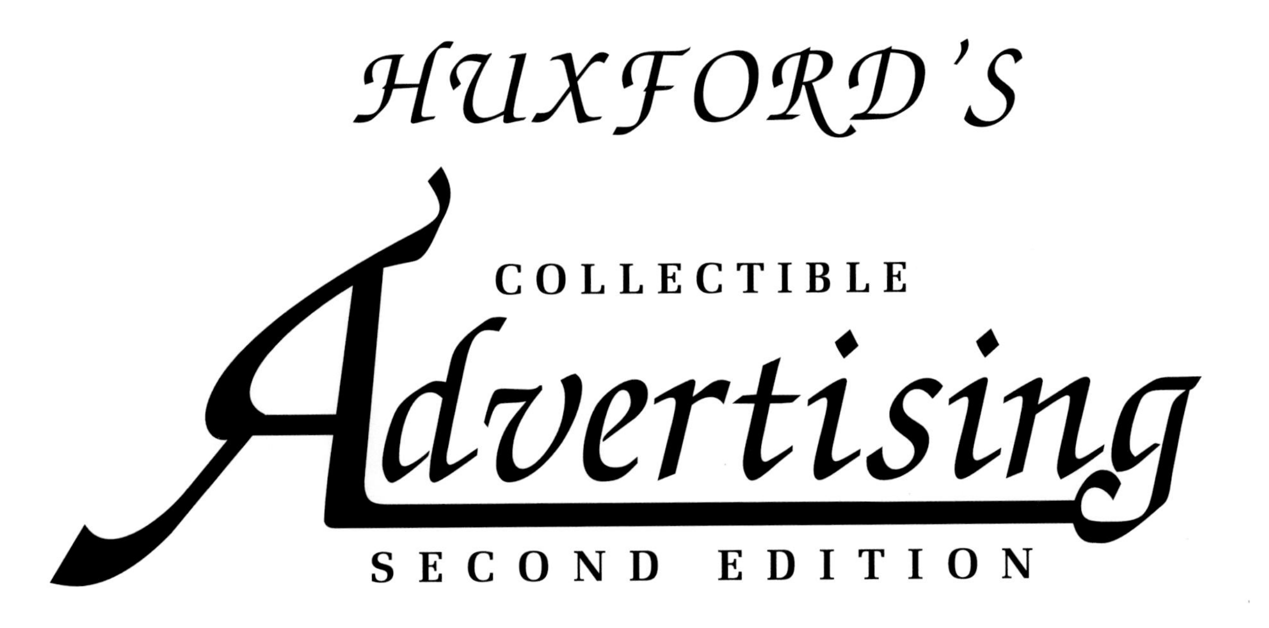

Sharon & Bob Huxford

COLLECTOR BOOKS
A Division of Schroeder Publishing Co., Inc.

On the Cover:

Pepsi-Cola, die-cut tin sign, 1950s, 18" diameter, NM, A, $230.00 (Photo courtesy Gary Metz)

Old Glory Coffee, 1-lb canister, EX, D, $4,000.00

Red Goose Shoes display figure, 11", NM, D, $100.00

Aunt Jemima and Uncle Moses dolls, stuffed cloth, from a set of four that includes Wade and Diana, 12½" x 8¾", complete set, EX, D, $625.00

Webster Tobacco tin, hinged lid, 3½" x 5", VG, D, $45.00

Wonder Bread, Howdy Doody, die-cut cardboard sign, movable joints, 13", NM, D, $33.50.

Editorial Staff:

Editors
Sharon and Bob Huxford

Research and Editorial Assistants
Nancy Drollinger and Donna Newnum

Cover Design
Beth Summers

Book Design
Karen Long

Searching For A Publisher?

We are always looking for knowledgeable people considered to be experts within their fields. If you feel that there is a real need for a book on your collectible subject and have a large comprehensive collection, contact us.

COLLECTOR BOOKS
P.O. Box 3009
Paducah, Kentucky 42002-3009

The current values in this book should be used only as a guide. They are not intended to set prices, which vary from one section of the country to another. Auction prices as well as dealer prices vary greatly and are affected by condition as well as demand. Neither the Authors nor the Publisher assumes responsibility for any losses that might be incurred as a result of consulting this guide.

Additional copies of this book may be ordered from:

COLLECTOR BOOKS
P.O. Box 3009
Paducah, KY 42002-3009

@$24.95. Add $2.00 for postage and handling.

Introduction

The field of collectible advertising is vast and varied. Offering an almost infinite diversity of items, it has the obvious potential to appeal to nearly anyone, with any interest, within any budget. With this in mind, we have attempted to compile a guide that would be beneficial to all collectors of advertising memorabilia. This book includes over ten thousand descriptive listings and hundreds of photos. The format has been kept as simple as possible, and we've added an index to further facilitate its use.

Items are sorted primarily by alphabetizing the product name as worded on each specific sign, tray, tin, etc. For instance, you'll find listings for Pabst Blue Ribbon Beer, others under Pabst Brewing Co., still another under Pabst Malt Extract. Each variation indicates the primary, most obvious visual impact of the advertising message. There are some exceptions. Even though many examples of Coca-Cola advertising are simply worded 'Coke,' all have been listed under the title 'Coca-Cola' The advertising message as it actually appears is given in the description. There are several other instances where this applies—Planters (Peanuts), Cracker Jack, and Pepsi-Cola, for example. When they seemed appropriate, cross-references were added.

After the product (or company) name, the form of the item is given, i.e. sign, tin, mug, ash tray, etc. (Trays having 'deep dish' or rolled rims are so described; when the type of rim is not mentioned, you may assume it is the more common tray style.) Circa is given when that information was available. Following phrases describe graphics, colors, and sizes. When only one dimension is given, it is height; and height is noted first when two or more are noted. Often there is a detailed description of any damage; in lieu of specific details, condition is indicated by standard abbreviations: M for mint, NM for near mint, EX for excellent, VG for very good, and G for good. Plus and minus signs were used to indicate levels in between. See the section 'Condition and Its Effect on Value' for more information.

We have given actual sizes when that information as available to us, otherwise sizes are approximate.

Because our listings have been compiled from many sources, we have coded each line to indicate that the suggested value is (A), an auction result or a price actually realized by another type of sale, or (D), a dealer's 'asking' price. As everyone is aware, auction prices are sometimes higher than dealer's prices, but they are just as apt to be lower. At any rate, they are legitimate prices for which merchandise actually changed hands and have always been used by dealers as a basis for their evaluations. As an added feature, this edition will also contain many listings with codes identifying the dealer or collector who provided us with that information. Feel free to contact these people if you are interested in buying that item or similar items. Though they may have already been sold, many of these descriptions were taken directly from selling lists. Many dealers tend to specialize in specific areas of advertising, and even if they no longer have the item in question, they may be able to locate it for you. We'll tell you how to decipher the codes in the following pages. Please remember, as you should regard any price guide, this one is offered as only a tool to be used in addition to your own personal observations of market dealings, show sales, and trade paper ads. alongside your personal observations of market dealings, show sales, and tradepaper ads.

Acknowledgments

We are indebted to the following auction galleries who have contributed catalogs, photographs, listings, and other information, all of which was vital to the production of this guide:

Noel Barrett Antiques & Auctions Ltd.
P.O. Box 1001
Carversville, Pennsylvania 18913

Cerebro
P.O. Box 327
East Prospect, Pennsylvania 17317

Collectors Auction Services
RD 2, Box 431; Oakwood Rd.
Oil City, Pennsylvania 16301

Dynamite Auction Company
Franklin Antique Mall & Auction Gallery
280 Franklin Ave.
Franklin, Pennsylvania 16323

Franks Antiques
Box 516
Hilliard, Florida 32046

James D. Julia Inc.
Box 830
Fairfield, Maine 04937

Bob Kay
P.O. Box 1805
Batavia, Illinois 60510-1805

Gary Metz's Muddy River Trading Company
4803 Lange Lane S.W.
Roanoke, Virginia 24018

Mike's General Store
52 St. Anne's Rd.
Winnipeg, Manitoba, Canada R2M 2Y3

Wm Morford
RD #2
Cazenovia, New York 13035

Anthony J. Nard & Co.
US Rt #220
Milan, Pennsylvania 18831

Nostalgia Publications
Mr. Allan J. Petretti
21 South Lake Dr.
Hackensack, New Jersey 07601

Richard W. Oliver Inc.
Box 337
Kennebunk, Maine 04043-0337

Richard Opfer Auctioneering Inc.
1919 Greenspring Dr.
Timonium, Maryland 21093

Victorian Images
P.O. Box 284
Marlton, New Jersey 08053

Witherell's Americana Auctions
P.O. Box 804
Healsburg, CA 95448

Dave Beck
P.O. Box 435
Mediapolis, Iowa 52637

Hake's Americana & Collectibles
P.O. Box 1444
York, Pennsylvania 17405

Photo Credits:

David Allen
Dunbar's Gallery
Donald Friedman
Darryl Fritsche
Henry Hain III
Eric Hardesty
David Hirsch
David Horvath
Bob Kay
Mike's General Store
Gary Metz

Identification of Coded Dealers and Collectors

Many of our listings contain 2-character codes indicating the dealer or collector who provided us with the description and value of specific items. These codes are located at the very end of the line. At the time we entered our data, they actually had these items for sale, and though they were in no way required to retain their stock until our book was published, some things may still be available. As all collectors know, lapse time between data entry and the actual release date of a price guide can involve several months. During that time these dealers may buy and sell identical or very similar pieces of merchandise several times, and since they must sometimes pay more to restock, their prices will fluctuate, so don't regard the prices they sent us as though they were etched in stone! Over the months that elapse, market values may appreciate, and if you're an advertising collector, you should hope that this is the case. An active market is healthy for both dealers as well as collectors. But even if the item you want to purchase is no longer in stock, as I'm sure you're aware, there is a nationwide network of dealer connections, and the merchant you contact may be able to steer you to someone else that will be able to help you.

Please, if you are making your inquiry by mail, send the dealer a self-addressed, stamped envelope. This is common courtesy. In the long run it not only makes the transaction more convenient for the dealer, but it assures you that his response will make its way back to the proper address. Handwritten addresses are often difficult to make out. If you call and get his answering machine, when you leave your message and your number, tell him by all means to call you collect with his response.

If you're a dealer who regularly or even occasionally puts out a 'for sale' listing of merchandise and would like to be involved in our next edition, please contact us at Huxford Enterprises, 1202 7th Street, Covington, Indiana 47932.

(B1)
Dave Beck
P.O. Box 435
Mediapolis, Iowa 52637
(319) 394-3943

(B2)
Ann Brogley
P.O. Box 16033
Philadelphia, Pennsylvania 19144
(215) 824-4698

(C1)
Cairn's Antiques
P.O. Box 44026
Lemoncove, California 93244
(209) 597-2242

(C2)
Cerebro
P.O. Box 1221
Lancaster, Pennsylvania 17603
(800) 695-2235

(C3)
CC Cowboys
RR#1 Box 430
Chester, South Carolina 29706
(803) 337-8225

(D1)
Darryl's Old Advertising Signs
Darryl Fritsche
1525 Aviation Blvd.
Redondo Beach, California 90278
(310) 376-3858

(D2)
Dennis & George Collectibles
3407 Lake Montebello Dr.
Baltimore, Maryland 21218

(D3)
Dunbar's Gallery
Howard and Leila Dunbar
76 Haven St.
Milford, Massachusetts 01757
(508) 634-8697; FAX (508) 634-8698

(F1)
Donald Friedman
660 W. Grand Ave.
Chicago, Illinois 60610
Days: (708) 656-3700; Evenings and weekends:
(312) 226-4741

(G1)
Gaylord's Mercantile
Bill Gaylord
1015 Second St.
Sacramento, California 95814
(916) 444-5738

(G2)
Gumballs Galore
Randy and Sue Razzoog
716 Fairfield
Grand Rapids, Michigan 49504
(616) 453-8044

(H1)
Henry F. Hain III Antiques & Collectibles
2623 N. Second St.
Harrisburg, Pennsylvania 17110

(H2)
Hesson Collectibles
1261 S. Lloyd Ave.
Lombard, Illinois 60148

(H3)
David Horvath
27 Cockpit St.
Baltimore, Maryland 21220
(410) 686-1279

(M1)
Gary Metz's Muddy River Trading Co.
4803 Lange Lane S.W.
Roanoke, Virginia 24018
(703) 989-0475

(M2)
Mike's General Store
52 St. Anne's Rd.
Winnipeg, Manitoba, Canada R2M-2Y3
(204) 255-3463

(M3)
Signs of Age
Robert and Louise Marshall
115-117 Pine St.
Catasaugua, Pennsylvania 18032
(215) 264-8986

(N1)
Violet Newcomb
2251 W. Washington Apt 302
Springfield, Illinois 62702-4648
(217) 787-9497

(N2)
Duane Nycz
P.O. Box 923
Soap Lake, Washington 98851
(509) 246-0672

(P1)
Paper Pile Quarterly
Ada Fitzsimmons
P.O. Box 337
San Anselmo, California 94979-0337
(415) 454-5552

(P2)
Judy Posner Collectibles
RD #1 Box 273
Effort, Pennsylvania 18330
(717) 629-6583; FAX (717) 629-0521

(P3)
Postcards International
Marty Shapiro
P.O. Box 2930
New Haven, Connecticut 06515-0030
(203) 865-0814; FAX (203) 495-8005

(P4)
John and Sheri Pavone
29 Sullivan Rd.
Peru, New York, 12972
(518) 643-8152

(S1)
Don Shelly
P.O. Box 11
Fitchville, Connecticut 06334
(203) 887-6163 (afer 5 pm)

(S2)
The Sign Sez
Larry and Nancy Werner
P.O. Box 188
Winfield, Illinois 60190
(708) 690-2960

(S3)
Steve Sourapas
1413 N.W. 198th St.
Seattle, Washington 98177
(206) 542-1791

(S4)
Craig and Donna Stifter
511 Aurora Ave #117
Naperville, Illinois 60540
(707) 717-7949

(S5)
Rex Stark
49 Wethersfield Rd.
Bellingham, Massachusetts 02019

Condition and Its Effect on Value

Condition, possibly more than any other consideration, is very important when assessing the value of advertising collectibles. On today's market items in good to very good condition are slow to sell unles they are extremely rare. Mint or near mint examples are high.

On the occasion when no condition is given in our listings, assume the item to be in excellent condition. Every effort has been made to describe any damage fully; so nearly every line has either specific mention of fading, rust, chips, etc. or a condition code. Tins are evaluated with original lids unless noted otherwise. Items that we found selling or offered for sale more than once are sometimes listed twice, when conditions varied.

The following criteria are generally used by most dealers and auction galleries when describing condition (corresponding numbers are sometimes used instead of letter codes; these are also given).

Mint (M) (10) — Unused, absolutely no wear, like new.

Near Mint (NM) (9) — Appears new, but on closer examination minor wear, a few very light scratches, or slight dullness can be seen.

Excellent (EX) (8) — General appearance is very pleasing with only a few very minor dents, scratches, and loss of paint to distract.

Very Good (VG) (7) — Still attractive to display, but with more defects than one in excellent condition; has some rust, pitting, and fading.

Good (G) (6) — Used, faded; has paint wear, dents, scratches, and rust. Generally not collectible unless the item is especially hard to find.

Good- (G-) (5) — Has serious problems; heavily rusted, scratched, pitted; has little if any value.

To help you arrive at values for items in conditions other than those specifically given, we suggest the following guidelines. These are only in general, and there are of course exceptions to the rule.

Using excellent as a basis, equate the same item in mint condition at 2x; NM at 1.5x; VG at -.5x; and G at -.75x. For instance, an item in EX condition at $100 used as a basis makes the same in M condition $200; NM, $150; VG, $50 (or less).

A

A Haas Brewing Co, stained glass window, curved sides, embossed metal tag on frame reading 1858-1954, 10x59", G, A **$400.00**

A Overholt & Co Pure Rye, sign, reverse-painted glass with paper insert picturing the founder, mirror back, framed, image: 24x36", EX, A **$550.00**

A&P, bank, 1970s, red vinyl pig with logo on each side, 2x3x5", VG, A **$20.00**

A&P, pin-back button, A&P encircled by I'm An A&P Salesman, On To Chicago Contest, 1" dia, NM, A **$14.00**

A&P, pin-back button, pictures A&P workers, large, EX, D2 .... **$40.00**

A&P, tea bin, wood, metal interior, 6-sided, slanted lid, red with 2 red & gold logos, 2 gold geometric bands, worn, 30", A **$210.00**

A&P, trade card, die-cut cardboard, basket of flowers, reverse lists location of branch stores & products, 9x10", EX, H1 .... **$25.00**

A&P, see also Atlantic & Pacific Tea Co

A&P Teas & Coffees, sign, ca 1880, paper, historical image of people rushing to be on time, Ten Minutes..., framed, image: 22x32", VG, A **$850.00**

A-Treat, display, die-cut cardboard, boy in beany atop panel reading Drink A-Treat, M-m-m So Good, easel missing, 10x6", VG, A **$125.00**

A-Treat, display, die-cut cardboard, Drink A-Treat Beverages on banner above Santa in sleigh above rooftops, 22x28", EX, M3 .... **$45.00**

A-Treat, display, die-cut cardboard stand-up, waving Santa, 42x27", EX+, M3 .... **$85.00**

A-Treat, menu board, tin, red, white & blue A-Treat panel above black chalkboard, 20x14", EX, M3 .... **$35.00**

A-Treat, thermometer, tin, white with Serve above A-Treat on scrolled banner above green bottle, rounded ends, 30x8", NM, M3 .... **$125.00**

AAA Service Station, sign, convex half-circle lenses in blue & white mounted in metal case, ...Auto Club Of Missouri, 13½" long, VG, A **$155.00**

Abbey & Imbrie, postcard, 1906, pictures fisherman beside colorful tarpon, used, A **$26.00**

Abbey's Effervescent Salt, sign, die-cut cardboard standup, waist-length girl in yellow ready-to-drink product, lettering below, 10x7½", EX, D **$300.00**

Abbott's Angostura, sign, 1899, tin, man in tuxedo pouring himself a glass of bitters, ...Aids Digestion, original frame, 44½x32", G, A **$150.00**

Abbott's Bitters, thermometer, painted wood, yellow outlined in blue, man above, product name below, arched top, 21x5", VG+, A **$185.00**

Abbott's Bitters, thermometer, 1899, round metal case, glass front, degrees above man on oval at right of product name, 9" dia, EX, A **$110.00**

Abbotts Ice Cream, sign, painted tin, Abbotts Ice Cream & serving girl in oval above empty flavor panel, 29x13", EX, A **$90.00**

ABC Beer, label, 1933-36, Aztec Brewing Co, U-type permit number, VG, A **$10.00**

ABC Beer, sign, tin, Grecian girl in front of temple overlooking factory scene, American Brewing Co on frame, 30x23", EX, A $2,200.00

ABC Chewing Gum, sign, paper, ABC bathing girl image above box of product, It's Up To You, Go Get It!, matted & framed, 28x13", EX, A **$110.00**

ABC Power Washer, pocket mirror, pictures lady using washer, product name above, 2⅛" dia, EX, A **$160.00**

ABC/Allen Bros Co Food Products, pocket mirror, ABC arched above large building, lettering below, oval, 1¾x2¾", EX, A **$110.00**

Abercrombie & Fitch Co Camp Outfits, catalog, 1905, camp scene on front, fly fishing scene on back, well illustrated, 302 pages, scarce, EX, A **$210.00**

Abercrombie Camp Outfitters, catalog, 1939, 72 pages, VG, D **$25.00**

Absaraka Cigars, box label, inner lid, Indian with arrows & peace pipe, 6x9", M, C3 .... **$35.00**

AC Auto Parts, mechanical pencil, 1940s, gold-plated, floating AC oil filter inside, EX, D2 .... **$35.00**

AC Oil Filters, sign, 1941, painted tin, Oil Filters on band across bottom of circle with oil filter image & large AC, 9x18", EX, A **$65.00**

AC Service, sign, 1947-48, flange, 2-sided, round AC atop Service with chains linking Oil Filter & Fuel Pump panels, 18x11", VG+, A **$150.00**

AC Spark Plug Cleaning Station, sign, 1945, painted tin, 2-sided, winking horse taking shower atop Registered..., spark-plug graphic, 16x11", VG/G, A **$140.00**

AC Spark Plugs, display case, cylinder shape with large spark plug graphic giving off rays over AC, lettering above & below, 17", EX, A **$125.00**

Acco Spinach, can label, pictures atlas with sphere & spinach, Atlanta NY, 6½x20", EX, G1 .... **$10.00**

Ace No 70 Boot Cement, can with contents, product name on ace of diamonds, screw top, 1-qt, NM, A **$15.00**

Acid Iron Mineral Tonic, sign, tin, Acid Iron Mineral lettered above man in leopard skin with anvil left of advertising, framed, vertical, EX, M1 .... **$265.00**

Acme Coffee, tin, Acme Brand Coffee lettered above American in oval center, dots surround lower portion, screw top, 1-lb, EX, A **$66.00**

Acme Cowboy Boots, sign, light-up, painted metal emblem with yellow neon lettering at left of plastic boot, 20" long, G, A **$160.00**

Acme Cowboy Boots, sign, light-up, painted metal emblem with yellow neon lettering at left of plastic boot, works, 20" long, EX+, A **$750.00**

Acme Folding Boat Co, trade card, black on green, boat at top, Safe, Handsome, Compact..., EX, A **$38.00**

Acme Granite Floor Paint, trade card, before & after scene with Black lady, prejudicial slang below, EX, A **$20.00**

Acme Lawn Mower, trade card, ca 1880, pictures well-dressed Victorians on lawns, mowers on front & back, 4 pages, 3¼x5", EX, P1 .... **$37.50**

Acme Quality Paints, sign, porcelain, 2-sided, large paint can in white with black highlights on red background, 20x14½", VG, A **$55.00**

Acorn Stoves & Ranges, sign, zinc, 2-sided acorn shape in 2 shades of green, gold relief lettering, very rare, 48x48", EX, A $3,850.00

Acorn Stoves & Ranges, trade card, folder, leaf & acorn logo on front, 1881 calendar inside, minor stain, VG, A.. **$16.00**

Acorn Stoves & Ranges, trade card, unhappy couple opens to lovely dinner setting, EX, A **$22.00**

Acropolis Sifted Peas, can label, colorful view of Parthenon, M, C3 .... **$12.00**

Active Andes Stoves, trade card, 3-color litho picturing a stove, Phillips & Clark Stove Co, Geneva NY, folded/creased, 6x4", D **$18.00**

Adam Scheidt Brewing Co, calendar, 1907, man standing beside 2 women in sailor attire, floral border, full pad, framed, image: 29½x21", VG, A **$600.00**

Adam Scheidt Brewing Co, pocket mirror, Valley Forge Special arched above large bottle, company name below, oval, 2¾", EX, A **$40.00**

Adam Scheidt Brewing Co, tip tray, Standard Beer lettered across gent lifting glass of brew, Healthful & Strengthening, 4⅜" dia, VG+, A **$130.00**

Adams Chewing Gum, dispenser, cast metal with labeled glass front, 6 push tabs, A Flavor For Every Taste, 17½", VG+, A **$70.00**

Adams Express Co, sign, reverse-painted glass, G, D .. **$375.00**

Adams Hair Brush No 269, pocket mirror, pictures hair brush with product name above, Its Use Insures A Healthful Scalp..., 2⅛" dia, VG+, A **$70.00**

Adams Motor Graders, token, ca 1920, You Pay lettered on arrow, Round & Round She Goes, Where She Stops Nobody Knows, VG+, D **$10.00**

Adams Pepsin Tutti-Frutti, cabinet, oak with glass front & mirrored back, product name embossed on marquee, 17½x12½x6", VG+, A **$700.00**

Adams Pepsin Tutti-Frutti, pocket mirror, product name arched above girl displaying tray of gum, Good For Digestion, oval, 2¾", EX, A **$675.00**

Adams Pepsin Tutti-Frutti, sign, glass, Adams Pepsin Tutti-Frutti Sold Here lettered on mottled background, wood frame, horizontal rectangle, VG, A **$120.00**

Adepa, crate label, Spanish citrus, flying sea gulls & flag, EX, C3 .... **$4.00**

Adloff & Hauerwaas Breweries, calendar, 1908, die-cut cardboard, fishing scene, factory inset below, full pad, matted & framed, image: 20x13", EX+, A **$1,250.00**

Admiral Parts & Accessories, thermometer, dial, 10" dia, NM, B1 .... **$65.00**

Admiral Rough Cut, tin, encircled portrait with product name above & below, pull top, NM, A **$250.00**

Admiration Cigars, display, counter-top, tin, pictures woman admiring herself in mirror, 7½x5¾", VG, A **$100.00**

Admiration Miniatures, sign, ca 1920, tin hanger, black with green ad emblem showing lady looking in mirror, Deco border, 7x5½", NM, D3 .... $350.00

Adriance, Platt & Co, see also Buckeye Harvester

Adriance, Platt & Co Agricultural Machinery, sign, ca 1900, paper, features vignettes of equipment in use, strong colors, lined back, minor stain, EX, A **$550.00**

Adriance, Platt & Co Mowers & Reapers, trade card, pictures young maiden with flowers, ...Buckeye Works, Poughkeepsie NY... EX, A **$38.00**

Aetna Auto Ass'n of the USA, sign, die-cut porcelain, 2-sided, white stars above white image of USA, red lettering on blue shield, 14x20", EX, D3 .... **$650.00**

Aetna Insurance Co, calendar, 1891, port scene with mountain beyond, full pad, glass is cracked, matted & framed, image: 6½x9½", G-, A **$25.00**

Aetna Insurance Co, ledger marker, horizontal image of Mt Vesuvius erupting, Insure With..., Kellogg & Bulkeley litho, 12½x3", G, A $100.00

After Dinner Egyptian Cigarettes, print, loving couple encircled above lettering, Archiv stamp right of image, framed, circular image: 8¼" dia, EX, A $30.00

AG Spalding & Bros, pocket mirror, football image with company name & address, 2¾" long, EX, A $160.00

Air Chief Motor Oil, can, 1930-50, product name & airplane on white, Guaranteed 100%... below on red, screw lid & handle, 2-gal, 13", VG, A $80.00

Air Float Baby Powder, tin, light blue with dark-blue & white lettering above & below baby's portrait, shaker top, tall round shape, EX+, M2 ....$105.00

Airflite Motor Oil, can, red, white & blue, Airflite lettered above twin-engine plane, Motor Oil on red band below, scarce, 2-gal, EX, D3...............................$335.00

Airship, crate label, 1940s, California orange, old 4-prop commercial plane on royal blue, Fillmore Citrus Assoc, 10x11", M, C1..$12.00

Ajax Alcohol, sign, 1920s, embossed tin, green on silver, ...Completely Denatured Alcohol, 10x14", EX, D.$25.00

Ajax Heavies Ammunition, sign, ca 1925, die-cut cardboard, full-color image of hunter & boat with shell in black & gold, 16x27½", G, D...............................$35.00

Akron Brewing Co, sign, 1930s-40s, wood, painted-on image of the factory, black background, logo below, minor soiling, 24½x36", A...................................$375.00

Al Foss Fishing Tackle, ad cover, 1918, shows bass going after pork spinner, VG, A $60.00

Alaska Fur Co, sign, carved wood seal over flat wood sign with wrought iron moldings, seal & lettering in gold leaf, 51x76", VG+, A....................$17,600.00

Alaska Lager Beer, label, 1933-36, Pilsener Brewing Co of Alaska, U-type permit number, 11-oz, EX, A........$23.00

Albert Talc, tin, flat oval shape with floral motif surrounding product lettering, baby in tub on reverse, gold shaker top, EX+, M2 ....$190.00

Alberta High Grade Marshmallows, tin, lettering bordered by dash marks above & below, pry lid, round, EX, A $95.00

Albion, crate label, 1920s, California orange, bouquet of roses, Placentia Mutual Orange Assn, 10x11¾", M, C3 ....$16.00

Alden Fruit Vinegar, trade card, full-color image of young girl with flowers, 4x6", VG, D $4.50

Alden Fruit Vinegar, trade card, pictures a heron by lake with child & lamb, 4x6", G, D $4.50

Aldens, catalog, 1937, Spring/Summer, VG+, H2.......$55.00

Aldens, catalog, 1960, Christmas, VG+, H2 ....$100.00

Aldens, catalog, 1966, Fall/Winter, VG+, H2.............$25.00

Aldens, catalog, 1975, Christmas, VG, D $40.00

Alf & Alf Ale & Beer, label, 1933-50, oval shape, Modesto Brewery Inc, Internal Revenue Tax Paid statement, 11-oz, EX, A $21.00

Alfred Wright White Violet Borated Talcum, tin, paper label, white violets surround product lettering, dome top, 5¾x2⅝" dia, EX, D..$25.00

Alice Rose Sugar Corn, can label, ear of corn & large red rose, VG, C3 ....$10.00

Alka-Seltzer, clock, shaped like Alka-Seltzer tablet, MIB, D...$50.00

Alka-Seltzer, dispenser, metal, 3-sided, horizontal base with 2 rows of lighographed product boxes, plus 2 product bottles, EX, A.......................................$200.00

Alka-Seltzer, dispenser, metal, 3-sided with single row of lithographed product boxes, Speedy on ad panel atop, 14x7x5", EX, A...$100.00

Alka-Seltzer, display, large cardboard product box with white lettering on dark blue, light-blue & white border, 6x24x6", EX, A $5.00

Alka-Seltzer, ice bucket, oversized tablet box, boycotted Moscow Olympics version, few made, EX, D2 ....$45.00

Alka-Seltzer, sign, Alka-Seltzer in silver with diamond grid above Be Wise -- Alkalize in gold, framed with glass top, 9x21", VG, A $190.00

Alka-Seltzer, squeeze toy, 1960s, Speedy, molded vinyl, 5½", NM, D $250.00

Alka-Seltzer, store display/tape dispenser, colorful tin, tape dispenser on reverse, EX, P2...............................$95.00

All American, crate label, Washington apple, shield with stars & stripes on black panel, yellow & white lettering, 9x11", EX, G1...$5.00

All Fruit Crushes, sign, cardboard hanger, girl in sombrero picking fruit, Orange, Lemon, Lime... below, 13x9½", NM, B1 ....$15.00

All Jacks Cigarettes, sign, 1940s, tin, pictures large pack of cigarettes, Hard To Beat below, 10x14", EX, D....$35.00

All Star Brew, label, World Champion Packer Squad Of 1936, Rahr Green Bay Brewing Corp, Green Bay Wisconsin, 12-oz, M, A $43.00

All Strikes Cigars, box label, inner lid sample, 1890s, early bowling scene, OL Schwencke & Co litho, EX+, A .$242.00

All-American Draught Beer, label, 1933-50, Columbus Brewing Co, Internal Revenue Tax Paid statement, 1/2-gal, EX, A $26.00

Allen & Ginter Tobacco, sign, paper, features cigarette cards of women jockeys, Racing Colors Of The World, framed, 28x18", VG+, A..................................$4,800.00

Allen Square Cigars, box label, lithographer's proof, early 1900s, corner building & street scene, EX, A $90.00

Allenbury's Malted Milk, container, aluminum, ...Made In Canada, knob lid, EX, A $160.00

Allens Red Tame Cherry, display, chalkware figurine, girl in green dress & gold pinafore holding cherries on round lettered base, 26", EX, A **$450.00**

Allens Red Tame Cherry, sign, embossed die-cut tin, boy & girl at table enjoying product, Drink Allens...And You'll Smile Too, 36x24", NM, A.................$15,000.00

Alliance Coffee, sign, die-cut cardboard, chef holds lettered cup, base reads For Coffee Contentment Serve..., 16x13", EX, A **$225.00**

Allied Mills Inc, sign, die-cut porcelain, red, white & black flour-sack shape with silhouette of soldier on horseback, 34x21", EX, D3......................$475.00

Allied Van Lines, doll, printed cloth, minor discoloration on 1 leg, D **$5.00**

Alligator Rainwear, sign, 1950s, counter-top, pictures an alligator, 5x10", G, D **$22.00**

Allis Chalmers, sign, porcelain, A-C Allis-Chalmers lettered on circle with zigzag edge on red diagonal square, 11x11", NM, A **$110.00**

Allis Chalmers Tractors Sales & Service, sign, porcelain, 2-sided, white on green, 28x20", EX, D **$300.00**

Alma Cigars, box label, inner lid sample, 1907, close-up portrait of pretty lady, Moehle Lithographic Co, EX, A ...**$31.00**

Alma Polish, trade card, 1885, park scene with statue & girl with tennis racket, 3½x5", EX, P1 ....**$15.00**

Almond Smash, display, die-cut cardboard, Christmas wreath surrounds Drink Almond Smash on red, It's Good on blue, 11x13", NM, M3........................**$15.00**

Alox Shoe Laces, sign, 1930s, die-cut cardboard shoe, Pay The Clerk, 11x19", EX, D **$14.00**

Alpen-Rose Cigars, box label, outer, woman & snow-capped mountains, 4½x4½", M, C3 ....**$16.00**

Amalie Motor Oil, clock, glass lens, Amalie on horizontal oval in center, oil cans at 12-3-6-9, numbers in between, 15" dia, EX+, A **$230.00**

Amalie Motor Oil, decal, paper, Push lettered above product can, 6x3½", NM, A **$18.00**

Amaretto Di Saronno, ceiling swag lamp, Tiffany style, EX, D **$35.00**

Amaretto Di Saronno, floor mat, pictures Amaretto bottle with black border on red background, EX, D......**$30.00**

Amaretto Di Saronno, mirror, pictures bottle of Amaretto, wood frame, 18x21½", EX, D **$20.00**

Amberlite Beer, label, pre-Prohibition, Fresno Brewing Co, EX, A **$35.00**

Ambrew Beer, label, 1933-36, American Brewing Co Ltd, U-type permit number, 11-oz, EX, A....................**$12.00**

Ambrosia Lager Beer, label, 1933-50, eagle above product name, South Side Brewing Co, Internal Revenue Tax Paid statement, 12-oz, EX, A **$5.00**

America Cigars, box labels, inner & outer sample set, 1877, classical figures posed on marked base, Heppenheimer & Maurer, VG/EX, A........................**$162.00**

America's Delight, crate label, 1920s, Washington apple, mountain orchards with large apple in foreground, Seattle, 9x10½", M, C3 ....**$4.00**

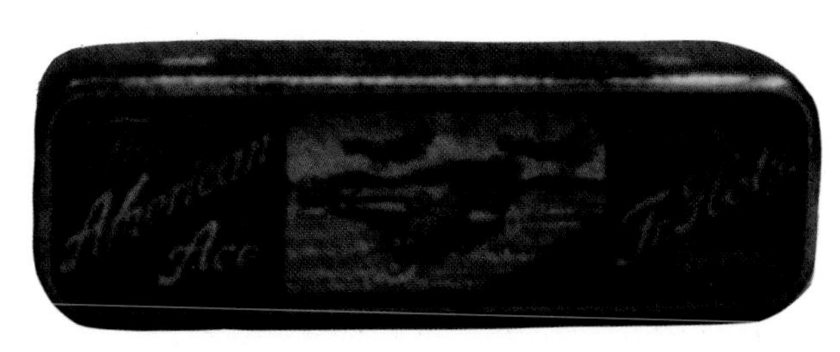

American Ace Harmonica, tin, The American Ace & Made By Fr Hotz Germany in gold script flank 3 planes flying over water pictured on lid, EX, D3..............$48.00

American Airlines, playing cards, MIB, P4 ....**$4.00**

American Airlines, timetables, 1951, EX, D **$9.50**

American Beauty Corsets, pocket mirror, 3 large roses above product name & other lettering, 2¾x1¾", NM, A **$54.00**

American Boiler & Pipe Covering Co, trade card, pictures a pipe cover, company name & text in gold on black, EX, A **$46.00**

American Bond Cigars, box label, inner lid, 1936, eagle on red, white & blue stripes, 6x9", M, C3............**$45.00**

American Brake Shoe Co, statuette, 1970s, painted plaster, 3", EX, D **$35.00**

American Breakfast Coffee, pail, American Breakfast in white outlined in red on gold above white Coffee on red, gold slip lid, bail, EX+, M2........................**$65.00**

American Brewing Co, match striker, stoneware, incised logo of eagle & emblem, 3x3¾" dia, VG, A **$170.00**

American Brewing Co's Beers, sign, glass, foiled lettering on red, white & blue background, framed, 22x17", EX, A...**$385.00**

American Carriage Co, catalog, 1899, 48 pages, VG, D.**$20.00**

American Cartridge Co, box, American Eagle arched above eagle with wings spread, Shot Shells Loaded With Smokeless Powder above company, VG, A **$28.00**

American Central Insurance Co, sign, 1920, embossed brass, Pierce Arrow limousine & logo in bottom corners, black lettering, rare, 10x14", EX, A $800.00

American Central Insurance Co, sign, 1920, embossed brass, Pierce Arrow limo, buffalo & Indian logos in lower corners, rare, 10x14", NM, D3 ....**$1,475.00**

American Condensed Milk Co, sign, ca 1885, paper, matron & mother watching little girl dance on huge can of product in garden, 14x20", NM, A.................**$325.00**

American Draught Beer, label, 1933-50, American Brewery Inc, U-type permit number, 64-oz, EX, A.......**$13.00**

American Express, globe, milk glass with 2 reverse-painted glass lenses, red, white & blue, flag with world globe in center, 16", VG, A................................**$250.00**

American Express Co, sign, porcelain, white on blue, Money Orders, Foreign Checks, Travelers Cheques..., surface scratches, 13x17", G, A **$175.00**

American Express Money Orders, clock, light-up, metal with glass lens, red & blue lettering on beige with red & blue highlights, 13x13", EX, A **$75.00**

American Express Travelers Cheques/Conoco, sign, porcelain, white American... on blue above 2 orange Conoco logos flanking Accepted Here on white, 5x10", VG+, A **$200.00**

American Family Soap, sign, die-cut tin, eagle atop box of soap on American shield, Jas S Kirk & Co, 20x19½", VG, A **$3,750.00**

American Gas, gas globe, 1920-40, Gill body, product name in white on blue, red dot in center outlined in white, 13½" dia, EX..**$325.00**

American Gems Cigars, box label, inner lid sample, 1890s, ladies' portraits surround large box of cigars, OL Schwencke & Co litho, EX, A **$26.00**

American Girl Cigars, box label, outer, girl wearing daisies, 4½x4½", EX, C3 ....**$14.00**

American Granulated Cut Plug, pocket tin, upright, product name & ornate graphics on green background, VG, A **$182.00**

American Journal Newspaper, sign, Victorian woman with parasol flying over New York, Have You Seen This Girl..., matted, image: 16x20½", NM, A.......**$150.00**

American Lager Beer, sign, embossed tin under glass, eagle on shield flanked by lettering, Rochester NY below, framed, 30x41", G+, A **$600.00**

American Lager Beer, sign, reverse-painted glass, eagle on shield flanked by lettering, Rochester NY below, framed, G-, A...**$450.00**

American Line/Red Star Line, letter folder, International ocean liner under full steam, lists ships of the line & offices on reverse, 12x3", EX+, A.......................**$250.00**

American Manure Spreader, match holder, tin, horse-drawn manure spreader in oval above lettering, ...Harrow Co, Detroit Mich, 5", VG, A **$380.00**

American Mills Mocha Java, tin, mythological man with lion & swan, white, red & gold, JS Silvers & Bro, press lid, oval, 6x4", EX+, A **$60.00**

American Nut Company's Salted Pecans, tin, white with red product name above red, blue & silver circular logo, company name below, pry lid, EX, D3.....**$175.00**

American Old Line Insurance Co, watch fob, pictures Indian head, G, D **$40.00**

American Powder Mills, barrel, wood, lettering on ends, contains some powder, 8x6", VG, A..................**$190.00**

American Powder Mills Dead Shot Gun Powder, envelope, 1891, pictures can of gun powder above return address, VG, A **$130.00**

American Protectorate Cigars, box label, inner lid, portrait of President James Monroe, 6x9", M, D...........**$6.00**

American Protectorate Cigars, box label, outer, portrait of James Monroe, 4½x4½", M, D **$4.00**

American Stamp Company, sign, embossed tin, red, white & blue, 10x27", EX, D.................................**$50.00**

American Standard Loads, box label, unused, EX, A.**$140.00**

American Steel & Wire Co's Zinc Insulated Fences, jigsaw puzzle, 1933, giant boots walking through farm fields, Take This Step For Better Farm Protection, 9x12", EX, F1..**$35.00**

American Steel Farm Fences, match holder, tin, red, green & white, company name above fence graphic, Quality & Efficiency Guaranteed..., EX, D..........**$125.00**

American Woolen Co, booklet, 1924, illustrated work on how wool is processed into cloth, 40 pages, EX, D .**$5.00**

Amlico Premium Gasoline, pump plate, 1950s, porcelain, Premium lettered on green center band, Amlico... in white above & below, 10" dia, EX, A **$110.00**

Amlico Regular Gasoline, pump plate, 1950s, porcelain, Regular lettered on green center band, Amlico... in white above & below, 10" dia, EX, A **$95.00**

Ammen's Powder, tin, pictures baby's face on paper label, EX, D...**$12.50**

Ammon & Person Baby Brand Butterine, pocket mirror, pictures small girl spreading butter on bread, lettering above & below, 2¾", VG, A **$2,100.00**

Amoco, ball point pen, retractable, red, white & black, EX, D **$20.00**

Amoco, gas globe, 1920-40, Gill body, Amoco in white on black band, red ground, 13½" dia, EX, A... **$325.00**

Amoco, sign, 1940s, porcelain, 2-sided, red, black & white logo above Courtesy Cards Honored Here in black, 15x24", VG, A **$120.00**

Amoco American Gas, mechanical pencil with oil sample in end, red, white & black, EX, D **$25.00**

Amoco Motor Grease, can, 1940s, logo above cream & black lettering, green background, pry lid, minor scratches, A **$15.00**

Amoco Winter Lubricants, banner, cloth, oval snow-covered sign looms over silhouette of car, Your Car Needs Winter Lubricants!, 35x38", NM, A **$85.00**

Amoco 586, bank, oil-can shape with 3 gold bands at top, Amoco oval above 586, Special Piston & Valve Stem Oil, 3", NM, A **$11.00**

Amorita Cigars, sign, paper, 2-sided, yellow & red, 7" dia, M, D **$4.50**

Anchor Pain Expeller, calendar, 1893, die-cut cardboard, Imported Anchor Pain... around 2 kids above January page on red anchor, 13x8", VG, A **$45.00**

Anchor White Lead Paint, string holder, 2-sided die-cut tin hanger, Dutch Boy on knee painting window frame, bucket below, 31x14", EX, A $4,000.00

Anderson's Concentrated Soups, pocket mirror, Jewish man with hot bowl of soup & showing soup can, Each Can Makes 6 Plates, 2⅛" dia, VG+, A **$190.00**

Andre Champagne, mirror, wood frame, 18x25", EX, D. **$12.00**

Angelica Uniforms, catalog, 1953, 75th anniversary, 50 pages, VG, D **$6.50**

Angelina, lug box label, grapes, Italian lady holding basket of grapes, Victor, EX, G1 .... **$2.00**

Angelus Marshmallows, pocket mirror, features blond cherub, oval, 2¾", NM, A **$55.00**

Angelus Marshmallows, pocket mirror, features brunette cherub, oval, 2¾", EX, A **$45.00**

Angelus Marshmallows, pocket mirror, 2 cherubs leaning on large box of marshmallows, minor wear, horizontal oval, 2⅜" long, VG, A **$50.00**

Angelus Marshmallows, pocket mirror, 2 cherubs leaning on large box of marshmallows, horizontal oval, 2⅜" long, NM, A **$111.00**

Angelus Marshmallows, tape measure, 1917, Cracker Jack Co, G, D **$215.00**

Angelus Marshmallows, tin, Angelus lettered in oval above Marshmallows, glass lid, round, EX, A **$55.00**

Angelus Marshmallows, tin, Angelus lettered in oval above Marshmallows, slip lid, round, EX, A **$25.00**

Anheuser-Busch, bottle, light blue with embossed logo on side, 9", VG, D **$14.00**

Anheuser-Busch, charger, tin, couple with man on right pouring beer into fondue, Say When , EX, A **$400.00**

Anheuser-Busch, matchbook cover, horses & wagon on front, colorful, 40 strike, front strike, NM, R1 .... **$7.00**

Anheuser-Busch, pocket knife, enamel over brass jack-knife, trademark logo & lettering, 3-blade & corkscrew variety, 3¼" long, G, A **$145.00**

Anheuser-Busch, print, 'Custer's Last Fight,' Home Of Budweiser & other lettering below, framed, 36x46", EX, A **$275.00**

Anheuser-Busch, print, 1896, 'Custer's Last Fight,' Anheuser-Busch Brewing Association below, framed, image: 32x42", EX+, A **$2,300.00**

Anheuser-Busch, prints by Oscar Beringhaus, 'Relief Train,' 'Attack On An Emigrant Train,' etc, original frames, set of 5, 14x23", EX, A **$650.00**

Anheuser-Busch, sign, ca 1907, paper, Budweiser girl in red dress, logo in lower right corner, matted & framed, 38½x23½", EX, A **$750.00**

Anheuser-Busch, sign, paper, Budweiser girl holding bottle of beer beside a tree, product name on original frame, 38½x23½", G, A **$500.00**

Anheuser-Busch, sign, paper, panoramic factory view, America's Largest & Favorite Brewery above, original frame, 41x53", VG, A **$5,000.00**

Anheuser-Busch, sign, plaster & chalk, panoramic factory view, America's Largest & Favorite Brewery above, framed, 45x58", EX+, A $6,750.00

Anheuser-Busch, sign, red & white case glass, bold lettering & logo in decorative hand-painted frame, 54½x80", VG, A **$1,750.00**

Anheuser-Busch, sign, self-framed tin, girl with basket of hops and bottle of beer, 37½x25½", G, A **$600.00**

Anheuser-Busch, sign, tin, panoramic factory scene, Home of Budweiser... lettered below, original frame, 15¾x37", G-, A **$500.00**

Anheuser-Busch, tray, factory scene surrounded by eagle & hops logo, ...America's Largest & Favorite..., oval, 15½x18½", G, A **$450.00**

Anheuser-Busch, tray, Victory with cherubs holding variety of products, decorative border, oval, 10½x13", VG, A **$275.00**

Anheuser-Busch, tray, 1895-1901, Victory with cherubs holding variety of products, decorative border, oval, 13½x16½", EX, A **$425.00**

Anheuser-Busch, see also Budweiser

Anheuser-Busch, see also Busch

Anheuser-Busch Malt Nutrine, sign, self-framed tin, doctor following stork's shadow on path to house, 7½x12½", EX, A **$400.00**

Anheuser-Busch Malt Nutrine, sign, 1900-20, self-framed tin, stork carrying bottles to nest of babies, town scene below, 15½x19½", EX, A **$400.00**

Anheuser-Busch Malt Nutrine, sign, 1910, self-framed tin, doctor in horse-drawn buggy chasing stork with baby, A Hurry Call, 7½x12½", VG, A **$190.00**

Animal Crackers, tin, 1989, sealed, 2½x8x6", D.......**$12.50**

Ann Arundel Pride Tomatoes, can label, horse-drawn wagon with tomatoes, M, C3 ....**$6.00**

Anteek Beer, display, painted composition, figural waiter on round base, hand holds beer, embossed product name on apron, EX, A $300.00

Anthony Cigars, box labels, inner & outer sample set, Anthony in classical setting with labeled banner, Heppenheimer & Maurer, EX/M, A **$36.00**

Anthracite Beer Co, pocket mirror, celluloid, pictures Santa with bag full of toys, ...Lager, Ale & Porter, rare, 2" dia, EX, A **$250.00**

Anthracite Brewing Co, pocket mirror, bust-length portrait of a girl, lettering above, minor soiling/wear, oval, 2¾x1¾", VG, A **$65.00**

Antikamnia Chemical Co, calendar, 1899, each page shows a different skeleton image, GH Buck & Co Litho NY, 10x7", EX, A **$300.00**

Antikamnia Tablets, tip tray, pictures reclining woman, G, D **$85.00**

Antler German Beer, label, 1933-50, logo above product name, Moose Brewing Co, Internal Revenue Tax Paid statement, 12-oz, EX, A **$9.00**

Apache Talc, tin, pictures people in various poses, tall round can with shaker top, EX, A **$25.00**

Apollinaris Table Water, sign, tin, rider standing beside horse, Queen Of Table Waters, Pretty Polly... on original frame, 13½x17½", VG, A **$175.00**

Apple a Day, crate label, Washington apple, blue & white 3-D lettering on black background, red trim, 9x11", EX, G1 ....**$2.00**

Appleton Brand Apples, crate label, 1915, ranch scene flanked by Art Nouveau lady & apples, Watsonville Cal, 10½x9", M, C1 ....**$5.00**

Aqua Velva, sign, cardboard stand-up, pictures Mamie Van Doren, Your Barber Recommends... above, 24x16", NM, B1 ....**$18.00**

AR Rugaber Furniture, pocket mirror, features St Bernard biting on chain, Special Prices To Newlyweds, 2⅛" dia, EX, A **$625.00**

Araban Coffee, tin, Arab man in profile with steaming cup of coffee, white product lettering above, gold screw lid, 1-lb, EX, A $350.00

Arabela Cigars, trolley sign, 1920s, cardboard, Arabela Cigars on fan-shaped graphic next to cigar, 5¢ Each, 11x21, EX, M2 ....**$45.00**

Aratex Semi-Soft Collars, trolley sign, product name & advertising left of illustrated image of man's head, 35¢ Each, 3 For $1.00, 11x21", EX, A **$70.00**

Arbuckles' Coffee, sign, embossed tin, Arbuckles' on diagonal band, Pure -- Wholesome above, Coffee below, elongated rectangle, EX, A **$50.00**

Arbuckles' Coffee, thermometer, An Old Friend above & Coffee below Arbuckles' on the diagonal, product below, squared corners, 19", VG, A **$40.00**

Arcadia Brewing Co Special Brew, label, pre-1920, company name above Special Brew in script, G, A....**$70.00**

Arcadia Lager Beer, label, 1933-36, U-type permit number, 1/2-gal, EX, A $36.00
Arenas, lug box label, California grape, red carnations on white lettering, on black ground, Los Angeles, G1...$2.00
Aristocrat Milk, pin-back button, 1930s, red & white, EX, D....................$4.00
Arizona Star, crate label, California grapefruit, pastel shaded grove with mountains in background, Sacramento, G1 ....$5.00
Arm & Hammer, booklet, 1916, 'The Twin Farms,' 8 pages, EX, D $4.00
Arm & Hammer, booklet, 1923, 'A Friend In Need,' product illustrations, girl & mother on cover, 32 pages, 4½x3½", VG, H1 ....$6.00

Arm & Hammer, recipe book, 1916, 'Book of Valuable Recipes,' 69th edition, 32 pages, EX, D $14.00
Arm & Hammer, recipe book, 1933, 'Good Things to Eat,' 105th edition, 32 pages, EX, D $12.00
Arm & Hammer, recipe book, 1936, 'Good Things to Eat,' 32 pages, VG, D $6.00
Arm & Hammer, recipe book, 1936, 'Successful Baking For Flavor & Texture,' 4th edition, 38 pages, 6¾x4¾", EX, H1 ....$8.00
Arm & Hammer, recipe book, 1938, 'Good Things to Eat,' 15 pages, EX, D $10.00
Arm & Hammer, recipe book, 1948, 'New Old Fashioned Recipes,' 14 pages, EX, D $8.00
Arm & Hammer Brand Soda, sign, litho on paperboard, box of baking soda with product name arched above & below, black ground, 12x16", G, A $20.00
Armory & Sharps Rifle Co, letterhead, 1877, engraved factory vignette, VG, A $40.00
Armour & Co, recipe book, 1920s, '60 Ways to Serve Ham,' colorful illustrations, 27 pages, minor stains, EX, H1 ....$4.50
Armour & Co Packers, trade card, 2-sided, continuous scene of boys playing at fence, EX, A $20.00
Armour Poultry Products, pin-back button, 1950s, pictures rooster in red sleeveless sweater, black, white & red, EX, D $8.00
Armour's Choice Sausage, key-chain tag, 1930s, die-cut tin, red & gold, overall finish wear, D $4.00
Armour's Corn Flakes, sign, self-framed tin, features bowl of cereal between box & bouquet of roses, advertising above, 15x20½", VG, A $140.00
Armour's Star Ham, pin-back button, 1920s, blue, white & yellow, EX, D $28.00
Armour's Veribest Peanut Butter, pail, straight sides, bail handle, 12-oz, A $55.00

Armour's Veribest Peanut Butter, pail, yellow with lettered horizontal oval above nursery rhyme vignettes, pry lid & bail, 1-lb, EX, A..............$225.00
Armour's Veribest Peanut Butter, sign, tin over cardboard, shows sandwich on pedestal plate behind product jar, product name below, 9x13", VG, A $250.00
Armour Soap, premium catalog, 1915, VG, D..........$20.00
Armour Star, sign, self-framed tin, pictures Black man slicing ham, G, D $550.00
Armours Simon Pure Lard, pail, no lid, 2-lb, D......$16.00

Armstrong's Quaker Rugs, jigsaw puzzle, early 1930s, boy & girl playing on rug with blocks that spell out company name, 9x6", EX, F1 ....$45.00
Armstrong Tires, display rack, 1930s-40s, tin, red with white lettering & black highlights, ...Insured Tires, minor paint chips, A $20.00
Arnholt & Schaefer Brewing Co, tip tray, bottle flanked by A&S Braun Beer & Weiner Export, Imperial Malt Extract... above & below, 4½" dia, EX, A $160.00

Around the World Motor Oil, can, 1925-45, early touring cars encircling world globe, product name above, pour spout & handle, 2-gal, 10½", VG, A **$85.00**

Arrow Beer, clock, wood case, stenciled tin face, white letters on red circle, black numbers, Anytime Is..., 15½x15½", VG+, A **$80.00**

Arrow Beer, globe, glass, 2-sided, arrow logo with product name above & below, original fitter rings & screw caps, 17x15" dia, EX, A **$900.00**

Arrow Beer, sign, self-framed tin, King Gambrinus enjoying flagon of beer, Mellow By Nature, Strengthened By Repeal, 17" dia, VG, A **$225.00**

Arrow Borax Soap, sign, hanging, die-cut cardboard arrow, ...America's Best, box of soap hanging below, unused, EX, D **$225.00**

Arrow Collar, trolley sign, man's head in decorated oval frame left of product name & advertising, Chase..., 20¢ Each, 11x21", VG, A **$55.00**

Arrow Collars & Shirts, sign, canvas, JC Leyendecker-style scene of man & woman taking Sunday cruise in boat, 20x30", EX, D3 ....**$550.00**

Arrow Shirts, sign, Arrow Shirts in blue neon on base with proprietor's name in black, 7½x25", EX, A.............**$275.00**

Arrowhead Hosiery, box, cardboard, Arrowhead lettered on an arrowhead below teepee & Indian lady on horse, 15x4½x1½", EX+, A **$40.00**

Artie Cigar, counter display, tin, pictures Artie atop building, decorative border, 9½x6¼", EX, A **$400.00**

Artie Cigar, sign, tin, pictures Artie sitting atop building facing product lettering, TJ Dunn & Co Makers, 10x14", G, A...**$375.00**

Artie Cigar, sign, tin, pictures Artie sitting atop building facing product lettering, TJ Dunn & Co Makers, framed, EX+, A $725.00

AS Davis Dry Cleaners, sign, glass, company name above For Better Service... at right of man in suit, small, EX, M1 ....**$300.00**

Asbach Uralt German Brandy, display bottle, glass, 20", EX, D...**$18.00**

Ash Grove Cement, sign, porcelain, yellow, blue & white, Cowles-White Lumber Co, chips, 20x14", D.........**$45.00**

Ashland Brand Tomatoes, can label, pictures big red tomato & green leaves, Ashland Va, M, C1 ....**$3.00**

Ashland Flying Octanes, lens, glass, Ashland in red receding letters appearing to speed above Flying Octane in green, minor wear, 14" dia, NM, A **$200.00**

Ashland Plus, gas globe, 1930s-40s, plastic body, product name in white on large red A, 13" dia, EX, A **$125.00**

At Leisure Cigars, box labels, inner & outer sample set, 1870s, girl lounging by garden pond, Heppenheimer & Maurer litho, EX/M, A **$85.00**

Ath-Lo-Pho-Ros, display, die-cut cardboard, street scene with 2 men in front of large sign, Searles Remedy For..., 19x28" open, EX+, A..**$200.00**

Athlete, crate label, 1930s, California orange, 3 runners reaching finish line in stadium, Claremont, 10x11", M, C1 ....**$5.00**

Athlete Smoking Mixture, tin, D Ritchie Co Manufacturers, Montreal, Canada, rectangular with rounded corners, 4x6", D..............................$500.00

Atkinson's Wormwood Cordial, sign, paper, Atkinson's arched above Original Wormwood Cordial..., Farwell print, original gilt frame, 13x11", NM, S5............**$250.00**

Atlanta Cigars, box labels, inner & outer sample set, 1870s, girl by flag draped over ship's anchor, Heppenheimer & Maurer, EX+/G, A **$344.00**

Atlantic, pump sign, porcelain, white with red & blue lettering, 9x13", EX, D3..**$110.00**

Atlantic & Pacific Tea Co, sign, die-cut cardboard, couple on early tricycle on which company name makes up spokes, ad on reverse, 10x7", EX, A **$130.00**

Atlantic & Pacific Tea Co, sign, die-cut cardboard standup, tomcat with top hat & cane teasing girlfriend, Don't Tommy Don't below, 10x8", EX, A **$110.00**

Atlantic Ammunition Co's Chamberlin Cartridges, box, product & company name above & below display of product, 20-gauge, VG, A **$160.00**

Atlantic Aviation Motor Oil, banner, 1940s, oilcloth, product name in white on blue above Zero Cold Test in red, minor staining, 36x60", A **$135.00**

Atlantic Aviation Motor Oil, can, metal, red product name above red plane & white Aviation on blue inverted chevron on white, 1-qt, unopened, D3..**$45.00**

Atlantic Aviation Motor Oil, can, 1935-45, Aviation superimposed over red airplane on blue arrowhead, product name above, 5-qt, 9½", EX **$60.00**

Atlantic Aviation Motor Oil, sign, painted metal, 2-sided, Atlantic above Aviation on inverted chevron, Motor Oil below, Keeps..., 11x18", VG+, A **$60.00**

Atlantic Aviation Motor Oil, sign, painted tin, We Sell Atlantic Paraffine Base... above plane, seal logo below, wood frame, 44x14", VG, A **$700.00**

Atlantic Aviation Motor Oil, sign, 1951, porcelain, 2-sided, red & navy on ivory, Keeps Engines Clean, navy border, 10x17", M, D3 ....$250.00

Atlantic Beer, label, 1933-50, Extra Pale in script above product name, Internal Revenue Tax Paid statement, 12-oz, EX, A **$6.00**

Atlantic Coast Line, sign, tin, black lettering on yellow, Georgia, Virginia, North Carolina... lettered around border, 29½" dia, VG, A **$120.00**

Atlantic Diesel Fuel, pump sign, 1951, porcelain, Atlantic in shadowed letters on red above blue Diesel Fuel on white, 13x17", VG, A... **$60.00**

Atlantic Flying 'A' Maps, map holder, metal, red with Flying 'A' emblem above Maps lettered in black, 36x9", NM, A.. **$95.00**

Atlantic Gasoline, globe, Atlantic in bold letters on wide center band in red, white & blue, glass case, 16½", VG+, A **$150.00**

Atlantic Gasoline, pump sign, porcelain, Atlantic lettered in white shadowed in blue with white lines above & below, 9x13", EX+, A **$35.00**

Atlantic Gasoline, sign, porcelain, white with Atlantic above emblem with 2 red crossed arrows, Gasoline below, 52x36", EX, A **$375.00**

Atlantic Imperial, pump sign, embossed tin, shield shape with Atlantic on inset upper left of Imperial in diagonal script, 17x13", EX, A... **$35.00**

Atlantic Kerosene, sign, porcelain, red, white & blue, 17x13", NM, B1 .... **$35.00**

Atlantic Premium, bank, tin, red & white gas pump with red, white, blue & black lettering & highlights, blue bottom, 5", NM, A **$45.00**

Atlantic Premium, globe, milk glass with red & blue inserts, Atlantic on diagonal band above Premium, 17x15", EX, A... **$200.00**

Atlantic Premium, sign, porcelain, Atlantic in shadowed letters on hanging sign image above Premium lettered across bottom, 11x13", VG, A.............................. **$65.00**

Atlantic Pure White Lead, sign, copyright 1906 by National Lead Co, Dutch Boy image above logo left of product name, black frame, 35x21", VG, A........ **$150.00**

Atlantic White Flash, matchbook cover, featuring the Americus Hotel, Allentown PA on front, 20 strike, front strike, NM, R1 .... **$6.25**

Atlantic White Flash, pump sign, 1949-50, metal, white & black on red, Atlantic above round White Flash logo, 17x13", M, D **$125.00**

Atlantic White Lead Paint, string holder hanging display, tin, 2-sided, features Dutch Boy seated in swing, bucket below, rare, 26½x15", NM, A $7,500.00

Atlas Battery, bank, tin, figural 6V battery, EX, D..... **$35.00**

Atlas Life Insurance Co, watch fob, brass, pictures Atlas holding world globe, lettering on back, EX, D **$15.00**

Atlas Perma-Guard, thermometer, tin, blue above, red below, white border, All-Winter Anti-Freeze, touched up, 36", VG, A **$25.00**

Atlas Perma-Guard, thermometer, tin, blue above, red below, white border, One Fill Lasts All Winter, round top & bottom, 36", G, A... **$15.00**

Atlas Photo Co, postcard, photo image of tired girl holding a candle, Wake Up Your Sales..., price list for prints on back, VG+, P3... **$40.00**

Atlas Prager Ale, label, 1933-36, Atlas Brewing Co, U-type permit number, 12-oz, VG, A **$30.00**

Atlas Prager Bock Beer, label, ca 1933-50, Atlas Brewing Co, Internal Revenue Tax Paid, 12-oz, EX, A **$7.00**

Atlas Special Certificate Brew, matchbook cover, features product name & Atlas Brewing Co, Chicago, 20 strike, M, R1 .... **$12.00**

Atlas Transit, matchbook cover, red, black & white, Fast Freight Service, Serving Arkansas, 20 strike, front striker, NM, R1 .... **$2.75**

Atlas Van Lines, doll, Atlas Annie, cloth, 15", EX, D... **$15.00**

Attracto Cigars, label, Attracto on scrolled banner borders top & Cigar Of Quality borders bottom of oval with castle & swan, 6x9", EX, D **$10.00**

Atwater Kent Radio, instruction booklet, 1927, illustrated, 47 pages, minor soiling, D....................................**$18.00**

Atwater Sweet Potatoes, can label, pictures sweet potatoes, Sunlit Fruit Co, G1 ....**$6.00**

Atwood's Coffee, tin, flat, key-wind lid, 1-lb, EX, D.**$20.00**

Aug Wolf & Co's Works, sign, paper, advertising around nighttime factory scene, matted & framed, 30x39", EX, D3..$975.00

August Flower German Syrup, clock, reverse-painted glass, silver & gold on black, round clock face in center, rare, 16x16", VG, D **$425.00**

August Flower German Syrup, thermometer, paper face, round with lettering in center, numbered perimeter, chipped repainted case, 9¼" dia, G+, A **$15.00**

Augustiner Beer, sign, embossed tin, Augustiner in shadowed letters above company seal at right of Beer Properly Aged, 14x20", VG+, A....................................**$35.00**

Aultman & Taylor Farm Machinery, sign, paper, barnyard scene with families & company's threshers, product lettering above, matted & framed, image: 15x36", G- A...**$350.00**

Aunt Jemima, creamer & sugar bowl with lid, plastic, yellow cups with Aunt Jemima & Uncle Mose on sides, F&F Mold & Die Co, EX, P2...............................**$150.00**

Aunt Jemima, dolls, Aunt Jemima, Uncle Moses, Wade & Diana, stuffed cloth, 12½" to 8¾", set of 4, EX, D..**$625.00**

Aunt Jemima, lapel pin, Aunt Jemima lettered on bendable tab above button, Breakfast Club & Eat A Better... around picture, VG+, A...**$14.00**

Aunt Jemima, paper plate, 1940s, smiling Aunt Jemima pictured in center with name lettered beneath, fluted edge, 9" dia, NM, P2 ....**$49.00**

Aunt Jemima, promotional banner, 1940, painted canvas, shows Aunt Jemima & stack of pancakes, Coming... In Person..., 33x56", NM, A.......................................**$330.00**

Aunt Jemima Pancake Flour, box, cardboard, picturing Aunt Jemima, 14x13x9", G-, A..............................**$55.00**

Aunt Jemima Pancake Flour, puzzle, die-cut cardboard, 2 product images on string attached to bust image of Aunt Jemima, 4x5", EX, D...................................**$125.00**

Aunt Jemima Pancake Flour, sign, copyright, 1917, cardboard hanger, 2-sided, Aunt Jemima seated in swing flanked by product, 18", EX+, A......$5,750.00

Aunt Jemima's Pancake Flour, mask, die-cut cardboard, Aunt Jemima's head wrapped in scarf with advertising, cutouts for eyes & nose, 13x12", M, A................**$200.00**

Aunty, crate label, Florida citrus, smiling Black lady holding a branch of citrus blossoms, 3½x8½", M, C1....**$2.00**

Aurora Brewing Co, label, 1933-50, encircled A logo above product name, Internal Revenue Tax Paid statement, 12-oz, EX, A **$11.00**

Aurora Brewing Co, tray, 1910, girl with flagon of beer against shrubbery, company name & Aurora Beer lettered on rim, 13x10½", G, A...............................**$160.00**

Austen's Forest Flower Cologne, trade card, young girl with big brown eyes wearing winter hat, G, D......**$4.00**

Austen's Forest Flower Cologne, trade card, young girl with wings holding pie & flowers, EX, D **$3.00**

Austin Ammunition, pin-back button, 3 dogs on gold background, round, EX, A...................................**$50.00**

Austin Healy 3000, sign, 1960s, MK 111 Sports Convertible with harbor scene in background, signed Johnston, 25x35", M, A **$110.00**

Austin Powder Co, sign, 1892, paper, image of 3 dogs, Compliments Of Austin Powder Co, Austin O at top, black frame, 22x17", VG+, A...........................**$1,200.00**

Austin's Dog Bread, sign, self-framed tin, 1 of 3, woman feeding dogs, Don't All Speak At Once, Chase Emerson illustration, 38x26", VG, A **$850.00**

Austin-Western Co LTD, match safe, ca 1905, celluloid & nickel, company name lettered diagonally over allegorical image, EX+, D **$380.00**

Auto Strop Razor, sign, tin, pictures hands & razor, G, D...**$365.00**

Auto-Lite Service, sign, painted metal flange, 2-sided, Auto-Lite on band wrapped around Authorized Service panel, 12½x19", VG/G-, A **$25.00**

Auto-Lite Spark Plugs, cabinet, painted metal, glass front, advertising marquee above, 2 rows of tin display boxes on each side, 19x13", VG+, A **$45.00**

Auto-Lite Spark Plugs, sign, porcelain, spark plugs & lettering in oval center, Better Motor Performance... above & below, 23x11", M, D **$95.00**

Autobacco Tobacco, tin, red with Autobacco lettered above pipe-smoking driver looking over steering wheel, SS Pierce Co, 5x5x3", VG, A **$60.00**

Autobacco Tobacco, tin, red with Autobacco lettered above pipe-smoking driver looking over steering wheel, SS Pierce Co, 5x5x3", G, A **$40.00**

Autocrat Coffee, tin, pictures a steaming cup of coffee with product name above & below, Brownell & Field Co, 3-lb, EX, A **$100.00**

Automobile Invincible Oil, pocket mirror, barrel shape, EX, D **$95.00**

Automobilist Cigars, box label, inner lid sample, 1890s, 3 people in early touring car, Schlegel litho, VG, A . **$176.00**

Avalon Cigarettes, sign, paper, lady's head in 3-quarter pose above large Avalon Cigarettes on white band & product pack, 18x12", NM, A **$15.00**

Avalon Cigarettes, sign, paper, sexy lady in flat wide-brimmed hat poses with cigarette, Avalon on white band & product pack, 15x10", NM, A **$10.00**

Avon, talcum tin, 1977, commemorates California Perfume Co, Trailing Arbutus, floral decor, gold highlights, 5½", NMIB, A **$10.00**

Avon Champion Spark Plug, cologne decanter, EX in box, P4 .... **$6.00**

Avon Products Co, catalog, ca 1951, 128 pages, VG, D . **$35.00**

AW Kenison Co, calendar, 1906, paper, girl in profile holding daisies, green background, matted & framed, 19½x14½", NM, A **$275.00**

AW Kenison Co, calendar, 1908, cardboard, portrait of a girl in oval center, full pad, matted & framed, image: 19½x14", VG, A **$125.00**

Ayer's Ague Cure, sign, tin, stork in marsh at lower left of product advertising, Excellent Remedy For Liver Complaints, 28x14", G, A **$850.00**

Ayer's Cherry Pectoral, trade card, girl with dove on her shoulder holding basket of cherries, ...For Colds, Coughs, Throat..., EX, A **$24.00**

Ayer's Hair Vigor, sign, paper, bare-chested nymph rising from a lily, For The Toilet, trimmed borders, 14x11", EX, A **$1,650.00**

Ayer's Hair Vigor, sign, 1896, cardboard hanger, girl with long hair holding product, product name below, 6½x4½", EX, S5 .... **$150.00**

Ayer's Pills, sign, paper, Black country doctor with child in his lap, ...The Best Family Physic, framed, image: 41x28½", EX, A **$9,500.00**

Ayer's Pills, trade card, 1880s, 'The Little Favorites,' group of girls holding banner, Ayer's Pills, Sugar Coated, EX, P1 .... **$15.00**

Ayer's Sarsaparilla, sign, ca 1880, tin, Victorian bedroom scene with 2 women tending to another, Purifying The Blood..., framed, EX, A **$1,000.00**

Azucena Cigars, box label, inner lid, 1884, Arab woman & various Arabian scenes, 6x9", M, C3 .... **$20.00**

Azur, sign, porcelain, 2-sided, Azur in blue arched lettering over blue & white star on white, orange border, 66" dia, VG, D3 .... $475.00

B

B&B Overalls, thermometer, porcelain, pictures man in overalls, G, D **$1,750.00**

B&S Brand Coffee, coffee-bean container, metal with glass sides, top shows dressed elephant left of emblem, blinks on & off, 28", EX, A **$200.00**

B-Wise, crate label, 1930s, California pears, pictures an owl on blue background, Sacramento, 7½x11", M, C3 . **$16.00**

B-1 Lemon-Lime Soda, bottle carrier, cardboard, logo & lettering on striped background, NM, B1 .... **$3.00**

B-1 Lemon-Lime Soda, decal, 1946, pictures sandwich & bottle of soda, Delicious, Nutricious below, 7x8½", EX, D **$8.00**

B-1 Lemon-Lime Soda, display, light-up panel beside bottle, round red & white logo above, More Zip In Every Sip!, NM, M3 .... **$85.00**

B-1 Lemon-Lime Soda, fan pull, cardboard, round with red B-1 on white dot above white Lemon-Lime Soda on red, EX, M3 .... **$10.00**

B-1 Lemon-Lime Soda, plate from push bar, tin, yellow product name on black, 3x16", NM, M3 .... **$20.00**

B-1 Lemon-Lime Soda, sign, cardboard hanger, B-1 in red on white circle above Lemon-Lime Soda, round, NM, B1 .... **$4.00**

B-1 Lemon-Lime Soda, sign, 1940, cardboard stand-up, girl in gingham dress with bottle, Up To Your Lips In Pleasure..., 11x28", EX, D **$36.00**

B-1 Lemon-Lime Soda, sign, 1940s, cardboard stand-up, pictures kids riding carousel, lettering above, 10x7", EX, D **$10.00**

B-1 Lemon-Lime Soda, thermometer, 1950s, embossed tin, logo & lettering on striped ground, 16x4½", EX, D .. **$44.00**

Bab-O, sample tin, EX, D **$35.00**

Baby Ruth, candy box, 1950s, cardboard, pictures the co-stars from the movie 'Gypsy,' 12x6", EX, A..........**$33.00**

Baby Ruth, jar, clear glass barrel shape, red & white tin lid with Curtiss Candy Co lettered over Baby Ruth, 3¾", EX, D..........**$15.00**

Baby Ruth, matchbook cover, full-length ad, ...5¢, Rich In Pure Dextrose, The Energy Sugar, full book, 20 strike, EX, R1..........**$6.00**

Baby Ruth, tape dispenser, porcelain with paper labels reading Curtiss Baby Ruth Candy & Gum, 2x10½", VG, A..........**$25.00**

Baby's Balm Unscented Talcum Powder, tin, baby seated by tub in gold-bordered circular inset above product lettering on textured ground, oval, 5x3", EX, D.**$110.00**

Baby's Dy-Dee Service, squeeze toy, 1950s, rubber, delivery truck with crowned infant seated atop, company name in red on sides, 4x5", VG, A..........**$35.00**

Baby's Own Talc, tin, Baby's Own Talcum lettered on fancy emblem over yellow background, shaker top, tall flat oval shape, EX+, M2..........**$62.00**

Bacardi Rum, rug, 20x17½", EX, D..........**$12.50**

Badger Mutual Fire Insurance Co, paperweight, 1887-1937, embossed cast-iron badger figure on oval base marked The Badger Mutual, EX, A..........**$45.00**

Badger Pure Barley Malt Extract, sign, tin, product name & logo on yellow, The National Beverage Distributing Co..., 12x18", EX+, M3..........**$65.00**

Bagdad Coffee, pail, Bagdad arched above 2 Arabs & camel, Coffee lettered below, screw lid & bail handle, 9x7" dia, EX, M2..........**$68.00**

Bagdad Smoking Tobacco, sign, ca 1909, man in profile smoking pipe with product in hand, Bagdad Short Cut etched in frame, 33¼x24", EX, A..$390.00

Bagley's Burley Boy Tobacco, lunch box, tin, trademark image of child boxing on oval insets, hinged lid & bail handle, rare, 5x6½x4", EX, A..........**$2,200.00**

Bagley's Old Colony Mixture Smoking Tobacco, pocket tin, upright, red oval bust portrait of woman in profile on white background, product name above & below, G, M2..........**$80.00**

Bagley's Old Colony Mixture Smoking Tobacco, pocket tin, upright, red oval bust portrait of woman in profile on gold background, product name above & below, NM, H3..........$500.00

Bagley's Red Belt Pipe or Cigarette Tobacco, pocket tin, upright, pictures a red belt with product name above & below, slip lid, EX, A..........**$15.00**

Bagley's Wild Fruit Tobacco, lunch box, Bagley's arched above Wild Fruit Tobacco, slip lid, bail handle, VG, A..........**$75.00**

Bailey, Farrell & Co, trade card, 1870-80, oval hunt scene surrounded by pictorial & lettered vignettes, black & white, VG, A..........**$130.00**

Bailey's Irish Cream, mirror, with map of Ireland, 17x21", EX, D..........**$30.00**

Bailey's Pure Rye, sign, ca 1902, self-framed tin, waitress carrying tray into room of costumed men & women, Shonk litho, 26x18", VG, A..........**$215.00**

Baker Furniture, catalog, 1931, 100 pages, VG, D...**$25.00**

Baker Guns, pocket catalog, 1928, pictures a rifle & various game birds in flight on cover, 8 pages, scarce, VG, A..........**$85.00**

Baker's Cocoa, cookie jar, glass, round with yellow images of the Chocolate Girl, 10", EX, A..........**$143.00**

Baker's Cocoa, tray, deep-dish with flat rim, Chocolate Girl & advertising in center, 14" dia, VG, A..........**$176.00**

Baker's Cocoa, see also Walter Baker or W/WH Baker & Co

Baker's Coconut, recipe book, 1934, 'The New Coconut Treasure Book,' 38 pages, EX, D..........**$10.00**

Baker's Delight Baking Powder, sign, cardboard, pictures Black cook, movable price wheels, 14x12", A..........**$10.00**

Baker's Hygrade Ice Cream, thermometer, wood, black on gold, portrait above product name, company name below, rounded top & bottom, 14", VG+, A..........**$40.00**

Baker's Pure Fruit Flavoring Extracts, recipe book, 24 pages, G, D..........**$18.00**

Bakers Choice, can label, bakery scene with baker trimming crust & lady stacking pies, 6½x10", EX, G1..........**$10.00**

Bakers Talcum, tin, stork with baby, EX+, D....**$150.00**

Bald Eagle Whiskey, pocket mirror, eagle perched on lettered mountain top before sunburst, filigree border, SF Petts Co, oval, 2¾", G, A................$60.00

Balkan Sobranie Turkish Cigarettes, box, yellow with black graphics of Turkish scenes bordered by lettered & scrolled banners & columns, 1x6x3", EX, A **$25.00**

Ball's Hip Skating Corset, trade card, 1870s, with corset inset, pictures girl skating, EX, P1.........................**$35.00**

Ballantine Ale & Beer, sign, cardboard, lady with glass of beer, America's Finest below, EX, A **$50.00**

Ballantine Ale & Beer, sign, cardboard, woman with Christmas gifts & bag of bottles flanked by Happy Holidays, framed, image: 12x17", EX, A **$65.00**

Ballantine Ale & Beer, tray, beer glass beside product name & 3-ring logo in black & red on white, star motif on background, 12" dia, VG, D............................**$18.00**

Ballantine's Breweries, calendar, 1908, cardboard, factory inset at top, decorative border, December sheet, framed, image: 20x12½", VG, A.........................**$320.00**

Ballantine's Canada Malt Ale, label, pre-Prohibition, EX, A...**$21.00**

Ballantine Scotch, display, inflatable snowman, 44", EX, D...**$18.00**

Ballistite & Empire Smokeless Powders, lapel stud, World's Best..., red, white & blue, VG, A............**$15.00**

Ballistite & Empire Smokeless Powders, pin-back button, ...The Best Smokeless Powders lettered on red, white & blue target, EX, A...................................**$35.00**

Ballistite Smokeless Powders, pin-back button, The Only Perfect Dense Smokeless Powder above & below Ballistite on large center band, round, EX, A **$15.00**

Balm of Tulips, display box, 2-sided, divided to hold 12 bottles of remedy, marquee above, has bottles & various cards, 8x4", NM, A **$250.00**

Baltimore American Ale & Beer, sign, embossed tin, Baltimore upper left of American in diagonal script, receding Beer & Ale 10¢, 18x36", VG, A **$80.00**

Baltimore Brewing Co, tray, oval image of woman holding glass of Special B-B, Each Glass Invites Another... on rim, 13¼x10½", G, A.....................................**$170.00**

Balyeat Mattresses, Pillows & Box Springs, ad, paper, lady seated on bed above frontal view of mattress, box springs & pillows, Insure Sleep, framed, A **$15.00**

Bambino Smoking Tobacco, pocket tin, upright, outlined product name above baseball player at bat outlined in white, VG, A...**$650.00**

Bambino Smoking Tobacco, pocket tin, upright, outlined product name above baseball player outlined in white, NM, A...**$1,546.00**

Bank Note Cigars, box, light brown bank note resembling currency, 5x9½x1½", EX, D **$15.00**

Bank Note Cigars, box label, inner lid, large brown note resembling currency, 6x9", M, D **$6.50**

Bank Note Cigars, tin, Bank Note above Five Cents surrounded by ornate border, slip lid, vertical rectangle, EX, A **$40.00**

Banneret Cigars, box label, outer, child holding a banner, 4½x4½", M, C3..**$12.50**

Banquet Ice Cream, sign, curved reverse-painted glass, We Sell Banquet above soda & sundae, Ice Cream & company name below, 37x23", EX, A **$1,200.00**

Banquet Tea, teapot, stoneware, white on brown, ...A Wonderful Flavor, Iced Hot, dome lid, VG+, A .**$140.00**

Banquet Tea, teapot, stoneware, white on brown, ...A Wonderful Flavor, Iced Hot, replaced lid/touched up, G, A..**$25.00**

Bar Special Pilsener Beer, label, 1933-50, Volk Brewery Co, Internal Revenue Tax Paid statement, 12-oz, EX, A..**$21.00**

Baranger Studios' Advertising Automaton, 'A Diamond Always Rings the Bell,' 18x17x16", EX, A....$2,250.00

Baranger Studios' Advertising Automaton, 'Cherubs Wedding Ring Factory,' 14½x20x13½", EX, A.**$3,250.00**

Baranger Studios' Advertising Automaton, 'Crew Hard at Work Building Wristwatch,' 13x12x12", As Is, A..**$4,500.00**

Baranger Studios' Advertising Automaton, 'Diamond in Safe,' 19½x17x12", EX, A.................................**$1,750.00**

Baranger Studios' Advertising Automaton, 'Diamond Workers Setting Stone,' (in large ring), 17x13½x13½", EX, A...**$5,200.00**

Baranger Studios' Advertising Automaton, 'For the Thrill of Her Life, One of Our Beautiful Diamonds,' couple in howdah on elephant, 22x19x12", EX, A...........**$2,500.00**

Baranger Studios' Advertising Automaton, 'From the Diamond in the Rough to the Finished Jewel,' 19x14¾x14", EX, A **$3,000.00**

Baranger Studios' Advertising Automaton, 'Gem from Mine to You,' 17x23x15", EX, A **$1,750.00**

Baranger Studios' Advertising Automaton, 'Get on the Bandwagon with One of Our Beautiful Diamonds,' 18½x18x15½", EX, A **$2,950.00**

Baranger Studios' Advertising Automaton, 'Have No Fear, One of Our Beautiful Diamonds Will Win Her,' Davy Crockett on carousel, 19x18½x9", EX, A **$2,950.00**

Baranger Studios' Advertising Automaton, 'Hold Your Horses, Don't Forget the Diamond,' 13x25x12", EX, A **$3,750.00**

Baranger Studios' Advertising Automaton, 'It's In the Cards Dear, You'll Buy Your Diamonds Here,' 15x15x12", EX, A **$2,200.00**

Baranger Studios' Advertising Automaton, 'Jewelry Factory at Work,' 22x18x14½", EX, A **$3,000.00**

Baranger Studios' Advertising Automaton, 'Let One of Our Diamonds Be Your Very Own Star,' 14x16" dia, EX, A **$3,250.00**

Baranger Studios' Advertising Automaton, 'Man Cutting Woman on Sawmill,' 17½x22¾x14½", EX, A **$2,000.00**

Baranger Studios' Advertising Automaton, 'Mounting Diamond in Setting,' (on large ring with ladder), 18½x12x9", EX, A **$3,650.00**

Baranger Studios' Advertising Automaton, 'Movie Star Collage with Diamond Cutters at Work,' 15x14x13¼", EX, A **$2,250.00**

Baranger Studios' Advertising Automaton, 'Our Diamond Inspectors at Work,' 14x14x10", EX, A **$2,750.00**

Baranger Studios' Advertising Automaton, 'Pirates at Their Work,' 20x19x12½", EX, A **$2,250.00**

Baranger Studios' Advertising Automaton, 'She Is a Happy Bride with One of Our Beautiful Diamonds,' 19x15½x12", EX, A **$3,500.00**

Baranger Studios' Advertising Automaton, 'She Is a Happy Bride with One of Our Four Beautiful Diamonds,' Jeep with top, 12½x17x12", EX, A **$3,000.00**

Baranger Studios' Advertising Automaton, 'The Old Woman Who Lived in the Shoe, Her Diamond Was Bought Here Too,' 16x22x13", EX, A **$5,000.00**

Baranger Studios' Advertising Automaton, 'Win Her the Easy Way,' 19x14¾x14", EX, A **$2,700.00**

Baranger Studios' Advertising Automaton, 'You Will Always Win if You Pick One of Our Diamonds,' jockey on horse within horseshoe, 17½x17x7", EX, A **$2,000.00**

Barbarossa Premium Beer, sign, embossed composition, King being served by gnomes with 2 crows dropping in, flaking/chipping, 13½" dia, G, A **$95.00**

Barbey's Sunshine Beer, clock, reverse-lit glass, Sunshine on large band above clock face, clock not working, 22" dia, G-, A **$350.00**

Barbey's Sunshine Beer, globe, yellow case glass body with reverse-painted glass inserts, minor chips to rim/edge inserts, 17x15" dia, EX, A **$825.00**

Barbock's Talc, tin, Oriental motif in golds & red, shaker top, round shape, EX, M2 ......**$105.00**

Barcardi Rum, bathroom scale, metal, working, 12½x10½", EX, D **$15.00**

Barcardi Rum, pool cue, with inscribed carrying case, EX, D **$18.00**

Barefoot Boy Tomatoes, can label, pictures little barefoot boy in rolled-up pants, M, C1 ......**$2.50**

Barker's Nerve & Bone Liniment, sign, ca 1883, paper, pictures variety of farm animals with river beyond, 24x30", G, A **$525.00**

Barnsdall Super-Gas, sign, porcelain, 2-sided, white with Barnsdall Super-Gas lettered above Ethyl logo, blue border, 30" dia, G+/G, A **$150.00**

Barq's, menu board, embossed tin, Drink above Barq's in diagonal script above Good lower right, chalkboard below, 28x20", VG+, A **$5.00**

Barq's Root Beer, can, steel, EX, D **$4.00**

Barrelhead Root Beer, can, steel, EX, D **$4.00**

Barrington Hall Bakerized Coffee, measure, tin with raised lettering, worn, 3½", D $8.00

Barry's Ale, label, 1933-50, New England Brewing Co, Internal Revenue Tax Paid statement, 12-oz, EX, A **$20.00**

Barry's Half & Half Ale & Porter, label, 1933-50, New England Brewing Co, Internal Revenue Tax Paid statement, 12-oz, EX, A **$20.00**

Bartels Beer, sign, sand & painted canvas, professor holding glass of beer, The Professor Says..., framed, image: 56x26", G-, A **$350.00**

Bartels Beer, tray, deep-dish, elderly man hoisting stein of beer, lettering on rim, 12" dia, EX, A **$250.00**

Bartels Malt Extract, sign, early, tin over cardboard, pictures bottle, An Ideal Tonic..., 6x13", NM, B1 ......**$125.00**

Bartels Pure Beer, sign, self-framed tin, bold lettering with logo in upper left, minor fading/scratches, 22¼x28", G, A **$600.00**

Bartholomay Beers & Ales, tray, deep-dish, girl on winged wheel among clouds, 12" dia, G+, A **$125.00**

Bastian Bros Co, pocket mirror, shows factory scene with busy sidewalk, lettering above & below, oval, 2¾" long, EX, A **$190.00**

Bata Bullets High-Top Sneakers, display, plaster shoe, 12x24x7", G, A **$25.00**

Batory Cigars, label, Batory arched over portrait of the Polish king, 4x4", EX, D....................................**$12.00**

Battle Creek Food Co, booklet, 'Healthful Living,' information on weight reducing & price list, 65 pages, EX, D....**$10.00**

Baum's Polish, display, die-cut cardboard stand-up, lady in open touring car with Baum's arched above, Wonderful..., 10x9", VG, A.......................................**$45.00**

Baum's Polish, display, die-cut cardboard stand-up, lady in open touring car with Baum's arched above, Wonderful..., 10x9", NM, A....................................**$175.00**

Bausch & Lomb, catalog, 1929, features microscopes & scientific instruments, 318 pages, VG+, H2..............**$75.00**

Bavarian Premium Beer, sign, tin on cardboard hanger or stand-up, man drinking beer behind product name, In 8 Ounce Splits, 6x9", NM, B1...............................**$12.00**

Bay Gasoline, sign, tin, 2-sided, S2...........................**$45.00**

Bay State Moulding Manufactory, trade card, coated stock, Proprietor Joseph F Paul, Boston Mass in oval center, red patterned background, gold border, EX, A...........**$145.00**

Bay State Paints, sign, 1940s, die-cut porcelain flange, Pilgrim with yellow paint, product name in white on green, 15x15", EX, A................................$130.00

Bay State Ranges, Furnaces & Stoves, trade card, pictures nighttime winter scene with cabin near water, 4½x3¼", EX, D..**$4.50**

Bayer Aspirin, sign, tin, Safe For Aches & Pains above Bayer Aspirin & aspirin pill, Does Not Depress The Heart below, 15x18", VG+, D1.............................**$49.00**

Bayle Peanut Butter, pail, pictures Scouting scenes, press lid & bail handle, 12-oz, VG+, A........................**$110.00**

Beacon Java Coffee, bin, tin, yellow with red & silver, Boyd, Leeds & Co arched above lighthouse, product name below, 22x13x13", EX, A..........................**$200.00**

Beacon Shoes, sign, reverse-painted glass, product name above vertical oval logo, With Goodyear Heels Attached, framed, 21x15", VG, A..........................**$70.00**

Beadle's Half Dime Library, broadside, engraved & hand-colored wood, portrait insets & listings of Half Dime novels, framed, image: 33x23", VG, A............**$1,500.00**

Bears' Elephant Cigarettes, tin, rectangular shape with hinged lid, red with yellow accents, elephant motif, VG, M2...**$110.00**

Beau Brummell Ties, advertisement, portrait of George Bryan Brummell in top hat, lettered frame, 29x22½", EX+, A..**$140.00**

Beau Geste, crate label, 1940s, California vegetable, foreign legion soldier playing bugle in desert, El Centro, 10½x9", M, C1..**$1.00**

Beautyskin, pocket mirror, Beautyskin on the diagonal above lady with head turned right, For Health & Beauty, oval, 2⅜", EX, A......................................**$60.00**

Beaver State Beer, label, 1933-50, product name on V-shape, Rose City Brewing Co, Internal Revenue Tax Paid statement, 64-oz, EX, A..**$18.00**

Bedwell & Co's Tobaccos, Snuffs & Cigars, broadside, 3 Black men rolling barrels on oval surrounded by lettered vignettes, framed, image: 14x18½", EX, A..............**$100.00**

Bee Brand Tomatoes, can label, 1933, pictures large tomato & beehives, M, C3...................................**$15.00**

Bee Hive Overalls, pocket mirror, Bee Hive Overalls Best Maid arched above shirtless girl in overalls, oval, 2¾x1¾", VG+, A...**$160.00**

Beech-Nut Chewing Tobacco, sign, porcelain, package of tobacco left of product name, EX+, A......................**$140.00**

Beech-Nut Chewing Tobacco, sign, porcelain, tobacco pouch left of product name, chipping/scratches/rust/edge wear, 10½x22", A..................................**$60.00**

Beech-Nut Chewing Tobacco, tin, photo image of early auto on oval on lid, Our Visit To The Beech-Nut Plant Will Stand Out..., 7x10x16", VG+, A.....................**$77.00**

Beech-Nut Coffee, tin, key-wind lid, 1-lb, G, D........**$16.50**

Beech-Nut Gum, billboard poster, ca 1951, man on pole beside large pack of gum, Any Time!..., Spurgeon-Tucker, 8 ft 6" x 19 ft 6", EX, A............................**$50.00**

Beech-Nut Gum, display, tin, little girl with stick of gum on marquee atop pedestaled case, Peppermint Flavored..., 5¢, 11x7x7", EX, A................................**$600.00**

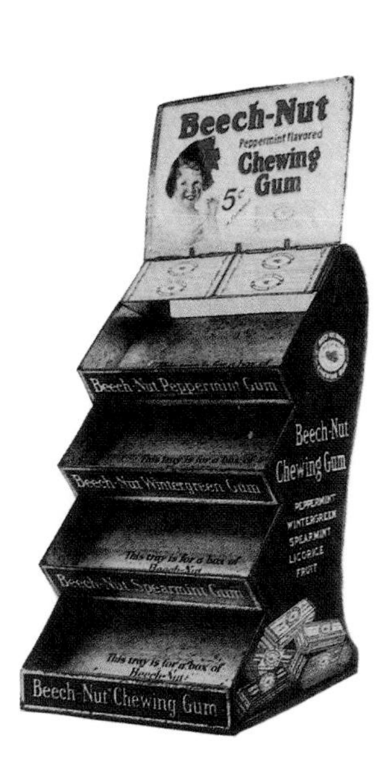

Beech-Nut Gum, display, tin, 4-tiered slanted shelves labeled with various flavors, allover advertising & girl on marquee, 15", EX, A..........................$450.00

Beech-Nut Gum, sign, cardboard stand-up, lady in red dress & hat gives thumbs-up to Beech-Nut Gum, advertising lower left, 17", VG+, A..............................**$250.00**

Beech-Nut Gum, sign, tin, pack of gum featured in lower left corner with Beech-Nut Peppermint Gum, Always Refreshing!, 16x30", EX, A..................................**$148.00**

Beech-Nut Gum, squeeze toy, 1960s, rubber, open pack of peppermint gum with silvered tips, VG, A...........**$37.00**

Beefeater Gin, display, wood & composition, figural castle guard holding spear on rectangular base with yellow lettering, 17x9", EX, A..**$75.00**

Beefeater Gin, water pitcher, EX, D..........................**$15.00**

Beeman's Pepsin Gum, pocket mirror, Beeman's on banner above man's portrait flanked by Pepsin & Gum, Good For Digestion, 2⅛" dia, EX, A..................**$140.00**

Beeman's Pepsin Gum, sign, tin, yellow with gum pack at left of red product name, Aids Digestion in black, 3x18", NM, A..**$375.00**

Bel Boy Beer, label, 1933-50, bellboy flanked by product name, Huntley Brewing Co, Internal Revenue Tax Paid statement, VG, A..**$33.00**

Belding's Emby. Silk, display case, oak frame with glass sides, hanging embroidery thread display inside, 28x24x24", G, A...**$500.00**

Belding's Spool Silk, display case, revolving rack in mahogany-stained wood with glass sides above 3 drawers, 32½", G+, A...**$800.00**

Belfast Tobacco, box, square, NM, H3.....................**$50.00**

Belknap Hardware, catalog, 1961, M, D..................**$60.00**

Bell Ethyl, gas globe, 1920s-30s, red plastic body, Bell lettered in blue above logo, 13½" dia, EX, A...$375.00

Bell Piano, bookmark, die-cut celluloid, owl shape with upright piano, The Wise Buy..., NM, A................**$90.00**

Bell Roasted Coffee, pocket mirror, pictures lettered bell, America's Best lettered above, Buy No Other below, 2⅛" dia, NM, A...**$44.00**

Bell's Imperial Coffee, pocket mirror, Imperial lettered over bell on dark background, JH Bell & Co Chicago below, scratches, 2¼" dia, EX, A..........................**$46.00**

Bell System, sign, porcelain, 2-sided, Bell System lettered on bell in center of arrow, Public Telephone above, 6x12¼", EX+, A..**$40.00**

Bell Telephone Cable, sign, 1940s, porcelain, encircled bell in center, blue & white, 7x3½", EX, D...........**$16.00**

Bella De Cuba Cigars, box label, inner lid, woman playing guitar, 6x9", C3...**$22.00**

Bellas Hess, catalog, 1958, Spring/Summer, VG+, H2..**$25.00**

Belle of Anderson Sour Mash, sign, reverse-painted glass, bare-breasted women by Turkish baths, star logo lower left, framed, image: 28x20", G-, A......................**$350.00**

Belmont Brewing Co, mug, ceramic, banded above & below hops decorated bell above Belmont Brewing Co, Martin's Ferry O, 5", EX, D.................................**$125.00**

Ben Bey Superfine Cigar, tin, Ben Bey above logo & Superfine Cigar..., logo surrounds border, hinged lid, rust/scratches, 3½x5", D..........................$35.00

Ben Hur Cigars, box label, end, Ben Hur in chariot pulled by 4 white horses, 2½x5", M, D.............................**$2.50**

Bendix Home Laundry, sign, 1940s, cardboard, little girl looking in old washer, Washes Rinses, Damp-Dry..., 11x28", EX, D..**$28.00**

Bendtsen Ice Cream, container, 1930s, pictures a cow, red & white, 4x3½" dia, EX, D...................................**$12.00**

Bengal Gin, display, roaring tiger figure, ...Imported (And Undomesticated!) on base, 9x6x7", G, A.............**$70.00**

Benham's Ice Cream, tray, deep-dish, large dish of ice cream encircled by Palmer Cox brownies, minor fading/scratches, 13¼x10½", VG, A........................**$150.00**

Bennett Bros, catalog, 1971, jewelry, appliances, toys & general merchandise, 762 pages, VG+, H2...........**$30.00**

Bentley & Bush Law Offices, sign, tin, 2-sided, gold lettering on black sand background, Frank S Bentley, Law Office... on reverse, worn, 12x17", A...................**$40.00**

Bentley & Bush Law Offices, sign, wood, 2-sided, Law-Offices, Bentley & Bush in gold letters on black sand background, 9½x31½", VG, A.............................**$80.00**

Berbiglia Beer, label, 1933-50, Capital Brewery Inc, Internal Revenue Tax Paid statement, 1-qt, EX, A.......**$15.00**

Bergdoll's Beer, calendar, 1902, elderly man & woman with glass of beer, circular logo in upper corners, framed, image: 16½x22", EX, A...........................**$400.00**

Bergdoll's Beer, sign, paper, stock image of Bavarian man sampling beer, logo on wall, framed, image: 19x14½", VG, A..**$95.00**

Berger's Storm King Cold Blast Lantern, postcard, pictures little girl climbing up a ladder with a lantern, Can't Keep Us Down, VG, P3 .... **$35.00**

Berghoff Beer, sign, self-framed tin on cardboard, pictures 2 hunting dogs in snowy scene, Right On Every Point, 13x21", EX, A **$55.00**

Bergner & Engel Brewing Co, match safe, celluloid over tin, trademark phoenix bird logo on front, girl with long hair on back, 3x1½", G, A **$60.00**

Bergner & Engel Brewing Co's Tannhaeuser, pocket knife, embossed nickel over brass, Tannhaeuser & phoenix bird logo, 3-blade & corkscrew, 3¼" long, VG, A **$60.00**

Bergner & Engel Brewing Co's Tannhaeuser, sign, embossed tin, phoenix bird logo with lettering above & below, framed, image: 29½x21½", G, A **$250.00**

Berina Malted Milk Food, sign, pre-1920, porcelain, Scottish gent looking out over ocean, product image & lettering at left, 24x60", EX, M2 .... **$410.00**

Bering Cigars, label, Bering arched above clipper ship before sunset, Very Mild lettered on ribbon banner below, 6x9", EX, D **$8.00**

Bering Cigars, label, Bering lettered above portrait of explorer in oval with gold border on solid gold background, 6x9", EX, D **$10.00**

Berkley & Jay Furniture, catalog, 1910, 32 pages, VG+, H2 .... **$35.00**

Berkshire Brewing Association, sign, paper, appears to be Teddy Roosevelt during the war toasting to the enemy, framed, image: 30x21½", VG, A **$1,600.00**

Berma Coffee, tin, cream & black on red, product name above plantation with mountains in the distance, screw lid, 1-lb, EX, A $85.00

Bernheim Distilling Co, sign, paper copy of 1897 photograph of a Black couple being married by local preacher, 12x16½", VG, A **$55.00**

Bernheimer & Schwartz Pilsener Brewing Co, calendar, 1915, large factory image, lettering above, full pad, framed, image: 29x20½", NM, A **$800.00**

Bernheimer & Schwartz Pilsener Brewing Co, sign, paper, pictures man on rearing horse in ornate oval, rectangular factory scene below, framed, image: 26½x18", EX, A **$525.00**

Berry Bros Automobile Color Varnishes, display, wood frame encloses strips of varnished wood on either end of center ad panel showing auto, 10x33", VG, A **$385.00**

Berry Bros Hard Oil Finish, trade card, pictures Uncle Sam supplying the world with Berry Bros Hard Oil Finish, EX, A **$19.00**

Berry Brothers Varnishes, packing crate made into child's wagon, wood, 20x30x18", G, A **$175.00**

Berry Brothers Varnishes, pocket mirror, children playing with dog & in wagon, The Berry Brothers' Toy Wagon lettered below, 2⅛" dia, G, A **$65.00**

Berry Brothers Varnishes, pocket mirror, pictures small farm boy pulling dog in yellow wagon with red wheels, oval, 2¾" long, EX, A **$225.00**

Berson Candy, display box, tin, double lid hinged in middle, advertising on sides, 12x14½", EX, A **$25.00**

Bertolli Pure Olive Oil, statuette/toothpick holder, 1970, composition, Bertolli Chef holding product on red base, 6", NM, D **$30.00**

Bertsch & HB Hard Pan Shoes, pocket mirror, girl resting elbows on table while holding flowers, ...For Men & Boys, oval, 2¾", EX, A **$300.00**

Besser Beer, label, 1933-50, Prima Co, Internal Revenue Tax Paid statement, 32-oz, EX, A **$13.00**

Best Quality Sewing Machine Needles, cabinet, wood case with embossed tin front picturing Presidents Washington & Lincoln, 17½" long, G, A **$60.00**

Best Selection Cigars, box label, inner lid, sunrise scene with singing bird & flowers, 6x9", EX, C3 .... **$12.00**

Bethlehem Liquor, tray, majestic elk in center, Pure Family Liquors lettered below, good sheen, 13¼x13¼", VG, A **$105.00**

Betsy Ross Shoes, pocket mirror, shows Betsy Ross seated while sewing flag, Locke Shoe Co, oval, 2¾", EX, A **$625.00**

Betsy Ross Tea, tin, image of Betsy Ross with flag flanked by Orange Pekoe & Pekoe, Plunkett-Jarell Grocer Co, press lid, VG, D $30.00

Betsy Ross 5¢ Cigar, sign, self-framed tin, oval portrait of Betsy Ross with American Flag, fading/scratches/chips, 24x20", G, A **$100.00**

Betty Ann Baking Powder, label, 1920s-30s, little red-headed girl in pink dress skipping rope, gilt border, Hastings Ne, 6-oz, M, C1 .... **$3.00**

Betty Crocker, recipe book, 1956, 'How To Have the Most Fun with Cake Mixes,' 34 pages, EX, D **$6.00**

Betty Crocker, recipe book, 1957, 'Cookie Carnival,' 38 pages, EX, D **$6.00**

Betty Crocker, recipe book, 1963, 'Festive Fixin's with a Foreign Flair,' 23 pages, EX, D **$4.00**

Betty Crocker, recipe book, 1967, '42 Hot Potato Ideas,' 15 pages, EX, D **$4.00**

Betty Crocker, recipe book, 1969, 'Ways with Hamburger,' 24 pages, EX, D **$2.50**

Betty Zane Pop Corn (sic), box, allover star graphics with product name flanking girl, Pop Corn 10¢, 2-oz, NM, A **$5.00**

Betty Zane Popcorn, can, Dwarf White Hulless arched above girl with stars on dress, Guaranteed To Pop below, no top, 10-oz, EX, A **$30.00**

Beverwyck Beer, can, cone-top, Famous Beverwyck Beer, red, green & silver, some rust, D **$24.00**

Beverwyck Beer, tray, deep-dish, Beverwyck lettered graphics in red & gold on green & black background, 12" dia, EX, A **$60.00**

Beverwyck Beer, tray, girl lifting glass of lager on draped background, lettering on rim, minor rim chips, 13" dia, EX, A **$150.00**

Beverwyck Irish Cream Ale, can, cone-top, label features clover-leaf logo, EX+, A **$50.00**

Beverwyck Irish Cream Ale, can, cone-top, label features clover-leaf logo, VG, D **$22.00**

Bevo, sign, self-framed tin, bottle & fox sitting on bench flank Bevo 10¢, The-All-Year-Round-Soft Drink, horizontal, EX, M1 .... $345.00

Bevo, tray, depicts 3-team horse-drawn delivery wagon with simulated wood-grain border lettered Bevo, 10½x13¼", G, A **$65.00**

Bewley's Anchor Feeds, sign, porcelain, pictures anchor, G, D **$360.00**

BF Goodrich, sign, painted tin, BF Goodrich over large glowing tire image BF G seal over bottom part of tire, 23x35", EX, A **$20.00**

BF Goodrich, see also Goodrich

BF Goodrich Tires-Batteries, sign, 1948, porcelain, BF G tire logos flank Tires-Batteries below bold BF Goodrich in cream on blue, 17x72", EX+, A **$100.00**

BF Gravely Tobacco, tin, square corners, NM, D ... **$225.00**

BH Douglass' Capsicum Cough Drops, plate, porcelain, black & white on mustard orange ground, ...For Coughs, Colds & Sore Throats, 6¼" dia, M, D.... **$150.00**

Bickmore Easy-Shave Cream, sign, die-cut cardboard stand-up, man applying cream to brush above large tube & 35¢, 31x21", VG, A.................................. **$10.00**

Bickmore Easy-Shave Cream, sign, die-cut cardboard stand-up, man applying cream to brush above large tube & 35¢, 31x21", EX, A **$50.00**

Bickmore Gall Salve, sign, 1940-50s, gray horses on a mountain path, ...For All Wounds... on navy blue, 22x34", EX, A **$50.00**

Big Ben Smoking Tobacco, pocket tin, upright, pictures famous London landmark, orange & yellow, slip lid, rare, 4½x3", EX, A **$425.00**

Big Boy Restaurant, ashtray, glass, M, P2 .... **$35.00**

Big Boy Restaurant, cigarette lighter, M, P2............. **$35.00**

Big Chief, crate label, Canada apple, Indian in full head-dress, 9x11", EX, G1 .... **$10.00**

Big Chief Soda-Water, sign, embossed tin, chief drinks from bottle at left of Drink Big Chief Soda-Water, Quality Beverages, rectangle, EX, A **$900.00**

Big Dutchman Beer, label, 1933-50, Vienna Brewing Co, Internal Revenue Tax Paid statement, 1-qt, EX, A... **$16.00**

Big Giant Cola, banner, cloth, yellow & blue with Big Giant Cola above 'weight-lifter' bottle lifting 16-oz weights, 33x56", VG+, M3 .... **$100.00**

Big Giant Cola, sign, tin, Big Giant Cola above 'weight-lifting' bottle, For A Real Lift, More For Your Money, 24x12", EX+, M3 .... **$100.00**

Big Horn Red Pimentos, can label, 1924, ram's head & red peppers, M, C3... **$6.00**

Big Nine Chewing Tobacco, sign, paper, Chew Big Nine (underlined) Again... at left of tilted product pack with Big 9 Clippings logo, 15x7", NM, A **$16.00**

Big Patch Vegetables, label, boy in patched trousers & dog looking at veggie patch, Watsonville, 6½x5", EX, G1... **$12.00**

Big Red, bottle, 1969, clear with red & white label, 10-oz, EX, D **$4.50**

Big Run Cigars, box labels, inner & outer sample set, 1890s, banner & horse shoe over cigar box surrounded by portraits, VG/M, A... **$825.00**

Big Smith Shirts, sign, cardboard stand-up, pictures WWII airplanes, G, D **$25.00**

Big Smith Work Clothes, clock, 1950s, light-up, working, G, D **$110.00**

Big Wolf Cigars, box label, inner lid, pictures angry wolf showing his teeth, 6x9", M, D **$6.00**

Big 10 Beer, label, 1933-50, W Gerst Brewing Co, Internal Revenue Tax Paid statement, 12-oz, EX, A........... **$16.00**

Bigger Hair Tobacco, canister, cardboard, paper label of Black person with nose ring & earrings, slip lid, minor scratches, 6x5" dia, VG, A **$120.00**

Bill Dugan Cigar, pin-back button, ca 1900, multicolored, minor spots, D **$8.00**

Billings-Chapin Paint, sign, cardboard cutout, house painter holding can of paint explains advantages of product to customer, 29x32", EX, A **$300.00**

Biltrite Cigars, tin, paper label, oasis & desert scene, Now 2 For 5¢, slip lid, oval, 6x6x4", EX, A **$95.00**

Biltrite Cord-On-End Soles, sign, embossed tin over cardboard, pictures the product, Will Not Slip, For Greater Safety..., 9x13¼", EX, D.. **$48.00**

Biltrite Heels & Shoes, thermometer, embossed tin, bulb on white shoe sole on dark background, We Rebuild Like New! above, 13½x6", EX, D1........................ **$40.00**

Biltrite Rubber Heels & Soles, door push bar, porcelain, silhouetted dancing couple on white dot left of white product name on red, 3x30", EX, M2................... **$65.00**

Binghamton Ice Cream, tip tray, girl in red scarf & hat eating dish of vanilla ice cream, Everybody's Favorite, oval, 6¼x4¼", EX, A.. **$195.00**

Binghamton Oil Refining Co's Petrolina Ointment, tin, ca 1880s, features oil derricks on lid, company emblem on sides with product listings, rare, Ginna, 7x5x5", EX, A **$185.00**

Birchola, sign, embossed tin, bottles flank Drink on band above Birchola in script, In Bottles below, elongated rectangle, EX, A **$50.00**

Birchola, sign, tin flange, 2-sided, Ice Cold on band above Birchola in script, Sold Here on band below, EX, A **$120.00**

Bird Valley, crate label, 1920s, California apple, large blue crow perched on a shield, Watsonville, 10½x9", M, C1 .... **$2.00**

Birds Eye Frozen Foods, pin-back button, red, white & blue, EX, D **$7.00**

Bireley's, sign, embossed tin, pictures display of bottles, For Real Fruit Taste Drink..., 15x36", NM........... **$125.00**

Bireley's, sign, 1940s, embossed tin, assorted fruits in front of tilted bottles, ...Natural Thing To Drink, 4x20½", EX, A.. **$110.00**

Bireley's Beverages, door push plate, Drink above bottle, NM, A... **$100.00**

Bireley's Non-Carbonated Beverages, sign, tin, yellow with red & cream, Drink upper left of product name, 10x28", EX, A... **$20.00**

Bireley's Orange Drink, sign, 1949, cardboard, girl on raft giving boy a drink, It's A Good Time For..., 19x34", EX, D... **$65.00**

Birk's Beer, label, ca 1933-50, lion logo above Birk Bros Brewing Co, Internal Revenue Paid statement, 1-qt, VG, A... **$16.00**

Birmingham Ledger, pocket mirror, building with lettering above & below, Our New Home 1911, cracked mirror/edge wear, oval, 2¾", VG, A.......................... **$30.00**

Bitner's Trymore Cough Drops, tin, Bitner's Trymore lettered on the diagonal above Cough Drops, pry lid, round, 10-lb, EX, A **$80.00**

Bixby's Shoe Polish, sign, paper, comical image of man having his oversized boots polished, smiling sun upper left, 12x17½", VG, A... **$375.00**

BK Bliss & Sons Garden, Field & Flower Seeds, trade card, lettered graphics, gold on black, EX, A....... **$34.00**

Black & Decker Mfg Co, catalog, 1954, features power tools, 24 pages, VG, D **$10.00**

Black Cat Cigarettes, ad, paper, Give Me Black Cat Every Time! lettered above lady holding black cat & cigarette, matted & framed, EX, D3 .... **$150.00**

Black Cat Cigarettes, sign, paperboard, woman enjoying cigarette while holding black cat, Give Me Black Cat Everytime!, framed, 27x19", VG+, A..................... **$90.00**

Black Cat Stove Cream, tin, pictures a cat on front & embossed cat on lid, EX, D **$35.00**

Black Diamond Whiskey, sign, paper, 2 dapperly dressed Black couples, ...Rich & Mellow, Coblentz & Levy, framed, image: 20x15", EX+, A $1,300.00

Black Gold Coffee, can, product name lettered above & below encircled horse's head on paper label, Johnson Coffee Co, slip lid, VG, A **$85.00**

Black Gold Tobacco, pocket tin, upright paper label, NM, D **$20.00**

Black Jack Gum, jigsaw puzzle, 1933, shows domineering woman putting piece of gum in husband's mouth, 7x10", EX, F1 .... **$40.00**

Black Kow, bottle, amber glass, cow's head above white horizontal oval lettered Black Kow, NM, M3 .... **$10.00**

Black Kow, sign, Drink upper left of oval lettered Black Kow, dressed cow with bottle left, In Bottles 5¢ at right, 23x12", G, A... **$43.00**

Black Kow, sign, tin, Drink above white oval lettered Black Kow, dressed cow with bottle below, In Bottles 5¢..., 35x23", VG+, A.. **$127.00**

Black Label Beer, bottle, amber glass in large barrel shape with red & gold neck label, cream lettering, screw cap, label wear, 18", EX, A **$5.00**

Black Label Beer, wall display, 1960s, hard plastic light-up, winter scene with man carrying 2 beer boxes, 22½x10½", EX, D.. **$45.00**

Black Oak Brand Tobacco, box label, marching drummer with army, town beyond, product name below, framed, image: 12⅜x6¼", M, A **$30.00**

Black Silk Stove Polish, tin, pictures man with tie, dome top, EX, D.. **$20.00**

Black Velvet, pitcher, clear glass with black & gold name patch on each side, round, D................................ **$6.00**

Black Velvet, pitcher, pottery, black & gold, open lip, rectangular, D... **$10.00**

Black Velvet Canadian Whiskey, display bottle, inflatable, 22", EX, D **$7.50**

Blackwell's Bull Durham Tobacco, clock, stained wood case, reverse-stenciled glass door with image of a bull, dial faded/stained, 33", G, A **$210.00**

Blake, Lamb & Co's Animal Traps, catalog, 1925, with price list, pictures a trap on cover, well illustrated, 14 pages, EX, A **$25.00**

Blakey's Boot & Shoe Protectors, display card, 1880s, cardboard, shows boy & girl hammering cleats into shoe & shoe sole with cleats, 10½x6", G, H1 ...... **$12.00**

Blankes Mojav Coffee, tin, pictures horse & rider with lettering above & below, round slip lid on square can, rounded corners, EX, A **$160.00**

Blatz Beer, display, chalk & plaster, figure of dancing barmaid holding mugs of beer, chips to painted surface, 19x9x6", G, A **$175.00**

Blatz Beer, display, 1950s, metal, figural Blatz man playing banjo on stage beside bottle, felt backdrop, 18x10x7", EX+, D **$95.00**

Blatz Beer, sign, ca 1913, oilette, outdoor tavern scene with man beside open touring car, Val Blatz Brg Co, framed, 27x35", EX+, A **$400.00**

Blatz Beer, sign, 1900-10, oleograph, people dining & drinking with early red touring car outside, rare, framed, 27x35", EX, A **$1,450.00**

Blatz Beer, store display, 1960, plastic, Blatz beer man carrying pitcher of beer, round base, 12", M, D $35.00

Blatz Beer, tray, embossed plastic, brown, 13¼" dia, D **$10.00**

Blatz Malt-Vivine, label, 1933-36, product name on center triangle, U-type permit number, 10-oz, EX, A **$5.00**

Blatz Old Heidelberg Beer, jigsaw puzzle, shows Cliff Thompson, world's tallest salesman standing at 8 ft 7" tall, 7x10", EX, F1 ...... **$30.00**

Blatz Old Heidelberg Beer, sign, cast plaster, barmaid atop barrel with steins of beer, oval top, 34x19¼", VG, A **$50.00**

Blazing Star, crate label, California pear, yellow flower in center box on blue background, Kelseyville, 8x11", G1 ...... **$5.00**

Bleriot Cigars, label, Bleriot lettered above the French aviator in fancy oval with lettered ribbon across bottom, 4x4", EX, D **$15.00**

Blevins Popcorn, tin, Bee Hive Hybrid lettered diagonally on shield with product name above & below, 10-lb, VG, A **$33.00**

Bliss Native Herbs, match holder, tin, product name above capitol building, oval portrait & lettering on striker, 6½", G-, A **$85.00**

Bliss Native Herbs & Rubbing Liniment, thermometer, tin, red & black on yellow, lettering above & below, rounded corners, surface stains, 11½", G, A **$45.00**

Bloch Bro's West Virginia Mail Tobacco, sign, paper, banners above man promoting product to crowd, lettering below, early, vertical, EX, M1 ...... **$1,600.00**

Bludwine Health Drink, sign, tin flange, Bludwine in script on diagonal band, Ice Cold & 5¢ above & below, bottle at right, 10x12", NM, D $750.00

Blue & Gold Beer, stained glass window, ...Wigwam Cafe, Billy Stevens & Fred Higson with floral border, framed, 12 ft 8"x29", VG, A **$3,500.00**

Blue & Gold Lager, stained glass window, ...Solano, Sharp & Steam, yellow, green, blue, red & white, original frame, 28x68", VG, A **$5,500.00**

Blue & the Gray, crate label, 1920s, Florida Oranges & Grapefruit, Milne-O'Berry Packing Co, St Petersburg, 9x9", M, C3 ...... **$15.00**

Blue Band Margarine, tin, shows African boy, EX, D **$20.00**

Blue Beacon Coal, sign, tin, Your Guide To Fuel Economy lettered on beacon coming from lighthouse left of product name, rectangle, NM, M3 ...... **$175.00**

Blue Bird Cigars, box label, outer, pictures a bluebird perched on a branch, 4½x4½", M, D **$2.50**

Blue Bird Marshmallows, tin, triangular shape with lid showing blue birds perched in tree watching group roast marshmallows, 7", EX, M2 ...... **$100.00**

Blue Bonnet Cigars, label, Blue Bonnet arched above encircled bonnet with Very Mild lettered on ties, Cured Ripe Tobacco below, 6x9", EX, D **$7.00**

Blue Bonnet Margarine, doll, Dutch girl, hard plastic, 8", MIB, D **$8.50**

Blue Bonnet Margarine, pin-back button, 1950s, yellow, blue & white, EX, D **$5.00**

Blue Coal, sign, embossed tin, flaming piece of coal & bag of coal flank Blue Coal Sold Here..., black border, 11½x24", EX, A **$95.00**

Blue Coat Cigars, box label, inner lid, 1913, Civil War Soldier with rifle, 6x9", EX, C3 .... **$45.00**

Blue Crown Spark Plugs, display, tin, large spark plug over lettered diagonal band, Get More Pep, Save More Gas..., 17x14", NMIB, A **$190.00**

Blue Diamond Almonds, tin, Art Nouveau design, EX, D **$42.00**

Blue Goose, crate label, 1940s, California orange, blue goose on orange ground, American Fruit Growers Inc, 10x11", M, C1 .... **$2.00**

Blue Grass Axle Grease, sign, painted tin, Indian Refining Company logo lower left of Use...For Tired Wheels, company name below, 7x14", VG+, A **$375.00**

Blue Heron, crate label, Florida citrus, grand blue heron stalking through cattails & reeds, 9x9", M, C1 .... **$2.00**

Blue Hill Corn, can label, pictures house by a river & white corn, M, C1 .... **$3.00**

Blue Jay, display, die-cut tin, man & woman with signs reading I'm Foot Gay With Blue-Jay & Sakes Alive..., 11x10½", VG+, A **$325.00**

Blue Jay Corn Plasters, display, die-cut tin, Grandma in rocker with knitting basket, Blue-Jay ad on front of knees, 14", EX+, A $290.00

Blue Jay Corn Plasters, display, die-cut tin, Grandpa in rocker whittling, Don't Whittle Corns, legs missing, 6x3¾x5½", VG, A **$130.00**

Blue Jay Corn Plasters, display, die-cut tin, Grandpa in rocker whittling, Don't Whittle Corns, lower part of legs missing, 14", G, A **$55.00**

Blue Jay Foot Aids, display rack, 4 slanted shelves with lettered marquee, Self Service, 27¼x16", EX, A **$5.00**

Blue Larkspur, crate label, Washington apple, racehorse with winner's wreath on blue background, white logo, Wenatchee, 9x11", G1 .... **$6.00**

Blue Lodge Cigars, box label, inner lid sample, 1880s, encircled Masonic alter with cherubs on either side, Geo S Harris litho, EX, A **$75.00**

Blue Mountain Oysters, can label, 1922, mountain scene & oysters, M, C3 .... **$50.00**

Blue Ribbon Cake, pin-back button, 1930s, blue & white, EX, D **$4.00**

Blue Ribbon Coffee, tin, 1920-30, white & black on red, Blue Ribbon Products... & 'R' intertwined, Pure Coffee below, 5-lb, EX, A **$100.00**

Blue Ribbon Malt, sign, cardboard, little boy in overalls & straw hat squatting beside dog & can, Wherever Do You Go..., 29x21", EX, A **$68.00**

Blue Ribbon Malt Extract, recipe book, 1928, 32 pages, EX, D **$12.00**

Blue Ribbon Pure Cayenne, tin, red, white & blue, Blue Ribbon arched above image of blue bow, Pure Cayenne below, vertical rectangle, EX, M2 .... **$7.00**

Blue Ribbon Pure Mace, tin, Blue Ribbon lettered above polka-dot bow, Pure Mace below, red, white & blue, pry lid, round, EX+, M2 .... **$8.00**

Blue Rocks, pin-back button, Shoot Blue Rocks above & below product image, black & yellow, scarce, round, VG, A **$140.00**

Blue Spots Cigars, box label, inner lid, peacock standing on cigar, 6x9", M, D **$12.50**

Blue Sunoco, bank, tin, 1950s-60s, gas pump with logo bottom center, blue, yellow & red, lift-off top, 4", EX, A **$35.00**

Blue Sunoco, gas globe, ca 1915, milk glass with blue border, diamond logo in center, minor scratches to lens, 14½" dia, A **$175.00**

Blue Sunoco, pump sign, die-cut porcelain, Blue Sunoco lettered on yellow diamond, 8x12¼", EX, A **$220.00**

Blue Sunoco, pump sign, die-cut porcelain, Blue Sunoco on yellow diamond with red arrow on vertical blue diamond, 22x19", EX, A **$190.00**

Blue Sunoco, see also Sunoco

Blue Sunoco 200, sign, porcelain, Blue Sunoco in yellow on blue diamond with red arrow over yellow vertical diamond, 20x15", M, D3 .... $365.00

Blue Wagon Staple Cotton, wall medallion, crystaline, pictures a wagon, ...Will Pay More Dollars Per Acre...S Maston Nixon, 6" dia, EX, A **$75.00**

Blue Winner, crate label, apple, cowboy in arena on horseback reaching down to pick up an apple, 10½x9", M, C1 .... **$2.00**

Bluff City Beer, sign, cardboard stand-up or hanger, blue, yellow & green, Swing To Bluff City Beer, 8x12", NM, B1 .... **$12.00**

Bluff City Special Lager Beer, label, 1933-50, Bluff City Brewery Inc, Internal Revenue Tax Paid statement, 12-oz, VG, A **$9.00**

Boar's Head Tobacco, sign, celluloid, product name lettered above circular inset of boar's head at left of product, 8x11", VG, A **$40.00**

Bob's Big Boy, ashtray, glass, G, D **$35.00**

Bob White, lug box label, apple, bob white sitting on a log & white lettering on red background, Stewartstown, EX, G1 .... **$3.00**

Bodega Wine & Liquor Co, sign, paper, features Indian princess posing with bow & arrow, small repair, ornate frame, image: 20x15", VG+, A **$50.00**

Bodegas Franco-Espanolas Logrono (Rioja), sign, tin, woman seated at cabriolet table with bottle of wine & vase of flowers, 18½x13", G, A **$50.00**

Boericke & Tafel, catalog, ca 1900, features homeopathic medicine, 144 pages, VG, D **$30.00**

Bokar Coffee, tin, black & gold, screw lid, 1-lb, VG, D .. **$22.00**

Boll's Sea Food & Oyster Market, blotter, 1920s, flapper girl in red hat, Chas E Boll, Prop, unused, 3⅜x6⅛", H1 .... $8.00

Bolla Wines, mirror, metal frame, 21x17½", EX, D.... **$15.00**

Boncilla Classic Beautifer Cream, sign, die-cut cardboard, lady with hands on face above large product tube, It Makes Your Face Feel So Good, 9x6", NM, M2 ..... **$45.00**

Bond Bread, blotter, shows The Lone Ranger on Trigger, The Lone Ranger Says...Always Be Careful!, EX, A **$225.00**

Bond Bread, blotter, 1940s, pictures SBD1 Navy Dive Bomber, unused, 6½x3½", D **$4.00**

Bond Bread, bread end label, shows Hopalong having shootout with bank robbers above Hopalong Cassidy's Favorite in script, EX, S1 .... **$7.00**

Bond Bread, recipe book, 1931, 'Mealtime Surprises Made with Bond Bread,' 28 pages, VG, D **$7.50**

Bond Bread, recipe book, 1933, 22 pages, G, D **$5.00**

Bond Bread, sign, porcelain, Bond Bread lettered in black with green outline on yellow, black & green scalloped border, 4x18", EX, A **$205.00**

Bond Bread, sign, porcelain, product name in fancy script, yellow & blue, 14x19", EX+, A **$33.00**

Bone Eagle & Co Red Cough Drops, tin, product name lettered on label with eagle above, smaller round lid on square can with rounded corners, 5-lb, EX, A... **$160.00**

Bonnette Coffee, tin, Dutch children at table, product name on bands above & below, slip lid, 1-lb, 5¾x4¼" dia, VG, A **$200.00**

Bonnie Bro's Distillers, sign, etched & reverse-painted glass, factory scene flanked by Joel B Frazier..., ornate gold leaf frame, 34x45", G, A **$900.00**

Boodles Gin, mirror, metal frame, 15½x19", EX, D... **$15.00**

Boone Cola, sign, pictures a bottle, S2 .... **$295.00**

Booster Cigar, sign, ca 1910, paper, gentleman waiting for lady to fix her stocking, Stirton & Dyer, London Canada, 30x18", EX, M2 .... $2,100.00

Borax, display, die-cut cardboard, theatrical image of the mule team flanked by people using product, 33x24x54", NM, A **$1,200.00**

Borden, award, 1960s, gold-colored metal, half-apple figure pictures Elsie in center, award for sales of cartons, 3x2x1", EX, A **$94.00**

Borden, birthday card, opens to birthday scene with Elsie at left, Happy Birthday from Elsie & All The Borden Family, EX+, P2 .... **$65.00**

Borden, board game, 1963, 'Elsie's Milkman Game,' complete with box, EX, A **$87.00**

Borden, book, 1946, 'Elsie & the Looking Club,' hardbound, P2 .... **$25.00**

Borden, bowl, pictures Elsie dancing in flowers, Cambridge, M, P2 .... **$125.00**

Borden, Christmas greeting intented to be placed on milk bottle, wreath surrounds Elmer with greeting card below, M, P2 .... **$35.00**

Borden, creamer, 1940s, glazed ceramic in shape of Elsie's head, tan with black & white accents, minor glaze cracking, 5", VG, D **$45.00**

Borden, doll, Elsie, 1950s, stuffed fabric with rubber head, premium, VG, A **$180.00**

Borden, drinking glass, pictures Elsie & family in 1776 decor, EX, P2 .... **$25.00**

Borden, drinking glass, 1950s, clear with white image of Elsie's head, tapered, 6x3" dia, M, D **$18.00**

Borden, ice cream dish, glass, full-color Elsie portrait on front, EX, P2 .... **$28.00**

Borden, jar, embossed glass, match striker on back, stopper top, EX, A **$60.00**

Borden, lamp, pottery, Elsie & Beauregard, M, P2 .. **$295.00**

Borden, place mat, full-color image of Elsie, 11x16¾", M, P2 .... **$12.00**

Borden, push puppet, 1950s, wood & paper, Elsie on green base, moos when pressed, 5", NM, D. $200.00

Borden, salt & pepper shakers, baby Beulah & Beauregard, EX+, P2 .... **$65.00**

Borden, salt & pepper shakers, ceramic, 2-piece Elsie with head resting on body, M, P2 .... **$110.00**

Borden, sewing needle book, pictures Elsie, several sewing needles mounted inside, 5½x4¾", VG, D **$6.50**

Borden, store display, rubber animated figure of Elsie's head, M, P2 .... **$1,400.00**

Borden, sweater, powder-blue V-neck with embroidered Elsie in daisy, large, M, P2 .... **$75.00**

Borden, toy watch, 1950s, white plastic border & numbers around raised head of Elsie, missing brass link bands, 1⅛" dia, G, A **$18.00**

Borden's Eagle Brand, recipe book, 1920s, Art Deco cover of woman in kitchen looking at cookbook while working, 32 pages, VG, H1 .... **$12.00**

Borden's Eagle Brand, recipe book, 1952, '70 Magic Recipes,' 24 pages, EX, D **$6.00**

Borden's Fine Dairy Products, clock, glass with metal frame, Borden's in script above Fine Dairy Products on upper half, 1-12, round, EX, D **$240.00**

Borden's Ice Cream, flavor board, plastic over cardboard, Elsie & Borden's...Very Big On Flavor above row of flavor panels, 26x13", NM, A **$100.00**

Borden's Ice Cream, sign, painted metal flange, 2-sided, red Borden's above white Ice Cream right of image of Elsie, 15x24", EX, A **$300.00**

Borden's Ice Cream, sign, porcelain, 2-sided, Borden's in script above Ice Cream, You Know It's Pure, checked top & bottom, 28x20", EX, A **$200.00**

Borden's Ice Cream, sign, porcelain flange, pictures Elsie at left of product name, 15x24", NM, D **$350.00**

Borden's Ice Cream, sign, tin, product name above image of Elsie, 28x20", EX, A **$66.00**

Borden's Malted Milk, container, aluminum, Borden's in script imprinted above Richer Malted Milk in red diamond, EX+, A $105.00

Borden's Malted Milk, container, aluminum, diamond logo with product advertising imprinted on front, EX, A .. **$120.00**

Borden's Malted Milk, container, glass, blue enameled lettering on white label, aluminum lid, NM, D **$350.00**

Borden's Malted Milk, container, glass with enameled label, stopper top, EX, A **$160.00**

Borden's Malted Milk, container, glass with stenciled milk glass label, embossed tin lid, 8½", EX, A **$575.00**

Borden's Malted Milk, sign, die-cut cardboard stand-up, maid standing sideways holds tray with product, A Food For Everyone, 5x4⅝", EX, D **$175.00**

Borden's Malted Milk, tip tray, server stands sideways displaying product on green, gold lettering & trim on brown rim, 4½" dia, VG+, A $400.00

Borden's Malted Milk Candy, container, glass with embossed metal top, flared bottom, 9x5½" dia, EX, A **$100.00**

Borden's Milk, paperweight, shaped as milk carton picturing Elsie, G, D **$22.00**

Borden's Powdered Lemon Juice, tin, lemons below product name, pry lid, minor wear, 5-lb, P2 .... **$45.00**

Borden's Sweetened Condensed Milk, recipe book, 1931, 'New Magic In The Kitchen,' 62 pages, G, D **$7.00**

Borden's Vanilla Ice Cream, carton, 1950s, pictures scoops of ice cream & Elsie's face, 2-qt, EX, D **$5.00**

Borkum Riff Tobacco, tin, round, NM, H3 .... **$10.00**

Boron Supreme, gas globe, 1940, porcelain, red & blue stripe points down to Boron in blue above red Supreme in script, 14" dia, EX, A $100.00

Boscul Coffee, bank, One Hour Fresh lettered above Boscul Coffee, Vacuum Packed below, 2¼x2½" dia, EX, A **$20.00**

Boscul Coffee, tin, waiter serving coffee, EX, D **$40.00**

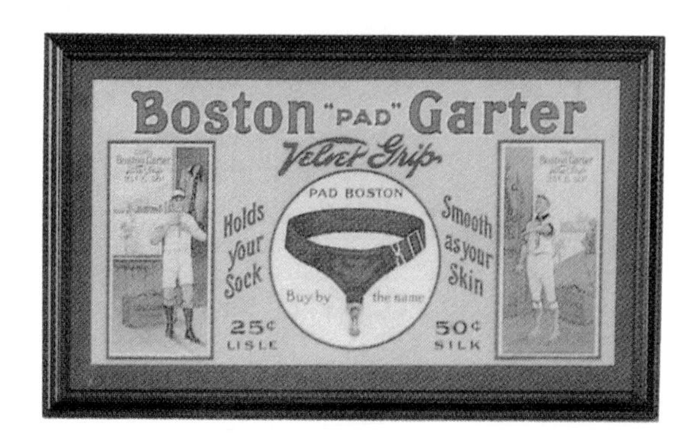

Boston 'Pad' Garter, sign, paper, product name above Velvet Grip garter flanked by 2 ball players utilizing product, framed, 21x11", EX, A $4,000.00

Boston Belting Co, sign, paper, colorful vignettes of factory, Boston White House & river scene, framed, image: 17¼x13½", VG, A **$105.00**

Boston Cartridge Co, sign, 1901, 'Comrades,' paper with metal strips top & bottom, pictures hunter with bird & dogs, 26x20", VG, A **$550.00**

Boston Herald Newspaper, pocket mirror, celluloid, pictures newsboy, EX+, D **$110.00**

Boston Herald Newspaper, sign, tin, The Boston Herald One Cent lettered in white on red, 12x23¼", G-, A **$80.00**

Boston Herald Newspaper, tip tray, ca 1905, shows running newsboy hawking newspaper, worn/some pitting, 4" dia, G, A **$55.00**

Boston Herald/Sunday Herald Newspaper, pocket mirror, shows running newsboy hawking newspaper, 1¾", EX, A **$80.00**

Boston Herald/Sunday Herald Newspaper, tip tray, shows running newsboy hawking newspaper, On Sale Everywhere, A Newspaper Made For All, 3½" dia, EX, A.. **$110.00**

Boston Sunday Globe Newspaper, sign, 1895, cardboard stand-up, jolly fat man in top hat & colorful suit with advertising on cummerbund & hat, 8", EX, A $85.00

Boston Varnish Co, pocket mirror, man's face reverses from happy to sad by turning mirror, Kyanize Varnishes & Enamels, 3½" dia, VG+, A **$25.00**

Bostonians Shoes for Men, shoe horn, engraved shield & crest emblem, black, 4" long, VG, P4 .... **$15.00**

Bounce Fabric Softener, doll, 1985, Montgomery Moose, brown plush body, knit shirt & corduroy pants, logo on shoe, 15", EX, N1 .... **$15.00**

Bounty Cigarettes, pocket tin, upright, pictures a cigarette with product name & other lettering above & below, hinged lid, NM, A **$50.00**

Bouquet Roasted Coffee, tin, coffee cup on white filigree image, white & red product lettering above & below on red, gold screw lid, 1-lb, NM, A **$175.00**

Bovine Beef, trade card, hold-to-light, pictures a Bovine steer, eyes open & close, My Life Was Saved By..., EX, A **$20.00**

Bower & Bartlett's Boston Blue Ribbon Brand Coffee, bin, metal, gold & black graphics on red, hinged lift top, 19x17½x14", G, A **$120.00**

Bowey's Hot Chocolate, container, stoneware, barrel shape, rolled rim & base, Bowey's Hot Chocolate Served Exclusively embossed on base, EX, A **$50.00**

Bowl of Roses Pipe Mixture, pocket tin, upright, pictures man enjoying cigar while reading the newspaper, EX, A ..**$75.00**

Bowler Bros Brewers, match safe, celluloid over metal, orange hop leaf design on both sides, Worchester, Mass, 2¾x1½", G, A **$35.00**

Bowler Bros Brewers, match safe, for Tadcaster Ale, celluloid over nickel-plated brass, pictures 2 bottles on reverse, 2¾x1½", EX, A **$90.00**

Boyce Moto Meter, sign, die-cut paper, Boyce above lettered Moto Meter & image of same in oval with floral decor, framed, 16x40", EX+, A **$1,250.00**

Boyce Moto Meter, sign, 1914, die-cut tin flange, 2-sided, woman points to hood ornament on car front, Authorized..., 19x22", EX, A............$4,000.00

Brach's, doll, 1972, scarecrow, cloth body with vinyl head, 16", EX, D **$25.00**

Brach's, doll, 1989, Wile E Coyote, plush, brown body with beige head & chest, 16½", M, N1..................**$15.00**

Brach's, growth chart for kids, 1989, shows Bugs Bunny holding a carrot, VG+, P4 ....**$8.00**

Brach's Candies of Quality, tin, 1930s-40s, gold on gold picturing candies & factory scenes, screw lid, 5-lb, 10", EX, A **$55.00**

Brach's Supreme White Marshmallows, tin, slip lid, some wear, round, A **$30.00**

Bradford Brewing Co, tray, stock image of girl with flowered lei in a landscape, lettering above, oval, 16½x13½", VG, A **$300.00**

Bradley's Fertilizers, trade card, interior scene with farmer sleeping in chair, vignettes of various crops above, shades of brown, EX, A **$48.00**

Braems Bitters, sign, aluminum, Drink Braems Bitters above bottle, For Appetite below, vertical, EX, A **$45.00**

Branigan Rubbers, sign, embossed tin, hanging, product name arched above lion, Sold Here below, 12½" dia, VG+, A **$55.00**

Breakfast Belle, crate label, Florida citrus, Black maid serving breakfast, 9x3½", M, C1 ....**$2.00**

Breethem, tin, shows a woman breathing, Breethem For The Breath, 5¢, EX, A **$10.00**

Breidt's Draught Beer, label, 1933-50, P Breidt Brewing Co, Internal Revenue Tax Paid statement, 1/2-gal, EX, A..**$20.00**

Breidt's Pure Beer, tip tray, girl with roses sipping a glass of beer, As It Is Made In Germany lettered below, 4¼", EX, A **$160.00**

Breinig's Oil Paints, sign, embossed tin, steeple painter hanging upside down from weather vane, Ready Mixed..., framed, image: 28x20", VG, A $9,750.00

Bremer Brau, label, 1928-33, Adam Scheidt Brewing Co, L-type permit number, 12-oz, EX, A **$41.00**

Brer Rabbit's Molasses, recipe book, ca 1930, 'Modern Recipes for Modern Living,' 48 pages, EX, D **$10.00**

Breuningers Milk, thermometer, celluloid, pictures stork with baby above product name, rounded ends, vertical, EX, A **$90.00**

Breyer's Ice Cream, sign, neon, leaf logo encircles Breyer's with Ice Cream below, no transformer, has break in tubing, A **$20.00**

Breyer's Ice Cream, spoon, Eat Breyer's Ice Cream, G, D **$48.00**

Bri-Nee's Fresh Roasted Peanuts, tin, pictures man rowing peanut-shaped boat, Teasingly Salty, 10-lb, EX, D **$75.00**

Briar Pipe Tobacco, store card, pictures Black child holding 2 packages of tobacco, minor soiling/overall wear, framed, 11¼x8", VG, A **$225.00**

Bridal Brand Coffee, tin, man & donkeys with harbor scene in background, slip lid, rare, oval, 1-lb, 5¾x4¾x3½", VG, A **$250.00**

Bridal Veil, crate label, 1930s, California lemon, Bridal Veil Falls at Yosemite Park & large lemon, Santa Paula, 9x12½", M, C1 ....**$5.00**

Bright Star Flashlights, display, for countertop, pictures flashlight with logo & star atop, red, black & white, 6-sided, 20x6" dia, EX, A **$235.00**

British America Assurance Co, letter folder, tin, pictures Canadian building & company's building, rare, 12½x3", EX, A **$525.00**

Broadway Brewing Co, tray, deep-dish, hand holding spear flanked by Pure & Beers, company name & Buffalo NY around rim, 12" dia, EX, A **$250.00**

Broadway of America, sign, porcelain, yellow image of US with black lettering & highway route on black, yellow line border, 14x24", EX, D3 ....**$750.00**

Brockway Motor Trucks, sign, 1920, embossed tin, product lettering above & below photo image of truck, framed, 20x28", VG, A **$600.00**

Brockway Motor Trucks, sign, 1920, embossed tin, product lettering above & below photo image of truck, framed, 20x28", EX+, D3....................$950.00

Bromo-Seltzer, dispenser, purple glass bottle on nickel-plated bracket, purple glass square base, 15¾", EX, A........**$180.00**

Bromo-Seltzer, pocket mirror, bottle of product with product name & Cures All Headaches circling banded rim, 2¼" dia, EX, A **$200.00**

Bromo-Seltzer, pocket mirror, bottle of product with product name & Cures All Headaches circling banded rim, 2¼" dia, G, A **$51.00**

Bromo-Seltzer, postcard, black & white photo image of horse-drawn wagon, pictures a bottle & lettering on wagon, EX, P3 ....**$30.00**

Bromo-Seltzer, tip tray, bottle of product with lettered rim, Cures All Headaches, 4¼" dia, EX, A **$130.00**

Bronco, crate label, 1920s, California orange, cowboy on running horse, Redlands Foothill Groves, 10x11¾", M, C3 ....**$5.00**

Brook's Thread, sign, paper, 1878 Paris Exposition with Victorian displays & figures, minor edges tears, 14x19¼", VG, A **$150.00**

Brooke Bond dividend Tea (sic), sign, porcelain, 20x30", appears EX, A...**$60.00**

Brooke Bond Tea, sign, porcelain, blue product lettering on red-orange background, black & white checked border, 30x20", EX+, M2 ....**$150.00**

Brookfield Pork Sausage, sign, cardboard, boy running in the snow with package of sausage, Swift & Company, USA below, 20x15", EX, A.................................**$175.00**

Brookfield Rye, sign, self-framed tin, girl in diaphanous gown holding bottle of liquor, Made Famous By Public Favor, 33x13", EX+, A.....................................**$1,000.00**

Brother Jonathon Fine Cut Chewing Tobacco, tin, shows lad seated among tobacco plants, smaller round lid with center loop handle on larger round can, rare, 5-lb, A **$1,750.00**

Brotherhood Overalls, pocket mirror, bare-breasted woman standing in center fastening overalls flanked by white lettering, 2⅛" dia, EX, A **$125.00**

Brotherhood Tobacco, lunch box, metal, Brotherhood in diagonal script & Tobacco lettered on emblem, VG, A...**$54.00**

Brotherhood Tobacco, sign, ca 1900, paperboard, worker & statesman beside train enjoying product, framed, 26x18", EX, A **$1,650.00**

Brotherhood Tobacco, sign, cardboard, text surrounded by colorful display of packages & tins, framed, image: 26x17½", VG, A **$125.00**

Brotherhood Tobacco, tin, product name above & below scroll design, slip lid, 4x6", VG+, A **$20.00**

Brown Dick Smoking Tobacco, tin, pat 1858, paper label featuring prancing horse with product name arched above, lettering below, NM, A **$195.00**

Brown's Jumbo Bread, display, die-cut tin elephant, product name lettered on orange & white blanket, 12½", VG, A...**$550.00**

Brown's Mule Tobacco, mold, 1920s, tin with 24 embossed mules, 12x12", EX, D............................**$16.00**

Brown Trucking Co, ruler, folding, Auto Trucks & Horse-Drawn Wagons For Hauling Of All Kinds, Ft Wayne, Ind, EX, D **$20.00**

Brown-Forman Co Distillers, tray, bulldog listening to echo from crock of Old Tucker Whiskey, Suspects His Master lettered below, 13" dia, VG, A.................**$225.00**

Browne & Sharpe Mfg Co, postcard, 1907-15, colorful factory image, VG, A..**$11.00**

Brownie Brand Salted Peanuts, tin, dark blue with gold & cream circular Brownie logo, pry lid, 10-lb, NM, D3...$275.00

Brownie Brand Salted Pecans, tin, brown with gold & cream circular Brownie logo, United Fig & Date Company, pry lid, 5-lb, EX+, D3 ....$210.00

Brownies, crate label, California orange, pictures mob of little people tapping big orange for juice, Lemon Cove, G1 ....**$10.00**

Browning Sporting Arms, foldout, 1938, opens in 12 panels to form large sheet with illustrations & prices, includes letter to dealers, EX, A **$15.00**

Bruck's Beer, label, 1933-50, Bruckman Co, Internal Revenue Tax Paid statement, 1/4 gal, EX, A **$30.00**

Bruck's Beer, sign, 1930s, tin, red, cream, black & blue, logo above Bruck's in script, 6x14", EX, D...........**$50.00**

Bruck's Bock Beer, label, 1933-50, ram's head at top, Bruckman Co, Internal Revenue Tax Paid statement, 12-oz, VG, A **$18.00**

Bruck's Hi% Beer, label, product name script, Bruckman Co, 12-oz, VG, A **$33.00**

Bruinoil/Bruin Gasoline, sign, tin flange, 2-sided, fierce-looking bear on oval with Bruinoil arched above & Bruin Gasoline below, NM, A **$1,850.00**

Brunswick Beverages, soda bottle, painted label, Enjoy Brunswick Beverages, 8-oz, EX, D..........................**$3.00**

Brunswick Cocoanut, tin, Cocoanut lettered on banner waving diagonally with Brunswick above, smaller round lid on square can, EX, A............................**$60.00**

Brunswick Havana Cigar, match holder/striker, ceramic, lettering on all sides, 4", G, A.............................**$220.00**

Brunswick Records, catalog, 1924, EX, D **$10.00**

Brunswick Soups, sign, paper, jovial man eating soup with large ladle, Rich & Delicious... on bowl, decorative border, 13x11", EX, A **$575.00**

BT Babbitt's 1776 Soap Powder, trolley sign, half-circle image reads Use It Every Day Monday To Saturday behind box of product, framed, 11x21", NM, A...**$81.00**

Bub's Beer, matchbook cover, red & white, Peter Bub Brewery, Winona Minn, 20 strike, front strike, NM, R1.....**$5.00**

Bubble Up, sign, celluloid, Just Pure Pleasure! in script above bubble logo, green background, oval, 9x13", NM, M1 ....$120.00

Bubble Up, sign, tin, red Drink & green Kiss Of Lemon/Kiss Of Lime on white arrow left of lettered bubbles on green, 12x28", NM, M3......................**$90.00**

Bubble Up, sign, tin, white Drink upper left of lettered bubbles, Kiss Of Lemon/Kiss Of Lime lower right on green, 12x28", M, B1 ....**$50.00**

Bubble Up, thermometer, pictures bottle, 16x6", G, D.**$45.00**

Bubble Yum, necklace, yellow fruit-gum pack on plastic cord, EX, D **$3.50**

Bubbling Over Coffee, tin, 1930-40, green, red & white, jockey on horse in horizontal oval, product name above & below, 1-lb, EX, A...............................**$215.00**

Buccaneer Private Stock Ale, label, 1933-36, Cleveland & Sandusky Brewing Co, U-type permit number, 12-oz, EX, A **$30.00**

Buchanan & Lyall's Choicest Tobacco, sign, velvet scroll, black, cream & gold on red, Planet & Neptune in bars above & below with logo & text, 16x12", VG+, A **$15.00**

Bucher & Bibbs Plow Co, pin-back button, farmer telling another gent that The 'Imperial' Is The Best Plow In The World..., round, EX, A **$49.00**

Buck Beverage, sign, 1930s, embossed tin, green, red & yellow, Drink...The Beer-y Beverage, 9½x19", EX, D..**$50.00**

Buck Cigars, humidor trunk, wood, tin cover with simulated wood finish on top & sides, tin liner, Made Good-Always..., 27" long, G, A....................................**$180.00**

Buckeye Fence, pocket mirror, ladies of the 4 seasons divided by close-up of wire fence, lettering on black border, 2" dia, G+, A..**$100.00**

Buckeye Forge Pumps, trade card, pictures Black man pumping water into burning house, lettering above & below, EX, A...**$30.00**

Buckeye Harvester, sign, paper, large B with harrow & mower insets, Adriance, Platt & Co, paper loss/edge tears, framed, image: 14x11", A..........................**$125.00**

Buckeye Lawn Mowers, trade card, surreal image of little boy riding an insect, lettering above & below, prices on reverse, EX, A **$16.00**

Buckeye Root Beer, mug, stoneware, circular logo in center, figural handle, crazing, 6", VG, A **$40.00**

Buckeye Root Beer, syrup dispenser, ca 1920, white ceramic with product name arched around oval Cleveland logo, not original pump, VG, A **$450.00**

Buckeye Root Beer, syrup dispenser, ceramic, black urn shape with white logo, not original pump/some restoration, VG+, A **$230.00**

Buckeye Root Beer, syrup dispenser, porcelain, foaming soda glass transfer on all sides, nut-buds decor, rare, ovoid, 17x7½" dia, VG, A **$500.00**

Buckingham, crate label, 1920s, California pear, cowboy riding a bucking pig, California Bartletts, Vacaville, 7¼x11", M, C1 ....**$3.00**

Buckingham's Dye for Whiskers, trade card, white-bearded man opens up to man with dark beard, ...For The Whiskers, 3x5½" open, EX+, A **$19.00**

Buckingham's Dye for Whiskers, trade card, white-bearded man opens up to man with dark beard, ...For The Whiskers, 3x5½" open, G, D **$8.00**

Buckingham Tobacco, pocket tin, upright, ornate graphics, slip lid, NM, H3...**$165.00**

Bud Lite, sign, neon, reads Lite above small Open in rectangular border with rounded corners, 3 colors, 2-way switch, EX, A **$45.00**

Bud Lite, statuette, 1980s, composition, Spuds MacKenzie in a party hat, ...Original Party Animal on octagonal base, 6½", M, D **$175.00**

Bud Lite, thermometer, pictures Spuds McKenzie, The Original Party Animal, 12" dia, EX, D **$12.50**

Budweiser, cookie jar, glass with fired-on paint, wood cover, M, P2..**$250.00**

Budweiser, light, 1960s, plastic, hanging, Budweiser horses & wagon rotate inside, rare, EX, A **$750.00**

Budweiser, lighter holders, metal can shape, disposable, pair, 3", VG+, P4...**$6.00**

Budweiser, plate, 1989, 'Winter Day,' 24k gold trim, 8½" dia, M, D...**$75.00**

Budweiser, salt & pepper shakers, 1970s, ceramic, Bud Man figures, EX+, P2..**$325.00**

Budweiser, sign, light-up, plastic with glass front, draft horse looks out over water, ...King Of Beers emblem below, 13x20", VG, A..**$35.00**

Budweiser, sign, tin, 4 small girls holding oversized beer bottle while goddess on pedestal crowns it, framed, image: 23x15", G-, A..**$350.00**

Budweiser, sign, 1907, paper litho, shows Budweiser girl in landscape, raised gilt on black oak frame, 39x24", EX, D...**$1,250.00**

Budweiser, sign, 1960s, tin, eagle logo & ornate graphics, red, black & gold, 26x17", EX, D..........................**$25.00**

Budweiser, stein, Endangered Species Edition II, shows Asian tiger, ceramic insert in lid, 6½", M, D.........**$25.00**

Budweiser, stein, 1980 Holiday, pictures Clydesdales & wagon, 5", M, D...**$110.00**

Budweiser, stein, 1982 Holiday, Clydesdales 50th Anniversary 1933-83, pictures Clydesdales & wagon in winter scene, 6½", M, D..**$95.00**

Budweiser, stein, 1986 Horseshoe Series, cobalt blue, West Germany, 7", M, D...**$50.00**

Budweiser, stein, 1988 Classic Edition I, 8", MIB, D......**$200.00**

Budweiser, stein, 1988 Winter Olympics, shows collage of events, 8½", MIB, D...**$75.00**

Budweiser, stein, 1989, ceramic Bud Man, Anheuser Busch Inc. 8½", M, D..$30.00

Budweiser, stein, 1989, Classic Edition II, 8", MIB, D...**$150.00**

Budweiser, tray, 'St Louis Levee In Early Seventies,' Budweiser & King Of Bottled Beers lettered on rim, 13x18", EX+, D...**$330.00**

Budweiser, tray, 'St Louis Levee In Early Seventies,' Budweiser & King Of Bottled Beers lettered on rim, 13x18", G, A...**$120.00**

Budweiser Bottled Beer, display, gold-painted metal base, reverse-incised glass plate with gold foil lettering, We Feature..., 17" long, EX, A..................................**$130.00**

Budweiser Faust, stained glass window, eagle logo, framed, image: 47x32", EX, A..........................**$4,000.00**

Budweiser Syrup, label, pre-1920, Anheuser-Busch Brewing Ass'n, 16-oz, EX, A..**$21.00**

Buehler Brothers Smoked Meats & Sausages, sign, tin, New Taste Thrills..., red, white & black, 6½x20", NM, B1..**$30.00**

Buell's Brighton Blend Coffee, tin, lady in profile with steaming cup of coffee with lettering above & below, screw lid, round, 1-lb, G, A.................................**$85.00**

Buffalo Brand Peanut Butter, pail, buffalo surrounded by lettered oval band in yellow on red ground, FM Hoyt & Co, press lid & bail, EX, A................$150.00

Buffalo Brewing Co, sign, self-framed tin, display of product bottles on table, minor fading/scuffs to border, 28¼x22¼", G, A...**$425.00**

Buffalo Brewing Co, tray, deep-dish, bust-length portrait of a woman in profile wearing straw hat, lettering on rim, 12" dia, EX, A..**$300.00**

Buffalo Cafe, pocket mirror, nude resting on river bank, Ludlow Ky, CY Sechrest Prop, Good For 5¢ In Trade, oval, 2¾x1¾", VG+, A..**$350.00**

Buffalo Courier Express, wagon, green-painted wood box with white lettering on all 4 sides, VG, A...**$525.00**

Buffalo Distilling Co, sign, embossed tin, charging buffalo surrounded by 4 barrels with logo, Sentenne & Green litho, framed, 13½x20", G, A.............................**$800.00**

Buffalo Motor Oil, can, 1915-25, buffalo on orange ground, Prairie Cities Oil Co below text in upper right, screw lid, 1/2-gal, 7", EX, A...............................**$295.00**

Buffalo Pitts Co, calendar, 1911, Indian killing charging buffalo, inserts of equipment below, full pad, framed, image: 23½x15", VG, A.......................................**$350.00**

Buffalo Rock Ginger Ale, sign, self-framed tin, bust portrait of lady holding bottle above inset reading Keep Healthy..., vertical, EX, M1 ....**$725.00**
Buffalo Scale Co, sign, hanging, wood, white lettering on black, ...Buffalo, Chicago, New York, 16x28", G-, A..**$85.00**
Buffalo Scale Co, trade card, interior & exterior factory vignettes with fancy graphics, scarce, minor edge flaws, 4⅝x7", VG, A **$75.00**
Buick, coloring book, 1958, G, D....................................**$10.00**
Buick, counter display, 1960, light-up, wood with glass front, Buick & advertising pictured on front, hinged lid, VG+, A **$50.00**
Buick, magazine, May 1951, EX, D **$5.00**
Buick, pin-back button, I'm A Buick Man lettered in white on red, round, EX, A...**$21.00**
Buick, pin-back button, Simplicity-Durability arched over Power above early open car, Buick in script below, round, EX, A **$26.00**
Buick, puzzle, plastic, Best Buy & Buick lettered on small white & black squares that move about in larger square frame, EX, D **$25.00**
Buick, sign, porcelain, Buick in white diagonal script on red dot with Valve above, In Head below, white border, 20" dia, M, D3 ....**$550.00**

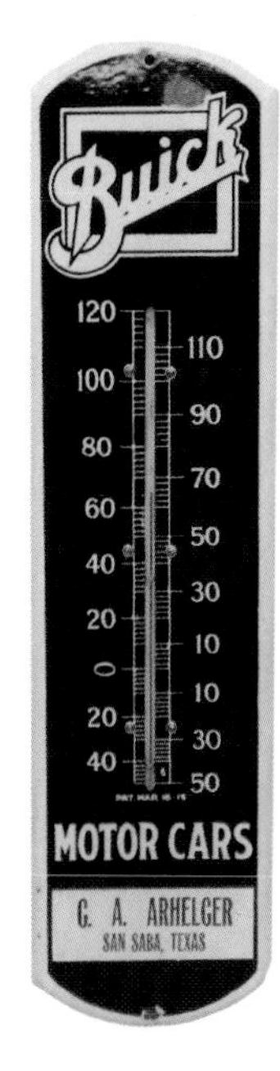

Buick Motor Cars, thermometer, porcelain, blue & white with white border, rounded ends, dealer's name on white panel below, 28x7", EX, D3 ..$675.00
Buick Valve In Head Motor Cars, pin-back button, Buick lettered diagonally over lettered rectangle logo with decorative border,⅞" dia, EX, A **$25.00**
Bull Brand Feeds, sign, 1930s-40s, tin, black & white cow on 2 large B's flanked by Cost Least, Produce More, framed, 36x72", VG, A **$210.00**
Bull Dog Cut Plug Tobacco, pocket tin, upright, bulldog in oval with product name above & below, slip lid, G-, A **$75.00**
Bull Durham Smoking Tobacco, display, copper-clad plaster figure of a bull on oblong base embossed with advertising, 17x21", EX, A **$1,430.00**
Bull Durham Smoking Tobacco, sign, paper, Indian on rearing stallion raising rifle, Defies The World... below, minor paper loss, 10x7", VG, A..........................**$500.00**
Bull Durham Smoking Tobacco, sign, paper, instructor & children at blackboard, Teaching Time below, framed, 27½x20½", EX, A..**$1,200.00**
Bull Durham Smoking Tobacco, sign, paper, Spanish bull-fighting scene, A Royal Victor, original frame, 23½x35", NM, A..**$600.00**
Bull Durham Smoking Tobacco, sign, 1930s, cardboard, Black woman smoking pipe at the General Store, My! It Shure Am Sweet Tastin', 10x25", VG, A..............**$110.00**
Bull Durham Smoking Tobacco, trolley sign, bull image upper right & product image lower left of patriotic emblem, So-long..., framed, 11x21", EX, A.........**$350.00**
Bull of the Woods Quality Chewing Tobacco, sign, tin, Bull Of The Woods above snorting bull, Quality Chewing Tobacco below, yellow background, 18x12", NM, M3 ....**$85.00**

Bulldog Safety Switches, display, papier-maché, bulldog with brown on back extending over eyes, white legs & underbody, 16x30", EX, A.....$1,100.00
Bully Boys, box label, inner lid sample, 1890s, group of men brawling, OL Schwenke & Co litho, EX, A............**$825.00**
Bunker Hill Breweries, celluloid litho, features trademark bulldog on orange background, Oh Be Jolly!, rare, 7" dia, EX, D3 ....**$750.00**
Bunnies Salted Peanuts, tin, Bunnies Salted Peanuts lettered above dressed rabbit holding product, GE Barbour Co, very rare, 10-lb, EX, A.........................**$210.00**
Bunny Bread, door push plate, 1930s, embossed tin, white on red, Reach For Bunny Bread, 3x28", EX, D **$40.00**
Bunte Bros & Spoehr's Fine Candies, sign, paper, pictures mountain climbing scene with eagles protecting rock-bound chicks, matted & framed, image: 21x15½", VG, A **$650.00**
Bunte Marshmallows, tin, pictures youth standing at left of marshmallow tin with lettering at right, pry lid, rare, 10-lb, A **$500.00**
Burch's Jumbo Popcorn, tin, pictures Jumbo, 10-lb, 13x6" dia, EX, D **$130.00**

Burdock Blood Bitters, trade card, pictures little girl holding doll & product, EX, A **$12.00**

Burgefeuer Cigars, box label, inner lid, knight in armor with sword, 6x9", M, C3..**$7.00**

Burger Beer, clock, ca 1938, wood case with embossed tin front, oval center with lettering, nonworking, 15x19x2½", G, A..**$75.00**

Burger Beer, sign, self-framed tin, Tempting in script on border above portrait of elegant lady, product name below, 27x18", VG, A...**$95.00**

Burger Bock Beer, label, 1933-50, ram's head in center, 12-oz, EX, A **$27.00**

Burger Bohemian Beer, sign, self-framed painted tin, pipe & matches in ashtray beside frothy glass & bottle by vining post, 21x16", EX, A **$110.00**

Burger Bohemian Beer, sign, tin on cardboard, proud fisherman showing buddy his catch at campsite, Drink Burger Bohemian Beer, 15x20", VG+, A.............**$210.00**

Burger Brewing Co, tray, deep-dish, elderly couple enjoying a beer, lettering on rim, rare, oval, 12½x15¼", VG, A...**$120.00**

Burger King, ashtray, metal, 3" dia, NM, P4 ....**$3.00**

Burger King, doll, 1970s, stuffed cloth, red, yellow & black outfit with Burger King on necklace & belt buckle, 13½", EX, D..**$7.00**

Burgerliches Brauhaus Imported Pilsner Beer, sign, factory scene & gold medal awards surrounded by embossed nouveau border graphics, framed, vertical, VG, A **$145.00**

Burgermeister Ale, label, ca 1933-50, San Francisco Brewing Co, Internal Revenue Tax statement, 11-oz, EX, A **$10.00**

Burgess Batteries, thermometer, tin, yellow, red, green, white on black, text above, factory below, mounting tabs top & bottom, 14", VG+, A **$130.00**

Burgess Gun, trade card, 1893, pictures a gun above lettering, 12-Gauge Repeating Shotgun..., more guns on back, VG, A **$35.00**

Burgess Seeds & Plants, catalog, 1949, VG, D **$18.00**

Burgh Brau Beer, label, 1933-36, Frank McDermott Brewing Co, U-type permit number, 12-oz, EX, A **$12.00**

Burma Coffee, tin, black & gold, screw lid, 1-lb, EX, D..**$25.00**

Burma Shave, sign, wood, 3 panels reading Burma Shave Does What You Think It Should with Burma Shave on reverse, each panel: 17x40", G, A......................**$225.00**

Burnett's Cologne Water, trade card, pictures little geese walking on a country road, 5¾x4½", VG, D...........**$4.00**

Burnham Apple Sauce, can label, apples & red lettering on ivory background, gold trim, Newark NY, G1..**$3.00**

Burt's Fine Shoes, sign, paper, interior scene with several families trying on shoes, overall soiling, matted & framed, 17½x22", VG, A **$800.00**

Burton-Peel Dry Foods Co, sign, 1906, paperboard, elegant woman wearing a hat, Store Ahead..., signed Philip Boileau, framed, 20x15", VG, A...............**$250.00**

Busch Bavarian Beer, mug, 1970, metal, can shape, EX, D...**$10.00**

Busch Extra Dry Ginger Ale, sign, porcelain, Busch above Anheuser eagle logo, Extra Dry below on label left of America's Finest..., 11x21", VG+, A..........**$250.00**

Buscs A L'Ours, sign, cardboard, pictures bears trying on & inspecting corsets, minor surface chips, framed, image: 16x21½", EX, A..**$375.00**

Bush Hill Creamery Butter, trade card, red & green on white, product name in large letters above farm scene with cattle, EX, A...**$10.00**

Buss Auto Fuses, display, tin, man scratching head in front of car as others pass, Why Be Helpless..., 10 fuse boxes, 8x9", VG+, A...**$65.00**

Buster Brown Bread, pin-back button, Buster & Tige displaying lettered sign with Buster Brown Bread lettered around rim, 1¼", NM, A.......................................**$38.00**

Buster Brown Bread, sign, ca 1915-20, embossed tin, Buster & Tige flank Golden Sheaf Bakery advertising, black frame, 22x30", NM, A $1,800.00

Buster Brown Bread, sign, ca 1915-20, embossed tin, Buster & Tige flank Golden Sheaf Bakery advertising, framed, 20x28", VG+, A **$968.00**

Buster Brown Cameras, booklet, 1917, 'Buster Brown Cameras-How to Make Photographs,' Ansco Co, 12 pages, 6x4¼", EX, D **$7.50**

Buster Brown Children's Clothes, banner, cloth, Buster & Tige in tug-of-war, ...Since 1904, red, black & yellow on white with red border, 35x58", VG, A.............**$30.00**

Buster Brown Cigar, tin, elderly man blowing smoke at Buster & Tige, signed RP Outcault, slip lid, scarce, 5x5" dia, EX+, A **$3,544.00**

Buster Brown Hose Supporter, pin-back button, ca 1900, multicolored, EX, D..**$15.00**

Buster Brown Shoes, birthday card, 1960s, pair holding balloons reading Buster Brown & Tige, inside reads Wish A Happy Birthday, EX, A **$15.00**

Buster Brown Shoes, display, plaster, Buster Brown straddling Tige holding Buster Brown Shoes sign, 16½ x 8" dia, VG, A...**$410.00**

Buster Brown Shoes, mask, ca 1905, stiff die-cut paper, upper portion of Buster Brown's head in red hat, ad text on reverse, 8x10", VG, A **$75.00**

Buster Brown Shoes, mirror, Brown Bilt Shoes lettered above Buster Brown Shoes, adjustable metal stand, wood frame, 21½x16", VG, A **$55.00**

Buster Brown Shoes, pin-back button, ca 1920, shows a winking Buster Brown & a smiling Tige on black background, 1½" dia, VG+, A........................$225.00

Buster Brown Shoes, pocket mirror, Buster & Tige head images with Buster Brown Shoes above, For Boys & Girls below, 1¾" dia, NM, A...............................**$150.00**

Buster Brown Shoes, pocket mirror, Buster holds shoe above Tige's head while he holds shoe box, lettering around rim, 2¼" dia, G+, A **$60.00**

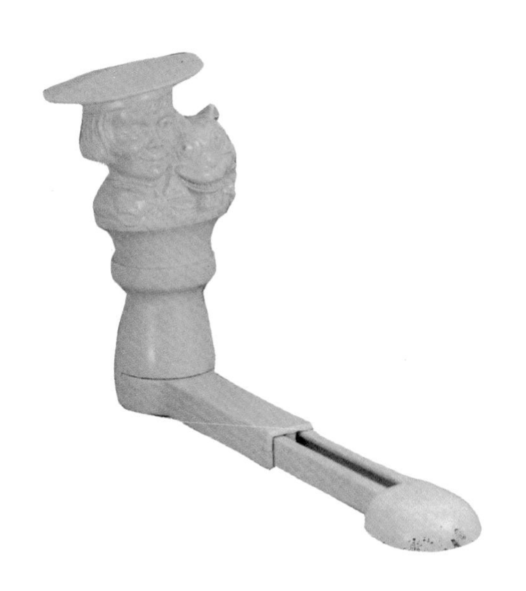

Buster Brown Shoes, shoe tree, plastic, figures of Buster & Tige at top, 4½", NM, D.....................$35.00

Buster Brown Shoes, sign, Buster & Tige on black background, Buster Brown Shoes Are Sold Here, original label on back, 10" dia, VG+, A **$1,900.00**

Buster Brown Shoes, store bench, 1905, oak, features Buster & Tige, strong color, scarce, 33x51x17", EX, D.....**$3,500.00**

Buster Brown Shoes, store rug, features head poses of Buster & Tige with Buster Brown lettered below, star border, needs binding, 48" dia, A **$130.00**

Buster Brown Shoes, store runner, triple image of Buster & Tige, For Boys, For Girls..., overall wear, 26½"x9 ft, G, A..**$100.00**

Buster Brown Shoes, thermometer, paper dial with oval image of Buster & Tige, lettering below, brown & white, 9" dia, EX, A...**$170.00**

Buster Brown Shoes, tote bag, 1960s, NM, D...........**$40.00**

Busy Bee Restaurant, pocket mirror, Keep Smiling & Eat At The above portrait of Uncle Sam, Busy Bee Restaurant below, oval, 2¾", VG+, A............................**$225.00**

Butte City 5 Cent Cigars, sign, ca 1905, paper, elegant woman amidst vivid red flowers, brass & metal frame, 20x15", EX, A...**$605.00**

Butter Krust Bread, pin-back button, 1930s, red, white & blue, EX, D **$8.00**

Butter Krust Bread, sign, ca 1909, embossed tin, Butter Krust boy with milk can, rust/chips/dents, framed, image: 38½x26½", G-, A **$125.00**

Butter Krust Bread, sign, 1920s-30s, die-cut porcelain, Butter Krust boy holding up slice of bread, rare, 18½x15", NM, M1.......................................$2,800.00

Butter-Nut Bread, labels, uncut sheet of 8 labels picturing Hopalong Cassidy, framed, 32x14½", EX, A.........**$30.00**

Butter-Nut Bread, sign, cardboard, The Jolly Baker presenting Butter-Nut Bread, Rich As Butter, Sweet As A Nut, framed, 22x16", EX, A..................................**$25.00**

Butter-Nut Bread, sign, embossed tin, yellow product name on black with Rich As Butter, Sweet As A Nut, yellow lined border, 6x14", NM, M3 ....**$80.00**

Butter-Nut Bread, sign, 1920s, die-cut cardboard, grocer handing girl a loaf of bread, 13x11", EX, D..........**$24.00**

Butter-Nut Bread, sign, 1920s, die-cut cardboard, little girl eating slice of bread, 13x11", EX, D.....................**$18.00**

Butter-Nut Bread, sign, 1924, cardboard, product name in elongated oval flanked by 2 little girls with loaves of bread, 11x21", EX, D..**$28.00**

Butter-Nut Coffee, tin, nonpictorial, keywind lid, 1-lb, EX, A..**$12.00**

Butterfinger, matchbook cover, Rich In Pure Dextrose, 20-strike, NM, R1 ....**$2.00**

Butterick Patterns, cabinet, oak, 20 compartments with glass inserts (some missing), Butterick Patterns stenciled above, 57x31", G, A **$450.00**

Butterine, sign, paper, girl riding calf over blooming field, Purity & Pride, In A Field Of Our Own, framed, 9½x13", G+, A $180.00

Buttermilk Toilet Soap, trade card, wallet-shaped card opens down into colorful 4-panel 4-part story of Jack & Jill, EX, A...$20.00

Button's Raven Gloss Shoe Dressing, trade card, 1880s, palette motif with woman in jockey outfit, 2½x4", VG, P1 ....$6.00

Buxom, crate label, fruit, farm girl in low-cut sunsuit & straw hat, 4¼x10", M, C1 ....$1.00

Buy the Best, crate label, California pear, view of central valley with orchard & mountains, beige background, 8x11", EX, G1..$3.00

Buy-Rite Pineapple, can label, grocer holding can of pineapples, M, C3...$6.00

Buzzer Cigars, label, Buzzer arched above butterfly with a cigar body, 4x4", EX, D..$12.00

C

C Conrad & Co, sign, watercolor on paper, woman surrounded by cherubs, gnomes & product, oval, matted & framed, image: 7x11", EX, A...........................$250.00

C Person's Sons Importers & Distillers, sign, 1910-20, tin, features buffalo encircled by red ring with white lettering, Buffalo Club Rye Whiskey, framed, 37x27", EX, A .$550.00

C Schmidt & Sons Brewing Co, recipe book, 1913, 'Dainty Home Lunches,' woman in period hat holding glass of beer on cover, 8 pages, G, H1..................$7.00

C&H Sugar Twin, doll, Hawaiian girl, in original package, 15", M, D $8.00

Cabanas Cigars, box label, outer, woman flanked by world globes, 4½x4½", M, C3 ....$4.00

Cadbury Chocolate, puppet, Clovis Cow, white & brown plush, inside lined with nylon, 12", M, N1 ....$13.00

Cadet, crate label, apple, cadet in dress attire & US seal, 9x10½", M, C3...$10.00

Cadillac, pencil, 1920s, pictures a golfer, For A Long Drive-Cadillac, Wilbur Dunn Cadillac Co, red, white & blue, EX, A $39.00

Cadillac, sign, porcelain, 2-sided, Cadillac in white script above emblem, white Authorized Service below on blue, 48x48", VG+, A $650.00

Cadillac Eldorado, sign, tin, crown & shield encircled by leaf design above ...1977, gold background, wood frame, 24x18¼", NM, A $60.00

Cadillac Engine, booklet, 1949, 20 pages, NM, D.......$8.00

Cadillac Service, sign, Cadillac Service arched above & below crown logo, 42" dia, G, D $900.00

Caf-Fee-No, pocket mirror, sickly bulldog rests head against wall, Got A Headache? Caf-Fee-No Will Cure It, oval, 2¾", G+, A $300.00

Cal-Cola, sign, embossed die-cut cardboard, Dutch sailing scene in oval surrounded by flowers above, Drink...5¢, vertical, NM, A..$100.00

Calabash Smoking Mixture, pocket tin, upright, product name encircled in center, flat top, rare, VG+, A ..$330.00

Calagras, crate label, California asparagus, crew loading asparagus on wagon, Sacramento, G1......................$2.00

California Dream, crate label, 1920s, Sunkist oranges, 2 peacocks & castle with lots of gilt, Bradford Bros Inc, Placentia, 10x11", M, C1.......................................$12.00

California Fig Syrup Co, sign, paper on linen, woman picking figs by the Pacific ocean, One Enjoys Syrup Of Figs..., 52x80½", VG, A $2,500.00

California Insurance Co of San Francisco, sign, porcelain, white on green, minor chips, 18x12", D.....$150.00

California Interstate Telephone Co, plaque, embossed metal, white on blue, shaped as open phone book with desk phone, 18x24", NM, D1 ....$225.00

Calkins Farm Wagon, catalog, 1924, features horse-drawn flat-bed freight wagons, 42 pages, EX, D $8.00

Call Again 5¢ Cigar, sign, stenciled & embossed tin, Call Again lettered above Cigar flanked by 5¢, A Welcome Smoke, framed, 12x36", EX, A..............................$50.00

Call Again 5¢ Cigar, sign, tin, white lettering on blue & red bands, white border, rounded corners, 3x13¾", NM, A $25.00

Callanan's English Coffee, tin, decorative logo, round screw lid on tall square can, A.............................$85.00

Calotabs, thermometer, wood, black on white, Calotabs For Biliousness...Torpidity above, product below, rounded top, 15", G, A..$35.00

Calox Tooth Powder, pocket mirror, Your 32 Teeth Are 32 Reasons For Using Calox, The Oxygen Tooth Powder..., oval, 2¾", NM, A..$44.00

Calso Gasoline, map holder, metal, red, 3-tier with encircled Calso Gasoline flanked by Road & Maps in white, 20x12½", VG, A $95.00

Calumet Baking Powder, display, cardboard with tin can in center of Calumet Kid & can image above plate of biscuits & ad text, 10x12", EX, A........................$225.00

Calumet Baking Powder, recipe book, 1942, 'Baking Secrets,' 34 pages, EX, D...$8.00

Calumet Baking Powder, recipe book, 1947, 'Learn To Bake, You'll Love It,' 80 pages, EX, D $4.50

Calumet Baking Powder, sign, cardboard, with removable price wheels, EX, A..$15.00

Calumet Baking Powder, thermometer, wood, blue & red lettering & multicolored can on yellow, Best By Test, Trade Here & Save, 22", G+, A...........................$310.00

Calumet Baking Powder, thermometer, 1920-40s, wood, Call For above baking powder tin, Best By Taste above little boy, 22x6", EX, A **$350.00**

Cambridge Blend Coffee, tin, Cambridge in script above Blend Coffee, vertical rectangle with round lid, 1-lb, A **$40.00**

Camden Beer, label, 1933-50, Camden Beverage Co, Internal Revenue Tax Paid statement, 1-qt, EX, A **$11.00**

Camel, crate label, 1930s, California pear, camel & master in desert scene, Loomis, 7¼x11", M, C1 .... **$2.00**

Camel Cigarette 100s, tin, round with Camel logo, pry lid, EX, A **$40.00**

Camel Cigarettes, can cooler, 1991, vinyl, Camel Joe smoking a cigarette, 4", M, D **$10.00**

Camel Cigarettes, cap, corduroy with embroidered Camel Joe & insignia, EX, P4 .... **$10.00**

Camel Cigarettes, cup, 1980s, plastic, features Camel Joe, Hardpack, 12-oz, EX, D **$30.00**

Camel Cigarettes, sign, ca 1942, test pilot & pack of cigarettes with vintage warplanes beyond, 11x21", EX, D **$60.00**

Camel Cigarettes, sign, tin, Camel arched above Camel Joe dressed in tux holding cigarette pack on yellow background, 27x18", NM, M3 .... **$18.00**

Camel Cigarettes, sign, tin, cigarette pack with advertising above & below, vertical rectangle, EX, D .. **$135.00**

Camel Cigarettes, sign, 1960s, paper, actor James Daly promoting Camels at right of Have A Real Cigarette... above pack, 11x21", EX, M2 .... **$25.00**

Camel Cigarettes, thermometer, embossed painted tin, shows open pack, Camels Sold Here, Have A Real Cigarette, 13½x5¾", VG+, H1 .... **$38.00**

Camel Cigarettes, tin, pictures a camel, Turkish & Domestic Blend, dents/scratches, 4½x5¾", D..$30.00

Camel Cigarettes, 3-D bottle holder, Camel Joe, vinyl head, NM, P4 .... **$10.00**

Camel Cigars, box label, inner lid, pictures Arab riding camel in desert, 6x9", M, D **$8.00**

Camel Cigars, tin, camel & rider flanked by 5¢ & triangular logo, slip lid, VG+, A **$40.00**

Cameron's Fine Smoking Tobacco, tin, orange & gold, lettered label on paisley background, slip lid, rounded corners, 2x4½x3½", EX, A **$25.00**

Camp Fire Blend Coffee, tin, 1931, circular inset of man tending campfire, lettering above & below, lid missing, 2 1/2-lb, EX, A **$450.00**

Campbell & Co's Edinburgh Ales, sign, paper, lettered ribbons flank gold crest logo, company name above, product name below, framed, 23x29", EX, A **$20.00**

Campbell's Alphabet Soup, word game, cardboard canister with tin lid, shows Cambell Kids, contains red plastic letters, EX, D $22.00

Campbell's Coffee, tin, 4-lb, EX, D **$55.00**

Campbell's Soup, badge for contractor, metal with celluloid, Campbell Soup above number, Contractor typewritten below, 1¾" dia, NM, A **$220.00**

Campbell's Soup, banner, red felt, Campbell's in white script above running Campbell Kid, Soups lettered vertically below, 17¾", EX, A **$135.00**

Campbell's Soup, booklet, 1979, 'Light Eating Menu Planner,' colorful illustrations of the Campbell Kids, 20 pages, M, D **$6.00**

Campbell's Soup, bowl, 4" dia, M, D **$8.50**

Campbell's Soup, calendar, 1980, paper, M, D **$10.00**

Campbell's Soup, child's fork, Campbell Kid's head engraved above M-m-m Good on handle, EX, D... **$5.00**

Campbell's Soup, coloring book, 1976, 'A Story of Soup,' uncolored, 14x11", M, D **$20.00**

Campbell's Soup, doll, ca 1973, Campbell Girl, stuffed cloth, blue bibs with red & white checked shirt, 15½", EX, D **$65.00**

Campbell's Soup, dolls, 1976, Campbell Kids as Paul Revere & Betsy Ross, vinyl, 10", MIB, D **$200.00**

Campbell's Soup, electrical soup kitchen with can opener, display rack & mugs, 1955, Ready In A Jiffy, 27x19x12", EX, A **$400.00**

Campbell's Soup, invitation for radio program, 'The Christmas Carol,' 1933, colorful front pictures 3 Campbell Kids, 5x8", EX, P1 .... **$25.00**

Campbell's Soup, jigsaw puzzle, 1986, #319, 'All Aboard,' 28 pieces, VG, D **$30.00**

Campbell's Soup, lunch box with thermos, 1968, metal, domed, brown, rare, G/VG, D **$250.00**

Campbell's Soup, lunch box with thermos, 1973, mostly blue showing kids at play, thermos is red & white with logo, 7x9x3½", G, D..**$275.00**

Campbell's Soup, menu board, shows Campbell Kid & bowl of soup with Today's Specials, Good & Hearty..., lined board below, 23x18", EX, A **$55.00**

Campbell's Soup, pin, 1970s, enamel on brass, figural Campbell's Girl, inscribed New Jersey Jaycee-Ettes Are M'm-M'm Good, 1¾", EX, A..................................**$50.00**

Campbell's Soup, pocket mirror, large can of soup flanked by 21 Kinds & 10¢ A Can, Campbell's above, Soups below, 2¾x1¾", EX, A..**$99.00**

Campbell's Soup, pocket mirror, pictures can of soup flanked by 6 Plates & 10 Cents, lettering below, 1¾" dia, VG+, A **$80.00**

Campbell's Soup, potholder, 1968-70, soup-can shape with magnet inside, minor discoloration, D **$10.00**

Campbell's Soup, recipe book, 'Campbell's 100 Best Recipes,' 160 pages, EX, D **$8.00**

Campbell's Soup, recipe book, 1950, 'Easy Ways to Good Meals-99 Delicious Dishes,' 48 pages, EX, D **$10.00**

Campbell's Soup, salt & pepper shakers, plastic, Campbell Kids with cooking utensils, 4¼", EX, D **$70.00**

Campbell's Soup, sign, 1980, Captain America & the Campbell Kids, Help Save Energy, 24x16", EX, D **$7.50**

Campbell's Soup, snack can, ca 1966, slip lid, large, rare, EX, D **$85.00**

Campbell's Soup, storybook, 1954, pictures Campbell Kids on cover, Rand McNally, 8x6½", VG, D................**$25.00**

Campbell's Soup, thermometer, 1940s, 2-D plaster plaque, Campbell Kid in striped shirt next to thermometer, 7x3½x1", VG+, A...**$202.00**

Campbell's Soup, tin, 1966, round with red & white logo, rare, 16x12" dia, G, D **$85.00**

Campbell's Soup, toy electric mixer, 1960s, pictures Campbell Kids on sides, Mirro, rare, MIB, D **$225.00**

Campbell's Soup, toy tea set, 1982, plastic, includes 4 plates, cups, tray, dish & utensils, shows the Campbell Kids, MIB, D **$65.00**

Campbell's Soup, toy truck, 1985, white cab, red trailer promoting Campbell's products on sides, Truck Load Of Good Food, 5x18", NM, D...............................**$95.00**

Campbell's Soup, warming dish, 1930s, shows early Campbell Kids, girl crying & boy holding candy, 1x7½" dia, VG, D..**$90.00**

Campbell's Soup, warming dish, 1930s, shows early Campbell Kids, girl holding doll & boy holding flowers, signed Grace Drayton, G, D **$75.00**

Campbell's Tomato Soup, magnet, 1989, can shape, in original package, M, D **$4.00**

Campbell's Tomato Soup, sign, 1910s-20s, die-cut porcelain, can shape depicting famous label, edge chips/minor staining, 22½x15", G, A **$1,000.00**

Campbell's Tomato Soup, sign, 1910s-20s, die-cut porcelain, can shape depicting famous label, original bracket & screws, 22½x13", EX+, A **$2,200.00**

Campbell's Vegetable Garden, bank, tin, can shape w/paper label, pictures Campbell Girl, Money Saving..., 4½", EX, D...........**$9.50**

Campbell's Vegetable Soup, sign, steaming bowl of soup & soup can among grouping of fresh vegetables, When You're Hungry, 11x21", EX, A **$55.00**

Campfire Marshmallows, tin, Campfire lettered diagonally above Marshmallows, slip lid, round, some wear, A **$25.00**

Campfire Supreme Marshmallows, tin, pictures campfire scene with figures standing by teepee, slip lid, round, 1-lb, EX, A..**$50.00**

Canada Dry, bottle topper, die-cut cardboard, logo above list of flavors & assorted fruit, 10", NM, B1.............**$6.00**

Canada Dry, clock, plastic face with metal frame, 12-3-6-9 with dots in between surround Canada Dry logo, 16x16", EX, M2 ....**$35.00**

Canada Dry, door push plate, hand holding bottle before product emblem, The Best Of lettered on diagonal band below, NM, A...**$100.00**

Canada Dry, menu board, tin, crown logo & Champagne Of Ginger Ales above chalkboard, vertical rectangle with rounded corners, EX, M2 ....**$30.00**

Canada Dry, sign, cardboard, Canada Dry in quotes above 2 bottles & glass over snowy stream, Cool Off dot lower left, 34x28", VG, A **$15.00**

Canada Dry, sign, embossed die-cut tin, Canada Dry lettered over crown emblem, 15x14", M, A **$45.00**

Canada Dry, sign, 1950s, embossed tin, product name on shield above hand holding bottle, Best Of Them All lettered below, 12", VG, A **$10.00**

Canada Dry Spur, door push plate, 1930s, embossed tin, pictures tilted bottle & large 5¢, 12x3½", EX, D...**$70.00**

Canada Dry Spur, fan hanger, 2-sided, large tilted bottle of Spur before palm trees, The Delicious Cola 5¢, 7¾x4⅛", NM, A **$4.00**

Canada Dry Spur, sign, embossed tin, green Canada Dry above red Spur above tilted 5¢ bottle, Zip In Every Sip! below, 12x4", NM, M3..**$45.00**

Canada Dry Spur, sign, 1940s, die-cut cardboard hanger, 2-sided, pictures tilted bottle & palm trees, 5¢ below, 8x5", EX, D **$10.00**

Canada/Luxor Paints, sign, tin flange, 2-sided, paint brush atop paint can, 1 Canada Paint, 1 Luxor, Quality In Every Drop, 18x13", EX+, M2.............................**$150.00**

Canadian Club Cigars, box label, inner lid, 1950s, pictures colorful leaf, Millions Sold For 5¢ Each, The Same Cigar Now..., 7x8", M, C3 ....$3.00

Canadian Club Cigars, sign, Canadian Club lettered above 3 men in conversation with product & 5¢ below, Sumatra Wrapper, framed, vertical, A **$90.00**

Canadian Club 5¢ Cigar, fan hanger, 2-sided, Different From All Others arched above Canadian Club lettered over maple leaf, 7" dia, NM, A **$8.00**

Canadian Lord Calvert, water pitcher, EX, D........... **$12.00**

Canadian Pacific Express, sign, tin, bold white letters on blue background, minor chip/scratches, 13x20", G, A..... **$350.00**

Candee Rubbers, trade card, pictures puppy in a shoe, sepia tones, advertising on back, EX, A **$17.00**

Candee Rubbers, trade card, pictures 2 women trying on boots, sepia tones, advertising on back EX, A **$14.00**

Canton Ginger, tin, 5x3x1½", EX, D **$16.50**

Cantrihum Overalls & Coats, pocket mirror, side of boxcar with Cantrihum on the diagonal, Union Made above, horizontal oval, 2¾" long, EX, A............ **$110.00**

Cap'n Crunch, frame-tray puzzle, M, D2.................. **$25.00**

Cap'n Crunch, kaleidoscope, 1970s, cardboard cylinder with paper label showing 6 different characters, 7¼x2" dia, VG+, A **$10.00**

Cape Cod Cranberries, crate label, 1924, 2 boys in sailor attire eating cranberries, M, C3.............................. **$7.00**

Capital Brand Peanut Butter, pail, features children playing, EX, A **$1,200.00**

Capital Pak, crate label, 1940s, California asparagus, view of California capitol building, Sacramento, G1....... **$2.00**

Capitan Parlube Motor Oil, can, 1925-45, pictures car on mountain road below product name, pour spout & handle, 2-gal, 10½", EX+, A................................ **$105.00**

Capitol City Brewing Co, pitcher, embossed stoneware, trademark emblem on 1 side, shield with leaves & lettering on other, 8½x5½" dia, G, A **$275.00**

Capitol Motor Oil, can, 1940s, dome of capitol building on circular inset, red, white & blue, pour spout & handle, 2-gal, 10½", NM, A **$45.00**

Capitola Flour, pocket mirror, Capitola lettered diagonally above factory scene encircled by product advertising, 2⅛" dia, EX, A.. **$76.00**

Caporal Sweet Tobacco, label, paper, soldier standing at ease with a burning building in background, minor soiling, 21½x9", EX, A... **$160.00**

Capper's Farmer Protective Service, sign, tin, red, black & white, lettering within eagle, 8x14", EX, D....... **$25.00**

Capper's Farmer Protective Service, sign, tin, This Farm Protected above company name on eagle, Cash Rewards, Thieves Beware lettered below, edge rust, 8x14", B1... **$12.50**

Capt Morgan Spiced Rum, display mirror, light-up, 13x19", EX, D **$30.00**

Capt Morgan Spiced Rum, mirror, 16x21", EX, D.... **$20.00**

Capt Morgan Spiced Rum, pennant, white silk, pictures Capt Morgan, 15x15", EX, D **$4.50**

Capt Morgan Spiced Rum, sign, tin, 16x20", EX, D. **$15.00**

Carborundum File, sign, tin stand-up, pictures farmer sharpening blade, Sharpens Mower & Reaper Sections..., 19½x14", G, A **$220.00**

Card Seed Co, display rack with seed packets, metal, slanted front with 5 rows, labeled front, 24¾x16x10", EX, A **$85.00**

Cardinal Beer, tip tray, pretty girl with flowers in her hair, lettering on rim, minor soiling/edge chips, 4¼" dia, VG, A... **$130.00**

Cardinal Cherry, dispenser, painted metal on wrought-iron stand, cardinal under tree lifts glass, Cardinal Cherry 5¢ below, 58", VG, A **$700.00**

Carey Shingles, thermometer, cardboard & actual piece of shingle, 10x5", EX, D **$45.00**

Cargray Gold, pump sign, 1930s, porcelain, black Cargray lettered on gold winged tire by Gold lettered on black, 10" dia, M, D3 .... $195.00

Carhartt Overhalls, Trousers & Shirts, decal, Carhartt 100% Union Made lettered on wheeled trailer superimposed over heart, From Mill To Millions, 6x9", EX, M2.................. **$4.00**

Carhartt's Clothing, sign, curved porcelain, railroad emblem over heart above lettering, red, white & blue, 28x22½x5½", EX, A **$750.00**

Carigas, can, 1910-25, ...Emergency Gasoline Tank above Aetna logo, red & yellow, pour spout, 1-gal, 12½", NM, A **$20.00**

Carl Dunbar Cigars, trade card, features elderly man & children, Calvert Lithography Co, 6x4", EX, H1 ..... **$5.00**

Carling's, sign, self-framed tin on cardboard, 9 English bobbies seated in a row drinking Carling's, Nine Pints Of The Law, 12x21", VG, A **$105.00**

Carling's Black Label Beer, salt shaker, vinyl, miniature beer can, M, D **$5.00**

Carlton Club Mixture, sample tin, upright, logo with product name above & below, EX+, A **$42.00**

Carmen Complexion Powder, pocket mirror, Carmen Complexion Powder lettered above bust portrait of girl in oval, 1¾" dia, EX, A **$30.00**

Carnation Evaporated Milk, door plate, porcelain, Pull lettered above can of product, 7x3½", EX+, A ... **$550.00**

Carnation Evaporated Milk, door plate, porcelain, Push lettered above can of product, 7x3½", NM, M1.. **$650.00**

Carnation Gum, sign, self-framed tin, girl with floral bouquet, Chew Carnation Gum & Taste The Smell, 13¾x13¾", EX, A... **$800.00**

Carnation Ice Cream, postcard, pictures billboard, M, D **$20.00**

Carnation Malted Milk, container, aluminum, red & white background with Carnation logo, Malted Milk in black below, 8½", EX+, A **$150.00**

Carnation Malted Milk, container, glass, Barbie premium offer on label, unused, D **$125.00**

Carnation Malted Milk, container, milk glass with aluminum lid, product name lettered on front, EX, A **$145.00**

Carnation Malted Milk, container, porcelain with aluminum lid, Carnation in script on red above flowers, Malted Milk on white below, EX+ A **$450.00**

Carnation Milk, recipe book, 1932, '100 Recipes by Mary Blake,' colorful photos, red & white cover, EX, D. **$4.00**

Carnation Milk, recipe book, 1959, 'Teen Time Cooking with Carnation,' 16 pages, EX, D **$6.00**

Carnation Milk, sign, 1950s, die-cut porcelain, product name & bottle on red, white & green emblem, 15x14", EX, D3 .... $525.00

Carnation Toilet Co, catalog, 1922, features perfumes, dental creams, medicines, etc, well illustrated, 32 pages, EX, D **$9.50**

Caroga Can Syrup, can label, 1940, Black waiter holding tray with syrup, EX, C3 .... **$30.00**

Carr Chain Works Inc, sign, image of tire in gold & silver chains splashing through water, Look Better & Last Longer..., vertical, EX, A **$10.00**

Carro Amano, crate label, 1920s, California orange, Gypsy selling oranges from pushcart, East Highlands, 10x11¾", M, C3 .... **$4.00**

Carroll Rye, sign, 1907, paper, baseball player catching a bottle of whiskey, Caught On The Fly, 1 of 2, framed, image: 18x12", EX, A **$1,500.00**

Carstairs, lamp, metal seal shape, M, P2 .... **$125.00**

Carstairs White Seal Gin, sign, 1950s, glass diamond shape, red, white, blue & silver seal & logo, minor paint chips, 13x10½", EX, D **$38.00**

Carstairs White Seal Whiskey, charm, ca 1940s, plastic, pictures white seal balancing red ball, miniature, EX, D .. **$4.00**

Carter Rice & Co, blotter, 1938, pictures luggage, tennis racket & golf clubs, 2-tone green, black & brown, unused, 6x3½", D **$6.00**

Carter's Buccaneer Typewriter Ribbon, tin, pictures a buccaneer, EX, D **$10.00**

Carter's Fountain Pen Fluid, inkwell, brass insert in glass block with etched lettering on sides, minor edge chips, 3x4x4", VG, A **$35.00**

Carter's Inks, blotter, 1903, The Old Bookkeeper's Verdict, unused, 6x3⅜", H1 .... **$6.50**

Carter's Inks, showcase, glass & oak with decaled horn & quill on front, lettering on 1 side, 14¼x22x11¼", VG, A.. **$350.00**

Carter's Inks, sign, 1900s, embossed tin, bookkeeper at desk in oval center, After All, No Ink Like Carter's, 25x18½", VG, A **$600.00**

Carter's Little Liver Pills, sign, reverse-painted glass with foil back, black background with silver highlights, 11½x10¼", EX, A **$220.00**

Carter's Little Nerve Pills, sign, reverse-painted glass with foil back, black background with silver highlights, 11½x10¼", EX, A **$175.00**

Carter's Pants, Overalls, Shop Coats, sign, porcelain, Carter's above Watch The Wear in diagonal script between images of train & working men, horizontal, EX, M1 .... **$1,600.00**

Cartwright Borden Crackers, pocket mirror, box of product encircled by Your Health Depends Upon What You Eat, with damaged box, 2⅛" dia, EX, A **$250.00**

Cascade Beer, tray, Uncle Sam & others sampling product, We Never Disagree... below, Union Brewing & Malting Co on rim, 11x14", G-, A $150.00

Cascarets Candy Cathartic, pin-back button, ca 1900, purple & white, EX, D **$6.00**

Cascarets Candy Cathartic, pocket mirror, lady reclining on tail of letter 'C' in Cascarets, Just For The Bowels lettered above, 2⅛" dia, VG, A **$55.00**

Cascarets Candy Cathartic, trade card, constructed with sand, shows constipated child, when turned over sand drops in clear window, EX, A **$55.00**

Case Agency, sign, tin flange, full color image of eagle atop ball, HD Beach litho, faded/scratches, 23½x16", G, A **$550.00**

Casey & Kelly Brewery, tray, colorful image of King Gambrenas with glass of beer, Peerless Beer... on rim, scuffs/soiling, 13¼" dia, G, A **$250.00**

Casey & Kelly Munster, Bohemian Beer & Carbonated Ale, tray, bust-portrait of girl with flowers in her hair, lettering on decorative rim, oval, 16¾x13¾", EX, A .**$375.00**

Cashew Nut Crunch, tin, 1950s, pictures children, EX, D **$45.00**

Cashmere Bouquet Perfume, trade card, pictures young lady with tray of flowers, die-cut bird at top, Colgate & Co, EX, D **$5.00**

Castanea Beer, tray, stock image of 3 dogs chewing playing cards, ...FC Lucas, Brewer lettered on rim, oval, 13½x16½", EX, A **$475.00**

Castellanos Cigars, box label, inner lid, bust of a woman & royal coat-of-arms, 6x9", M, C3 ....**$5.00**

Castle Dome Cigars, box label, inner lid, top of castle in view over trees, 6x9", M, C3................................**$30.00**

Castrol, thermometer, red Castrol on white geometric design on green ground, red numbers on white border, 12" dia, NM, M3..**$95.00**

Caswell Club Cigars, cigar cutter & ashtray, nickel-plated, fancy footed ashtray & oval emblem with embossed lettering, 7", EX, A..**$300.00**

Caswell's Coffee, tin, 1924-28, yellow & blue, lady in profile sipping coffee in filigree oval inset, lettering above & below, 3-lb, EX, A..**$210.00**

Cataract Cream Ale, label, Cataract Brewing Co, U-type permit number, 12-oz, G, A...................................**$5.00**

Catawissa Sparkling Beverages, sign, embossed tin, red on white, bottle left of product name & Dial 2252 Catawissa, red lined border, 12x18", NM, M3.......**$90.00**

Catcher Rough Cut Pipe Tobacco, tin, burning pipe below product name, pull top, 5" dia, VG+, A.....................**$20.00**

Catlin's Patent Pouch Smoking Tobacco, sign, 1890s, paper, hissing cat atop product box by fence eyeing pipe-smoking cat in window, 12x9", NM, D3 ....$850.00

Cattaraugus Cutlery Co, display case, oak & glass, ...Little Valley NY, trapezoid, 11½x18x4½", EX, A **$250.00**

Cattaraugus Cutlery Co, display case, wood box frame, glass hinged top, Indian trademark & ...The Better Quality Knife on box, 31x20", EX, A **$150.00**

CBC Krausened Beer, label, 1933-36, Carondelet Brewing Co, U-type permit number, 12-oz, EX, A.............**$21.00**

CD Kenny Co, pin-back button, early 1900s, Welcome United Singers below crossed flags, advertising on back, 1½" dia, VG, A..**$12.00**

CD Kenny Co, tip tray, complimentary Thanksgiving Greetings, pictures boy entering door with a live turkey, 5⅛" dia, EX, A...**$240.00**

CE Hidlebaugh Saddlery Co, thermometer, black & white stenciled wood, arched top, squared bottom, damaged at mounting holes, 47", G, A...........**$210.00**

Cellarmaster, sign, applique & hand-painting on leather, portly monk sampling glass of alcohol, framed, image: 24" dia, G, A **$50.00**

Celluloid Corset Clasps, sign, paper, 2 women wearing corsets in front of mirrored dresser, Side & Dress Steels..., minor soiling, 21x15", EX, A $3,400.00

Centennial Bock Beer, label, 1933-50, Christian Diehl Brewing Co, Internal Revenue Tax Paid statement, 12-oz, EX, A **$10.00**

Central Beer, sign, case glass with double window, red & white, framed, 28½x76½", VG, A **$500.00**

Central Brewing Co, charger, tin, tavern scene with men conversing with barmaids, minor chips/scratches, 24" dia, VG, A **$300.00**

Central Brewing Co, tray, factory scene with harbor & street scene in foreground, lettering on rim, oval, 13¾x16¾", EX, A **$700.00**

Central Market Coffee, tin, pictures Miss Liberty, scarce, 4-lb, EX, D **$650.00**

Central National Fire Insurance, sign, eagle decal on oak, lettering above & below, framed, image: 22x16", EX, A **$600.00**

Central Union Cut Plug Tobacco, lunch pail, gold on red, shows girl in crescent moon, brass catch, handled, NM, A **$155.00**

Central Union Cut Plug Tobacco, tin, girl in crescent moon flanked by Cut & Plug, gold & red, slip lid, 4x6", EX, A ...**$31.00**

Century Beer, label, 1933-36, Ph Schneider Brewing Co, U-type permit number, 12-oz, EX, A **$14.00**

Ceresota Flour, ashtray, ceramic, brown image of Ceresota boy in center of round dish with 4 cigarette rests, gold trim, 7" dia, NM, A **$5.00**

Ceresota Flour, booklet, ca 1910, 'Household Hints,' 32 pages, EX, D **$14.00**

Ceresota Flour, match holder, die-cut tin, Ceresota boy slicing bread above light blue flour box holder, 5½x2½", VG, A $225.00

Ceresota Flour, match holder, die-cut tin, Ceresota boy slicing bread above Prize Bread Flour on barrel holder, 5½x2½", NM, A $350.00

Ceresota Flour, pin-back button, ca 1900, multicolored, EX, D **$20.00**

Ceresota Flour, pocket mirror, Ceresota boy facing left slices bread, Prize Bread... above, Ceresota Flour below, 2⅛" dia, VG, A **$70.00**

Ceresota Flour, pocket mirror, Ceresota boy facing left slices bread, Prize Bread... above, Ceresota Flour below, 2⅛" dia, NM, A **$186.00**

Ceresota Flour, pocket mirror, Ceresota boy facing right slices bread, Ceresota Flour above, Pure-Wholesome... below, 2⅛" dia, NM, A **$186.00**

Cerveza Superior White Star, label, pre-1920, eagle & star logo flanked by White Star, Cerveza Superior above, Congress Brewing Co, EX, A **$5.00**

CF&I Coals, sign, porcelain, product name in red & black lettering at right of 3 devils with black coal bags, 9x20", EX, A **$285.00**

Chadwick's Spool Cotton, cabinet, oak with 6 lettered drawers, Chadwicks Best Six Cord..., lift lid, 15x32", VG, A **$550.00**

Chalmers-Motor-Car-Co, sign, cardboard, blue on cream, Chalmers-Motor-Car-Co, Detroit Mich USA surround CMC logo, 21x20½", VG, A **$145.00**

Chamberlain's Tablets, store jar, glass, yellow decal features product name & advertising on 2 sides, not original top, 12x5½" square, VG, A **$45.00**

Champ, crate label, 1930s, Louisiana Sweet Potatoes & Yams, Dupuis Produce Co, 9x9", M, C3 .... **$4.00**

Champagne Lager Beer, label, pre-1920, product name above eagle & star logo, Congress Brewing Co lettered below, EX, A **$15.00**

Champagne Velvet Beer, sign, tin on cardboard, fisherman with lunch trying to escape from 2 skunks, ...Million Dollar Flavor, 14x19", VG, A **$80.00**

Champagne Velvet Beer, sign, tin on cardboard, man hanging on to boat while friend tries to reel in fish, 14x19", EX, A **$100.00**

Champion Brew, label, 1933-50, Dallas Ft Worth Brewing Co, Internal Revenue Tax Paid statement, 12-oz, EX, A ... **$21.00**

Champion Brewery, tray, stock image of girl in white veil, Extra Brewed For Bottling..., cherubs & flowers on rim, oval, 17x14", VG, A **$145.00**

Champion Spark Plugs, clock, 1920-30, metal light-up, America's Favorite..., metal rusted away at top of clock, 14x26", VG, A **$80.00**

Champion Spark Plugs, display, tin, yellow with embossed Champion logo, 2 spark plugs on metal panel, lettering below, 12x18x6", VG, A **$200.00**

Champion Spark Plugs, man's jewelry set, ca 1940, 2 cuff links, lapel button & tie clip, each has white porcelain spark plug, EX, P1 .... **$40.00**

Champion Spark Plugs, radio, gray & white spark plug on black base, Champion lettered in red, round gold label on base, 14", EX+, A **$55.00**

Champion Spark Plugs, sign, 1920-35, porcelain, Champion logo on yellow, More Power, More Speed, 14x30", EX, A $1,000.00

Champion Spark Plugs, thermometer, wood, spark plug shape, 21x5", VG, D **$425.00**

Championship Cigars, box labels, inner & outer sample set, 1880s, man pinning medal to boxer's chest, Geo S Harris litho, VG/G, A **$256.00**

Champlin HI-V-I Motor Oil, sign, porcelain, 2-sided, ...On The Ground Or In The Sky, 20x32", NM, S2 ...... **$265.00**

Champlin Motor Oils, sign, porcelain, 2-sided, white with Champlin Motor Oils lettered around 'C' logo reading Use Champlin Oils, 30" dia, G, A **$120.00**

Chancellor Cigar, sign, porcelain, Mild, Fragrant..., maroon, black & white, edge chips/overall wear, 12x36", VG, A **$140.00**

Chandler's Kidney Pellets, display card with 3 boxes of pellets, 1941, pictures a girl in square inset at top, 12x7", EX, D **$14.00**

Chandon Brut Imperial, display bottle, plastic, 27", EX, D **$18.00**

Channel, crate label, California lemon, pictures gulls flying around vignette of Santa Barbara Channel, Goleta, 9x12", G1 .... **$3.00**

Charles Denby Cigars, tin, Charles Denby in script above oval portrait, slip lid, 5½x3½", NM, A **$60.00**

Charles Fox Cigars, box label, outer, 1909, overweight well-dressed man, 4½x4½", M, C3 ....**$24.00**

Charles Williams Stores, catalog, 1921, Spring/Summer, features automobile supplies, 66 pages, VG+, H2.......**$40.00**

Charm of the West Chewing Tobacco, tin, slip lid, rectangular with rounded corners, EX, A **$175.00**

Charms, sign, paper, tipped box of raspberries & pack of Raspberry Charms left of product advertising, framed, 13x22", EX, A..**$200.00**

Charter Oak Stoves, trade card, young man wooing girl with sheepish suitor looking on, 3x4½", VG, D.....**$4.50**

Chas A Grove's Sons Whiskey, tray, Indian on horseback chasing a buffalo, ...Golden Rod Spring Grove lettered on rim, round corners, 13¼x13¼", VG, A $625.00

Chas A Grove's Sons Whiskey, tray, 2 dogs at table smoking cigars, ...Golden Rod, Spring Grove lettered on rim, square corners, 14x14", EX, A **$450.00**

Chase & Sanborn Coffee, booklet, 1914, epochs of US history, chromolitho Indian chief on cover, 10 pages, EX, D...**$7.50**

Chase & Sanborn Coffee, jigsaw puzzle, pictures Ceylon girl picking tea, G, D **$30.00**

Chase & Sanborn Coffee, poster, paper, 1897 view of elderly men conversing in a New England grocery, matted & framed, image & mat: 20x23", G, A..........**$150.00**

Chase & Sanborn Coffee & Tea, blotter, pictures elderly woman sipping from mug, multicolored, unused, minor edge damage, 6x3½", D..**$6.00**

Chase & Sanborn's Choice Quality Coffee, tin, red round milk-can shape with white lettering, domed top with small round lid, bail handle, 5-lb, NM, A **$285.00**

Chase & Sanborn's High Grade Teas & Coffees, display, metal, adjustable shelf on vertical stand with green & gold lettering, 33x15½x10", G+, A........................**$95.00**

Chase & Sanborn Standard Java, trade card, frontal view of little boy on a donkey, backview on reverse, Where Is The Boy?, Here I Am, 6½x3", EX, P1 ....**$45.00**

Chase & Sanborn Standard Java, trade card, little girl hugging cat surrounded by text, Standard Java Record lettered above, EX, A **$17.00**

Chase's Liquid Glue, sign, reverse-painted glass, colorful bottle, gilded wood frame with raised leaf & vine pattern, 25½x17½", G-, A..**$100.00**

Checkers Tobacco, pocket tin, upright, Checkers in script on red & black checked background, slip lid, 4½x3", VG, A **$225.00**

Checkers Tobacco, sample box, cardboard with paper label, tin top & bottom, red lettering on white, slip lid, rare, VG+, A **$300.00**

Cheer Up Soda, fan pull, die-cut cardboard, green bottle shape with red & white label, EX, M3 ....**$18.00**

Cheer Up Soda, sign, red, white & green bottle & drinking glass on simulated wood-grain background, 11½x9½", EX, D..**$48.00**

Cheerio Coffee, tin, pictures bird in a top hat on a branch, Cheerio lettered above, Coffee below, no top, 1-lb, EX, A...**$51.00**

Cheerios, cereal bowl, bright yellow, You Made Cheerios Number One around rim, You Did It in bowl, 6" dia, EX, D..**$20.00**

Cheerios, cereal box, with Lone Ranger Deputy badge, movie film & flashlight ring offers, full, EX, D...**$165.00**

Chelsea Seed Corn, bag, 1930s, cloth, pictures a plantation gate, 34x15", EX, D **$12.50**

Chemists' Borated Talcum Infant Powder, tin, floral motif surrounding product lettering, shaker top, flat oval, EX, M2 ....**$60.00**

Cheon Tea, tip tray, oriental lady serving iced tea on tray, lettered border, CD Kenny Co, 4¼" dia, EX, A ..**$230.00**

Chero-Cola, blotter, Drink Chero-Cola, There's None So Good lettered on oval with octagon-shaped border, NM, A **$18.00**

Chero-Cola, pocket mirror & pin holder, In A Bottle Thru A Straw arched above Drink Chero-Cola with underline, 2⅛" dia, VG, A..**$33.00**

Chero-Cola, sign, cardboard, Drink Chero-Cola In The Twist Bottle lettered above landscape, matted, horizontal, EX, A...........**$20.00**

Cherry Blossoms, blotter, bottles and flowers flank oval logo, NM, A **$18.00**

Cherry Blossoms, blotter, 1920s, pictures glass & straight-sided bottle, Drink Cherry Blossoms, A Blooming Good Drink, 8x3½", EX, D..**$17.50**

Cherry Blossoms, bottle topper, cardboard, Cherry Blossoms on red trapezoid above white oval with green lettering, floral decor, EX, M3.................................**$45.00**

Cherry Blossoms, bottle topper with embossed bottle, cardboard, girl's face shown in lettered cherry blossom, red 5¢ below, EX, M3 ....**$75.00**

Cherry Blossoms, fan hanger, character pouring from bottle to glass, Make Mine Cherry Blossoms, A Blooming Good Drink!, 7½x6", NM, A **$8.00**

Cherry Blossoms, fan hanger, girl's head poking out from cherry blossom sipping from straw in 5¢ glass, 8½x6", NM, A **$22.00**

Cherry Blossoms, sign, cardboard, white & red on black, Drink above Cherry Blossoms on red panel, 5¢, A Blooming Good Drink below, EX, M3.................**$15.00**

Cherry Blossoms, sign, embossed tin, bottle on oval left of Ask For above Cherry Blossoms above A Blooming Good Drink, 20x28", EX, A.......**$110.00**

Cherry Blossoms, sign, tin, yellow with black Drink above Cherry Blossoms on red trapezoid shape, A Blooming Good Drink below, 13x19", EX, M3.......**$95.00**

Cherry Blossoms, sign, 1921, tin with glass bottle, 10", NM, A.......$1,300.00

Cherry Blossoms, tray, features bottle on white oval, In Bottles Only, oblong, VG+, A.......**$75.00**

Cherry Blush, sign, tin, Cherry Blush lettered in white over sprig of cherries, Cherries Only Rival, 6x9", EX, M1.......$400.00

Cherry Smash, bottle topper, die-cut cardboard, colonial boy with glass surrounded by cherries, EX, A.......**$65.00**

Cherry Smash, bottle topper, plastic, 2-sided, Cherry Smash lettered on stylized bow tie shape with Drink above, 4⅛x7¼", NM, A.......**$10.00**

Cherry Smash, pin-back button, pictures George Washington, G, D.......**$35.00**

Cherry Smash, postcard, Black servant serving Cherry Smash on the lawn of Mt Vernon, Cherry Smash lettered on lawn, VG+, P3.......**$40.00**

Cherry Smash, sign, cardboard hanger, glass & trail of cherries left of Always Drink 5¢..., Our Nations Beverage, 6x11½", EX, A.......**$60.00**

Cherry Smash, sign, embossed tin, Drink above Cherry Smash lettered in shape of bow tie, In Bottles lettered below, 9x23¾", G, A.......**$45.00**

Cherry Smash, sign, light-up, celluloid, red Cherry Smash flanks drinking glass on branch above lady enjoying drink, framed, 14x11", NM, A.......**$1,550.00**

Cherry Smash, sign, tin, red Cherry Smash flanks 5¢ over 3 cherries on branch marked Fowler's, curled corners, 4x9½", NM, A.......$2,000.00

Cherry Smash, syrup bottle, label under glass, metal cap, label stained, 11½", G, A.......**$110.00**

Cherry Smash, syrup dispenser, ceramic potbelly shape, 5¢ glass shown on front & back, gold trim, hairlines/drilled hole, 14x8½", VG, A.......**$500.00**

Cherry Smash Sundae, sign, cardboard hanger, sundae with trail of cherries around bottom, Cherry Smash Sundae Is Delicious, 6x11½", VG+, A.......**$165.00**

Cherry Sparkle, sign, 1930s-40s, embossed tin, animated homely fella with bottle & straw at left of Exquisite... emblem, 6x13", EX+, A.......**$350.00**

Chesapeake Steamship Co, print, paper, company name & home ports lettered below view of steamship, lined border, matted & framed, 25x35", EX, A.......**$400.00**

Chesmore's Reliable Seeds, dispenser, revolving, tin, round with company name & address on front, minor rust, 24", VG, A.......**$425.00**

Chesterfield Cigarettes, apron, cotton canvas, pictures burning cigarette, Always Buy Chesterfields, They Satisfy, EX, D.......**$25.00**

Chesterfield Cigarettes, ashtray, metal, shaped like cigarette pack, G, D.......**$14.00**

Chesterfield Cigarettes, display, die-cut cardboard, college couple promoting Chesterfield, Sound Off For..., Much Milder..., 16x11½", EX, A.......**$10.00**

Chesterfield Cigarettes, door plate, 1920s-40s, porcelain, pack of cigarettes in center, white lettering above & below, 9x4", EX, A.......**$140.00**

Chesterfield Cigarettes, sign, ca 1950, porcelain flange, Buy Chesterfield Here on oval above 2 unopened packs, 17x11x1½", EX, D3.......**$110.00**

Chesterfield Cigarettes, sign, cardboard, Every Time It's Chesterfield over lady with basketball, The Golden Jubilee Of Basketball, 21x11", NM, A.......**$50.00**

Chesterfield Cigarettes, sign, cardboard, Much Milder Chesterfield above actor Paul Douglas promoting product, ...Premium Quality, 21x22", M, D.......**$65.00**

Chesterfield Cigarettes, sign, cardboard, shows 2 large packs of cigarettes with advertising ...Best For You, No Adverse Effects..., 22x21", M, D............................**$65.00**

Chesterfield Cigarettes, sign, die-cut metal flange, 2-sided, Buy...Here on oval above 2 packs of different sizes, 17x12", EX+, A...**$30.00**

Chesterfield Cigarettes, sign, embossed painted tin, Chesterfield in alternate red & blue above pack over tobacco leaves, 29x19", EX, A **$25.00**

Chesterfield Cigarettes, thermometer, pictures tobacco leaves & cigarette pack, 13½x6", G, D.................**$50.00**

Chevalier's Life For The Hair, sign, paper, lady with long hair on horseback flanked by list of remedies, minor paper loss/soiling, 10x13", VG, A **$350.00**

Chevrolet, almanac, 1945, 32 pages, EX, D..............**$10.00**

Chevrolet, bank, cardboard, pictures a 4-door car, truck & logo, yellow, blue & white, in original envelope, EX, D..**$20.00**

Chevrolet, banner, 1952, cloth, wood rod & string hanger across top, fringed bottom, New Carburation... above Chevy on road, EX, A **$145.00**

Chevrolet, clock, neon with metal case, bow tie logo on dial, McClellan Chevrolet, Zurich, Kansas at top, 21" dia, EX, A...**$475.00**

Chevrolet, coin, 1954 Corvette, Motorama commemorative, gold color, EX, D..**$15.00**

Chevrolet, display, cardboard, features various trucks, The Great American Truck Value, ...Truck For Every...Need, 42x63", VG, A..**$210.00**

Chevrolet, display, electrical, 2 front-end models demonstrating Old & New Methods of Front End Contruction, framed, 20x31", EX, A.....................................**$1,320.00**

Chevrolet, hat visor, cardboard, blue & white logo, 20 Years-Sales Leadership, EX, D...............................**$5.00**

Chevrolet, key ring, 1962, 50th anniversary, EX, D ..**$15.00**

Chevrolet, pen & pencil set, The Heartbeat Of America, Parker, in original box, EX, D **$15.00**

Chevrolet, pin-back button, character drawing of smiling face wearing cap encircled with Chevrolet For You In '42, ¾" dia, NM, A **$22.00**

Chevrolet, pin-back button, Decision Maker '57 lettered above logo, blue & white, round, EX, A **$36.00**

Chevrolet, sign, embossed tin, white on black, For Economical Transportation above Chevrolet emblem, 12x23", EX, D3 ....**$350.00**

Chevrolet, sign, light-up, die-cut owl perched atop Chevrolet emblem, For Economical Transportation, 34x22", G, A **$700.00**

Chevrolet, sign, neon, blue Chevrolet logo on black bordered circle with Super Service in yellow tubing, restored, 42", EX, D **$2,200.00**

Chevrolet Dealer, Used Car Committee 1937, cigar box, Syroco wood, very ornate with embossed lettering & emblem on diamond center, hinged lid, 3x12x9", EX, A **$100.00**

Chevrolet Motor Cars, calendar, 1920, green with white lettering & lined border, farm scene with car & family above full pad, 31x16", VG, A...........................**$145.00**

Chevrolet Sales & Service, screwdriver, bow tie logo, metal handle, EX, D **$25.00**

Chevrolet Sales & Service, sign, porcelain, 2-sided, white on blue, scattered chips, 40x28", EX, D.............**$175.00**

Chevrolet Service, sign, painted tin, Chevrolet emblem above Service & short arrow pointing left, worn paint, wood frame, 45x76", VG, A...............................**$190.00**

Chevron, booklet, 1970, car care guide & lube chart, EX, D...**$15.00**

Chevron, Tonka truck, #XR101, tan & white with blue & red Chevron logo, 15¾" long, MIB, D **$185.00**

Chicago, Rock Island & Pacific Railway, sign, reverse-painted glass, mother-of-pearl locomotive & passenger cars, ornate frame, 42½x53½", EX, A ..$14,000.00

Chicago, Rock Island & Pacific Railway, sign, 1902, reverse-painted glass, features the Rocky Mountain Limited against mountain range, framed, image: 23x99", VG+, A...**$25,000.00**

Chicago, Rock Island & Pacific Railway, time table, 1881, paper, Victorian woman in fancy railroad dining car, Kosak & Clark, 10x6½", NM, A **$150.00**

Chicago Club Beer, label, 1933-50, Chicago lettered above Club, United States Brewing Co, Internal Revenue Tax Paid statement, 12-oz, G, A **$11.00**

Chicago Flexible Shaft Company, booklet, 1910, expert instructions on shearing sheep by machine, 23 pages, cover loose, G, D **$10.00**

Chicago Pneumatic Tool Co, catalog, 1909, features air compressors, 102 pages, EX, D **$16.00**

Chicago Shot Tower Co, trade card, comical image of owls in tree looking down at hunter, You Don't Scare Us, You Don't Use..., VG, A **$35.00**

Chicken Dinner Candy, sign, embossed tin, red, yellow & blue, Chicken Dinner Candy 5¢, 2½x22", NM, B1 ..**$30.00**

Chicken Dinner Candy, sign, waxed cardboard, Eat Chicken Dinner Candy, 5¢, red, yellow & blue, 12x24", NM, B1 ....**$22.00**

Chickie, crate label, 1950s, asparagus, fluffy yellow chick walking toward bunch of asparagus, San Francisco, M, C1 ....**$2.00**

Chiclets, front panel of vendor, porcelain, shows lady in circle with lettering above & below, vertical, edge chips, A..**$370.00**

Chiclets, paper cup, EX, G2 .... **$22.00**
Chiclets, puzzle, NMIB, D **$8.00**
Chiclets, sign, 1916, die-cut tin, features monkey, very rare, EX, D **$995.00**
Chiclets, tin, shiny green, 3½x5½", EX, D **$10.00**
Chief Beer, label, 1933-36, Indian in full headdress, Montgomery Brewing Co, U-type permit label, 12-oz, VG, A **$15.00**
Chief Cook Cigars, box label, inner lid sample, 1880s, man at hearth with roasted bird, other game & cooked food, Geo S Harris litho, VG, A **$42.00**
Chief Joseph, crate label, apple, Indian chief on blue background, 10½x9", M, C1 .... **$2.00**
Chief Metal Ware, salesman's sample, aluminum trash can, Northwest Metal Products, 3¾", EX, A **$65.00**
Chief Paints, sign, tin, 2-sided, Indian's head in feathered headdress left of Chief Paints in yellow on dark blue, 12x28", NM, M3 .... **$65.00**
Chiffon Margarine, doll, Mother Nature, cloth, in package, M, D **$20.00**
Chilean Nitrate Co, note pad, bearded Black farmer beside 2 sacks of Chilean Nitrate, orange, white, black & yellow, framed, 9½x7", VG, D **$30.00**
Chimo Baking Powder, can label, 1924, 2 images of the same monk, G, C3 .... **$5.00**
Chiquita Bananas, doll, 1980, Olympic Raccoon, printed cloth with white plastic vest, M, N1 .... **$10.00**

Chiquita Bananas, figurine, 1951, Sebastian miniature, 4", NM, D $500.00
Chiquita Bananas, recipe book, 1950, colorful covers & illustrations, United Fruit Co, 24 pages, EX, H1 ..... **$4.50**
Cho Cho Ice Cream Bar, sign, 1940s, paper, clown admiring ice cream bar, Try The New Taste Thrill!, 10x15", EX, D **$30.00**
Choctaw Rentals-Service, sign, porcelain, Indian head in profile in circle with Rentals-Service above, Choctaw below, 10x10", VG, A... **$150.00**
Choice Family Tea, pail, product name with decorative bands above & below, Winslow, Rand & Watson, slip lid & bail, 4x4" dia, EX, A **$65.00**
Choisa Coffee, tin, lion on shield superimposed over eagle above product name, SS Pierce Co, screw lid, 1-lb, EX, A **$50.00**
Chore Boy Brand Sponges & Scouring Pads, toy, 1991, molded vinyl, Chore Boy with open arms standing on a sponge, Reckitt & Coleman Household Products, 6", M, D **$20.00**
Chr Heurich Brewing Co's Original Lager, sign, tin with embossed border, lettering & logos, wear to border/minor chips/dents, 17¼" dia, VG, A **$50.00**
Christener Trucking, calendar, 1936, die-cut truck shape, complete, D **$100.00**
Christian Brecht Lager & Export Beer, calendar, 1898, girl on the beach writing in sand, lettering above, full pad, framed, image: 22x15", VG+, A **$1,000.00**
Christian Moerlein Brewing Co, tray, encircled portrait of the founder & logo, floral rim, darkening due to age/rim chips, oval, 15x18½", G, A.................... **$300.00**

Christies Infant Food, sign, paper, pictures child in highchair reaching for can of food from cherubs perched on tail of 'C', 14x24", EX+, A.......... $750.00
Christines Ice Cream, sign, light-up, little girl enjoys dish of ice cream at left of company name above list of flavors, gold frame, EX, A...................................... **$225.00**
Christmas Brew, label, 1933-36, Auto City Brewing Co, U-type permit number, 12-oz, EX, A **$11.00**
Christy Bros 5 Ring Wild Animal Show, poster, colorful image of caged animals & large crowd of people, minor chipping and wear, 28x42", EX, A **$450.00**
Chrysler Motors, pin-back button, ...San Francisco surrounded by Golden Gate International Exposition, round, EX, A **$26.00**
Chrysler-Plymouth Sales & Service, license plate topper, blue & white with both logos, EX, D................... **$25.00**
Chunk-E-Nut Popcorn, box, light cardboard, Crispy Delicious above couple enjoying popcorn, product name in circle below, 10-oz, NM, A **$6.00**
Chunk-E-Nut Popcorn, box, 1930s, pictures 2 kids with carousel in background, 10x7", EX, D **$12.50**
Church's Cow Brand Soda, sign, paper, pictures a setter running in tall grass, product lower right, signed Arnholt, framed, 25x16½", VG, A **$90.00**

CIE JL Mathieu Remedies, sign, tin, encircled portrait above banner & products, En Vente Ici below, Canadian, framed with glass, 20x14", EX, M2 ....**$185.00**

CIL Ammunition, sign, cardboard, large moose with head up at water's edge, some wear, 25x20", M2 ....**$85.00**

Cincinnati Burger Beau, clock, wood case with tin front, bearded man holding frothy mug & lettering on oval center, 14½x19x2½", VG, A **$130.00**

Cincinnati Lowenbrau, label, 1933-50, Burger Brewing Co, Internal Revenue Tax Paid statement, 12-oz, EX, A...**$66.00**

Cinco, cigar lighter, resembles table lamp, lettering on reverse glass shade, Stick To..., nickel-plated building on pedestal base, 11", G, A **$450.00**

Cinco Tobacco, lunch pail, NM, H3 ....**$70.00**

Cinderella Ice Cream, sign, cardboard, 14x11", M, D .**$150.00**

Cinnamon Toast Crunch Cereal, see General Mills

Ciot & Co's Paint, trade card, pictures a church painted in 3 colors, This Church Painted With..., EX, A........**$25.00**

Circle A Soda Water, art plate, Circle A logos on decorative rim flank Texas Cotton Palace in Waco Texas, NM, A **$606.00**

Cities Service, sign, 1930s, porcelain, 2-sided, black lettering & logo on white clover shape with black iron frame, 60x60", NM, D3 ....$575.00

Cities Service Koolmotor, gas globe, 1920s-30s, porcelain with glass body, product name in black & red surrounded by black clover, 14" dia, EX, A **$500.00**

Cities Service Motor Oil, sign, tin flange, 2-sided, oil can right of Cities Service Oil Sold Here, If It's...It Has To Be Good, 12x22", VG, A **$165.00**

Cities Service Oils, gas globe, 1928, metal body, cloverleaf logo & product name on white ground, 15" dia, EX, A **$250.00**

Cities Service Road Aids, map holder, metal, 3-tier in dark green with white logo & lettering, rust/chips/dents, 20x12½", VG, A **$80.00**

City Club Cigars, pocket tin, upright, man enjoying cigar while reading the paper, Crushed Cubes lettered below, EX, A...**$225.00**

City Tea & Coffee Co, tin, cream with gold & blue accents, shows Winnipeg Old City Hall, Chinese man with boxes on reverse, 9x7x5", EX, A **$275.00**

CJ Fell & Brother Spice Co, sign, paper, landscape above product name flanked by colorful illustrations of spices & lettering, 18½x16", EX, A..$425.00

CL Centlivre Brewing Co, sign, paper, panoramic factory scene, oval portrait of the founder lower left, framed, image: 24½x38", NM, A......................................**$575.00**

CL Centlivre's Nickel Plate Bottled Beer, sign, interior view of railroad dining car with couple being served by Black waiter, framed, image: 24x19½", G-, A.....**$150.00**

CL Centlivre's Tonic, sign, ca 1905, cardboard, nurse at left of ad panel, ...Builds Up The System..., For Sale Here, 12x22", VG, D **$170.00**

CL Centlivre's Tonic, sign, ca 1905, cardboard, nurse at left of ad panel, ...Builds Up The System..., For Sale Here, 12x22", EX+, A **$275.00**

Clabber Girl Baking Powder, grocer's want book, pictures can of baking powder, lined pages inside, 8x3¾", EX+, D...**$12.00**

Clabber Girl Baking Powder, pencil clip, 1930s, red & white, EX, D **$14.00**

Clabber Girl Baking Powder, recipe book, 1934, 18 pages, EX, D **$10.00**

Clabber Girl Baking Powder, sample tin, EX, D **$65.00**

Clabber Girl Baking Powder, sign, 1940s, tin litho, yellow, red & black, 12x34", N2...............................**$55.00**

Clanky Chocolate Flavor Syrup, container, 1963, plastic, Clanky character, brown with yellow lettering & cap, 10", NM, D...**$25.00**

Clarendon Pianos, trade card, ca 1900, pictures girl & 2 black dogs, Haddorff Piano Co, Rockford Ill, 4x2½", EX, P1 ....**$10.00**

Clark Candy Bars, squeeze toy, 1960s, molded vinyl, Clark boy holding a candy bar, Beatrice Foods Co, 8½", M, D **$90.00**

Clark's Confections of Taste, tin, 1900-15, logo flanked by 2 elves, DL Clark Co, Pittsburg Pa, press lid, 5-lb, dents/scratches, 7x6" dia, A.................................**$15.00**

Clark's Elephant Sewing Cotton, store card, heavy paper, product name above & below girl standing before ocean sunset, matted & framed, 22x13", EX, D3 ....**$550.00**

Clark's Mile-End Spool Cotton, trade card, 1879, 'A Bare Chance,' comical image of bear with rifle aiming at man in stream, Currier & Ives, VG, A **$28.00**

Clark's Mile-End Spool Cotton, calendar, 1886, girl seated under oriental parasol above January page showing advertising, framed, 30x20", M, D3..$650.00

Clark's Mile-End Spool Cotton, trade card, 1879, 'Caught Napping,' hunter & dog sleeping under a tree with fox sneaking by, Currier & Ives, VG, A......................**$26.00**

Clark's Mile-End Spool Cotton, trade card, 1880, 'A Bite All Around,' comical fishing scene, Currier & Ives, trimmed at top, A...**$35.00**

Clark's ONT Boilfast Thread, display, metal with slanted glass front, blue with yellow ONT circles on sides, 3 shelves with dividers, 7x15x10", EX, A..............**$275.00**

Clark's ONT Spool Cotton, sign, paper, cowboy roping longhorn steer with spool cotton, product name below, minor scratching, 16x20½", VG, A.....................**$700.00**

Clark's ONT Spool Cotton, trade card, pictures mother & baby elephant, circular logo upper right, Jumbo At Coney Island lettered below, EX, A.....................**$10.00**

Clark's Peanut Butter, pail, moose hunter & Indian in canoe with snow-covered mountains beyond, slip lid & bail, 3½x4" dia, VG, A..**$550.00**

Clark's Teaberry Gum, matchbook cover, full book, 20 strike, front strike, NM, R1......................................**$2.00**

Clark's Teaberry Gum, sign, tin, A Happy Thought! upper left of large pack of gum, That Mountain Tea Flavor lower right, 9x12", EX+, A...............................,..**$300.00**

Clarke's Pure Rye, pocket mirror, man getting ready to sip some whiskey, Peoria's Famous Whiskey...Bottled In Bond, 2⅛" dia, EX, A..**$140.00**

Clary Liquor Company, corkscrew, wood & metal, corkscrew turns into center of rod, EX, D.............**$6.00**

Class & Nachod Brewing Co, sign, paper, rustic tavern scene with people dancing, Solitaire Beer Is Good, framed, image: 15x20", EX, A............................**$180.00**

Classic Beer, label, 1933-50, Centlivre Brewing Co, Internal Revenue Tax Paid statement, 12-oz, EX, A...........**$23.00**

Clauss Cutlery, sign, reverse painting on curved glass, for gas illumination, product name above & below cutlery image, 24x17x12", EX, A.................................**$2,640.00**

Clauss Shear Co, cabinet, wood frame, glass panels, 4 round shelves on center spindle, lettering on front panel, 32x13x13", EX, A....................................**$950.00**

Clauss Shears, sign, die-cut cardboard, Victorian woman holding up a pair of large sheers, bent/broken in 2 pieces, 51x20", G, A...**$20.00**

Clay Export Co, brochure, 1919, 'Trapping Secrets,' pictures a hunter & fox, brown & blue, 16 pages, pocket - size, VG, A...**$15.00**

Clayton & Russell's Stomach Bitters, sign, surreal image of man fighting off 3-headed dog, If You Want A Good Appetite..., framed, image: 41½x18", EX+, A ..**$1,750.00**

Clearock Beverages, door pull plate, Pull above with We & Serve flanking upper part of bottle, NM, A **$70.00**

Clement Bicycles, watercolor, pictures bare-breasted woman with hammer & anvil, factory scene beyond, 5x4", M, D...**$350.00**

Cleo Cola, sign, embossed tin, Genuine Cleo In 12-Ounce Bottles left of seated Egyptian queen, Cola lower right, 12½x27", G, A...**$230.00**

Cleopatra Chocolates, tin, 1930s-40s, pictures lady's face in gold & red on dark label in top corner, 1 1/2-lb, EX, A..**$25.00**

Cleveland & Sandusky Brewing Co, sign, self-framed tin, bald man about to sample foaming glass of beer, oval, 28½x22½", EX, A..**$400.00**

Cleveland & Sandusky Brewing Co, tray, factory image surrounded by hops, decorative border, overall fading/minor rim chips, 14" dia, G, A.....................**$150.00**

Cleveland & Whitehall Co, pocket mirror, Masquerader above nude in open shirt asking 'Girls, Girls, Where Are My Keystone Overalls?,' oval, EX, A **$750.00**

Cleveland Faucet Co Beer Pump Makers, display, cardboard, vignettes of people using the Champion Pump which is displayed in upper right corner, framed, 26x19", G, A...**$150.00**

Clicquot Club Beverages, sign, tin, yellow, Clicquot Club above Eskimo boy in red circle over 3 horizontal lines, Beverages below, 18x48", NM, M3 ....**$145.00**

Clicquot Club Beverages, thermometer, tin, white with red Drink Clicquot Club Beverages above green bottle at right of bulb, 13x6", EX, M3.............................**$55.00**

Clicquot Club Ginger Ale, bank, 1930s, plaster half-figure of Eskimo boy holding large bottle, coin slot on top of head, 7x5½x4", EX, A.........$345.00

Clicquot Club Ginger Ale, calendar, 1942, paper, girl & Eskimo child with bottle on bike, 24x12", M, M3.......**$95.00**

Clicquot Club Ginger Ale, sign, die-cut cardboard, Eskimo boy in white fur snow suit holding large bottle, Kleek-O Coming Your Way, 42x19", VG, A...................**$75.00**

Clicquot Club Ginger Ale, sign, die-cut cardboard hanger, bottle shape, 7", NM, B1..**$6.50**

Climax Peanut Butter, pail, Climax arched above Peanut Butter on center band in oval center, press lid & bail, 16-oz, EX+, A..**$100.00**

Clint Ford Cigars, box label, inner lid, pictures Clint Ford in 2 scenes, 6x9", M, D **$4.50**

Clinton Brewing Co, tray, stock image of girl holding glass, Drink Pointer Bottle Beer... lettered on rim, 13¼x13¼", EX, A...**$175.00**

Clix Blades, display card with 20 full boxes, 1930s, pictures barber pole with man's face atop, EX, D **$44.00**

Clossman Hardware Co, sign, tin, touring car & sign reading Since 1876 pointing to billboard with company name & address, horizontal, NM, M1 ....**$900.00**

Cloth of Gold Succotash, can label, fancy bronze lettering on salmon-pink background, Westernville NY, EX, G1 ....**$4.00**

Clover Leaf Ice Cream, sign, painted metal, wrought-iron hanger, green 4-leaf clover with red product lettering above & below, 45x46", EX, A...........................**$340.00**

Cloverdale Soft Drinks, menu board, tin, white product name on red panel above chalk board, white border, 24x18", EX+, M3 ....**$45.00**

Club Night Cigars, box label, inner lid sample, 1890s, 4 gentlemen playing game of cards in parlor setting, George Schlegel litho, EX, A **$96.00**

Clubb's Mixture, tin, pictures a 3-leaf clover above product name & other lettering, slip lid, EX, A...........**$55.00**

Clubs Cigars, box label, inner lid sample, 1880s, English bobby surrounded by buildings, shield & flowers below, Heppenheimer & Maurer, VG, A **$96.00**

Cluett, Coon & Co's Shirts, Collars & Cuffs, trade card, 2-sided, World's Fair exhibit, description of manufacturers & Liberal Arts building on reverse, EX, A.......**$35.00**

Clysmic Table Waters, tip tray, nymph & deer at water's edge, Clysmic, King Of Table Waters lettered around gold rim, minor rust, 6x4", VG+, A..................$180.00

Co-op Golden Tires, ashtray, 1959, ornate brass with embossed tire in center, 2¾x4", EX, D **$25.00**

Coak, sign, cardboard, black on tan, Call For & Demand above Coak in script, Bottled By Litchfield Bottling Works, EX+, A **$70.00**

Coast 2 Coast, gas globe, 1920-30, milk glass, Coast 2 Coast in cross-shape pattern, green lettering & border, rare, 15½" dia, EX, A..**$900.00**

Coates Thread, trade card/calendar, 1880, Victorian fishing scene on front, calendar & advertising on back, VG, A..**$30.00**

Cobakco Bread, display case, oak with glass front, blue & white decal with Indian on horseback above loaf of bread, 48x36", G, A..**$300.00**

Cobb Aldrich & Co Green Coffee, tin, round lid on square can, A...**$35.00**

Cobbs Creek Whiskey, thermometer, tin, whiskey bottle above, Select Your Drink According To The Temperature, rounded top & bottom, 39", G+, A..............**$25.00**

Cobcut Corn, can label, 1930s, pictures hand cutting corn from cob onto plate, M, C3 ....**$10.00**

Coca-Cola, ad, black & white newsprint, early fountain scene encircled by arrow pointing to 5¢ glass, framed, 21x18", EX, A...**$15.00**

Coca-Cola, ad, 1914, picture & biography of baseball player, Mathewson, large curved arrow points down to flared glass, 16x6", M, D...................................**$100.00**

Coca-Cola, ad from magazine, 'Saturday Evening Post,' water skier confronts giant hand with glass, The Answer To Thirst..., VG, A......................................**$5.00**

Coca-Cola, ad from magazine, 1905, features Lillian Nordica with Coca-Cola logo centered below, 3 minor tape marks on back, NM, A...............$100.00

Coca-Cola, ad from magazine, 1905, Lillian Nordica by urn-shaped stand, Delicious & Refreshing flank coupon below, 10x6", VG, D3 ....**$250.00**

Coca-Cola, ad from magazine, 1905, pictures women & children sampling Coke, matted & framed, image: 7½x9½", EX, A...**$25.00**

Coca-Cola, ad from magazine, 1905, 2-page, women & children at ornate soda fountain flanked by lettering, framed, 9x13½", VG, A **$200.00**

Coca-Cola, ad from magazine, 1921, from the 'Delineator,' features cityscape with large Coca-Cola logo on side of building, EX, A **$5.00**

Coca-Cola, ad from magazine, 1922, 'Ladies Home Journal,' hand with glass above skiers on slope, Thirst Knows No Season, EX+, A **$5.00**

Coca-Cola, ad from magazine, 1923, 'Ladies Home Journal,' farm girl drinks Coke from straw, Enjoy Thirst, Coca-Cola logo, EX+, A **$5.00**

Coca-Cola, aisle marker, die-cut tin, 1950s-60s, Serve Coca-Cola At Home panel between numbered circles on iron hangers, EX+, A..**$230.00**

Coca-Cola, apron, 1930s, featuring a bottle, Pause Refresh, Ice Cold In Bottles, EX+, A....................................**$70.00**

Coca-Cola, apron, 1930s-40s, double pockets, Drink Coca-Cola In Bottles, VG, A...**$15.00**

Coca-Cola, apron, 1960s, double pockets, contour logo with Enjoy Coca-Cola, M, A..................................**$10.00**

Coca-Cola, apron, 1960s, Stir Up A Blizzard With Fresca, Smirnoff & Lime, M, A **$15.00**

Coca-Cola, ashtray, glass, black center with gold lettering, 3 cigarette rests, round, M, A................................**$22.00**

Coca-Cola, ashtray, 1950s, ceramic, oval shape with round metal Drink Coca-Cola insert, EX+, A..................**$23.00**

Coca-Cola, ashtray, 1970s, metal, Coke Adds Life To Everything Nice, 5x4", EX, D **$7.50**

Coca-Cola, ashtray, 1974, ceramic, Chattanooga Coca-Cola Bottling Co 75th anniversary, World's 1st Bottler, 6½" dia, EX, D **$15.00**

Coca-Cola, ashtrays, 1950s, ruby glass, set of 4 shaped as heart, club, diamond & spade, NMIB, A...$575.00

Coca-Cola, award medallion, 1961, gold with 3 diamonds, 100,000 Gallon Club, features bottle & recipient's initials, M, A...**$1,518.00**

Coca-Cola, backpack, 1960s-70s, canvas, Enjoy Coca-Cola, EX+, A **$7.00**

Coca-Cola, bag rack, 1930s-40s, metal, 6 For 25¢ carton of Coke in circle at left of Take Home Carton Of Coca-Cola, 17x36", EX+, A..**$375.00**

Coca-Cola, bag rack, 1940s-50s, metal, For Home Refreshment above Sprite boy pointing to Coca-Cola logo, 17x36", VG+, A..**$325.00**

Coca-Cola, ball, 1980s, rubber, red & black lettering on white, Enjoy Coca-Cola..., It's The Real Thing, 2½" dia, VG+, A **$18.00**

Coca-Cola, Ball of Fame, 1961, baseball motif, table format gives details of American & National League players from 1901-60, NM, A..**$300.00**

Coca-Cola, bang gun, 1920s, Drink Coca-Cola In Bottles, Pure As Sunlight!, NM, A **$150.00**

Coca-Cola, bang gun, 1950s, Drink Coca-Cola In Bottles, NM, A **$70.00**

Coca-Cola, bank, plastic, upright vending machine, flat top, Play Refreshed, 5¢, EX, A **$25.00**

Coca-Cola, bank, plastic, upright vending machine with slightly arched top, Work Refreshed, EX, A **$65.00**

Coca-Cola, bank, red cardboard & tin can with white lettering, Drink Coca-Cola, Delicious & Refreshing, In Bottles 5¢, 3", EX, M2 ....**$32.00**

Coca-Cola, bank, red upright vending machine with slip-lid top, white Drink Coca-Cola above, Ice Cold below, NM, M2 ....**$65.00**

Coca-Cola, bank, 1950s, battery-operated dispenser, white on red, 2 clear front panels with 3 glasses, Marx, EX+, M2 ....$440.00

Coca-Cola, bank, 1960s, red plastic upright dispenser with paper cup, top white decal with red lettering, with box, VG, M2...**$85.00**

Coca-Cola, bank, 1980, plastic, shaped as dispenser, NMIB, A...**$110.00**

Coca-Cola, banner, lady with bottle & tray, Does Entertaining Frighten You?, Send 10¢ For This Book On Home Entertaining..., G, A..**$81.00**

Coca-Cola, banner, paper, Coca-Cola on wavy band above smiling lady with tray of food & bottles, Enjoy Food, EX, A **$170.00**

Coca-Cola, banner, paper, Drink Coca-Cola flanked by 5¢ on red, white border, NM, A **$20.00**

Coca-Cola, banner, paper, To Introduce Bottled Coca-Cola Into The Home, See Valuable Coupon..., Electric Iron, 7x16", EX, A **$60.00**

Coca-Cola, banner, 1890s, cloth, Drink..., Delicious & Refreshing, Cures Headache..., At Soda Fountains 5¢, framed, 15x27", VG, A..........................$2,600.00

Coca-Cola, banner, 1941, paper, COLD carved from ice upper left of bottle tilted on iceberg, Drink... disk at right, 19x57", NM, D **$330.00**

Coca-Cola, banner, 1950s, paper, Refreshing in 3-D letters with button logo & tilted bottle shrouded with icicles, 18x60", NM, D **$300.00**

Coca-Cola, banner, 1960s, pictures Santa in chair with elf pouring Coke, The Pause That Refreshes, 11½x24", EX, D...**$20.00**

Coca-Cola, banner, 1972, pictures Santa at tree with gifts, 56x35", EX, D **$15.00**

Coca-Cola, banner, 1986, heavy cardboard, Celebration Of The Century, 26x72", EX, D **$7.50**

Coca-Cola, baseball bat, 1968, wood, inscribed Compliments Of Coca-Cola, VG+, A................................**$35.00**

Coca-Cola, baseball cap, 1950s, felt, red & white, EX, D..**$4.50**

Coca-Cola, beach bag, mesh with plastic lining, Can't Beat The Feeling, 21x14", EX, D....................................**$5.00**

Coca-Cola, bell, 1920s, stamped metal, 1 side reads Bottled Coca-Cola Roddy Mfg Co, other has cow & Our Only Competitor, 3", NM, A..**$550.00**

Coca-Cola, bell, 1930s, stamped metal, Refresh Yourself, Drink Coca-Cola In Bottles lettered on both sides, 3¼", NM, A...**$425.00**

Coca-Cola, bingo card, 1930s, green, NM, A.............**$30.00**

Coca-Cola, bingo card, 1941, wood-grain, EX+, A.....**$15.00**

Coca-Cola, bingo card, 1950s, EX, D **$3.00**

Coca-Cola, blotter, traffic policeman with bottle before yellow ground, Stop For A Pause & Go Refreshed flank disk logo, NM, M2..**$35.00**

Coca-Cola, blotter, 1904, blue on white, Drink Coca-Cola, Delicious + Refreshing, Coca-Cola Co, Home Office, Atlanta Ga, EX, M2..**$85.00**

Coca-Cola, blotter, 1906, red on white, Restores Energy above & Strengthens The Nerves below Delicious & Refreshing emblem, EX, D3 ....**$110.00**

Coca-Cola, blotter, 1909, red on white, Delicious-Refreshing-Invigorating above Drink... flanked by flared glasses, NM, M2...**$80.00**

Coca-Cola, blotter, 1915, Pure & Healthful above Drink... Delicious & Refreshing 5¢... emblem flanked by bottles, bordered, NM, M2 ....**$60.00**

Coca-Cola, blotter, 1923, red on white, Drink Coca-Cola Delicious & Refreshing emblem flanked by bottles, bordered, NM, M2..**$36.00**

Coca-Cola, blotter, 1926, blue & red on white, Refresh Yourself in blue above red Drink... Delicious... flanked by bottles, NM, M2..**$38.00**

Coca-Cola, blotter, 1935, receding logo at left of dog running along side of boy riding bicycle, green background, NM, M2 ....**$15.00**

Coca-Cola, blotter, 1937, blue with tilted bottle before Cold in 'icy' letters, red diamond logo & Refreshment in script, NM, M2 ....**$29.00**

Coca-Cola, blotter, 1938, green with hand holding bottle flanked by Drink...Delicious... disk logo & Drink Everybody Loves, NM, M2 ....**$35.00**

Coca-Cola, blotter, 1940, clown with bottle & Drink...Delicious... disk logo on green, The Greatest Pause On Earth, NM, M2 ....$42.00

Coca-Cola, blotter, 1942, girl in rowboat & disk logo, Wherever Thirst Goes, white border, NM, M2 .....**$15.00**

Coca-Cola, blotter, 1942, girl in yellow skirt & blue jacket lying on stomach enjoying Coke, I Think It's Swell, disk logo, NM, M2...**$10.00**

Coca-Cola, blotter, 1944, full-color image of 3 girls behind fountain, 3½x8", EX, D..**$12.50**

Coca-Cola, blotter, 1947, couple with bottles on white with Have A Coke on green & Coca-Cola on red panels, Canadian, NM, M2..**$28.00**

Coca-Cola, blotter, 1947, pictures large hand with bottle before ski couple on slope, Coke Knows No Season, NM, M2 ....**$12.00**

Coca-Cola, blotter, 1948, 2 girls entertaining guy on green sofa flanked by Hospitality & button logo, Canadian, NM, M2 ....**$28.00**

Coca-Cola, blotter, 1950, Boy Scout offering bottle from cooler, Be Prepared, Be Refreshed, NM, M2........**$40.00**

Coca-Cola, blotter, 1951, Drink Coca-Cola lettered on arrow pointing at bottle, Delicious & Refreshing below, NM, B1 ....**$6.00**

Coca-Cola, blotter, 1952, Coke bottle in snow seen through frosty window, Have A Coke & arrow marked on window, button logo, NM, M2 ....**$36.00**

Coca-Cola, blotter, 1952, 50th Anniversary emblem & Drink Coca-Cola button side-by-side on white background, NM, M2 ....**$50.00**

Coca-Cola, blotter, 1953, Sprite boy with large Coke bottle in snow, Drink... button at left, Good! upper right, Canadian, NM, M2...**$25.00**

Coca-Cola, blotter, 1954, Coke Time lettered above father handing out bottles from cooler to family, vertical, NM, M2 .... **$26.00**

Coca-Cola, blotter, 1956, hand with bottle before world globe at right, Friendliest Drink On Earth & Drink pennant at left, NM, M2 .... **$10.00**

Coca-Cola, blotter, 1957, pictures bottle & altitude records as of 1957, 7½x3½", EX, D **$10.00**

Coca-Cola, blotter, 1958, Over 58 Million A Day above Drink...In Bottles button & large bottle, Sign Of Good Taste below, NM, M2 .... **$10.00**

Coca-Cola, blotter, 1960, Over 60 Million A Day lettered above large bottle, Enjoy That Refreshing New Feeling below, NM, B1 .... **$6.00**

Coca-Cola, book, 'At Work Handbook Manual,' address cooler location, sampling, selling, sales presentations, etc, EX, A **$355.00**

Coca-Cola, book, 'Cooler Service Training Guide,' features organization outlines, training schedules, assignments, etc, EX, A **$50.00**

Coca-Cola, book, 1915, 'Universal Beverage' detailing bottle & fountain service, embossed logo with Elaine holding umbrella, EX, A **$150.00**

Coca-Cola, book, 1928 copyright, 'Alphabet Book Of Coca-Cola,' cartoon images & poems, NM, A **$60.00**

Coca-Cola, book, 1950s bottlers refrigeration, advertising & display handbook, NM, A **$220.00**

Coca-Cola, book, 1960s, 'Comprehensive Advertising Price Lists Of Items From The Early 60s,' complete with pictures, EX, A **$120.00**

Coca-Cola, book, 1986, 'Coca-Cola The First 100 Years' many color plates, hard-bound, original jacket, M, A **$85.00**

Coca-Cola, book, 1986, 'Coca-Cola The First 100 Years,' many color plates, hard-bound, original jacket, VG+ A **$25.00**

Coca-Cola, book cover, 1915, 'Universal Beverage,' embossed logo & Elaine holding umbrella, VG+, A **$25.00**

Coca-Cola, booklet, 1923, 'Facts...,' girl by sundial on front cover, hand holding bottle in front of waterfall on back, M, B1 .... **$40.00**

Coca-Cola, booklet, 1941, 'Coolers For Coca-Cola,' pictures coolers & Mills vending machines inside, cover worn, otherwise EX, B1 .... **$75.00**

Coca-Cola, bookmark, 1904, pansies with glass in holder & Drink...5¢ above Lillian Nordica posed by screen, 6x2", EX, A **$325.00**

Coca-Cola, boomerang, 1950s, EX, D **$7.50**

Coca-Cola, bottle, amber glass, straight-sided, embossed Wheeling West Virginia, 6 1/2-oz, EX, A **$65.00**

Coca-Cola, bottle, clear glass, straight-sided, Montreal Canada, foggy/small chip on lip, rare, M2 .... **$90.00**

Coca-Cola, bottle, clear glass, straight-sided with diamond-shaped paper label, full with sealed cap, extremely rare, 8", EX, A **$250.00**

Coca-Cola, bottle, dark-blue glass, straight-sided, misprinted 'Coca-Coca,' EX+, M2 .... **$40.00**

Coca-Cola, bottle, green glass, straight-sided, Canadian, scarce, EX+, M2 .... **$79.00**

Coca-Cola, bottle, green glass, straight-sided, embossed Salem NH, EX, A **$45.00**

Coca-Cola, bottle, green glass, straight-sided, printed lettering, Rochester NY, 30-oz, EX+, M2 .... **$150.00**

Coca-Cola, bottle, light-blue glass, straight-sided, Canadian, EX+, M2 .... **$29.00**

Coca-Cola, bottle, light-blue glass, straight-sided, script lettering, Rochester NY, 30-oz, EX+, M2 .... **$160.00**

Coca-Cola, bottle, 1977, Huntsville 75th anniversary, salutes 3rd Cola Clan Convention, EX, D **$25.00**

Coca-Cola, bottle, 1983, Tampa 80th anniversary, only 3,456 made, EX, D **$20.00**

Coca-Cola, bottle, 1984, Sacramento Cola Clan Convention, EX, D **$20.00**

Coca-Cola, bottle, 1986, Washington Redskins 50th anniversary, EX, D **$10.00**

Coca-Cola, bottle caps, in Lucite, set of 6: Iran, Ethiopia, Japan, Germany, Turkey & Argentina, Coca-Cola Export Corp, NMIB, A **$25.00**

Coca-Cola, bottle carrier, cardboard, white Coca-Cola on red diamond on yellow next to red Coke on white diamond on red, unused, M2 .... **$12.00**

Coca-Cola, bottle carrier, wood, For The Home, 25¢ Plus Deposit, dovetailed corners, rope handle, holds 6 bottles, VG+, A **$65.00**

Coca-Cola, bottle carrier, 1920s, wood, dovetailed corners, Refresh Yourself above ...In Bottles, handled, holds 6 bottles, EX+, A $140.00

Coca-Cola, bottle carrier, 1924, light cardboard, Drink Coca-Cola diminishing logo, This Hardy Six-Pack Serve Ice Cold below, NM, A **$110.00**

Coca-Cola, bottle carrier, 1930s, cardboard box with punch-out handle, Six Bottles Coca-Cola emblem with band around bottom, G+, A **$40.00**

Coca-Cola, bottle carrier, 1930s, light cardboard, red with white lettering, Six Bottles Coca-Cola, Serve Ice Cold, NM, A **$110.00**

Coca-Cola, bottle carrier, 1930s, light cardboard, Six Bottles Coca-Cola in emblem, Serve Ice Cold on band below, NM, A **$100.00**

Coca-Cola, bottle carrier, 1930s, yellow wood with red logo, 1923 Christmas bottle on ends, middle divider, holds 6 bottles, G, A **$65.00**

Coca-Cola, bottle carrier, 1930s-40s, wood, 'winged' logo on ends, Drink Coca-Cola In Bottle on sides, pull-up handle, NM, A....................................$70.00

Coca-Cola, bottle carrier, 1939, cardboard, 6-pack featuring Season's Greetings on handle, holly design on carton, VG, M2...**$30.00**

Coca-Cola, bottle carrier, 1940s-50s, aluminum, rectangular body with rounded corners, pull-up handle, holds 6 bottles, EX+, A..**$45.00**

Coca-Cola, bottle carrier, 1950s, aluminum, ribbed with Delicious Refreshing logo, pull-up handle, with 6 green bottles, 8", EX, A........................$55.00

Coca-Cola, bottle carrier, 1950s, aluminum with lift handle, holds 12 bottles, VG, A...**$50.00**

Coca-Cola, bottle carrier, 1963, cardboard, red Coke lettered on white, holds 12 bottles, 7x14", NM, D **$6.00**

Coca-Cola, bottle carrier, 1982, cardboard, white Coke lettered on red background, holds 8 10-oz bottles, 7½x9½", NM, D ..**$3.00**

Coca-Cola, bottle carrier for grocery cart, 1950, white on red, Enjoy Coca-Cola While You Shop, Place Bottle Here, 4x6", NM, D..**$45.00**

Coca-Cola, bottle case, 1920s-30s, cardboard, yellow Drink Coca-Cola In Sterilized Bottles on red oval, holds 24 bottles, VG, A...**$60.00**

Coca-Cola, bottle case, 1920s-30s, wood with green Coca-Cola logo, cut-out handles on ends, holds 24 bottles, worn, G, A..**$30.00**

Coca-Cola, bottle case, 1940s, cardboard, disk logo with Coca-Cola underlined left of In 6 Bottle Cartons, holds 24 bottles, NM, A...**$80.00**

Coca-Cola, bottle case, 1940s, cardboard, red & green, disk logo left of In 12 Bottle Cartons, VG, A................**$70.00**

Coca-Cola, bottle opener, metal, incised flat bottle shape, EX+, M2 ....**$12.00**

Coca-Cola, bottle opener, 1910, brass, red & black enamel inlay, rounded ends, 1 end as open-mouthed opener, Coca-Cola logo, EX, A...**$35.00**

Coca-Cola, bottle opener, 1910-20, steel, red enamel inlay, rounded ends, 1 end as opened-mouthed opener, Coca-Cola logo, VG, A...**$20.00**

Coca-Cola, bottle opener, 1950, bottle-cap form with protruding opener, commemorates 50th anniversary, opener NM/box EX, A **$65.00**

Coca-Cola, bottle opener & cap catcher, features the Sprite boy looking from behind Coke bottle, NMIB, A..**$15.00**

Coca-Cola, bottle topper, cardboard, pictures Santa with bottle of Coke, Stock Up For The Holidays below, 7½x7", NM, B1..**$15.00**

Coca-Cola, bottle topper, Spanish advertising on pleated shape above contour logo, 11x6½", EX, A **$12.00**

Coca-Cola, bottle topper, 1927, cardboard, 20s girl with parasol & scarf around neck, US Printing & Litho, 10½x8", G+, A **$140.00**

Coca-Cola, bottle topper, 1950s, plastic, red button logo with Drink Coca-Cola 'Coke' with We Let You See The Bottle on base, NM, A.......................$800.00

Coca-Cola, box of jumbo straws, 1960s, fishtail logo on 4 sides, Be Really Refreshed, EX, A **$60.00**

Coca-Cola, box of straws, cardboard box shows tilted bottle, 8¾x3¾", G, A..**$50.00**

Coca-Cola, box of straws, features bottle on 3 sides with cut-out front, Delicious & Refreshing, nearly full, VG+, A...**$200.00**

Coca-Cola, bracelet, Rachel Welch, EX, D **$35.00**

Coca-Cola, bumper sticker, America -- You're The Real Thing, EX, D **$2.00**

Coca-Cola, bumper sticker, Enjoy Coca-Cola, Adds Life To Safe Driving, unused, D **$5.00**

Coca-Cola, calendar, 1898, elegant lady with glass seated at table surrounded by pansies & text, 12 months below, 7x10½", EX, A $5,500.00

Coca-Cola, calendar, 1899, embossed cardboard, girl at desk in oval, roses at side, months in scattered design below, 13x7", VG, A **$4,000.00**

Coca-Cola, calendar, 1901, paper, fancy lady holds glass of Coke within filigree border surrounded by pansies, no pad, 13x7", G, A...**$1,350.00**

Coca-Cola, calendar, 1903, pictures Hilda Clark, Drink Coca-Cola 5¢ lower left, March page only (might be a copy), NM, A **$4,100.00**

Coca-Cola, calendar, 1904, cardboard, woman with glass in front of screen, rare, May pad, matted & framed, image: 15x7½", G, A **$1,500.00**

Coca-Cola, calendar, 1913, smiling lady in wide-brimmed hat lifting glass, signed Hamilton King, May pad, 22½x13½", G, A..**$1,200.00**

Coca-Cola, calendar, 1914, Betty in a bonnet, full pad, EX, A...**$1,000.00**

Coca-Cola, calendar, 1914, Betty in a bonnet, full pad, NM, A...**$1,600.00**

Coca-Cola, calendar, 1915, Elaine with bottle & folded parasol at knee, landscape beyond, February-December pad, EX+, A **$4,700.00**

Coca-Cola, calendar, 1915, Elaine with glass of coke & folded parasol at knee, landscape in the distance, full pad, EX+, A...**$3,600.00**

Coca-Cola, calendar, 1916, Elaine leaning on hand looking over her shoulder holding glass of Coca-Cola, July sheet only, NM, A **$1,150.00**

Coca-Cola, calendar, 1917, girl seated at table with folded parasol enjoying a glass of Coke, small distributor size, 19½x8", NM, A **$1,000.00**

Coca-Cola, calendar, 1917, girl seated at table with folded parasol enjoying a glass of Coke, April-December sheets, EX, A..**$850.00**

Coca-Cola, calendar, 1918, oval depiction of June Caprice in wide-brimmed hat holding glass, full pad, framed, 9x5", EX, A...**$180.00**

Coca-Cola, calendar, 1918, oval depiction of June Caprice in wide-brimmed hat holding glass of Coca-Cola, full pad, NM, A...**$275.00**

Coca-Cola, calendar, 1919, girl in floppy hat with bottle of Coke & her knitting, people in distance, July sheet, EX, A...**$750.00**

Coca-Cola, calendar, 1919, girl in floppy hat with bottle of Coke & her knitting, people in distance, partial pad, NM, S4 ....**$1,000.00**

Coca-Cola, calendar, 1920, girl in floppy hat leans on chair with folded parasol holding bottle with straw, full pad, EX+, A...**$1,050.00**

Coca-Cola, calendar, 1920, girl in yellow dress holding glass, pad missing, 27½x12", VG, A...................**$175.00**

Coca-Cola, calendar, 1921, autumn girl wearing a tam seated on garden bench with glass, full pad, NM, A **$1,400.00**

Coca-Cola, calendar, 1922, girl in pink dress at baseball game lifts glass of Coke, bottle on ledge, no pad, corner damaged, VG, A **$275.00**

Coca-Cola, calendar, 1923, girl in blue dress & white stole lifting bottle with straw, full pad, dry mounted, VG+, A **$250.00**

Coca-Cola, calendar, 1924, party girl by garden pool with glass, bottle on ledge, full pad, few creases near top, EX+, A **$550.00**

Coca-Cola, calendar, 1925, party girl in blue turban & white turban fox stole lifting glass, full pad, M, S4..........**$475.00**

Coca-Cola, calendar, 1925, party girl in blue turban & white fox stole lifting glass, March-December pad, G+, M2 ....**$220.00**

Coca-Cola, calendar, 1926, tennis girl seated holding glass, full pad with cover sheet, VG+, A **$375.00**

Coca-Cola, calendar, 1927, seductive lady holds glass, bottle lower left, logo above full pad, metal strip intact, EX, A **$525.00**

Coca-Cola, calendar, 1928, lady in gold gown & white stole with glass, Fremont Pharmacy ad above full pad, framed, 18x14", NM, A......................$1,000.00

Coca-Cola, calendar, 1929, lady in green dress & long strand of pearls holds glass, bottle at left, July sheet, framed, VG, A **$2,100.00**

Coca-Cola, calendar, 1931, boy in straw hat resting under tree enjoys a Coke & sandwich while dog watches, full pad, NM, A **$650.00**

Coca-Cola, calendar, 1932, boy rests on edge of well with bucket of Cokes, dog begging, July sheet, by N Rockwell, framed, VG+, A **$250.00**

Coca-Cola, calendar, 1932, boy rests on edge of well with bucket of Cokes, dog begging, full pad, by N Rockwell, NM, A **$625.00**

Coca-Cola, calendar, 1933, blacksmith & school boy enjoying a Coke, full pad with cover sheet, light staining, EX+, A **$450.00**

Coca-Cola, calendar, 1934, southern couple enjoying Coke on porch, full pad with cover sheet, NM, A **$525.00**

Coca-Cola, calendar, 1935, fishing boy with bottle & dog perched on stump, full pad with cover sheet, NM, A **$525.00**

Coca-Cola, calendar, 1936, old clam digger resting on red rowboat enjoys a Coke with little girl, full pad, NM, A $725.00

Coca-Cola, calendar, 1937, boy with 2 bottles of Coke & dog going fishing, billowing clouds in the distance, EX+, A **$625.00**

Coca-Cola, calendar, 1937, desk-type with easel back featuring 2 Coke bottles, Coca-Cola Bottling Co of New York, 6x8", NM, A **$35.00**

Coca-Cola, calendar, 1938, girl in lavender seated in front of Venetian blinds with bottle resting on lap, full pad, VG, A **$85.00**

Coca-Cola, calendar, 1939, girl in black dress with white collar ready to pour Coke, Thirst Asks Nothing More, full pad, G, A **$120.00**

Coca-Cola, calendar, 1939, girl in black dress with white collar ready to pour Coke, Thirst Asks Nothing More, full pad, NM, A **$550.00**

Coca-Cola, calendar, 1940, girl with bottle & glass in lap, disk logo lower left, Pause That Refreshes, full pad, framed, VG+, A **$275.00**

Coca-Cola, calendar, 1940, girl with bottle & glass in lap, The Pause That Refreshes, full pad with cover sheet, NM, A **$525.00**

Coca-Cola, calendar, 1941, ice skater on log with bottle, round logo at right, full 2-month pad, G+, A **$75.00**

Coca-Cola, calendar, 1943, nurse in cape holding bottle of Coca-Cola, round logo lower right, full 2-month pad, EX+, A **$300.00**

Coca-Cola, calendar, 1944, girl in hat with 1 side of brim pulled back holds bottle, round logo, full 2-month pad, M, S4 .... **$100.00**

Coca-Cola, calendar, 1945, features young pin-up girls, EX+, A **$230.00**

Coca-Cola, calendar, 1946, metal strip missing, G, ... **$85.00**

Coca-Cola, calendar, 1947, September/October sheet shows blond with pair of skis, red disk logo & bottle lower left, EX+, A **$180.00**

Coca-Cola, calendar, 1948, EX, A **$110.00**

Coca-Cola, calendar, 1949, sheets EX/NM, A...... **$110.00**

Coca-Cola, calendar, 1950, M, S4 .... **$80.00**

Coca-Cola, calendar, 1951, January/February sheet shows party girl with Coke bottle, red disk logo lower left, VG+, A **$100.00**

Coca-Cola, calendar, 1952, EX, A **$60.00**

Coca-Cola, calendar, 1953, smiling Santa holding up Coke bottle, Talk About Being Good!, stain on 1 page, 22¼x12¼", EX, A **$75.00**

Coca-Cola, calendar, 1954, EX,.A **$90.00**

Coca-Cola, calendar, 1955, small home-type, NM, A.**$20.00**

Coca-Cola, calendar, 1955, tin, small metal button at top, Drink Coca-Cola In Bottles, NM, A **$525.00**

Coca-Cola, calendar, 1956, January/February sheet shows mom at sewing machine being served Coke by daughter, button logo, EX, M2 .... **$85.00**

Coca-Cola, calendar, 1956, small home-type, with envelope, NM, A **$45.00**

Coca-Cola, calendar, 1957, EX+, A **$70.00**

Coca-Cola, calendar, 1958, snowman in bottle-cap hat holding bottle & standing between couple, full pad, EX, D **$85.00**

Coca-Cola, calendar, 1960, NM, A **$35.00**

Coca-Cola, calendar, 1960s, metal, Things Go Better With Coke, July-December pad, NM, A **$80.00**

Coca-Cola, calendar, 1961, NM, A **$55.00**

Coca-Cola, calendar, 1962, NM, A **$100.00**

Coca-Cola, calendar, 1962, small home-type, with envelope, NM, A **$45.00**

Coca-Cola, calendar, 1963, features December 1962 with Santa playing with train by Christmas tree, button logo, EX+, M2 .... **$80.00**

Coca-Cola, calendar, 1963, metal, fishtail logo, partial pad, NM, A **$200.00**

Coca-Cola, calendar, 1964, NM, A **$75.00**

Coca-Cola, calendar, 1966, NM, A **$80.00**

Coca-Cola, calendar, 1967, NM, A **$80.00**

Coca-Cola, calendar, 1968, VG, A **$15.00**

Coca-Cola, calendar, 1969, NM, A **$30.00**

Coca-Cola, calendar, 1970, NM, A **$25.00**

Coca-Cola, calendar, 1971, NM, A **$7.00**

Coca-Cola, calendar, 1972, NM, A **$5.00**

Coca-Cola, calendar, 1973, NM, A **$5.00**

Coca-Cola, calendar, 1974, cloth, 2 girls with heads together enjoying bottles of Coke, 12 months below, It's The Real Thing, M, A **$18.00**

Coca-Cola, calendar, 1980 Olympics, EX, D **$5.00**

Coca-Cola, calendar, 1982, NM, A **$7.00**

Coca-Cola, calendar, 1983, NM, A **$5.00**

Coca-Cola, calendar, 1985, NM, A **$7.00**

Coca-Cola, calendar, 1986, NM, A **$10.00**

Coca-Cola, calendar (perpetual), 1970s, tin, 1950s style with button atop, In Bottles, Have A Coke, full 1973 pad, G+, A **$140.00**

Coca-Cola, calendar holder, 1970s, tin, It's The Real Thing lettered above contour logo, space for calendar below, vertical, NM, A **$17.00**

Coca-Cola, calendar remnant, 1898, embossed cardboard, lady in blue at table, oval Coca-Cola emblems on elegant border, 8x6", NM, A $550.00

Coca-Cola, calendar sheet, 1953, May/June, 22x12", NM, D **$45.00**

Coca-Cola, calendar top, 1910, features the Coca-Cola girl by Hamilton King, matted & framed, 11⅛x8¾", EX+, A **$200.00**

Coca-Cola, calendar top, 1918, 2 ladies at the beach enjoying a Coke, 1 with parasol, EX, A **$900.00**

Coca-Cola, calendar top, 1921, autumn girl wearing a tam seated on garden bench with glass of Coca-Cola, framed, VG+, A **$210.00**

Coca-Cola, calendar top, 1922, girl with glass at baseball game looks over her shoulder, bottle rests on ledge, VG, A **$130.00**

Coca-Cola, calendar top, 1923, girl in blue dress & white stole lifting glass, VG, A **$75.00**

Coca-Cola, calendar top, 1925, lady in blue turban & white fox stole looking at glass of Coca-Cola, bottle rests on ledge, G, A **$60.00**

Coca-Cola, calendar top, 1928, lady in gold gown & white stole with glass, Coca-Cola emblem-type logo centered at bottom, VG+, A **$220.00**

Coca-Cola, calendar top, 1930, girl in white swimsuit with bottle seated on rock with feet in water, logo center bottom, EX, A **$110.00**

Coca-Cola, can, 1939, tin with paper label, red Coca-Cola on round white graphic on green ground, One Gallon lettered above, EX, A **$90.00**

Coca-Cola, can, 1980s, Play It! Tops contest can, EX, D ... **$3.00**

Coca-Cola, can, 1985, NASA Challenger mission, First Soft Drink In Space, 1 of 80 fitted with special flow release, rare, NM, D **$1,000.00**

Coca-Cola, carton insert, Coke Is A Natural! on banner above stylized Christmas tree, singing angel below, M, A **$12.00**

Coca-Cola, carton insert, 1930s, cardboard, round with billboard logo above, Easy To Serve lettered in center, EX, A **$130.00**

Coca-Cola, carton insert, 1930s, cardboard, round with billboard logo above, Refresh Your Guests lettered in center, EX, A **$160.00**

Coca-Cola, carton insert, 1930s, die-cut cardboard, round with billboard logo above, Good With Food lettered in center, EX, A **$140.00**

Coca-Cola, carton insert, 1936, lady's hand appears to be carrying carton, Take Home This Handy Six Bottle Carton, G+, A **$65.00**

Coca-Cola, carton insert, 1944, die-cut cardboard, Sprite boy points down to where bottles would be, Take Some Home, EX+, A $200.00

Coca-Cola, case insert, 1953, cardboard, advertising Memorial Day, 18x12", EX, A **$40.00**

Coca-Cola, case insert, 1954, cardboard, featuring Eddie Fisher on the radio brought to you by Coca-Cola, 20x12", NM, A **$150.00**

Coca-Cola, cassette player with headphones, 1980s, shaped as vending machine, D **$40.00**

Coca-Cola, change purse, 1907, gold bottle image at left of When Thirsty Try A Bottle, Coca-Cola Bottling Company, EX+, A **$80.00**

Coca-Cola, change purse, 1920 or before, burgundy, top part with metal clasp folds over, G-, A **$10.00**

Coca-Cola, change purse, 1920s, round with clasp at both ends, rust on metal parts, worn, G-, A **$15.00**

Coca-Cola, change receiver, 1890s, ceramic, banded rim, lettered center, The Ideal Brain Tonic..., 10½", rare, NM, A..**$7,500.00**

Coca-Cola, change receiver, 1907, glass, Drink Coca-Cola 5¢, scroll design above & below, NM, A.........**$3,200.00**

Coca-Cola, change receiver, 1940s, glass, square with round bowl, decaled, NMIB, A **$275.00**

Coca-Cola, charm bracelet, 1950s, NFL Cleveland Browns, EX, D..**$75.00**

Coca-Cola, charms, silver-plated, bottle form, set of 3, EX+, A..**$30.00**

Coca-Cola, check, 1910, Waycross Coca-Cola Bottling Co, complete in ink & signed by the Secretary-Treasurer, EX, D..**$15.00**

Coca-Cola, checkerboard, 1930s-40s, 2-sided, Chinese checkers on 1 side, plain checkers on reverse, silhouette girl logo, VG+, A...**$50.00**

Coca-Cola, checkers, 1940s, Dragon brand, NMIB, A..**$40.00**

Coca-Cola, checkers, 1950s-60s, NMIB, A **$30.00**

Coca-Cola, Chinese checkers board, 1940s, no marbles, EX, A..**$85.00**

Coca-Cola, Christmas tree dangler, 1976, 3-D, 24x14", EX, D..**$12.50**

Coca-Cola, cigar band, 1930s, bottle logo, NM, A..........**$50.00**

Coca-Cola, cigar box, features Lillian Russell, 2 for 5¢, general wear, G, A **$25.00**

Coca-Cola, cigarette box, 1936, frosted glass, embossed 50th Anniversary, few small chips caused during manufacturing, NM, A **$425.00**

Coca-Cola, clock, Baird, composition, figure-8 shape, embossed lettering, The Ideal Brain Tonic..., rare, 30½x18x4½", G, A **$11,000.00**

Coca-Cola, clock, Baird, 1896-1900, embossed tin, Manufactured By The Coca-Cola Co, Atlanta, Chicago, Dallas, 30x20x5", VG, A $32,000.00

Coca-Cola, clock, Gilbert regulator, 1910, wood case with decaled girl sipping from Coke bottle on glass front, EX, A..**$5,000.00**

Coca-Cola, clock, Gilbert regulator, 1916-20, wood case with In Bottles 5¢ lettered in gold leaf on glass front, numbered 1-12, EX, A.......................................**$800.00**

Coca-Cola, clock, Gilbert regulator, 1930s, wood case, round numbered face above lower glass front with Coca-Cola In Bottles, VG, A...........................**$1,000.00**

Coca-Cola, clock, Gilbert regulator, 1930s, wood case with Coca-Cola In Bottles lettered in gold leaf on glass front, numbered 1-12, G, A **$600.00**

Coca-Cola, clock, Ingraham school regulator, octagonal face, Delicious, Drink..., 5¢, Refreshing on face, rare, 25x17x4", VG, A...**$3,250.00**

Coca-Cola, clock, Ingraham store regulator, 1905-07, wood case with Regulator lettered in gold leaf on glass front, numbered I-XII, VG, A **$900.00**

Coca-Cola, clock, light-up, plastic & metal, vertical with clock above panel featuring skating couple & Drink Coca-Cola, NM, A...**$400.00**

Coca-Cola, clock, light-up, 1920s-30s, round metal frame with glass front, round logo with Drink Coca-Cola & silhouette girl, EX, A..**$285.00**

Coca-Cola, clock, light-up, 1930s, Ice Cold Coca-Cola above silhouette girl on diamond logo, neon perimeter, 1-12, rare, VG, A **$2,000.00**

Coca-Cola, clock, light-up, 1930s-40s, round clock with Drink Coca-Cola atop base showing 6-pack & It's Time..., VG+, A...$5,200.00

Coca-Cola, clock, light-up, 1941, neon octagon shape with Ice Cold Coca-Cola above silhouette girl, 1-12, works, 18" dia, NM, D..**$1,200.00**

Coca-Cola, clock, light-up, 1942, square metal frame, Drink Coca-Cola & bottle on octagon shape in center, 1-12, 16x16", NM, A...**$525.00**

Coca-Cola, clock, light-up, 1950, counter top, square clock left of Drink...In Bottles sign atop Have A Coke base, works, VG+, A..**$425.00**

Coca-Cola, clock, light-up, 1950s-60s, white round frame, Drink Coca-Cola on red serrated circle on lens, numbered 1-12, NM, A **$575.00**

Coca-Cola, clock, light-up, 1957, bottle on green background, Pam Clock Co, EX, A **$570.00**

Coca-Cola, clock, light-up, 1960s, outdoor, Things Go Better... above round Drink... logo, 1-12 around square border, 24x24", EX, A **$100.00**

Coca-Cola, clock, light-up, 1960s, round with fishtail logo in center, green numbers, 15" dia, A **$170.00**

Coca-Cola, clock, light-up, 1970s, modern pendulum with simulated wood case, light-up base with the Coca-Cola logo, EX+, A **$45.00**

Coca-Cola, clock, metal, 1941, thick round frame, red circle with Drink... above silhouette girl, numbered 1-12, EX+, A...**$350.00**

Coca-Cola, clock, metal, 1948, 3-ring wire rim around white face with red button on 'wing' panel, dots for numbers, 36" wide, EX, A...................................**$325.00**

Coca-Cola, clock, plastic, 1960s, red fishtail logo with green numbers & hands, 16x16", EX, M3 ....**$95.00**

Coca-Cola, clock, plastic, 1960s, white face, green numbers, Things Go Better With... upper left, Drink button lower right, NM, M3 ....**$80.00**

Coca-Cola, clock, plastic, 1974, Betty in bonnet decal on face with Drink Delicious Coca-Cola on plaque below, VG, A **$30.00**

Coca-Cola, clock, plastic, 1975, giant pocket-watch complete with hanging chain, MIB, A **$35.00**

Coca-Cola, clock, wood, 1920s-30s, round paper face on square frame with raised border, numbered 1-12, 14x14", VG, A **$210.00**

Coca-Cola, clock, wood, 1939, square Drink...In Bottles on red disk logo, Trade Mark on tail of C, 1-12, 16x16", VG+, A **$225.00**

Coca-Cola, clock, wood, 1939, square with Drink...In Bottles on red disk logo, Trade Mark under tail of C, 1-12, 16x16", EX+, A...**$375.00**

Coca-Cola, clock, 1910, leather bottle shape with easel back, round face with decorative border, Coca-Cola in gold below, EX, A $1,050.00

Coca-Cola, coaster, 1940s, metallic, pictures Golden Gate bridge, 4x4", EX, D...**$5.00**

Coca-Cola, coaster, 1950s, Please Put Empties In The Rack, green & white, EX, D **$3.00**

Coca-Cola, coaster/ashtray, 1940s-50s, features the Sprite boy, gold trim, round, NM, A **$50.00**

Coca-Cola, coin changer, 1950s, Vendo, Have A Coke, Get Your Nickels Here, overall restoration, NM, A...**$725.00**

Coca-Cola, cooler, ca 1930, Model E110A-K, vertical door at right opens to dispense bottles, center opener, G, A **$505.00**

Coca-Cola, cooler, Glascock, 1920s, oak frame, 4 painted tin panels, 2 lift doors on top, 32x32x22", G, A **$625.00**

Coca-Cola, cooler, Glascock, 1929, single case on legs with original castors, restored green body, oval Coca-Cola logo, VG, A...**$500.00**

Coca-Cola, cooler, Glascock, 1929, single case table top with drain spigot & opener, oval Drink... logos on sides, G, A **$575.00**

Coca-Cola, cooler, 1950s, red vinyl with white Drink...In Bottles, zipper top with 2 handles & white piping, 9x14x5", EX, D3..**$85.00**

Coca-Cola, coupon, 1908, offers free glass of Coca-Cola at any fountain with dispenser, some restoration, EX+, A...**$30.00**

Coca-Cola, coupon, 1915, offers free 1915 Elaine calendar, NM, A **$30.00**

Coca-Cola, coupon, 1929, for Tickle Toes the wonder doll with rubber legs & arms, NM, A...........................**$70.00**

Coca-Cola, cribbage board, 1930s, with instructions, EX+, A **$15.00**

Coca-Cola, cribbage board, 1940s, with instructions, in original box, box EX/board NM, A **$40.00**

Coca-Cola, cuff links, silver-plated, bottle form, some wear to plating, VG+, A **$30.00**

Coca-Cola, cup, 1920s-30s, tin, reads in bottom Use This Cup For Water, But Drink Coca-Cola In Bottles..., NM, A...**$45.00**

Coca-Cola, cup holder, plastic, white beveled base with Coca-Cola, Always Refreshing in red, holds 2 stacks of cups, EX, A **$25.00**

Coca-Cola, cup or can holder, 1950s, folding aluminum, NM, A **$35.00**

Coca-Cola, cutout for children, 1927, light cardboard, 'Circus Miniature...,' 1 large sheet, framed, VG+, A...**$45.00**

Coca-Cola, cutout for children, 1929, light cardboard, 'Store Miniature...,' 1 large sheet, VG, A **$40.00**

Coca-Cola, cutout for children, 1930s, light cardboard, '...Toonerville Town,' 1 large sheet, VG+, A **$170.00**

Coca-Cola, cutout for children, 1931, light cardboard, 'Uncle Remus Story,' 1 large sheet, VG, A............**$60.00**

Coca-Cola, cutout for children, 1932, light cardboard, 'Circus' (with Coke glass), 1 large sheet, VG+, A **$40.00**

Coca-Cola, dart board, 1940s, EX+, A.........................**$90.00**

Coca-Cola, dart board, 1950s, EX+, A.........................**$42.00**

Coca-Cola, darts, 1940s-50s, wood with feathered ends, box of 3, NM, A...**$90.00**

Coca-Cola, decal, Things Go Better With Coke lettered above hand holding cup of Coke & Enjoy A Large Size, 10x8", NM, B1...**$10.00**

Coca-Cola, dish, 1930s, ceramic, light green with embossed Drink Coca-Cola, Ice Cold, widely fluted side & edge, Vernonware, NM, A **$450.00**

Coca-Cola, dish, 1967, glass, square with logos & symbols from around the world, 11½x11½", NM, A...........**$60.00**

Coca-Cola, dish, 1967, smoked glass, button logo in center over world map, ruffled rim depicts different scenes, 7¼" dia, NM, A **$35.00**

Coca-Cola, display, cardboard, the 4 seasons on 5 ornate panels, some damage to second panel, extremely rare, A **$18,000.00**

Coca-Cola, display, cardboard, 1957, 3-D rocket form with Santa at window holding bottle of Coca-Cola, 33x13", G, A **$30.00**

Coca-Cola, display, cardboard, 1957, 3-D rocket form with Santa at window holding bottle, 33x13", NM, S4 .... **$150.00**

Coca-Cola, display, cardboard bifold, 1937, lady with glass in Deco frame, It's The Refreshing Thing To Do..., 34x52", NM, A **$3,500.00**

Coca-Cola, display, cardboard trifold, die-cut, 1935, Madge Evans with glass by chair in oval flanked by ad text, 31x42", G+, A $1,400.00

Coca-Cola, display, cardboard trifold, 1934, features Wallace Berry & Jackie Cooper flanking Coke bottle, 31½x43", VG+, A **$2,100.00**

Coca-Cola, display, crepe paper, 1920s-30s, fragment from large roll with orchid & oval Drink Coca-Cola logo above, 17x10", NM, A **$170.00**

Coca-Cola, display, die-cut cardboard, features Toonerville with comic characters & various Coca-Cola logos, 15 pieces, EX+, A **$2,600.00**

Coca-Cola, display, die-cut cardboard, large clown with bottle overseeing 3-D circus scene with many pieces, EX, A $3,500.00

Coca-Cola, display, die-cut cardboard, 1926, girl holding tray that could hold bottles, Daddy—Here It Is!, 14x11½", NM, A **$3,100.00**

Coca-Cola, display, die-cut cardboard, 1940, girl standing by cooler with bottle, The Pause That Refreshes, 42½x32½", EX, S4 .... **$375.00**

Coca-Cola, display, die-cut cardboard, 1950s, 2-sided, clown with 12-pack balancing himself with 1 finger on bottle, 60x48", VG+, A **$2,500.00**

Coca-Cola, display, die-cut cardboard, 1960, Santa enjoys a Coke with elves, A Merry Christmas Calls For Coke, 48x31¾", EX, A **$30.00**

Coca-Cola, display, die-cut cardboard, 1960s, Coke bottle with fluted sunburst design behind base of bottle, Ice Cold below, NM, A **$160.00**

Coca-Cola, display, die-cut cardboard, 1960s, hand holds Coke can, fluted sunburst design at base of can, Ice Cold below, NM, A **$230.00**

Coca-Cola, display, die-cut cardboard, 1960s, paper cup with fluted sunburst design behind base of cup, Refreshing below, NM, A **$160.00**

Coca-Cola, display, die-cut cardboard, 3-piece panels showing The Dahlias, Coca-Cola logo atop center panel, very rare, EX, A **$35,000.00**

Coca-Cola, display, die-cut cardboard bifold, 1922, pictures girl on wooden surfboard, 44x22", EX+, S4 .... **$1,500.00**

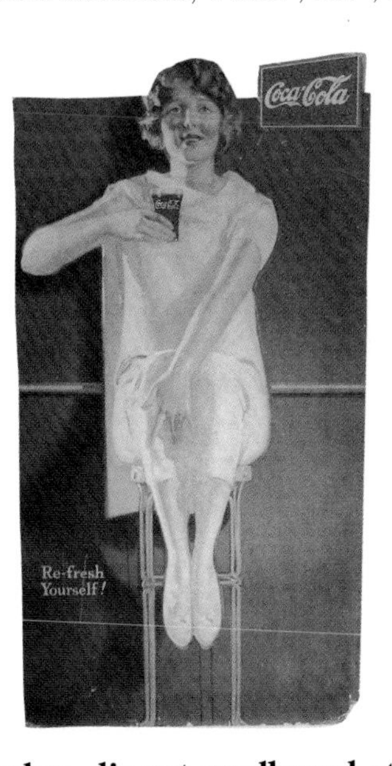

Coca-Cola, display, die-cut cardboard stand-up, 1926, girl with glass sitting on tall stool, Refresh Yourself!, 30x16", EX+, A $1,250.00

Coca-Cola, display, die-cut cardboard stand-up, 1940, girl with bottle at cooler looks over shoulder, The Pause..., 42x32", NM, A **$1,000.00**

Coca-Cola, display, die-cut cardboard stand-up, 1940s, Santa on steps with bag saying They Remembered Me, 50x27", EX+, A **$400.00**

Coca-Cola, display, die-cut cardboard stand-up, 1940s, woman holding 6-pack of Coke, restored/water damage/worn, 60", G-, A **$450.00**

Coca-Cola, display, die-cut cardboard stand-up, 1941, Santa beside cooler, Thirst Asks Nothing More, 32x40", VG+, A **$200.00**

Coca-Cola, display, die-cut cardboard stand-up, 1942, They Remembered Me on scrolled banner below Santa with Coke bottle, 18x9½", NM, A **$550.00**

Coca-Cola, display, die-cut cardboard stand-up, 1944, service girl in light uniform with hand on hip, 64x25", G, A **$95.00**

Coca-Cola, display, die-cut cardboard stand-up, 1945, Santa behind Coca-Cola disk & scrolled Greetings banner, 14x9", EX, A $90.00

Coca-Cola, display, die-cut cardboard stand-up, 1945, Santa with bottle & toy bag at fireplace, Greetings From..., 12x5", EX, A **$140.00**

Coca-Cola, display, die-cut cardboard stand-up, 1945, Santa with bottle standing next to grandfather clock, 19x10", NM, A **$310.00**

Coca-Cola, display, die-cut cardboard stand-up, 1945, Santa with bottle reading his mail, Greetings on banner below, 48", EX+, A **$290.00**

Coca-Cola, display, die-cut cardboard stand-up, 1948, bag of toys on chair before Santa at refrigerator with bottle, 54", EX+, A **$225.00**

Coca-Cola, display, die-cut cardboard stand-up, 1948, shows Santa standing before open refrigerator, 14x8", EX+, S4 ....**$100.00**

Coca-Cola, display, die-cut cardboard stand-up, 1950, kids put Cokes in fridge for Santa, button logo & Santa above, 14x9", NM, A **$180.00**

Coca-Cola, display, die-cut cardboard stand-up, 1953, The Gift For Thirst & button logo before Santa with gifts, 18x9", NM, A **$185.00**

Coca-Cola, display, die-cut cardboard stand-up, 1956, girl being handed a glass, Have A Large Coke At Our Fountain!, 19x18", EX, A **$273.00**

Coca-Cola, display, die-cut cardboard stand-up, 1958, Santa with 3 bottles in each hand, Sign Of Good Taste button, 48x26", EX+, A **$100.00**

Coca-Cola, display, die-cut cardboard stand-up, 1960s, Santa at tree with gifts & dog, 24x16", NM, A....**$140.00**

Coca-Cola, display, die-cut cardboard stand-up, 1960s, Santa on ladder, Free New Holiday Ideas In Cartons Of Coke, 60x28", EX, M3 ....**$150.00**

Coca-Cola, display, die-cut cardboard stand-up, 1962, boy dreams of Santa & helicopter, Season's Greetings, 47x32", NM, A **$150.00**

Coca-Cola, display, die-cut cardboard stand-up, 3-D, girl with glass pulling net over eyes, Have A Coke, button logo, 18x17", VG, A **$450.00**

Coca-Cola, display, 1933, die-cut cardboard stand-up, Ida Bailey Allen Recommends..., designed to hold 6 household items, EX+, A **$3,600.00**

Coca-Cola, display bottle, glass, 1923 Christmas, with cap, 20", bottle MN/cap G-, A **$320.00**

Coca-Cola, display bottle, glass ACL bottle with plastic cap, 20", NM, A **$160.00**

Coca-Cola, display bottle, styrofoam, painted gold, no cap, 42", VG+, A **$160.00**

Coca-Cola, display bottle, 1923, 75% original paint, no chips or cracks, EX, M2 ....**$270.00**

Coca-Cola, display bottle, 1930s, 1923 Christmas bottle, with cap, NM, D **$350.00**

Coca-Cola, display bottle, 1940s, handmade & hand-painted, registered logo, 22", G+, A $3,200.00

Coca-Cola, display bottle, 1940s-50s, die-cut tin, 9 ft, NM, A **$350.00**

Coca-Cola, display bottle, 1950s, styrofoam, 48", VG+, A **$900.00**

Coca-Cola, display bottle, 1960s, with plastic cap, 20", NM, A **$75.00**

Coca-Cola, display rack, folding metal, Coca-Cola on arched panel atop 4-tiered rack, EX, A..............**$160.00**

Coca-Cola, display syrup dispenser, rubber, white urn shape with gold trim, red Coca-Cola on front, worn decals/leans, 19", VG, M2 ....**$380.00**

Coca-Cola, Dixie cup, 1960s, Coke logo, 2½x2½" dia, EX, D **$2.50**

Coca-Cola, doll, 1950s, Buddy Lee, plastic, cap bill, tie & belt have been replaced, 12", EX, A **$425.00**

Coca-Cola, doll, 1950s-60s, Santa holding bottle of Coca-Cola, stuffed cloth, red suit with black boots & white mittens, EX, A **$35.00**

Coca-Cola, doll, 1980s or earlier, Christmas elf, stuffed felt with vinyl hands & head, 12", EX, A....................**$43.00**

Coca-Cola, domino set, Coke Is It, NMIB, A **$25.00**

Coca-Cola, domino set, yellow box with red & black graphics, dominos have bottle images, complete, EX, M2 .... **$55.00**

Coca-Cola, door awning, 1930s, canvas with metal rods, red & white stripe, ...Refreshment Center in green & white, rare, VG, A **$700.00**

Coca-Cola, door knob, 1913-15, brass ball shape with embossed Coca-Cola, NM, A **$900.00**

Coca-Cola, door knob, 1913-15, steel ball shape with embossed Coca-Cola, NM, A **$525.00**

Coca-Cola, door palm press, 1930s, porcelain, white Have A in script above Coca-Cola on red, horizontal with rounded ends, EX, M1 .... **$225.00**

Coca-Cola, door plate, 1930s, porcelain, Thanks Call Again For A... in diagonal script, rounded top & bottom, EX, M1 .... **$245.00**

Coca-Cola, door plate, 1940s-50s, Pull on white above Refresh Yourself on green, round Drink Coca-Cola In Bottles below, 6x3", M, A $230.00

Coca-Cola, door plate, 1940s-50s, Push on white above Refresh Yourself on green, round Drink Coca-Cola In Bottles below, 6x3", M, A $225.00

Coca-Cola, door plate, 1942, porcelain, red with Come In! Have A in yellow above white Coca-Cola, yellow border, 54x18", EX, M2 .... **$110.00**

Coca-Cola, door plate, 1960s, Push, Drink Coca-Cola, Be Really Refreshed on red vertical fishtail logo on white, rare, NM, A **$418.00**

Coca-Cola, door plate, 1970s, aluminum, Coke Is It! lettered diagonally above contour logo, 10x4", NM, D **$40.00**

Coca-Cola, door plates, early 1900s, aluminum, Drink Coca-Cola, Delicious & Refreshing, 5¢ above Push/Pull lettered vertically, pair, NM, A **$1,233.00**

Coca-Cola, door pull, 1930s, aluminum bottle shape with round Drink Coca-Cola logo above, reproduced in heavy cast iron, NM, A **$575.00**

Coca-Cola, door pull, 1950s, plastic & metal bottle-shape with oval Have A Coke! logo atop, minor paint chips, NM, A **$160.00**

Coca-Cola, door pull, 1950s, plastic bottle with white Have A Coke on red metal bracket, M, A **$275.00**

Coca-Cola, door push bar, porcelain, red Enjoy & Here on yellow fields flank white Coca-Cola on red field, 3x30", EX, M2 .... **$150.00**

Coca-Cola, door push bar, porcelain, yellow with red lettering, ...Refreshing New Feeling, 3x36", EX+, D3 .... **$195.00**

Coca-Cola, door push bar, 1930s, porcelain panel with tab ends on wrought-iron brackets, white Drink Coca-Cola on red, 4x27, EX, D $300.00

Coca-Cola, door push bar, 1950s, porcelain, Iced & Here in yellow flank lettering white Coca-Cola on red, 3x30", EX, M2 .... **$89.00**

Coca-Cola, door push bar, 1950s, porcelain, Take Some & Home Today (underlined) flank Coca-Cola, VG+, A **$200.00**

Coca-Cola, door push bar, 1950s-60s, porcelain, red Refreshing & New Feeling flank red Coca-Cola on white, adjustable, NM, A **$250.00**

Coca-Cola, draperies, 1960s, Things Go Better With Coke, 1 pair, G, A **$25.00**

Coca-Cola, drinking glass, 1912, flared rim with etched Coca-Cola logo within large 5¢ symbol & syrup line, large size, EX+, A **$525.00**

Coca-Cola, drinking glass, 1912-13, flared rim with etched Coca-Cola logo within large 5¢ symbol & syrup line, small size, NM, A $675.00

Coca-Cola, drinking glass, 1923-27, modified-flare rim with etched Coca-Cola logo, Trade Mark lettered on tail of C, NM, A **$210.00**

Coca-Cola, drinking glass, 1929-40, bell-shaped with etched Coca-Cola logo, Trade Mark lettered on tail of C, NM, A **$20.00**

Coca-Cola, drinking glass, 1930s, pewter, bell-shaped, leather pouch missing/few small dents/loss of shine, EX, A **$300.00**

Coca-Cola, drinking glass, 1950, bell-shaped, gold dipped, 50th Anniversary, without plastic display stand, worn gold, VG, A **$35.00**

Coca-Cola, drinking glasses, 1950s-60s, bell-shaped, 10-oz, Federal, box of 12, NM, A **$25.00**

Coca-Cola, drinking glasses, 1950s-60s, bell-shaped, 12-oz, Libby, box of 12, NM, A **$50.00**

Coca-Cola, drinking glasses, 1950s-60s, bell-shaped, 6-oz, Libby, box of 12, NM, A **$45.00**

Coca-Cola, drinking glasses, 1960s, Around The World set of 8, NM, A **$50.00**

Coca-Cola, entertainment stand, 1950s-60s, features dancing couple on irregular-shaped stand, G, A **$200.00**

Coca-Cola, fan, ca 1905, paper, 2-sided, Drink Coca-Cola above geisha girl drinking from glass in Japanese garden, VG, A $400.00

Coca-Cola, fan, 1900, rice paper with bamboo handle, 2-sided, Drink Coca-Cola 5¢ in horizontal oval/scene with flared glass, VG, A **$150.00**

Coca-Cola, fan, 1900, rice paper with bamboo handle, 2-sided, Drink...At Soda Fountains/butterfly & flowers, EX+, A **$180.00**

Coca-Cola, fan, 1911, rice paper, 2-sided with Oriental motif & flared glass with arrow & 5¢ on reverse, Keep Cool, EX, A **$90.00**

Coca-Cola, fan, 1930s, cardboard, wood handle, paddle shape with Drink Coca Cola above bottle on yellow dot, small crease, EX, A **$40.00**

Coca-Cola, fan, 1930s, pleated, blue with foil effect, boldly marked Property Of Coca-Cola on both sides, for display, 32", EX, A **$200.00**

Coca-Cola, fan, 1950, cardboard with wood handle, pictures hand holding bottle, 8x8", EX, D **$45.00**

Coca-Cola, fan, 1950s, cardboard, wood handle, shows hand with bottle bursting through paper, Drink Coca-Cola below, 12x8", NM, D **$40.00**

Coca-Cola, fan pull, 1930s, 2-sided, promotes Ray Noble & His Orchestra, Refreshment Time lettered on musical staff, 5" dia, G, A **$300.00**

Coca-Cola, fan pull, 1957, 2-sided, Santa shape, Family Size, Serve Coca-Cola, EX, D **$15.00**

Coca-Cola, festoon, 1912, round center portion only of couple in clown suits enjoying glasses of Coke, slight fading, rare, VG, A **$450.00**

Coca-Cola, festoon, 1918, 3 girls under parasols, floral arms hinged to piece with grommets, VG, A $1,000.00

Coca-Cola, festoon, 1922, Autumn Leaves, without envelope, NM, A **$1,400.00**

Coca-Cola, festoon, 1922, Verbena, with envelope, 5 pieces, NM, A $1,150.00

Coca-Cola, festoon, 1927, couple with glasses flank girl lifting glass in center, leaf background, with envelope, 5 pieces, NM, A **$4,500.00**

Coca-Cola, festoon, 1934, icicles surround Drink Coca-Cola emblems, The Pause That Refreshes..., with envelope, 5 pieces, NM, A **$700.00**

Coca-Cola, festoon, 1934, wood flowers decorate large oval Drink Coca-Cola logo, Drink, Be Alert, with envelope, 3 pieces, NM, A **$475.00**

Coca-Cola, festoon, 1937, rosy-cheeked girl surrounded by snow bough & flanked by full glasses, with envelope, 5 pieces, NM, A **$4,000.00**

Coca-Cola, festoon, 1938, swans flank disk logo, Pause, Refresh, with envelope, 5 pieces, EX+, A **$1,500.00**

Coca-Cola, festoon, 1938, wild rose decor, Delicious & Refreshing, with envelope, 5 pieces, VG, A **$650.00**

Coca-Cola, festoon, 1939, open locket with lady's face flanked by round logos with filigree borders, with envelope, 5 pieces, NM, A **$950.00**

Coca-Cola, festoon, 1939, open locket with lady's face flanked by round logos with filigree borders, with envelope, 5 pieces, EX, A **$675.00**

Coca-Cola, festoon, 1939, Petunia, ladies drinking from glasses flank Thirst Stops Here, with envelope, 5 pieces, NM, A **$950.00**

Coca-Cola, festoon, 1951, cardboard, Refreshment Through The Years 1886-1951, 5 pieces, NM, A...........**$1,200.00**

Coca-Cola, festoon, 1951, girls in various poses within filigree borders, ...Add Zest..., no envelope, 5-pieces, VG+/EX/NM, A **$1,300.00**

Coca-Cola, festoon, 1953, World-Time, Refreshing Anytime-Anywhere globe with time-zone clocks & full glasses, complete, NM, A **$938.00**

Coca-Cola, festoon, 1960s, Birthstones & Find Yours on ribbon banner with 12 gems, full glasses & fishtail logos, 4 pieces, EX+, A......................................**$275.00**

Coca-Cola, figurine, white porcelain figure of the Coca-Cola Santa seated on oval base holding bottle, German, 4½", NM, A **$330.00**

Coca-Cola, flag with pole, white Enjoy... contour logo on red cloth, EX, A **$45.00**

Coca-Cola, fly swatter, 1920s, leather paddle with wood handle, ...Every Bottle Sterilized & Washed 8 Times..., NM, A..**$210.00**

Coca-Cola, fly swatter, 1940s, advertising on wooden handle, EX, D...**$8.00**

Coca-Cola, flyer, illustrates & promotes the bottler's service emblems available to be ordered from Atlanta, NM, A **$20.00**

Coca-Cola, folder, 1964-65 World's Fair, Come On Along in triangle above World's Fair entrance, NM, B1......**$30.00**

Coca-Cola, folding chair, red with white lettering, from Mexico, D **$150.00**

Coca-Cola, game, 1930s-40s, chess, checkers, dominoes & backgammon by Milton Bradley, instruction booklet, box VG+/contents NM, A **$80.00**

Coca-Cola, game, 1930s-40s, table tennis, original box, box VG+/game NM, A..**$50.00**

Coca-Cola, game, 1938, 'Steps To Health,' complete, 26x11", NM, M2 ....$150.00

Coca-Cola, game, 1957, 'Shanghi,' NMIB, A..............**$10.00**

Coca-Cola, game board, 1940s-50s, 'Winko Baseball,' Milton Bradley, VG+, A..**$45.00**

Coca-Cola, goblet, clear glass with red lettering, 16-oz, D.**$9.50**

Coca-Cola, hat, driver's, green with red patch, size 7 1/8, EX+, A...**$90.00**

Coca-Cola, hat, soda jerk's, 1950s-60s, white linen with red lettering, M, A..**$50.00**

Coca-Cola, hat, soda jerk's, 1970s, paper, red & black on white, It's The Real Thing, adjustable, EX, D **$4.00**

Coca-Cola, ice tongs, 1920s, Compliments Of Coca-Cola Bottling Co, Greencastle Ind with 3-digit phone number, NM, A **$450.00**

Coca-Cola, inflatable bottle, made to hang or stand, 24", NM, A...**$30.00**

Coca-Cola, inflatable can, 1960s, diamond logo, 12", NM, A **$30.00**

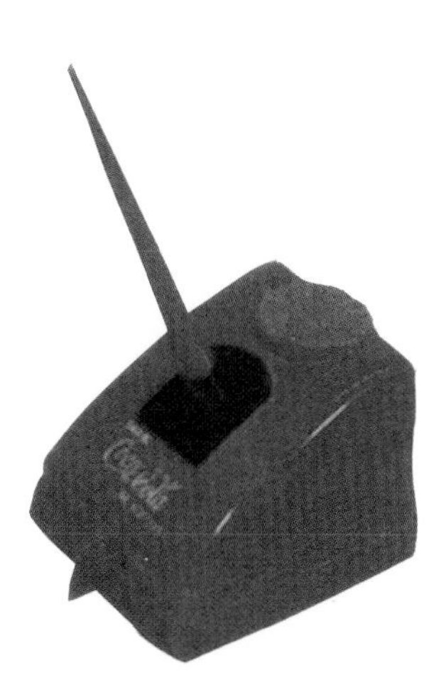

Coca-Cola, ink well, 1940s-50s, red plastic slant-front base with black & red fountain pen, white logo, front drawer opens, NM, A..........................$300.00

Coca-Cola, jacket, 1986, 100th anniversary, size large, M, D..**$50.00**

Coca-Cola, kite, 1930s, High Flyer featuring Coca-Cola above 6-oz bottles, major tears on either side of bottle, G, A...**$45.00**

Coca-Cola, kite, 1930s, High Flyer featuring Coca-Cola above 6-oz bottle, EX+, A..................................**$140.00**

Coca-Cola, knife, 1930s, Coca-Cola Bottling, Delicious & Refreshing, blade marked Stainless USA, EX, D...**$85.00**

Coca-Cola, lamp, painted milk glass bottle on round cast-metal base with embossed Coca-Cola, missing cap, 20", EX, A...**$3,300.00**

Coca-Cola, lamp shade, 1920s, stained glass in the Coca-Cola logo with metal leaf design on rim, 18" dia, NM, A..**$3,000.00**

Coca-Cola, letterhead, 1930s, Eastman Coca-Cola Bottling Co, pictures hand holding bottle, EX, D................**$5.00**

Coca-Cola, light globe, milk glass with green stripe around edge, red Drink Coca-Cola, NM, A.................**$1,300.00**

Coca-Cola, light globe, 1930, milk glass with original metal tassel & hardware, Coca-Cola lettered in red script, EX, A..**$1,800.00**

Coca-Cola, light pull, die-cut cardboard, Sprite boy holding bottle, 15x10", EX, A **$225.00**

Coca-Cola, lighter, applied gold bottle on a Barlow, narrow & tall, EX, A **$25.00**

Coca-Cola, lighter, applied gold bottle on a Scripto butane, EX, A **$15.00**

Coca-Cola, lighter, embossed bottle form, pulls apart in middle to expose lighter, tin cap, EX, A **$45.00**

Coca-Cola, lighter, metal flip-top with enameled cooler in red & white, VG, M2 .... **$36.00**

Coca-Cola, lighter, 1940s, round desktop, athletic activities around sides, EX, A **$180.00**

Coca-Cola, lighter, 1950s, bottle shape, EX, D **$25.00**

Coca-Cola, lighter, 1950s, metal with colorful bottle graphics, button logo on reverse, EX+, M2 .... **$50.00**

Coca-Cola, lighter, 1950s, metal with white Drink Coca-Cola on red body, EX+, M2 .... **$42.00**

Coca-Cola, lighter, 1960s, can shape with Enjoy Coca-Cola diamond logo on red, 1½", EX, A **$25.00**

Coca-Cola, lighter, 1960s, metal flip-top, red band above red Drink Coca-Cola lettered on clear plastic body, EX+, M2 .... **$36.00**

Coca-Cola, lighter, 1960s, metal flip-top, Zippo, centered bottle image EX+, M2 .... **$45.00**

Coca-Cola, lighter, 1963, musical, red with white logo, plays theme song from 1940s, works, NMIB, A $160.00

Coca-Cola, lighter, 1963, musical, white with red logo, Things Go Better With Coca-Cola, works, NMIB, A **$150.00**

Coca-Cola, lighter, 1970s, can shape with contour logo, 1½", EX, A **$40.00**

Coca-Cola, magazine cover, 1910 (June), front & back of 'The Housewife,' 2 ladies & dog at soda fountain, mounted, VG, A **$120.00**

Coca-Cola, map of North America, 1940s, paper, advertising across top with scenes from 1492-1942, 30x36", NM, A **$35.00**

Coca-Cola, map of North America, 1940s, shows railroad routes instead of highways, 30x36", D **$55.00**

Coca-Cola, marbles, 1950s, in original bag with tag reading Free With Every Carton..., EX+, A **$50.00**

Coca-Cola, match holder ashtray, 1930s-40s, round ashtray base with bottle holding up match holder, worn decals, G, A **$725.00**

Coca-Cola, match striker, porcelain, Drink Coca-Cola above Strike Matches Here, edge chip, square with rounded corners, EX, M1 .... **$260.00**

Coca-Cola, matchbook, 1929-35, Refresh... & tilted bottle on 1 side, receceding logo on reverse, with matches, NM, M2 .... **$15.00**

Coca-Cola, matchbook, 1937-43, bottle image on 1 side with Coca-Cola on reverse, Delicious & Refreshing on top end, EX, M2 .... **$8.00**

Coca-Cola, matchbook, 1960s, pictures Santa with elves, Promote Coca-Cola, EX, D **$15.00**

Coca-Cola, matchbook, 1970s, Coke Adds Life To Everything Nice, large size, EX, D **$3.00**

Coca-Cola, matchbook, 1970s, features It's The Real Thing, EX, D **$1.50**

Coca-Cola, matchbook cover, 100 Great Years '86, Coca-Cola, 20 strike, back striker, NM, R1 .... **$8.00**

Coca-Cola, matchbook holder, brass, Drink Coca-Cola In Bottles, with matches, M, A **$170.00**

Coca-Cola, matchbook holder, brass, has 50th Anniversary matchbook, EX, A **$40.00**

Coca-Cola, matchbook holder, 1959, tin, complete with matches, M, A **$95.00**

Coca-Cola, matchbooks, 1965 Miami Convention, box of 10, EX, A **$25.00**

Coca-Cola, mechanical pencil, 1940s-50s, 2-toned red & burgandy case with incised silver advertising, die-cut bottle on clip, NM, A **$50.00**

Coca-Cola, medallion, 1986, bronze, commemorates 100th anniversary celebration, NMIB, A **$15.00**

Coca-Cola, menu, 1902, paper, 2-sided, girl in plumed hat seated holding mug, 6x4", EX+, A **$800.00**

Coca-Cola, menu board, cardboard, button logo above, Take Home & 6-pack below black board, rounded corners, 29x17", EX, M3 .... **$225.00**

Coca-Cola, menu board, Coca-Cola on fishtail above lined board, vertical, EX, A **$110.00**

Coca-Cola, menu board, Drink...Be Refreshed on red oval atop chalk board, Have A Coke! on red panel below, Canadian, 26x18", EX, M2.................................. **$100.00**

Coca-Cola, menu board, with bag of numbers & letters used to arrange menu, A **$50.00**

Coca-Cola, menu board, wood, Drink... button between slotted menu panels, bottle flanked by scrolled design atop, 34", G+, A **$350.00**

Coca-Cola, menu board, 1930, horizontal oval Drink Coca-Cola logo above Specials To-Day, board below, red border, G-, A **$50.00**

Coca-Cola, menu board, 1930s, Drink Coca-Cola above Specials To-Day, 2 yellow lines down left side, 2 red lines at bottom, G+, A **$150.00**

Coca-Cola, menu board, 1930s, Drink Coca-Cola above Specials To-Day, 2 yellow lines down left side, 2 red lines at bottom, EX+, A **$300.00**

Coca-Cola, menu board, 1930s, painted & laminated plywood, Drink... panel above 11 menu slots, silhouette girl below, VG+, A **$425.00**

Coca-Cola, menu board, 1930s, Specials Today above Drink... oval, Refresh Yourself & bottle with straw below, rope border, VG+, A **$220.00**

Coca-Cola, menu board, 1932, Coca-Cola on horizontal diamond above with 3 lines down left side, 2 lines across bottom, EX, A..**$230.00**
Coca-Cola, menu board, 1934, tin, M, S4................**$135.00**
Coca-Cola, menu board, 1940, Drink...Delicious... disk above green board, Makes Good Food..., Canadian, 26x18", VG, M2..**$120.00**
Coca-Cola, menu board, 1940, embossed Coca-Cola logo at top, silhouette girl below, EX+, A.......................**$250.00**
Coca-Cola, menu board, 1950s-60s, masonite, fishtail logo above 10 metal slots used for menu inserts, vertical, EX+, A..**$190.00**
Coca-Cola, menu board, 1960s, tin, embossed fishtail logo above horizontal lines, arched top, unused, 30x20", NM, A..**$325.00**
Coca-Cola, menu board, 1962, tin, fishtail logo above Good With Food, menu area on either side, 8 ft long, EX, A..**$45.00**
Coca-Cola, menu card, 1901, Hilda Clark leans forward with mug, What Shall We Drink?, Drink Coca-Cola 5¢ on back, 4x12", VG, A....................................**$1,000.00**
Coca-Cola, menu card, 1952, cardboard hanger, pictures bacon & tomato sandwich & bottle of Coke, 40¢, 16x11", EX, D..**$50.00**
Coca-Cola, menu card, 1952, cardboard hanger, pictures ham & eggs & bottle of Coke 55¢, 16x11", EX, A..**$50.00**
Coca-Cola, menu signs, 1960s, plastic, 2 sandwiches, 1 hamburger, 1 hot dog, Things Go Better... logo, set of 4, 16x10", EX/EX+, M2...**$40.00**

Coca-Cola, mileage meter, 1950s, red plastic with white lettering, Travel Refreshed, EX+, A....$950.00
Coca-Cola, miniature billboard, 1959, with insert, NM, A.**$70.00**
Coca-Cola, miniature case with bottles, plastic, 2½x3½", NM, B1...**$20.00**
Coca-Cola, miniature music box, 1950s, with original instruction sheet, NM, A....................................**$230.00**
Coca-Cola, miniature picnic cooler, 1950s, red plastic box with squared wire handle, white Drink...In Bottles logo, 6" long, EX, M2...**$90.00**
Coca-Cola, miniature wooden case with 12 clear glass bottles, 1930s, E X, D...**$85.00**
Coca-Cola, miniature 6-pack, cardboard carrier with wire slide-up handle & 6 bottles painted to look full, metal caps, NM, A...**$85.00**
Coca-Cola, monthly puplication, 'The Red Barrell,' Sept 15, 1932, pictures girl with glasses of Coke, EX, D....**$25.00**
Coca-Cola, mug, 1912, brown earthenware with blue Drink & Coca-Cola impressed inside arrow shaped as 5¢, handle missing, o/w NM, A....................................**$950.00**
Coca-Cola, mug, 1920, ceramic, light green with embossed Coca-Cola logo, slight loss on embossing/few chips, o/w NM, A..**$750.00**
Coca-Cola, music box, 1950s, plays 'Let Me Call You Sweetheart,' red chest-type cooler form, white lettering, EX, A...**$120.00**
Coca-Cola, napkin, 1911, rice paper, red on white, lady seated at left of arrow encircling advertising, matted, 16x16", NM, D..**$130.00**
Coca-Cola, napkin holder with napkins, 1988, cooler shape, Italy, 5x5½x3½", EX, D............................**$20.00**
Coca-Cola, needle case, 1924, lady seated with hand on hip holding glass, bottle on ledge, glass & bottle on reverse, NM, A...**$60.00**
Coca-Cola, needle case, 1925, girl in turban & stole standing in profile looking at glass, glass & bottle on reverse, VG+, A...**$35.00**
Coca-Cola, note pad, 1903, celluloid, Hilda Clark lifting glass, pyramid on reverse, 5x2½", G, A.............**$175.00**

Coca-Cola, note pad, 1903, celluloid, Hilda Clark lifting glass, pyramid on reverse, EX+ A................$500.00
Coca-Cola, note pad & pencil caddy, plastic, EX, D....**$7.50**
Coca-Cola, note pad holder for candlestick phone, 1920s, original paper, number of local bottling company & ...In Bottles, NM, A..**$100.00**
Coca-Cola, notebook, 1987, 'Coca-Cola Advertising Schedule,' spiral bound, EX, D..**$7.50**
Coca-Cola, ornament, 1986, hard plastic figurine, Santa with small girl, Christmas Is Love, 3¾", MIB, D...**$12.50**
Coca-Cola, paddle & ball, 1940s-50s, rubber band attached, reads In Bottles, NM, A..**$55.00**
Coca-Cola, padlock, brass on 1 side, engraved Coca-Cola, by Best, NM, A..**$35.00**

Coca-Cola, pamphlet, 1931, showing 8 different New Coca-Cola billboards for 1931, 4-pages, NM, A **$30.00**

Coca-Cola, pants, bell-bottoms with It's The Real Thing & Enjoy Coca-Cola contour logo, EX, A **$15.00**

Coca-Cola, paperweight, lettered Coke Is Coca-Cola, 3½x2½", EX, A **$40.00**

Coca-Cola, paperweight, 1930s, glass, mirror on reverse, Beeville Coca-Cola Bottling, Bottled Purity, rectangular, NM, A **$106.00**

Coca-Cola, paperweight, 1960, bronze with bottle & emblem, given for plant production, EX, D **$10.00**

Coca-Cola, pen holder & perpetual calendar, leatherette top with knobs to turn day, date & month, stamped lettering, EX+, A **$200.00**

Coca-Cola, pen/pencil, Drink Coca-Cola In Bottles Sample No 515, with cap, NM, A **$42.00**

Coca-Cola, pencil, 1950s, Drink Refreshing Coca-Cola, 7½", EX, D **$2.50**

Coca-Cola, pencil case, 1930s, with pencils, 1 blotter, ruler, eraser & other original pieces, EX+, A........................**$35.00**

Coca-Cola, pencil holder, shaped like early ceramic urn syrup dispenser, EX, A..**$170.00**

Coca-Cola, pencil sharpener, 1933, metal, bottle shape, red, EX, D **$30.00**

Coca-Cola, perfume bottle, glass bottle form with cork stopper, NM, A **$55.00**

Coca-Cola, perpetual counter, 1907, cardboard, Drink Coca-Cola, Relieves Fatigue, minor creasing & soiling, EX, A $100.00

Coca-Cola, plate, clear glass with embossed contour logo, 13" dia, M, A **$60.00**

Coca-Cola, plate, 1920s-30s, china, Coca-Cola in gold leaf around rim, may be sample, 6¼" dia, EX, A **$210.00**

Coca-Cola, plate, 1931, Drink... & Refresh... on decorative flat rim, bottle & glass in center, Knowles China, 7¼", NM, A..**$375.00**

Coca-Cola, plate, 1931, Drink... & Refresh... on decorative flat rim, bottle & glass in center, Knowles China, 7¼" dia, EX, A...**$150.00**

Coca-Cola, plate, 1940s-50s, china, Drink Coca-Cola & Good With Food lettered on rim, stamped Sample, Wellsville, 6½" dia, NM, A **$450.00**

Coca-Cola, plate, 1954, silverplate, 50th Anniversary of bottling works, Presented By...To...In Memory Of..., 8¾" dia, EX+, A...**$200.00**

Coca-Cola, playing card, 1910, Gibson Girl, single card, EX, A **$80.00**

Coca-Cola, playing card, 1915, Elaine seated with folded parasol at knee, single card, EX, A **$25.00**

Coca-Cola, playing card, 1939, girl in red sweater with bottle & glass, single card, EX, A...............................**$35.00**

Coca-Cola, playing cards, features 8-bottle carton with contour logo, double deck, sealed, M, A...................**$25.00**

Coca-Cola, playing cards, 1915, Elaine seated with folded parasol at knee, plain edge, complete, with box, EX, A **$2,039.00**

Coca-Cola, playing cards, 1915, joker features straight-sided bottle, ace of spades with bottle crown, not original box, G, A **$700.00**

Coca-Cola, playing cards, 1928, girl drinking through straw from bottle, red border, 25 cards, EX, A...............**$70.00**

Coca-Cola, playing cards, 1938, green & gold with black stripe, Drink...In Bottles on front, rare, complete, with box, EX, A **$375.00**

Coca-Cola, playing cards, 1939, blue with Drink Coca-Cola In Bottles, vertical stripes & design on left edge, with box, EX+, A **$60.00**

Coca-Cola, playing cards, 1943, Coke bottle before girl in circular inset with autumn leaves around, complete, with box, EX, A **$75.00**

Coca-Cola, playing cards, 1943, Scottie dog, yellow border, complete, with box, EX, A **$350.00**

Coca-Cola, playing cards, 1943, service girl with silhouette girl on reverse of sealed box, NM/M, A **$110.00**

Coca-Cola, playing cards, 1943, 2 ballerinas with bottle, Drink... disk logo lower right, complete, with box, box G/cards NM, A..**$175.00**

Coca-Cola, playing cards, 1943, 2 ballerinas with bottle, Drink... disk logo lower right, no jokers, box EX/cards VG, M2..**$70.00**

Coca-Cola, playing cards, 1951, close-up of cowgirl holding bottle, complete, with box, sealed, box NM/cards M, A **$120.00**

Coca-Cola, playing cards, 1951, party girl holding bottle, complete, with box, sealed, box EX+/cards M, A..**$80.00**

Coca-Cola, playing cards, 1956, ice skater being offered a bottle of Coke, Through The Years, complete, with box, NM, A..**$130.00**

Coca-Cola, playing cards, 1956, ice skater being offered a bottle of Coke, button logo below, complete, with box, EX, A **$60.00**

Coca-Cola, playing cards, 1958, 'Ice Man' holding bottle & Coca-Cola button, Welcome Friend, complete, with box, EX+, A **$65.00**

Coca-Cola, playing cards, 1958, girl in pool with bottle, Sign Of Good Taste upper right, complete, no box, EX, A.....**$30.00**

Coca-Cola, playing cards, 1958, Refresh in script above button logo surrounded by hands holding bottles, complete, with box, EX, A...**$60.00**

Coca-Cola, playing cards, 1959, girl in pool rests bottle on Drink...In Bottles disk logo, Sign Of Good Taste, cards EX+/box EX, M2..**$36.00**

Coca-Cola, playing cards, 1959, snowman between couple, button logo, Sign Of Good Taste, complete, with box, sealed, MIB, A **$190.00**

Coca-Cola, playing cards, 1960, features couple standing on beach with cooler full of Coca-Cola, no joker, box EX/cards NM, A **$30.00**

Coca-Cola, playing cards, 1960, masquerade party, Be Really Refreshed, complete, no box, EX, A..........**$27.00**

Coca-Cola, playing cards, 1961, girl holding bottle & score card to face, Coke Refreshes You Best, complete, with box, EX, A..**$50.00**

Coca-Cola, playing cards, 1961, girl with bowling ball & bottle, Coke Refreshes You Best!, complete, with box, sealed, M, A **$70.00**

Coca-Cola, playing cards, 1961, girl with bowling ball & bottle, Coke Refreshes You Best!, complete, with box, EX, M2...**$45.00**

Coca-Cola, playing cards, 1963, couple by fireplace, button logo, Zing! Refreshing New Feeling, complete, with box, EX, A $55.00

Coca-Cola, playing cards, 1963, couple resting under unplanted tree with bottles, Things Go Better..., complete, sealed, MIB, A **$30.00**

Coca-Cola, playing cards, 1963, couple with surfboard, button logo, Zing! Refreshing New Feeling, complete, sealed, MIB, A **$50.00**

Coca-Cola, playing cards, 1963, girl in profile with tray of Coke bottles, Things Go Better With Coke, still sealed, MIB, A...**$55.00**

Coca-Cola, playing cards, 1963, wheat design, complete, with box, EX, A **$55.00**

Coca-Cola, playing cards, 1970s, Tiffany design, complete, EX, D **$5.50**

Coca-Cola, playing cards, 1971, party food around Coke bottle, complete, with box, sealed, NM, M2.........**$19.00**

Coca-Cola, playing cards, 1971, pictures girl in grass, It's The Real Thing, sealed, M, D **$17.50**

Coca-Cola, playing cards, 1976, Coca-Cola Adds Life To Everything Nice, complete, with box, sealed, NMIB, M1....**$16.00**

Coca-Cola, playing cards, 1980, Cola Clan National Convention, Alexandria, complete, M, D **$40.00**

Coca-Cola, playing cards, 1980, 1940s scenes, double deck, complete, with box, M, A **$35.00**

Coca-Cola, pocket mirror, 1906, Juanita sipping from glass, Drink Coca-Cola above, hole at top/no mirror, oval, 2¾x1¾", G+, A **$190.00**

Coca-Cola, pocket mirror, 1907, bare-shouldered lady lifts glass, Drink Coca-Cola above, Relieves Fatigue, oval 2¾x1¾", EX, A..**$475.00**

Coca-Cola, pocket mirror, 1907, bare-shouldered lady lifts glass, Drink Coca-Cola above, Relieves Fatigue, oval, 2¾x1¾", G, A **$170.00**

Coca-Cola, pocket mirror, 1908, Victorian lady at founatin drinks from glass, Drink Coca-Cola above, oval, 2¾x1¾", EX, A..**$650.00**

Coca-Cola, pocket mirror, 1909, lady enjoying Coke, St Louis Fair in background, Drink Coca-Cola, oval, 2¾x1¾", EX, A..$300.00

Coca-Cola, pocket mirror, 1910, The Coca-Cola Girl in wide-brimmed hat & high collar above Drink Coca-Cola, 2¾x1¾", VG, A...**$235.00**

Coca-Cola, pocket mirror, 1910, The Coca-Cola Girl in wide-brimmed hat & high collar, Drink Coca-Cola below, 2¾x1¾", EX+, A **$400.00**

Coca-Cola, pocket mirror, 1911, lady in floral hat facing right above Drink Delicious Coca-Cola, oval, 2¾x1¾", G, A **$70.00**

Coca-Cola, pocket mirror, 1911, lady in floral hat facing right above Drink Delicious Coca-Cola, oval, 2¾x1¾", EX, A **$225.00**

Coca-Cola, pocket mirror, 1914, lady looking over right shoulder lifts glass, Drink Coca-Cola 5¢ below, oval, 2¾x1¾", EX+, A..**$525.00**

Coca-Cola, pocket mirror, 1914, lady looking over right shoulder lifts glass, Drink Coca-Cola below, oval, 2¾x1¾", G, A..**$210.00**

Coca-Cola, pocket mirror, 1916, Elaine seated looking over her shoulder with bottle of Coca-Cola, oval, 2¾x1¾", VG, A...**$175.00**

Coca-Cola, pocket mirror, 1916, Elaine seated looking over her shoulder with bottle of Coca-Cola, oval, 2¾x1¾", EX, A...**$250.00**

Coca-Cola, pocket mirror, 1920, garden girl in yellow dress & floppy wide-brimmed hat holding bottle, oval, 2¾x1¾", EX+, A **$475.00**

Coca-Cola, pocket mirror, 1920, garden girl in yellow dress & floppy wide-brimmed hat holding glass, oval, 2¾x1¾", G, A **$130.00**

Coca-Cola, pocket mirror, 1920s, cat's head shown front & back, opens to bottle & Drink Coca-Cola In Bottles, NM, A **$332.00**

Coca-Cola, pocket mirror, 1936, Coca-Cola memos, 50th Anniversary, vertical rectangle, EX+, A $210.00

Coca-Cola, pop gun, Santa airborne in white sleigh with Coco-Cola logo on back, 4½x7½", NM, A **$15.00**

Coca-Cola, popcorn box, 1970s, cardboard, Coke Adds Life To Going To The Movies, EX, D **$4.00**

Coca-Cola, postage stamp carrier, 1902, celluloid, girl in plumed hat lifts Coke glass, pyramid on reverse, 2½x1½", EX+, A **$700.00**

Coca-Cola, postcard, Merry Christmas flanked by bottle & Santa in sleigh above lettering & logo, NM, B1 ...... **$4.00**

Coca-Cola, postcard, 1910, pictures the Coca-Cola girl, Hamilton King artwork, EX, S4 .... **$395.00**

Coca-Cola, postcard, 1911, motor girl with bottle at steering wheel, Drink Bottled Coca-Cola..., So Easily Served, VG, A **$130.00**

Coca-Cola, postcard/coupon, 1950s, 65th anniversary, Free 6 Bottles, pictures wire-handled carton, EX, D **$5.00**

Coca-Cola, postcards, 1940s, set of 4 featuring Dick Tracy with Coca-Cola advertising on sleeve, giveaway to WWII soldiers, NM, A **$80.00**

Coca-Cola, pretzel bowl, 1930s, aluminum, 3 bottles attached to bowl, EX+, A **$275.00**

Coca-Cola, print, 1943, cardboard, Grumman 'Avenger' TBF torpedo bomber attacks warship, disk & bottle lower right, 13x15", EX, A **$135.00**

Coca-Cola, prints, complete set of 20 WWII airplanes on cardboard hangers, EX+, A **$625.00**

Coca-Cola, punch board, 1930s, features 2 babies, Coke bottle & 1¢ sale price above used board, very rare, NM, A **$1,250.00**

Coca-Cola, punch card, Win A 24-Bottle Case Of Coca-Cola For Only 5 Cents, 8x7", EX, D **$5.00**

Coca-Cola, puzzle, 1940s-50s, 2-piece bent wire, The Pause That Refreshes marked on both sides, NM, A **$10.00**

Coca-Cola, puzzle, 1950s, mounted on paper, party scene with pennants, bottles on ice & Sprite boy below, Canadian, 12x18", EX, M2 .... **$80.00**

Coca-Cola, puzzle maze, 1950s, Get The BB's In The Eyes Of The Sprite Boy, from Memphis TN bottling company, EX+, A **$20.00**

Coca-Cola, radio, can form, General Electric, red with white Coke lettered sideways, contour logo, EX, A **$10.00**

Coca-Cola, radio, white Enjoy Coke lettered sideways on red vending machine, Hong Kong, NM, A **$40.00**

Coca-Cola, radio, 1930s, bottle form, Crosley, rare, M, A $12,000.00

Coca-Cola, radio, 1930s, bottle form, Crosley, some modifications have been made, radio has been replaced, rare, 30", VG, A **$2,400.00**

Coca-Cola, radio, 1950s, red plastic cooler form with white lettering, 9½x12x7", EX+, S4 .... **$600.00**

Coca-Cola, radio, 1950s, red plastic cooler form with white lettering, 9½x12x7", G+, A **$260.00**

Coca-Cola, radio, 1963, vending machine with red Drink Coca-Cola on white across top, EX, A **$120.00**

Coca-Cola, radio, 1965, model of a Vendo vending machine with vertical row of bottles at left, red Drink... on white top, EX+, A **$220.00**

Coca-Cola, radio, 1970s, vending machine with Here's The Real Thing logo, vertical bottles, wood panel on front, EX+, A **$80.00**

Coca-Cola, radio, 1970s-80s, bottle form, NMIB, A.... **$30.00**

Coca-Cola, radio, 1982, vending machine form, AM/FM transistor, NMIB, A **$40.00**

Coca-Cola, record, 1971, 45 rpm, 'Buy The World A Coke,' 'It's The Real Thing,' 'Little Bit Of Sunshine,' EX, D .. **$7.50**

Coca-Cola, record album, 1971, 'Lone Ranger,' EX, D... **$20.00**

Coca-Cola, ring, Raquel Welch, EX, D **$25.00**

Coca-Cola, ruler, metal, pictures bottle & button logo on each end, 6", NM, B1 .... **$8.00**

Coca-Cola, sales manual, 1940s, leather binder with 18 individual booklets, EX, D **$225.00**

Coca-Cola, salesman's sample, cooler, red plastic, lid lifts to show soft drinks on paper roller, bottom shows percentage of sales, EX, M2 .... **$180.00**

Coca-Cola, salesman's sample, miniature cooler with flip top, NM, A **$160.00**

Coca-Cola, salesman's sample, 1929, Glascock double-case cooler, Serve Yourself...Please Pay the Clerk, 8x10½x13", VG+, A $5,000.00

Coca-Cola, salesman's sample, 1930s-40s, leather mustang key case showing 4 leather key cases available, NM, A **$60.00**

Coca-Cola, salesman's sample, 1939, cooler & carrying case, cooler with open bottom, A Business Builder lettered on case, EX, A $1,800.00

Coca-Cola, salesman's sample, 1939, cooler & carrying case, cooler with open bottom, A Business Builder on case, complete, VG+, A **$1,050.00**

Coca-Cola, salesman's sample, 1960s, dispenser, metal & plastic with canvas carrying case, Things Go Better..., 12x17", NM, A **$800.00**

Coca-Cola, salt & pepper shakers, 1920s, aluminum with red inlay, in original box marked Treasure Chest, VG+, A **$260.00**

Coca-Cola, sandwich toaster, 1930s, electric, round with Coca-Cola impressed in lid & bottom, used in soda fountains, EX, A **$600.00**

Coca-Cola, scarf, 1930s-40s, cloth, features bottles & bottle caps with couple at table & couple dancing, 36x36", EX+, A **$35.00**

Coca-Cola, scarf, features Kit Carson surrounded by western scenes & circle logos at 4 corners, VG, A **$30.00**

Coca-Cola, score pad for bridge, features nurse with bottle & Drink...Delicious & Refreshing red disk logo, 7x4", NM, M2 .... **$15.00**

Coca-Cola, screen panel, 1920s-30s, center section of the Dahlias trifold screen, some wear, 29x29", G+, A .. **$65.00**

Coca-Cola, seltzer bottle, clear glass, straight-sided, incised Coca-Cola Co, Joplin Missouri, with cap & spigot, EX, A **$85.00**

Coca-Cola, seltzer bottle, clear with red graphics, waiter carrying tray, ACL, Cairo Ill, EX+, A.... $85.00

Coca-Cola, seltzer bottle, green fluted glass with tapered sides, from Winona Minnesota, EX+, A **$200.00**

Coca-Cola, seltzer bottle, green glass, tapered sides, Louisiana Coca-Cola Bottling Co, missing silver cap & spigot, G, A **$160.00**

Coca-Cola, seltzer bottle, 1950s, glass with metal top, ...Bottling Works, Alliance Ohio, Content 26 Fl Oz, minor wear, 11½", A **$135.00**

Coca-Cola, sewing kit, 1940s, US Marines, NM, A **$55.00**

Coca-Cola, sheet music, 1927, minor crease lines, EX, D **$200.00**

Coca-Cola, shelf hanger, 1976, Santa with note from Jimmy, Coke Adds Life To Holiday Fun, 15x5", EX, D **$3.50**

Coca-Cola, shirt, 1930s, embroidered Drink Coca-Cola In Bottles, VG+, A **$15.00**

Coca-Cola, shorts, It's The Real Thing, Enjoy Coca-Cola contour logo, NM, A **$12.00**

Coca-Cola, shot glass, 1986, Merry Christmas, EX, D .. **$4.00**

Coca-Cola, sidewalk marker, 1920s-30s, solid brass, Safety First, NM, A **$110.00**

Coca-Cola, sign, button, red with white Drink Coca-Cola In Bottles, 24" dia, NM, A **$325.00**

Coca-Cola, sign, button, white Coca-Cola over bottle on red, 36" dia, NM, A **$975.00**

Coca-Cola, sign, button, 1940s-50s, white Coca-Cola over bottle on red, 24", M, A **$725.00**

Coca-Cola, sign, button, 1940s-50s, features white Drink Coca-Cola & yellow Sign Of Good Taste on red, 16" dia, G+, A **$110.00**

Coca-Cola, sign, button, 1950, features white Drink Coca-Cola & yellow Sign Of Good Taste on red, 12" dia, NM, A **$190.00**

Coca-Cola, sign, button, 1950s, plain white, no decal, 16", EX, A **$160.00**

Coca-Cola, sign, button, 1950s, white with decaled bottle, EX, A **$275.00**

Coca-Cola, sign, button, 1950s, white with decaled hand holding bottle, 16" dia, EX+, A **$275.00**

Coca-Cola, sign, button, 1950s, white with Sprite boy looking around bottle, Have A Coke on burst of yellow, 16" dia, NM, A **$425.00**

Coca-Cola, sign, button, 1950s-60s, painted, red Drink Coca-Cola In Bottles on white, 36" dia, EX+, A . **$275.00**

Coca-Cola, sign, button, 1950s-60s, white Drink Coca-Cola In Bottles on red, edge flaking, 36" dia, A **$240.00**

Coca-Cola, sign, button, 1951, white Coca-Cola over bottle on red, 48" dia, NM, A **$500.00**

Coca-Cola, sign, cardboard, die-cut, diminishing logo above ice bucket with bottles & empty glass, 7 Million A Day, vertical, NM, A **$500.00**

Coca-Cola, sign, button, 1957, white Drink Coca-Cola In Bottles on red, 12" dia, NM, A **$180.00**

Coca-Cola, sign, cardboard, die-cut, For Picnic Fun lettered on wooden sign at left of picnickers with cooler of Coke, EX, M1 .... **$145.00**

Coca-Cola, sign, cardboard, die-cut, hostess holding round tray with snacks & icy bottles of Coke, Serve Coke At Home, EX, A **$260.00**

Coca-Cola, sign, cardboard, die-cut, 1910s, couple with parasol at sundial reading It's Time To Drink Coca-Cola, 36½x30", VG, A $5,500.00

Coca-Cola, sign, cardboard, die-cut, 1930, diminishing logo upper left of bathing beauty standing with bottle, So Refreshing, VG, A **$425.00**

Coca-Cola, sign, cardboard, die-cut, 1932, Francis Dee & Gene Raymond on beach, The Pause That Refreshes, showcase frame, VG, A **$1,550.00**

Coca-Cola, sign, cardboard, die-cut, 1947, 3 wood-handled 6-packs with green dot reading Easy To Carry, 33x42", EX, A **$210.00**

Coca-Cola, sign, cardboard, disk logo by dark-haired girl in lavender drinking from bottle, You Taste The Quality, framed, EX, M3 .... **$175.00**

Coca-Cola, sign, cardboard, features Bill Cosby, Have A Coke And A Smile, 32x66", EX, A **$25.00**

Coca-Cola, sign, cardboard, For Extra Fun, Take More Than One above 2 girls on tandem bike, Take An Extra Carton..., 27x16", NM, M3 .... **$85.00**

Coca-Cola, sign, cardboard, grocer puts bottles in sack left of Take Some Home Today & Coca-Cola disk, horizontal rectangle, VG, A **$80.00**

Coca-Cola, sign, cardboard, illustrated football player on 2-color background, Things Go Better...lower left, 22x14", NM, A **$6.00**

Coca-Cola, sign, cardboard, the McGuire sisters in straw hats promoting King Size bottles, Be Really Refreshed, 27x16", VG, A **$300.00**

Coca-Cola, sign, cardboard, Today's Feature, Enjoy A Float With Coke & glass over skyscape with hot air balloons, 11x26", EX, M3 .... **$65.00**

Coca-Cola, sign, cardboard, toys & tree surround seated Santa holding up glass, Is There Plenty Of Coke & Sprite..., 26x16", EX, M3 .... **$45.00**

Coca-Cola, sign, cardboard, trolley, late 1910s, Anytime... & Favorite Beverage flank flared glass, Coca-Cola below, 11x21", EX, A $1,800.00

Coca-Cola, sign, cardboard, trolley, 1907, man serving Coke from fountain at right of text, Tired? Coca-Cola Relieves Fatigue, G, A **$644.00**

Coca-Cola, sign, cardboard, trolley, 1917, Drink Coca-Cola, very rare, horizontal rectangle, EX, A **$1,500.00**

Coca-Cola, sign, cardboard, trolley, 1918, white on red trimmed in green, Drink Coca-Cola, Made In Canada, some wear, VG+, A **$250.00**

Coca-Cola, sign, cardboard, trolley, 1920s, Drink Coca-Cola, Delicious & Refreshing, with border, heavy restoration, 11x21", EX+, A **$85.00**

Coca-Cola, sign, cardboard, trolley, 1923, ...Delicious & Refreshing... at right of 4 ladies dressed for the seasons, 11x21", NM, A **$1,400.00**

Coca-Cola, sign, cardboard, trolley, 1940, 4-pack nestled in basket lower left, Get It With Your Groceries..., 25¢, 11x21", EX, D **$395.00**

Coca-Cola, sign, cardboard, yellow sandals by girl with bottle lying on stomach by pool, disk logo above, framed, 26x44", NM, M3 .... **$225.00**

Coca-Cola, sign, cardboard, yellow with red Drink button & smiling boy flanking large bottle, Me Too!, 29x36", EX+, M3 .... **$400.00**

Coca-Cola, sign, cardboard, 1920s, 1915 bottles on white flank Drink Coca-Cola, Delicious & Refreshing, tin frame, 21x60", NM, A.......... **$1,150.00**

Coca-Cola, sign, cardboard, 1924, couple on horses talking to couple in touring car, another couple on foot, 18x33", EX, A.......... **$800.00**

Coca-Cola, sign, cardboard, 1926, girl with parasol sitting pretty, 7 Million Drinks A Day, 31x18", G+, A.. **$1,300.00**

Coca-Cola, sign, cardboard, 1929, girl on lifeguard stand holding a glass of Coke, Just A Drink But What A Drink, 29¾x17", G+, A.......... **$180.00**

Coca-Cola, sign, cardboard, 1930, girl on phone, Meet Me At The Soda Fountain & diminishing Coca-Cola logo below, 38x27", G+, A.......... **$270.00**

Coca-Cola, sign, cardboard, 1930, Ice Cold in 'icy' letters above Coca-Cola As Always Five 5 Cents, 2-toned border, 12x15", NM, A.......... **$1,200.00**

Coca-Cola, sign, cardboard, 1931, Tingling Refreshment lettered at feet of girl with glass & waving, Niagara litho, 38x21", G+, A **$280.00**

Coca-Cola, sign, cardboard, 1935, man wrapping towel around woman at beach, Drink Coca-Cola, Hayden Hayden artwork, 50x30", G+, A **$325.00**

Coca-Cola, sign, cardboard, 1936, Chinese girl with glass seated on bench, bottles on table, logo in Chinese above, 22x15", NM, A.......... **$1,150.00**

Coca-Cola, sign, cardboard, 1936, clown & girl in tutu watch boy playing with circus dog, Drink Coca-Cola above, vertical, G-, A **$150.00**

Coca-Cola, sign, cardboard, 1936, hostess reclining on arm of chair while holding a glass of Coke, Drink Coca-Cola, 50x30", VG, A **$200.00**

Coca-Cola, sign, cardboard, 1936, 2 bathing beauties seated with bottles, 1886 & 1936 in upper corners, 47x27", G+, A .. **$400.00**

Coca-Cola, sign, cardboard, 1937, girl with bottle shields face from sun, disk logo, Face The Sun Refreshed, 49x32", G, S4 .... **$200.00**

Coca-Cola, sign, cardboard, 1938, bathing beauty leaning against rocks at beach, red button logo upper left corner, 50x30", G+, A **$1,700.00**

Coca-Cola, sign, cardboard, 1938, snow-covered disk logo before bottle in snow, Cold lettered beyond, 43x21", G+, A.......... **$225.00**

Coca-Cola, sign, cardboard, 1939, bathing beauty with bottle on striped diving board, 50x29", NM, S4....... **$300.00**

Coca-Cola, sign, cardboard, 1939, girl with bottle & bicycle leaning against stone wall, disk logo above, 31½x14", VG, A **$300.00**

Coca-Cola, sign, cardboard, 1939, lady seated at table Inviting You To Refreshment, Drink... button logo, horizontal, VG+, A.......... **$475.00**

Coca-Cola, sign, cardboard, 1940, Drink...Delicious & Refreshing disk logo above girl with bottle on beach, 50x30", EX, A.......... **$900.00**

Coca-Cola, sign, cardboard, 1940, Ice Cold on posted sign beside snowman opening large bottle, Canadian, 27x16", EX+, A.......... **$266.00**

Coca-Cola, sign, cardboard, 1940, lady in red with fur holds bottle at ballgame, silver wood frame, Kay Displays, vertical, EX, A.......... **$1,600.00**

Coca-Cola, sign, cardboard, 1940, skater sits on snowy log holding Coke, The Year-Round Answer, 57½x27", EX, A **$550.00**

Coca-Cola, sign, cardboard, 1940, smiling girl putting 6-pack in refrigerator, 27x16", VG+, A.......... **$350.00**

Coca-Cola, sign, cardboard, 1940, The Good Old Pause That Refreshes & disk logo flank fishing girl on dock, framed, horizontal, EX, D **$500.00**

Coca-Cola, sign, cardboard, 1940, The Good Old Pause That Refreshes & disk logo flank fishing girl on dock, framed, 27x56", NM, A.......... **$625.00**

Coca-Cola, sign, cardboard, 1940, pictures 2 girls in locker room, Thirst Asks Nothing More, some holes, 27x16", VG, A.......... **$50.00**

Coca-Cola, sign, cardboard, 1940s, Be Refreshed above button at right of girl on sail rig & bottle, 28x53", EX, M2 .... **$475.00**

Coca-Cola, sign, cardboard, 1940s, couple building a snowman, Thirst Knows No Season, disk logo, 50x29", NM, M3 .... **$400.00**

Coca-Cola, sign, cardboard, 1940s, girl in purple sweater & yellow skirt on stomach by 6-pack, I Think It's Swell, 29x56", G+, M3.......... **$120.00**

Coca-Cola, sign, cardboard, 1940s, mother & son watch monkey & organ grinder, Pause & Refresh, gold frame, vertical, EX+, A.......... **$675.00**

Coca-Cola, sign, cardboard, 1941, autumn girl in round inset, So Refreshing above, Drink Coca-Cola below, gold frame, 27x16", EX, A.......... **$300.00**

Coca-Cola, sign, cardboard, 1941, Drink...Refreshing... disk logo above cowboy wiping brow & eyeing bottle, gold frame, NM, A.......... $1,150.00

Coca-Cola, sign, cardboard, 1941, girl holding bottle of Coke singing into microphone, Entertain Your Thirst, 20x36", EX+, A.......... **$525.00**

Coca-Cola, sign, cardboard, 1941, girl on beach blanket flanked by disk logo & Cool Contrast To A Summer Sun, framed, 27x56", EX, A....................**$650.00**

Coca-Cola, sign, cardboard, 1941, girl taking carton from drink rack, Easy To Take Home at bottom, 27x16", VG+, A....................**$275.00**

Coca-Cola, sign, cardboard, 1941, girl with bottle of Coke relaxing at garden's edge, The Pause That Refreshes, 27x56", EX+, A....................**$310.00**

Coca-Cola, sign, cardboard, 1941, girl with bottle shading eyes with hand, disk logo & Face The Sun Refreshed below, 50x30", EX+, A....................**$850.00**

Coca-Cola, sign, cardboard, 1941, girl with skates enjoys Coke at cooler, Refreshment... Out Of Bottle, gold frame, 27x16", VG+, A....................**$235.00**

Coca-Cola, sign, cardboard, 1941, man offering bottle of Coke from behind to seated lady, On The Refreshing Side, 50x30", VG+, A....................**$320.00**

Coca-Cola, sign, cardboard, 1941, mother, father & son with bottles, It's A Family Affair, Drink... disk logo, 20x36", G+, A....................**$175.00**

Coca-Cola, sign, cardboard, 1941, singer at microphone with bottle, Entertain Your Thirst, disk logo at right, 20x34", G+, A....................**$180.00**

Coca-Cola, sign, cardboard, 1941, 25¢ 6-pack & The Pause That Refreshes flank garden girl resting with Coke, framed, 27x56", NM, A....................**$650.00**

Coca-Cola, sign, cardboard, 1942, Accepted Home Refreshment & disk logo flank couple popping corn at hearth, framed, 27x56", NM, A....................**$700.00**

Coca-Cola, sign, cardboard, 1942, At Ease...For Refreshment left of army nurse, disk logo at right, gold frame, horizontal, NM, A....................$2,000.00

Coca-Cola, sign, cardboard, 1942, couple getting bottles from bowl of ice above 6-pack, The Drink They All Expect, 27x16", VG, A....................**$220.00**

Coca-Cola, sign, cardboard, 1942, gazing couple, he with bottle at right of Drink Coca-Cola, Delicious & Refreshing, 20x28", NM, A....................**$850.00**

Coca-Cola, sign, cardboard, 1942, girl holding bottle & umbrella by cooler, Talk About Refreshing, 27x16", VG, A....................**$110.00**

Coca-Cola, sign, cardboard, 1942, girl leans against open car enjoying Coke with friend, Right Out Of The Bottle, 56½x27", EX, A....................**$550.00**

Coca-Cola, sign, cardboard, 1942, pictures service girl at door of plane, I'm Heading For Coca-Cola, gold frame, EX, A....................**$525.00**

Coca-Cola, sign, cardboard, 1942, shows 2 ballet dancers enjoying Coke, Entertain Your Thirst, gold frame, 27x16", VG, A....................**$375.00**

Coca-Cola, sign, cardboard, 1942, shows 6-pack left of couple at party table, The Drink They All Expect, 20x36", EX, A....................**$475.00**

Coca-Cola, sign, cardboard, 1943, farm mom handing bottle to daughter on wagon, disk logo below, gold frame, rare, vertical, EX, A....................**$775.00**

Coca-Cola, sign, cardboard, 1943, Have A Coke above smiling girl holding 2 bottles, vertical, EX, A.....**$450.00**

Coca-Cola, sign, cardboard, 1944, bottle resting diagonally on iceburg, burst of sun behind, Have a Coke at right, 20x36", EX, A....................**$450.00**

Coca-Cola, sign, cardboard, 1944, shows cheerleader with bottle, Refresh Yourself above, gold frame, 27x16", NM, A....................**$1,100.00**

Coca-Cola, sign, cardboard, 1944, For People On The Go above military man & girl in sunsuit walking, 50x29½", VG, A....................**$700.00**

Coca-Cola, sign, cardboard, 1944, girl on bicycle with basket of Cokes, Refreshment You Go For, Drink...Delicious..., 20x36", NM, A....................**$675.00**

Coca-Cola, sign, cardboard, 1944, shows girl standing by cooler with bottle in each hand, gold frame, 16x27", NM, S4....................**$275.00**

Coca-Cola, sign, cardboard, 1944, Home Refreshment above serviceman & girl with bottle seated on railing, gold frame, EX+, A....................**$875.00**

Coca-Cola, sign, cardboard, 1944, lady in coat & scarf unloading basket of goodies, He's Coming Home Tomorrow, horizontal, EX+, A....................**$550.00**

Coca-Cola, sign, cardboard, 1944, lady looking up is being offered a bottle of Coke, Yes!, ...The Global High-Sign, 27x56", NM, A....................$950.00

Coca-Cola, sign, cardboard, 1944, Refreshment You Go For at left of girl on bicycle, disk logo at right, 28x56", G, A....................**$365.00**

Coca-Cola, sign, cardboard, 1944, So Refreshing & Drink Coca-Cola flank autumn girl with bottle in circular inset, 27x56", EX+, A....................**$450.00**

Coca-Cola, sign, cardboard, 1944, sun bather is offered bottle of Coke from hand, Yes lettered in center, disk logo, 11x28", NM, A **$325.00**

Coca-Cola, sign, cardboard, 1944, 2 girls flanking globe, Drink Coca-Cola, Here's To Our GI Joes, gold frame, horizontal, NM, A **$1,350.00**

Coca-Cola, sign, cardboard, 1945, soldier & girl sitting on sofa, Just Like Old Times above, button logo below, 27x16", VG, A **$100.00**

Coca-Cola, sign, cardboard, 1946, features Coke For Me Too & disk logo at left of couple with bottles, 20x36", EX+, A **$525.00**

Coca-Cola, sign, cardboard, 1946, couple at poolside (he in water) enjoying Coke, disk logo & So Refreshing below, 50x30", EX, A **$575.00**

Coca-Cola, sign, cardboard, 1946, majorette posed with bottle on cooler, Let's Have A Coke, yellow border, 50x30", VG, M3 ....**$225.00**

Coca-Cola, sign, cardboard, 1946, Mom Knows Her Groceries lettered above girl putting bottles in refrigerator, EX+, A $600.00

Coca-Cola, sign, cardboard, 1946, Right Off The Ice above skater with bottle, couples skating beyond, disk logo gold frame, 27x16", G+, A **$230.00**

Coca-Cola, sign, cardboard, 1946, Right Off The Ice above skater with bottle, couples skating beyond, disk logo, 50x30", VG, M3 ....**$225.00**

Coca-Cola, sign, cardboard, 1946, school girl with sandwich talking to mom with bottles, -- And Coke Too, disk logo, 27x16", VG+, A **$375.00**

Coca-Cola, sign, cardboard, 1947, Coke Headquarters above girl at fridge handing man a bottle, reproduced gold frame, 27x16", NM, A **$600.00**

Coca-Cola, sign, cardboard, 1947, girl in clown suit being handed a bottle, Party Pause, disk logo, framed, 20x36", EX+, A **$875.00**

Coca-Cola, sign, cardboard, 1947, girl in fencing attire leaning against cooler with bottle, Join Me, gold frame, 27x16", EX, A **$275.00**

Coca-Cola, sign, cardboard, 1947, girl in fencing attire leaning against cooler with bottle, Join Me, unframed, 27x16", VG, A **$90.00**

Coca-Cola, sign, cardboard, 1947, girl posed with glass & bottle, The Pause That Refreshes, disk logo, gold frame, 20x36", NM, A **$875.00**

Coca-Cola, sign, cardboard, 1947, Hospitality & disk logo flank 2 girls & guy enjoying Coke on sofa, 20x36", EX, A **$450.00**

Coca-Cola, sign, cardboard, 1947, Refreshing & disk logo flank blond holding bottle & sunglasses, repro gold frame, 20x36", NM, A **$1,600.00**

Coca-Cola, sign, cardboard, 1947, Refreshing & disk logo flank blond holding bottles & sunglasses, unframed, 29x56", EX, M3 ....**$300.00**

Coca-Cola, sign, cardboard, 1947, waitress serves sandwich & bottles, Lunch Refreshed above, gold frame, 27x16", NM, A **$900.00**

Coca-Cola, sign, cardboard, 1947, Yes upper left of girl with bottle posed in beach chair, disk logo lower left, 54x28", EX, D **$465.00**

Coca-Cola, sign, cardboard, 1948, Coke...For Hospitality upper left of barbecue scene, disk logo, gold frame, 20x36", NM, A $650.00

Coca-Cola, sign, cardboard, 1948, disk logo above woman & 2 girls with bottles, Friendly Pause lettered below, 27x16", VG, D **$150.00**

Coca-Cola, sign, cardboard, 1948, features girl in pants & hat posed with bottle atop cooler, Play Refreshed, vertical, G+, A **$250.00**

Coca-Cola, sign, cardboard, 1948, girl on carousel being handed bottle, Play Refreshed on canopy above, gold frame, 58x30", NM, A **$2,600.00**

Coca-Cola, sign, cardboard, 1948, hostess offering a tray with bottles of Coke, Hospitality In Your Hands, 20x36", EX+, A **$200.00**

Coca-Cola, sign, cardboard, 1948, man & woman archers enjoying Coke in front of target, Pause For A Coke above, 27x16", VG, A **$190.00**

Coca-Cola, sign, cardboard, 1948, To Be Refreshed & disk logo at left of girl holding up 2 bottles, gold frame, horizontal, NM, A **$825.00**

Coca-Cola, sign, cardboard, 1949, girl among the tulips with bottle at right of button logo, Home Refreshment, 20x36", EX+, A **$375.00**

Coca-Cola, sign, cardboard, 1949, girl holding up paper cup, Serve Yourself, Ice Cold Coca-Cola on red band, 13x10½", EX, A **$210.00**

Coca-Cola, sign, cardboard, 1949, girl with book & bottle lying on stomach, Serve Coke At Home, button logo, 27x16", VG+, A **$225.00**

Coca-Cola, sign, cardboard, 1949, Refreshment! lettered above party girl with cart holding bottles, vertical, EX+, A **$525.00**

Coca-Cola, sign, cardboard, 1949, Serve Yourself on white band above Ice Cold... button & hand with paper cup, 13x10½", VG+, A **$210.00**

Coca-Cola, sign, cardboard, 1949, service-station man putting case in trunk for lady, Let Us Put A Case In Your Car, 15x12", VG+, A **$350.00**

Coca-Cola, sign, cardboard, 1949, smiling girl with tray holding 4 bottles, Hospitality In Your Hands & button logo, 20x36", VG, A **$350.00**

Coca-Cola, sign, cardboard, 1949, features tennis girl with bottle seated on cooler, Play Refreshed, 27x16", VG+, A **$300.00**

Coca-Cola, sign, cardboard, 1949, tennis girl with bottle seated on cooler, Play Refreshed, gold Coca-Cola frame, 27x16", EX+, A **$475.00**

Coca-Cola, sign, cardboard, 1950, close-up of lady next to open refrigerator offering a Coke, Home Refreshment, 27x16", NM, A **$450.00**

Coca-Cola, sign, cardboard, 1950, fishing girl holds bottle with disk logo in middle & Play Refreshed at top, framed, 27x56", EX, A **$550.00**

Coca-Cola, sign, cardboard, 1950, large bottle at right of lady lighting candle, Hospitality & Coca-Cola in center, 20x36", EX+, A $1,050.00

Coca-Cola, sign, cardboard, 1950, party girl with bottle & date book, Take Some Home Today, gold frame, 27x16", EX, A **$575.00**

Coca-Cola, sign, cardboard, 1950, Pause! above clown handing bottle to ice skater & other performer, gold frame, 27x16", NM, A **$1,850.00**

Coca-Cola, sign, cardboard, 1950, Refresh Yourself My Friend... above group scene, bottle atop, round logo below, 22x13", NM, A **$200.00**

Coca-Cola, sign, cardboard, 1950, 2-sided, girl with bottle, Home Refreshment/hayloft party, Coke Belongs, vertical, EX, A **$525.00**

Coca-Cola, sign, cardboard, 1950s, hand with bottle above man by drink rack, ...Put 'Em Back In The Rack Mac!, 12x15", EX, M2 .... **$22.00**

Coca-Cola, sign, cardboard, 1950s, Hospitality above family around refrigerator full of Coke, button logo below, 50x30", EX, M2 .... **$150.00**

Coca-Cola, sign, cardboard, 1950s, house beyond lady with bottle standing by party table, Almost Everyone..., 50x30", VG, M2 .... **$95.00**

Coca-Cola, sign, cardboard, 1950s, loving couple with bottles under green parasol, Good Taste, gold frame, 27x16", VG, M3 .... **$135.00**

Coca-Cola, sign, cardboard, 1950s, Sprite boy & red can with white diamond, Buy Now Coca-Cola In The 12-ounce Can! 20x36", EX+, M3 .... **$145.00**

Coca-Cola, sign, cardboard, 1950s-60s, barbecue theme with Take Enough Home on ribbon, kitchen motif on background, 27x58, NM, A **$500.00**

Coca-Cola, sign, cardboard, 1950s-60s, cowboy enjoys Coke in center, bronco rider & button logo below, Talk About Good, 36x20, M, A **$220.00**

Coca-Cola, sign, cardboard, 1951, shows Call For Coke lettered at left of large bottle & phone rotary dial, 20x36", G+, A **$105.00**

Coca-Cola, sign, cardboard, 1951, circus man handing crowned lady a Coke, Here's Something Good!, button logo, 20x36", EX, A **$575.00**

Coca-Cola, sign, cardboard, 1951, shows cowgirl with Coke bottle at left of Play Refreshed & button logo, 20x36", NM, A **$575.00**

Coca-Cola, sign, cardboard, 1951, Drink Coca-Cola above circle with musical family, Home Hospitality, gold frame, 27x16", EX+, A **$575.00**

Coca-Cola, sign, cardboard, 1951, sun bather before silhouette of girl's head drinking, Now For A Coke! framed, 26x36", VG, A **$245.00**

Coca-Cola, sign, cardboard, 1951, 2-sided, girl & Home Refreshment/party girl with balloons & streamers, gold frame, 27x16", NM, A $600.00

Coca-Cola, sign, cardboard, 1952, girl getting bottles from cooler for friends in background, ...So Good With Food, 27x16", VG, A **$220.00**

Coca-Cola, sign, cardboard, 1952, 2-sided, sunbather, What I Want Is A Coke/majorette, Refresh!, gold frame, 20x36", EX+, A.....**$775.00**

Coca-Cola, sign, cardboard, 1953, bottle & button logo before bird above dinner bell, Come & Get It, aluminum frame, 27x16", NM, A.....**$210.00**

Coca-Cola, sign, cardboard, 1953, Drink pennant behind 3 cheerleaders being handed bottles, Refresh Yourself!, 20x36", EX+, A.....**$700.00**

Coca-Cola, sign, cardboard, 1953, fishing girl on pier being handed a Coke, What You Want Is... above, button below, 50x30", NM, D.....**$550.00**

Coca-Cola, sign, cardboard, 1953, girl in canoe being handed a Coke, signed Elvgren, in gold frame, image: 27x56", EX+, A.....**$675.00**

Coca-Cola, sign, cardboard, 1953, hostess putting last-minute touches on food table, So Easy, Serve Coca-Cola, 27x16", VG+, A.....**$275.00**

Coca-Cola, sign, cardboard, 1954, Coke Time above woman in sun visor being handed bottle, ...In Bottles button below, 27x18", EX, D.....**$380.00**

Coca-Cola, sign, cardboard, 1954, girl on trapeze reaching for bottle, Drink...In Bottles button, gold frame, horizontal, EX, A.....$500.00

Coca-Cola, sign, cardboard, 1954, group enjoying cooler of Coke, Join The Friendly Circle, horizontal, NM, A.....**$450.00**

Coca-Cola, sign, cardboard, 1955, Coke Time lettered above smiling cowgirl bordered by branding symbols, 27x16", VG, A.....**$260.00**

Coca-Cola, sign, cardboard, 1955, Coke Time lettered at upper left of cowgirl bordered by branding symbols, 20x36", EX+, A.....**$500.00**

Coca-Cola, sign, cardboard, 1955, lady holding striped umbrella & bottle, Extra Bright Refreshment, gold frame, 20x36", VG+, A.....**$110.00**

Coca-Cola, sign, cardboard, 1955, Sprite boy peering around Coke bottle above button logo & bottle, Now! Family Size Too!, NM, A.....**$100.00**

Coca-Cola, sign, cardboard, 1955, swimmers enjoy a cooler of Cokes on a raft, Coke Time, Join The Friendly Circle, 20x36", EX+, A.....**$300.00**

Coca-Cola, sign, cardboard, 1955, 2-sided, Coke Time, cowgirl bordered by branding symbols/girl & sporting figures, 20x36", EX, A.....**$250.00**

Coca-Cola, sign, cardboard, 1955, 2-sided, shows ice skater being offered a Coke/equestrian scene, 17x16", VG, A.....**$140.00**

Coca-Cola, sign, cardboard, 1956, lady being handed a bottle of Coke at left of button logo, The Best Of Taste above, 20x36", NM, A.....**$200.00**

Coca-Cola, sign, cardboard, 1956, Sprite boy & large bottle in snow, Ice Cold above, Have A Big King-Size Coke below, 20x36", EX, A.....**$400.00**

Coca-Cola, sign, cardboard, 1956, 2-sided, girl offered bottle, The Best Of Taste/cowboy & bottle, Talk About Good, 27x16", EX, A.....**$175.00**

Coca-Cola, sign, cardboard, 1957, shows growth of Coca-Cola production over the years, 58 Million A Day, 27x16", G+, A.....**$20.00**

Coca-Cola, sign, cardboard, 1958, carton of Coke with large bottle & full glass, Now King Size Too, 27x56", EX+, A.....**$90.00**

Coca-Cola, sign, cardboard, 1958, girl emerging from water holding bottle of Coke, Cooling Lift above, 27x16", NM, A.....**$280.00**

Coca-Cola, sign, cardboard, 1958, Now- King Size Too above 6-pack with full glass & half-full bottle, 27x16", NM, D.....**$120.00**

Coca-Cola, sign, cardboard, 1958, Welcome Aboard left of large bottle by lifeguard tower with button logo atop, NM, A.....**$325.00**

Coca-Cola, sign, cardboard, 1960s, girl in straw hat in pool holds bottle with straw, Refreshing New Feeling! Zing!, 20x36, NM, A.....**$280.00**

Coca-Cola, sign, cardboard, 1960s, man kisses woman above Things Go Better With Coke & button logo, food scene below, 27x16", NM, A.....**$15.00**

Coca-Cola, sign, cardboard, 1960s, Pause That Refreshes & bottle above couple with bottles seated in S-shaped chair, 27x16", EX, A.....**$55.00**

Coca-Cola, sign, cardboard, 1960s, 2-sided, saddle on fence rail with 2 bottles, button logo, Sign Of Good Taste, 20x36", EX, A.....**$425.00**

Coca-Cola, sign, cardboard, 1961, bottle & Coke fishtail logo with sandwich plate on wood-look background, 12x15", NM, M2.....**$25.00**

Coca-Cola, sign, cardboard hanger, die-cut, 1910s, girl in early swimsuit seated holding glass, 28x18", G+, A.....$1,400.00

Coca-Cola, sign, cardboard hanger, die-cut, 1931, receding logo & Every Bottle Sterilized above row of bottles, rare, 12x14", G, A **$640.00**

Coca-Cola, sign, cardboard hanger, die-cut, 1933, 3-D, diminishing logo with Cold & bottle image, some tatter, VG, A **$300.00**

Coca-Cola, sign, cardboard hanger, die-cut, 1933, 3-D, diminishing logo above hot dog & bottle, Great Together! 20x10", NM, A **$320.00**

Coca-Cola, sign, cardboard hanger, die-cut, 1938, bathing beauty with knees up holds Coke bottle, round background, 22" dia, EX, A **$625.00**

Coca-Cola, sign, cardboard hanger, die-cut, 1940, disk logo left of girl in beach chair holding bottle, 23x26", NM, A **$1,800.00**

Coca-Cola, sign, cardboard hanger, die-cut, 1944, Sprite boy peeks from behind bottle, Welcome Friend, Have A Coke, 15x30", NM, A **$575.00**

Coca-Cola, sign, cardboard hanger, die-cut, 1950s, Ice Cold lettered on 'icy' disk with bottle & Drink Coca-Cola below, 7x7", NM, D **$30.00**

Coca-Cola, sign, cardboard hanger, die-cut, 1960, 2-sided, white Drink Coca-Cola on red fishtail, 15" long, NM, D **$30.00**

Coca-Cola, sign, cardboard hanger, 1896, Drink Coca-Cola... above lady holding cup with glass insert, rare, 10½x6½", EX+, A $22,000.00

Coca-Cola, sign, cardboard hanger, 1930s, 1-sided, German, Trink Coca-Cola, Eisgekuhlt, beveled-looking edge, oval, 12½", EX+, A **$100.00**

Coca-Cola, sign, cardboard hanger, 1939, female shopper with list has hand on 25¢ 6-pack at checkout, 31x14", EX+, A **$1,200.00**

Coca-Cola, sign, cardboard hanger, 1940s-50s, Sprite boy tips hat from behind bottle, Welcome Friend, Have A Coke, NM, A **$525.00**

Coca-Cola, sign, cardboard hanger, 1945, Hamburger & Coca-Cola lettered diagonally below 25¢ glass & open hamburger, 18x12", NM, A **$200.00**

Coca-Cola, sign, cardboard hanger, 1950s, King Size above 6-pack with Puts You At Your Sparkling Best at left, 7 dia, G, D **$35.00**

Coca-Cola, sign, cardboard hanger, 1952, Bacon & Tomato Sandwich above plate of same, And Coca-Cola 40¢ with bottle, 16x11", EX, D **$95.00**

Coca-Cola, sign, cardboard hanger, 1952, Ham & Eggs above breakfast plate, And Coca-Cola 55¢ with bottle below, 16x11", EX, D **$95.00**

Coca-Cola, sign, cardboard hanger, 1964, 2-sided, couple with bottle kissing under mistletoe & Santa eyeing food, VG+, A **$44.00**

Coca-Cola, sign, cardboard stand-up, 1953, Get This Kit Carson Kerchief, Details In Every Carton Of Coke, 24x16", NM, A **$275.00**

Coca-Cola, sign, cardboard stand-up, 1955, Kit Carson Wants You To Have His Rodeo Tie, Details In Every Carton..., 24x16", NM, A **$180.00**

Coca-Cola, sign, cardboard stand-up, 1955, Sprite boy with 2 bottles & button logo, Now! Family Size Too!, 27x16", NM, A **$100.00**

Coca-Cola, sign, cardboard stand-up, 1960s, advertising Free Holiday Decorations In Cartons Of Coke, 27x16", NM, A **$20.00**

Coca-Cola, sign, cardboard stand-up, 1960s, space boy with sandwiches & Coke, Zing For Your Supper!... 27x16", VG, A **$90.00**

Coca-Cola, sign, cardboard stand-up, 1970s, Raquel Welch offers Groovy Accessories, Love Raquel on CBS-TV April 26, 27x19", NM, A **$80.00**

Coca-Cola, sign, celluloid, 1920s, black & gold, Drink Coca-Cola, beveled edge, 6x11¼", G, A **$700.00**

Coca-Cola, sign, celluloid, 1920s, Crystoglass, features Drink above embossed Coca-Cola, beveled edge, 6x11", G+, A **$550.00**

Coca-Cola, sign, celluloid, 1938, round with Drink Coca-Cola, Delicious & Refreshing on red, gold edge, 9" dia, NM, A $1,000.00

Coca-Cola, sign, celluloid, 1940s, round with Coca-Cola, Coke, Ask For It Either Way on red, gold edge, 9" dia, EX+, A **$800.00**

Coca-Cola, sign, celluloid, 1940s, round with Delicious above Coca-Cola, Refreshing below, gold-banded edge, 9" dia, EX, A **$350.00**

Coca-Cola, sign, celluloid, 1950s, round with Coca-Cola over bottle image, gold edge, 9" dia, EX, A.......**$200.00**

Coca-Cola, sign, celluloid, 1950s, round with Drink Coca-Cola 'Coke', ..Ask For It Either Way.., gold-banded edge, 9" dia, VG+, A **$600.00**

Coca-Cola, sign, fiberboard, 1940s, embossed disk reads Lunch With Us around Coca-Cola logo, Kay Displays, 13" dia, EX, A **$1,350.00**

Coca-Cola, sign, fiberboard, 1940s, embossed disk reads Please Pay When Served around Coca-Cola logo, Kay Displays, 13" dia, VG, A **$450.00**

Coca-Cola, sign, flange, die-cut, 1930, colonial-style emblem with Refresh Yourself! above ...Sold Here Ice Cold, 20x17", EX, A $1,900.00

Coca-Cola, sign, flange, porcelain, 1938, colonial-style emblem with Rafraichissez Vous above ...Vendu Ici Glace, 16", EX, M2 ....**$400.00**

Coca-Cola, sign, flange, porcelain, 1940, colonial-style emblem with Drink Coca-Cola Here on red, Canadian, EX+, A...**$600.00**

Coca-Cola, sign, flange, 1920s, Ice Cold & Sold Here on green bands above & below Coca-Cola on red, horizontal rectangle, EX, A **$525.00**

Coca-Cola, sign, flange, 1936, Drink Coca-Cola on emblem with inverted corners & scalloped cut-out top, American Artworks, EX+, A..**$600.00**

Coca-Cola, sign, flange, 1936, Drink...In Bottles on emblem with inverted corners & scalloped cut-out top, American Artworks, G+, A **$260.00**

Coca-Cola, sign, flange, 1940s, 2-sided, Drink Coca-Cola above cutout bottom with bottle on yellow dot, 20x24", VG, A **$300.00**

Coca-Cola, sign, flange, 1946, Drink Coca-Cola on red panel above bottle on yellow dot & cut-out design, American Artworks, VG, A **$300.00**

Coca-Cola, sign, flange, 1946, Drink Coca-Cola on red panel above bottle on yellow dot & cut-out design, American Artworks, EX+, A.................................**$875.00**

Coca-Cola, sign, flange, 1947, 2-sided, Drink Coca-Cola on red panel above cutout bottom with bottle on yellow dot, 21x24", EX+, D3 ....$475.00

Coca-Cola, sign, flange, 1948, Enjoy Coca-Cola In Bottles over bottle image, round, EX, A **$750.00**

Coca-Cola, sign, flange, 1955, white Drink Coca-Cola on red disk logo, bottle & Ice Cold on arrow at bottom, 16" dia, EX, A **$625.00**

Coca-Cola, sign, flange, 1960, fishtail logo & Sign Of Good Taste on white panel with lines & green raised border, 15x18", EX+, A...**$325.00**

Coca-Cola, sign, glass, metal frame, 1950s, Have A Coke on panel above Drink Coca-Cola on bottom panel, 8x18", NM, D **$350.00**

Coca-Cola, sign, glass, reverse-painted, 1932, Drink Coca-Cola in center with Please Pay... above, Thank You below, 11" dia, G, D **$225.00**

Coca-Cola, sign, glass hanger, Drink Coca-Cola on top panel attached to bottom panel reading Lunch With Us, scarce, 14x21", EX+, A $1,200.00

Coca-Cola, sign, light-up, neon, With Ice arched above Coke lettered vertically on glass, NMIB, A **$325.00**

Coca-Cola, sign, light-up, red & white neon, Enjoy Coca-Cola, M, A **$350.00**

Coca-Cola, sign, light-up, 1920s, reverse-painted, reads Drink Coca-Cola In Bottles, double-lined border, rare, 7x15x5", VG, A **$1,500.00**

Coca-Cola, sign, light-up, 1930s-40s, neon Coca-Cola atop base reading In Bottles, very rare, EX+, A **$4,000.00**

Coca-Cola, sign, light-up, 1948, Coca-Cola on trapezoid shape with decorative top on Please Pay Cashier base, 12x28", EX, A **$875.00**

Coca-Cola, sign, light-up, 1948, hanging, glass over Coca-Cola lettered on panel with decorative bottle emblem below, 12x20", G, A **$190.00**

Coca-Cola, sign, light-up, 1950s, counter-top, clock at left of ...In Bottles on base reading Please Pay When Served, EX+, A **$475.00**

Coca-Cola, sign, light-up, 1950s, counter-top, glass front, Lunch With Us on white above Drink Coca-Cola on red, 8x18", EX, A **$600.00**

Coca-Cola, sign, light-up, 1950s, counter-top, Pause on motion disk at left of Drink...In Bottles on Have A Coke base, EX+, A **$800.00**

Coca-Cola, sign, light-up, 1950s, counter-top, rippled glass in frame with rounded corners, Please Pay... above Drink..., VG+, A **$350.00**

Coca-Cola, sign, light-up, 1950s, glass front, beveled border, Please Pay... on smaller panel atop Drink Coca-Cola, 8x18", NM, A **$500.00**

Coca-Cola, sign, light-up, 1950s, plastic 2-sided hanging disk, Drink Coca-Cola, Sign Of Good Taste, needs new cord, NM, A **$400.00**

Coca-Cola, sign, light-up, 1950s, 2-sided revolving red globe reading Drink...In Bottles on base lettered Take Enough Home, EX+, A $925.00

Coca-Cola, sign, light-up, 1950s-60s, plastic frame, cardboard insert showing spilled popcorn box & button, Enjoy The Show, EX, A..................................... **$925.00**

Coca-Cola, sign, light-up, 1950s-60s, plastic round shape hangs from wall, Coca-Cola, Sign Of Good Taste, NM, A **$190.00**

Coca-Cola, sign, light-up, 1955, round metal body & plastic lense, features Drink Coca-Cola In Bottles, 16" dia, EX, A **$400.00**

Coca-Cola, sign, light-up, 1960s, hanging 4-paneled revolving coach type with advertising on each panel, red & white, NM, A **$425.00**

Coca-Cola, sign, light-up, 1980s, Coke With Ice in neon, M, D **$350.00**

Coca-Cola, sign, light-up, 1989, The Official Soft Drink Of Summer lettered around Coca-Cola Classic over palm tree, round, NM, A **$1,250.00**

Coca-Cola, sign, masonite, simulated as rustic piece of wood with metal hangers, silhouette girl, Kay Displays, 11½x36", EX+, A **$375.00**

Coca-Cola, sign, masonite, 1939-41, round with silhouette girl logo, attached aluminum arrow, Kay Displays, G+, A.. $450.00

Coca-Cola, sign, masonite, 1940, Drink Coca-Cola lettered at left of girl tipping bottle to mouth, oak frame, 12x34", NM, A.. **$425.00**

Coca-Cola, sign, masonite, 1940, red disk on aluminum arrow, Ice Cold... above bottle on yellow dot, Kay Displays, 17" dia, VG, A.. **$378.00**

Coca-Cola, sign, masonite, 1940s, cooler form in aluminum ring with arrow, Kay Displays, 16" dia, G, A **$200.00**

Coca-Cola, sign, masonite, 1940s, red disk on aluminum arrow, Ice Cold... above bottle on yellow dot, Kay Displays, 17" dia, EX+, A **$841.00**

Coca-Cola, sign, metal, 1985, made for 11th Cola Clan Convention in Dallas, pictures a cowgirl, 13½x17½", EX, D **$10.00**

Coca-Cola, sign, mirror, 1920s, Every Bottle Sterilized, 8x17¾", VG, A **$190.00**

Coca-Cola, sign, mirror, 1930s, lettered Ice Cold with bottle image, framed, 18¼x8¼", G+, A......................... **$190.00**

Coca-Cola, sign, mirror, 1977, 1 of 1000 featuring John Pemberton & Asa Candler with syrup dispenser in oval, 36x24", MIB, A.. **$425.00**

Coca-Cola, sign, paper, Delicious Sandwiches on banner above glass & plate with 2 sandwiches, Drink Coca-Cola, 18x36", EX, A **$60.00**

Coca-Cola, sign, paper, Treat Yourself above man with sandwich opening bottle, Drink..., Delicious... below, 20x12", G+, A **$220.00**

Coca-Cola, sign, paper, 1908, Victorian lady at soda fountain enjoys a Coke, Sold Everywhere 5¢, heavily enameled, 14x19", VG, A **$950.00**

Coca-Cola, sign, paper, 1920, boy with hot dog & holding bottle with straw, That Taste-Good Feeling, metal strips, 20x12", EX+, A **$1,100.00**

Coca-Cola, sign, paper, 1920, boy with hot dog & holding bottle with straw, That Taste-Good Feeling, metal strips, 20x12", G-, A **$275.00**

Coca-Cola, sign, paper, 1920s, ...Refresh Yourself lettered over crowd scene below lady admiring bottle, framed, 20x12", VG, A **$400.00**

Coca-Cola, sign, paper, 1920s, girl in hat eyeing bottle with straw, Drink..., Delicious & Refreshing below, 20x12", G+, A $300.00

Coca-Cola, sign, paper, 1920s, girl in profile admires bottle with straw above crowd, Pause..., metal strips, 20x12", EX+, A **$1,300.00**

Coca-Cola, sign, paper, 1920s, Treat Yourself Right lettered above man opening bottle, lettering below, metal strips, 20x12", VG, A **$325.00**

Coca-Cola, sign, paper, 1939, 2-sided, 100 Years Of Baseball, featuring the greats such as Babe Ruth, framed, vertical, EX+, A **$605.00**

Coca-Cola, sign, paper, 1941, Home Refreshment arched above 6-pack, horizontal, NM, A **$75.00**

Coca-Cola, sign, paper, 1951, Good With Food lettered at left of 6-pack of Coke & basket of goodies, 11x24", NM, D **$25.00**

Coca-Cola, sign, paper, 1952, close-up of Santa with Coke bottle, children & gifts beyond, The Gift For Thirst, 10x22", NM, D **$60.00**

Coca-Cola, sign, paper, 1970s, pictures Santa with dog, Keep Up The Tradition, 24x18", EX, D **$15.00**

Coca-Cola, sign, paper, 1976, Santa with bottle of Coke, Coke Adds Life To Holiday Fun, 24x10", EX, D.**$10.00**

Coca-Cola, sign, paper, 1985, pictures Santa, Merry Refreshment For All, 24x18", EX, D **$6.50**

Coca-Cola, sign, plastic, tilted bottle & Have A Coke button among ice cubes lettered Ice Cold, Pause-Refresh on panel below, EX, A **$100.00**

Coca-Cola, sign, plywood, die-cut, Work Refreshed on arched panel above educational theme, Drink Coca-Cola at right, 23" wide, EX, A **$550.00**

Coca-Cola, sign, plywood, 1930s, leaf design atop inverted triangle reading Drink... with applied bottle over leaf decor, G, A **$150.00**

Coca-Cola, sign, plywood, 1933, 1-sided, inverted triangle with Drink... over 'Ice Cold' arrow with applied 1923 bottle, G, A **$300.00**

Coca-Cola, sign, plywood, 1933, 1-sided, inverted triangle with Drink... over 'Ice Cold' arrow with applied 1923 bottle, NM+, A **$1,458.00**

Coca-Cola, sign, porcelain, die-cut, 1930, fountain taps flank Drink Coca-Cola, Fountain Service below, 14x27", NM, A **$1,150.00**

Coca-Cola, sign, porcelain, die-cut, 1930s, white Drink Coca-Cola in cut-out script outlined in black, EX+, A $825.00

Coca-Cola, sign, porcelain, die-cut, 1933, Fountain Service on band above, Drink Coca-Cola, straight top, curved bottom, EX, A **$600.00**

Coca-Cola, sign, porcelain, die-cut, 1934, emblem in diagonal 2-tone colors, Fountain Service above Drink..., 26x22", EX, A **$875.00**

Coca-Cola, sign, porcelain, die-cut, 1934, emblem in diagonal 2-tone colors, Fountain Service above Drink..., 26x22", NM, A **$1,700.00**

Coca-Cola, sign, porcelain, die-cut, 1940s, 2-sided, Cigars Candy Stationary on white above Drink... emblem, 54x36", NM, A **$600.00**

Coca-Cola, sign, porcelain, 1930s, Drink Coca-Cola with Trade Mark lettered on tail of C, yellow & green border, 10x30", EX, A **$725.00**

Coca-Cola, sign, porcelain, 1930s, white on red, Drink Coca-Cola with Trade Mark on tail of C, white lined border, 18x45", NM, D **$495.00**

Coca-Cola, sign, porcelain, 1930s, 1923 Christmas bottle on gray background, 18" dia, VG+, A **$199.00**

Coca-Cola, sign, porcelain, 1930s, 2-sided, hand pouring a Coke from red dispenser, white Drink Coca-Cola, rounded corners, G, A **$225.00**

Coca-Cola, sign, porcelain, 1930s, 2-sided, hand pouring a Coke from red dispenser, white Drink Coca-Cola, rounded corners, EX+, A **$450.00**

Coca-Cola, sign, porcelain, 1935, yellow Drug Store on green above white Drink..., Delicious... on red, 60x96", VG, D3 ....**$950.00**

Coca-Cola, sign, porcelain, 1939, white Drink... on red, yellow Sold Here..., yellow/green border, Canadian, 12x31", EX, M2 ....**$155.00**

Coca-Cola, sign, porcelain, 1939, 2-sided, early Drink... dispenser with hand pouring full glass, round corners, EX+, A **$850.00**

Coca-Cola, sign, porcelain, 1940s, Coca-Cola with Drink upper left, Ice Cold lower right, white border, round corners, EX, A **$245.00**

Coca-Cola, sign, porcelain, 1941, white Coca-Cola above yellow Sold Here Ice Cold on red, round corners, 12x29", NM, A **$350.00**

Coca-Cola, sign, porcelain, 1942, red with yellow & white lettering, rounded bottom, flaking to mount holes/edges, 15x26", A **$125.00**

Coca-Cola, sign, porcelain, 1950, features Drink... Ice Cold dispenser with full glass, metal edge, round corners, 28x27", NM, A **$950.00**

Coca-Cola, sign, porcelain, 1950, 2-sided, Drink/Pause/Refresh on ribbon around Coca-Cola emblem, Lunch below, 28x26", EX, A $800.00

Coca-Cola, sign, porcelain, 1950s, Drink Coca-Cola on red dot with Candy lettered above & Films below, 30x18", NM, A **$270.00**

Coca-Cola, sign, porcelain, 1950s, Drink... on red field pointing to Fountain Service divided by 3 wavy lines, 12x28", G, A **$130.00**

Coca-Cola, sign, porcelain, 1950s, Drink... on red field pointing to Fountain Service divided by 3 wavy lines, 12x28", NM, A **$575.00**

Coca-Cola, sign, porcelain, 1950s, Fountain Service divided by pin-stripe lines left of round Drink... logo, 12x30", NM, A **$350.00**

Coca-Cola, sign, porcelain, 1950s, green Gas & Oil flank fishtail logo above Good With Food, green raised rim, 16x96", M, D3 .... **$475.00**

Coca-Cola, sign, porcelain, 1950s, 2-sided, Drink...In Bottles on emblem, plain courtesy panel, NM, A **$800.00**

Coca-Cola, sign, porcelain, 1950s, 2-sided, Rx Drug Rx on panel above Coca-Cola, Store on panel below, 48x60", NM, A **$950.00**

Coca-Cola, sign, self-framed, tin, 1930s, shows tilted bottle on yellow dot at right of Drink Coca-Cola, 11x34", EX+, A **$130.00**

Coca-Cola, sign, tin, die-cut, embossed, bottle applied to red background, original silver & black wood frame, old new stock, A **$325.00**

Coca-Cola, sign, tin, die-cut, embossed, 1920s, Drink Coca-Cola oval with 4 arrow shapes making up corners, 15x20", VG, A $1,500.00

Coca-Cola, sign, tin, die-cut, embossed, 1929, Drink Coca-Cola oval with 4 arrow shapes making up corners, 15x20", EX+, A **$2,200.00**

Coca-Cola, sign, tin, die-cut, embossed, 1932, 1923 Christmas bottle form, 39", G, A **$375.00**

Coca-Cola, sign, tin, die-cut, embossed, 1932, 1923 Christmas bottle form, 39", EX+, A $1,050.00

Coca-Cola, sign, tin, die-cut, embossed, 1960s, white Coca-Cola on red fishtail logo, 42" long, NM, A **$220.00**

Coca-Cola, sign, tin, die-cut, white Coca-Cola on 2-tone fishtail logo, 54", NM, A **$200.00**

Coca-Cola, sign, tin, die-cut, 1927, 2-sided arrow shape with Sold Here & Ice Cold flanking Coca-Cola, 22x30", EX+, A **$650.00**

Coca-Cola, sign, tin, die-cut, 1930s, Coca-Cola in script, goes behind neon letters on top of neon canister sign, 7x24", NM, A **$150.00**

Coca-Cola, sign, tin, die-cut, 1937, 2-sided inverted triangle with filigree work above, 1923 bottle with Drink...Ice Cold, G/VG, A **$310.00**

Coca-Cola, sign, tin, die-cut, 1940s-50s, Ice Cold on chest cooler & Sprite boy on arrow pointing downward, Kay Displays, EX+, A **$650.00**

Coca-Cola, sign, tin, die-cut, 1940s-50s, ribbon shape reading Sign Of Good Taste, made to attach to 24" or 36" button, NM, A **$65.00**

Coca-Cola, sign, tin, die-cut, 1949, wet-looking bottle, white Trade Mark Registered in large letters under Coca-Cola, 6 ft., VG+ A **$310.00**

Coca-Cola, sign, tin, die-cut, 1950, 6-pack, red carton with metal handle, white Coca-Cola above 6 For 25¢, 12½x11", NM, A **$866.00**

Coca-Cola, sign, tin, die-cut, 1950s, Delicious & Refreshing 6-pack, EX+, A **$300.00**

Coca-Cola, sign, tin, die-cut, 1953, wet-looking bottle, white Trade Mark & copyright in small letters under Coca-Cola, 9 ft, NM, A **$500.00**

Coca-Cola, sign, tin, die-cut, 1954, in shape of 12-bottle carton, Chill until Cold, Serve In Bottles, 13x20", NM, A **$850.00**

Coca-Cola, sign, tin, die-cut, 1960s, white Coca-Cola on red fishtail on white panel, 7x16", EX+, A **$52.00**

Coca-Cola, sign, tin, die-cut, 1963, 6-pack, King Size band around top part of carton, fishtail logos below, NM, A **$650.00**

Coca-Cola, sign, tin, embossed, 1899, Drink Delicious... above Hilda Clark contemplating letter, 5¢ Coca-Cola below, 28x20", VG+, A..............$3,200.00

Coca-Cola, sign, tin, embossed, 1908, features straight-sided bottles flanking Drink Coca-Cola In Bottles 5¢, 12x36", VG, A **$675.00**

Coca-Cola, sign, tin, embossed, 1908, straight-sided bottles flank Tomese Coca-Cola, En Botellitas 6¢ Plata, unused, 12x36", NM, A **$800.00**

Coca-Cola, sign, tin, embossed, 1920s-30s, In Bottles & 5¢ flank Drink Coca-Cola with Trade Mark on tail of C, 6x23½", EX+, A **$200.00**

Coca-Cola, sign, tin, embossed, 1929, Drink Coca-Cola above 1923 Christmas bottle, Sold Here Ice Cold below, beveled edge, G, A **$300.00**

Coca-Cola, sign, tin, embossed, 1930s, Drink Coca-Cola with Trade Mark lettered under tail of C, by Dasco, 5¾x17¾", VG, A **$180.00**

Coca-Cola, sign, tin, embossed, 1930s, Drink... above bottle before yellow dot, gold octagonal Deco border, Kay Displays, NM, A **$950.00**

Coca-Cola, sign, tin, embossed, 1930s, Drink... above bottle before yellow dot, round gold wavy border, Kay Displays, EX, A **$400.00**

Coca-Cola, sign, tin, embossed, 1930s, In Bottles & 5¢ flank Drink Coca-Cola, 6x24", NM, A **$230.00**

Coca-Cola, sign, tin, embossed, 1930s, pictures 3 bottles, 19x54", NM, S4 .... **$250.00**

Coca-Cola, sign, tin, embossed, 1931, Drink above bottle image, Coca-Cola below, lined border, 12½x4½", NM, A......**$475.00**

Coca-Cola, sign, tin, embossed, 1931, 1923 bottle at left of Drink Coca-Cola In Bottles, Delicious & Refreshing, 10x28", EX+, A **$650.00**

Coca-Cola, sign, tin, embossed, 1932, Drink Coca-Cola with Trade Mark lettered on tail of C, lined border, 5½x17¼", VG, A **$175.00**

Coca-Cola, sign, tin, embossed, 1932, round with Ice Cold lettered above Coca-Cola, Sold Here below, 20" dia, G+, A **$210.00**

Coca-Cola, sign, tin, embossed, 1933, Ice Cold Coca-Cola Sold Here, 2-tone banded border, some wear/dents, 20" dia, G, A **$160.00**

Coca-Cola, sign, tin, embossed, 1933, stenciled, yellow & white on green, Curb Service, ...Sold Here Ice Cold, 28x19½", G, A **$190.00**

Coca-Cola, sign, tin, embossed, 1934, deminishing logo with Ice Cold...Sold Here left of bottle on white ground, 20x28", NM, A **$725.00**

Coca-Cola, sign, tin, embossed, 1934, 1923 bottle on white left of Drink Coca-Cola on red, Trade Mark on tail of C, 12x36", EX+, A **$400.00**

Coca-Cola, sign, tin, embossed, 1934, 3-color field with 1923 Christmas bottle left of Drink..., Ice Cold below, 20x28", NM, A **$875.00**

Coca-Cola, sign, tin, embossed, 1936, 50th Anniversary above Coca-Cola, 1886-1936 below on red, Kay Displays, round, VG, A **$850.00**

Coca-Cola, sign, tin, embossed, 1950s-60, Enjoy above Coca-Cola with reflective treatment on words, white border, 10x24", VG+, A **$20.00**

Coca-Cola, sign, tin, embossed, 1958, pictures bottle at right of fishtail logo, green raised rim, 12x32", EX, D..**$200.00**

Coca-Cola, sign, tin, pictures bottle at right of white Drink Coca-Cola on red background, 17x56", NM, S2.**$485.00**

Coca-Cola, sign, tin, round with red Sign Of Good Taste on white, raised red dots around edge, 27" dia, NM, A.**$30.00**

Coca-Cola, sign, tin, self-framed, yellow & white on red, ...Please Pay The Clerk, wood-grain frame, 11x21", G+, M3 .... **$120.00**

Coca-Cola, sign, tin, self-framed, 1905, portrait of Lillian Nordica, Delicious Refreshing, Drink Coca-Cola 5¢, 33x23", EX+, A $4,500.00

Coca-Cola, sign, tin, self-framed, 1914, Betty in a bonnet, ...Delicious & Refreshing, 41x31", G, A..........**$1,000.00**

Coca-Cola, sign, tin, self-framed, 1916, Elaine with glass of Coke leaning on hand looking over shoulder, 30½x20", VG, A **$525.00**

Coca-Cola, sign, tin, self-framed, 1927, Drink Coca-Cola above bottle on white, Sold Here Ice Cold below, 54x19", NM, A..**$650.00**

Coca-Cola, sign, tin, self-framed, 1930, receding logo & hand-held bottle over rays of green, Get It Here Ice Cold, 10x14", VG+, A...**$325.00**

Coca-Cola, sign, tin, self-framed, 1930s, carton in circle, Take Home A Carton at left, Drink Coca-Cola at right, 18x54", EX, A...**$170.00**

Coca-Cola, sign, tin, self-framed, 1931, Drink Ice Cold Coca-Cola above Gas Today, Drink Coca-Cola & Sold Here below, 54x18", G, A..................................**$400.00**

Coca-Cola, sign, tin, self-framed, 1932, Ice Cold & Sold Here logos above & below large dot with Gas To-Day, vertical oblong, VG, A **$825.00**

Coca-Cola, sign, tin, self-framed, 1936, tilted label with 5¢ Ice Cold above centered bottle, Drink Coca-Cola below, 54x18", EX+, A **$625.00**

Coca-Cola, sign, tin, self-framed, 1936, 2-toned ground featuring Drink Coca-Cola at right of bottle, 12x36", EX+, D..**$380.00**

Coca-Cola, sign, tin, self-framed, 1939, Pause & Drink above tilted bottle on yellow dot, Coca-Cola below, 54x18", EX, A..**$290.00**

Coca-Cola, sign, tin, self-framed, 1939, Pause & Drink above tilted bottle on yellow dot, Coca-Cola below, 54x18", NM, D **$400.00**

Coca-Cola, sign, tin, self-framed, 1940, smiling girl with bottle at right of Coca-Cola, 12x34", NM, A **$450.00**

Coca-Cola, sign, tin, self-framed, 1941, Drink...Delicious & Refreshing left of man offering lady a bottle of Coke, 22x28", NM, A...**$550.00**

Coca-Cola, sign, tin, self-framed, 1942, Drink Coca-Cola at left of guy offering girl a Coke, 11x35", NM, A..**$500.00**

Coca-Cola, sign, tin, self-framed, 1946, features Drink Coca-Cola at left of girl tipping bottle to mouth, 12x34", NM, A...**$700.00**

Coca-Cola, sign, tin, self-framed, 1946, Drink upper left of Coca-Cola, tilted bottle on yellow dot lower right, 20x28", NM, A..**$425.00**

Coca-Cola, sign, tin, self-framed, 1948, tilted bottle on yellow dot, Have A Coke above, Coca-Cola below, 54x18", NM, A...**$350.00**

Coca-Cola, sign, tin, self-framed, 1949, Drink...Ice Cold on red field pointing to Trade Mark bottle on white, 32x55½", EX, D3 ....$425.00

Coca-Cola, sign, tin, self-framed, 1952, full-color bottle, slot top, 40x16", EX, D..**$235.00**

Coca-Cola, sign, tin, self-framed, 1953, full-color 6-pack, Take Home A Carton Of Quality Refreshment, slot top, 40x16", EX, D **$235.00**

Coca-Cola, sign, tin, self-framed, 1958, red vertical fishtail logo above bottle, ...Refreshing New Feeling, 55x18", NM, D3 ....**$275.00**

Coca-Cola, sign, tin, self-framed, 1958, Sign Of Good Taste fishtail logo left of bottle & Ice Cold, green rim, 18x58", NOS, D3..**$275.00**

Coca-Cola, sign, tin, sidewalk, embossed, 1885, French Wine Coca 5¢ on diagonal 2-color ground, may be one-of-a-kind, 28x20", EX, A **$5,700.00**

Coca-Cola, sign, tin, sidewalk, embossed, 1938, Ice Cold...Sold Here in rounded rectangle within vertical squared rectangle, NM, A **$525.00**

Coca-Cola, sign, tin, sidewalk, embossed, 1940, Drink...Ice Cold disk with 3 bars above Delicious & Refreshing, vertical, EX, A..**$320.00**

Coca-Cola, sign, tin, sidewalk, embossed, 1941, 25¢ 6-pack in circle with 3 bars above Take Home A Carton, vertical, NM, A..**$425.00**

Coca-Cola, sign, tin, sidewalk, hand holding early narrow-waisted glass, For Headache & Exhaustion..., 5¢ A Glass, 32x20", G-, A.......................................**$4,400.00**

Coca-Cola, sign, tin, sidewalk, porcelain, 1940s-50s, 2-sided, 2-color field with Stop Here above Drink..., Canadian, EX+, A **$800.00**

Coca-Cola, sign, tin, sidewalk, porcelain, 1950s, 2-sided lollipop style on cast-iron base, Drink Coca-Cola Refresh!, VG, A $150.00

Coca-Cola, sign, tin, sidewalk, 1897, For Headache & Exhaustion Drink Coca-Cola 5¢..., may be one-of-a-kind, 28x20", G, A $6,200.00

Coca-Cola, sign, tin, sidewalk, 1930s-40s, 6-bottle carrier on yellow dot above Take Home A Carton, framed, 28x20", VG, A $150.00

Coca-Cola, sign, tin, sidewalk, 1931, Curb Service lettered above Coca-Cola, Sold Here Ice Cold below, 28x20", G, A..$100.00

Coca-Cola, sign, tin, sidewalk, 1939, round Drink Coca-Cola Ice-Cold logo above, Delicious & Refreshing below, 28x20", VG, A..$100.00

Coca-Cola, sign, tin, sidewalk, 1942, Drink... Ice Cold disk logo flanked by 3 bars above Delicious & Refreshing, 28x20", NM, A..$350.00

Coca-Cola, sign, tin, sidewalk, 1950s, 2-sided, Take A Case... in diagonal script above $1.00 dot, ...Delicious..., 28x20", NM, A..$325.00

Coca-Cola, sign, tin, sidewalk, 1955, 2-sided policeman on cast-iron base, Slow School Zone, round logo & bottle on reverse, EX, A $2,100.00

Coca-Cola, sign, tin, sidewalk, 1955, 2-sided policeman on cast-iron base, Slow School Zone, round logo & bottle on reverse, G, A $600.00

Coca-Cola, sign, tin, sidewalk, 1955, 2-sided policeman on cast-iron base, Slow School Zone, round logo & bottle on reverse, NM, A $3,200.00

Coca-Cola, sign, tin, sidewalk, 1960s, lollipop in original ring with cast-iron Coca-Cola base, Sign Of Good Taste, NM, A...$650.00

Coca-Cola, sign, tin, 1908, Drink Coca-Cola In Bottles 5¢ at right of straight-sided bottle, red, white & green, 12x35½", VG, A $275.00

Coca-Cola, sign, tin, 1920s, Coca-Cola on center red band, green bands above & below reading Ice Cold Sold Here, rectangular, EX, A $525.00

Coca-Cola, sign, tin, 1920s, 1915 bottle at left of Drink..., Delicious..., The Icy-O Sanitary Dispenser below, 11x17", VG+, A...$1,300.00

Coca-Cola, sign, tin, 1926, Drink Coca-Cola Delicious & Refreshing at right of 1916 bottle on green field, 12x36", NM, A $1,500.00

Coca-Cola, sign, tin, 1926, girl offering glass of Coke against Coca-Cola in script, tray-type rim, oval, 13x19", NM, A..$6,500.00

Coca-Cola, sign, tin, 1927, Drink Coca-Cola on oval within rectangle, gold beveled edge, 8½x11", G+, A....$250.00

Coca-Cola, sign, tin, 1927, girl offering bottle against Coca-Cola on red oval on green rectangle, gold beveled edge, 9x11", NM, A $525.00

Coca-Cola, sign, tin, 1927, Refresh Yourself! in diagonal script above Drink..., Sold Here Ice Cold below, 29½x28½", VG+, A $275.00

Coca-Cola, sign, tin, 1929, diagonal 2-tone ground with Gas Today left of triangle chalkboard, Drink...While You Wait, EX, A $1,900.00

Coca-Cola, sign, tin, 1930s, Candy/Ice Cream/Soda above red panel with Drink... & bottle on yellow dot, wood frame, 36x60", EX, D3..$475.00

Coca-Cola, sign, tin, 1930s, red with Drink... above bottle on yellow dot, silver scalloped border, Kay Displays, 10" dia, NM, A $484.00

Coca-Cola, sign, tin, 1933, rectangular with deminishing logo & 1923 Christmas bottle at right, banded edge, VG+, A $270.00

Coca-Cola, sign, tin, 1934, Ice Cold Coca-Cola Sold Here on deminishing rectangle left of bottle on white ground, 19x28", G, D $125.00

Coca-Cola, sign, tin, 1937, round with Coca-Cola lettered over middle of bottle, banded & lined border, 45" dia, NM, A..$750.00

Coca-Cola, sign, tin, 1937, tricolored field with 1923 bottle at left of Drink Coca-Cola, single dots flank Ice Cold below, EX+, A $500.00

Coca-Cola, sign, tin, 1940, diamond shape with Drink Coca-Cola above bottle on yellow dot, beveled edge, approx: 42x42", NM, A.......................................$425.00

Coca-Cola, sign, tin, 1940s, yellow Drink upper left of white Coca-Cola, bottle outlined in yellow at right on red, 17x57", VG, M2...$140.00

Coca-Cola, sign, tin, 1947, 16" Drink...In Bottles button atop white vertical panel with wire-handled 6-pack, Serve Coke..., NM, A..$500.00

Coca-Cola, sign, tin, 1948, red, white & yellow, features tilted bottle in circle at right of Drink Coca-Cola, 11x34", M, B1 ....$250.00

Coca-Cola, sign, tin, 1948, Trade Mark Registered bottle on white background with white raised rolled rim, 31½x14", EX+, A **$120.00**

Coca-Cola, sign, tin, 1949, Serve Coke At Home lettered above 6-bottle carton, raised border, fancy top, 40x16", EX+, A **$220.00**

Coca-Cola, sign, tin, 1950s, Lunches & Home Made Chili above Refreshing New Feeling fishtail logo, green raised rim, 35x65", M, D3 .... **$550.00**

Coca-Cola, sign, tin, 1950s, whirligig with 4 2-sided logoed buttons of different colors on rod attached to arched base, NM, A $750.00

Coca-Cola, sign, tin, 1954, Pick Up 6 & For Home Refreshment flank 6 pack on white, white raised rolled rim, 16x50", NM, A **$325.00**

Coca-Cola, sign, tin, 1956, rectangular shape curved to fit barrel, Drink Coca-Cola, There's Nothing Like A Coke!, NM, A **$100.00**

Coca-Cola, sign, tin, 1958, Sign Of Good Taste fishtail logo & Ice Cold flank bottle, green raised rim, 18x55", NM, D3 .... $275.00

Coca-Cola, sign, tin, 1960, bottle & Ice Cold at right of fishtail logo, Sign Of Good Taste, 18x54", NM, A **$210.00**

Coca-Cola, sign, tin, 1960, vertical fishtail with Drink..., Sign Of Good Taste above bottle, green raised rim, 54x18", NM, A **$255.00**

Coca-Cola, sign, tin, 1960-63, Enjoy That Refreshing... fishtail logo left of Ice Cold bottle, green raised rim, 18x54", NM, M3 .... **$135.00**

Coca-Cola, sign, tin, 1960s, Enjoy Coca-Cola Ice Cold left of bottle, courtesy panel above, white raised rolled rim, 36"x60", NM, A **$120.00**

Coca-Cola, sign, tin, 1960s, Enjoy Coca-Cola lettered on red at left of bottle, white background, white raised rolled rim, NM, A **$200.00**

Coca-Cola, sign, tin, 1960s, fishtail left of Ice Cold bottle, Sign Of Good Taste below, green raised rim, 36x60", NM, A **$110.00**

Coca-Cola, sign, tin, 1960s, Ice Cold above paper cup, Prepared By The Bottler Of..., green raised rim, 28x20", NM, A **$245.00**

Coca-Cola, sign, tin, 1960s, features Sign Of Good Taste fishtail logo on white, green raised rim, 24"x60", EX+, A ... **$120.00**

Coca-Cola, sign, tin, 1960s, wire hanger, Whatever You Do on panel above western saddle in oval, Drink Coca-Cola below, EX, A $195.00

Coca-Cola, sign, tin, 1960s, wire hanger, Wherever You Go on panel above pine cone & skier on slope in oval, Drink... below, EX+, A $275.00

Coca-Cola, sign, tin, 1960s, wire hanger, Whatever You Do on panel above English saddle in oval, Drink Coca-Cola below, EX, A $180.00

Coca-Cola, sign, tin, 1964, Drink...disk logo at left of bottle & Things Go Better With Coke, raised rim, 12x32", NM, A **$170.00**

Coca-Cola, sign, tin, 1964, Things Go Better With Coke at left of bottle on white ground, green raised rim, 24x24", EX, A **$150.00**

Coca-Cola, sign, wood, bottle displayed in 'R' of Refreshing at left of Drink... on red rectangle, Kay Displays, 13x31", EX, A $300.00

Coca-Cola, sign, wood, 1930s, Ye Who Enter Here... on rustic board with bottle, Drink... emblem below, Kay Displays, 11x39", G, A **$450.00**

Coca-Cola, sign, wood, 1940s-50s, round logo & bottle right of Refreshing on beveled panel, scrolled bracket, Kay Displays, NM, A **$375.00**

Coca-Cola, sign, tin, 1964, large bottle at right of Things Go Better With Coke in diminishing words, 23x23", NM, A........**$120.00**

Coca-Cola, sign from cooler, tin, 1930s, die-cut porcelain in black & white, Drink Coca-Cola in script, G, A.**$260.00**

Coca-Cola, sign from drink machine, tin over cardboard, 1950s-60s, Treat Yourself..., left of bottle & silhouette, 12x25", EX+, A........**$130.00**

Coca-Cola, sign from drink rack, embossed plastic, metal trim, 1950s, white Drink Coca-Cola on red fishtail, EX+, A........**$73.00**

Coca-Cola, sign from drink rack, Serve above Coca-Cola, Sign Of Good Taste on image with concave sides & pointed corners, EX, A........**$70.00**

Coca-Cola, sign from drink rack, tin, 1950s, Sprite boy peeks around bottle, Have A Coke on sunburst, Take Some Home, 24x16", NM, D........**$180.00**

Coca-Cola, sign from drink rack, tin, 2-sided, Enjoy Coca-Cola at left of Things Go Better With Coke, 21x19", EX+, A........**$95.00**

Coca-Cola, sign from drink rack, yellow, red & white geometric design with Enjoy Coca-Cola, Be Really Refreshed, 11x22", EX+, M2........**$68.00**

Coca-Cola, sign from truck cab, tin, 1950s, red Drink Coca-Cola In Bottles on white, VG+, A........**$60.00**

Coca-Cola, sign from truck cab, tin, 1950s, yellow Drink & Ice Cold flank white Coca-Cola on red, EX+, A........$140.00

Coca-Cola, siphon bottle, cobalt blue glass with acid-etched lettering, spigot, Bradford Pa, EX+, M2..**$240.00**

Coca-Cola, spoon, applied silver bottle on end of handle, NMIB, A........**$35.00**

Coca-Cola, spoon, 1970s, Delicious & Refreshing, in plastic case, M, D........**$25.00**

Coca-Cola, store plaque, 1950s, shows the time proprietor will return, NM, A........**$220.00**

Coca-Cola, straw box, 1930s, cardboard, features bottle on 4 sides, Delicious & Refreshing, EX, A........**$210.00**

Coca-Cola, straw box, 1940s, cardboard, tilted bottle with straw on red, The Pause That Refreshes on green bottom band, 11", EX, M2........**$110.00**

Coca-Cola, straw box with 500 paper straws, 1960s, Things Go Better With Coke, each straw marked Coca-Cola, EX, D........**$50.00**

Coca-Cola, string holder, 1930s, tin, 2-sided, Take Home...In Cartons above & below 6 pack on yellow dot on red, 16x12", VG+/EX, M2........**$450.00**

Coca-Cola, string holder, 1930s, tin, 2-sided, Take Home...In Cartons/Drink...In Bottles on red dot on white, 16x12", G/VG, A........**$190.00**

Coca-Cola, syrup bottle, clear glass with white logo & metal cap, straight sides, 12½x3¼", EX, A........**$180.00**

Coca-Cola, syrup bottle, 1910, Drink Coca-Cola centered in wreath, EX, A........**$575.00**

Coca-Cola, syrup bottle, 1920, foil label, Drink Coca-Cola on gold, aluminum cap, VG+, A........**$350.00**

Coca-Cola, syrup bottle, 1920s, clear glass with Coca-Cola in red block letters on white enameled label, metal cap, NM, A........**$475.00**

Coca-Cola, syrup bottle, 1920s, clear glass with Drink Coca-Cola & border in red, metal cap, NM, A...**$425.00**

Coca-Cola, syrup bottle, 1920s, glass, white applied label with red Drink Coca-Cola & gold leafing, metal cap, EX+, A........**$1,200.00**

Coca-Cola, syrup can, 1930-40, round shape with red paper label & white lettering, 1-gal, EX+, A.......**$210.00**

Coca-Cola, syrup dispenser, hard plastic with chrome-plated metal, 3 spigots, 23", G, A........**$70.00**

Coca-Cola, syrup dispenser, porcelainized metal, Drink Coca-Cola Ice Cold on side, Have A Coke on rounded back, handled, EX, A........**$110.00**

Coca-Cola, syrup dispenser, 1896, ceramic urn, embossed Coca-Cola, gold-leaf highlights, ring handle on lid, 18x10" dia, EX, A........**$7,500.00**

Coca-Cola, syrup dispenser, 1896, ceramic urn, embossed Coca-Cola, gold highlights, ring handle on lid, 18x10" dia, VG, A........$5,200.00

Coca-Cola, syrup dispenser, 1978, ceramic urn, reproduction by MarvArt of 1896 dispenser, NM, A........**$450.00**

Coca-Cola, syrup jug, 1930s, glass with paper label, screw cap, original box, 1-gal, EX, A........**$200.00**

Coca-Cola, syrup keg, wood, barrel shape with label, no tap, soiled/tears, 16", G, A........**$30.00**

Coca-Cola, syrup keg, wood barrel shape with bung, paper label on end, 5-gal, EX, A........**$130.00**

Coca-Cola, syrup keg, 1910s, wood, barrel shape, 95% of original label & part of original wooden spigot, 10-gal, VG, A........**$170.00**

Coca-Cola, tab knob, enameled, 2-sided, Drink Coca-Cola Coke, Ask For It Either Way, NM, A........**$60.00**

Coca-Cola, tab knob, 1960s-70s, round with 2 flat sides, Coke lettered in red on white, EX, A........**$10.00**

Coca-Cola, tab knob, 1960s-70s, 1-sided crown-type, Coca-Cola lettered in red on white, EX, A **$50.00**

Coca-Cola, table knife, Coca-Cola embossed on handle, minor tarnishing, A **$20.00**

Coca-Cola, table knife, silver, handle engraved Coca-Cola, by the Strauss Company, Richmond Va, EX, A **$70.00**

Coca-Cola, tablet, Coke=Coca-Cola lettered above large bottle & lettering, NM, B1 ....**$8.00**

Coca-Cola, tablet, pictures flags of the United Nations, bottle & logo in lower left, NM, B1 ....**$6.00**

Coca-Cola, telephone, cube with contour logo, USA Olympic rings & numbers, EX+, M2 ....**$30.00**

Coca-Cola, telephone, 10-oz bottle shape, exact size, MIB, M2 ....**$40.00**

Coca-Cola, thermometer, aluminum, 1948, Coke & 5¢ above & below hand with bottle, disk Coke logo below, arched ends, 39", EX, A **$2,500.00**

Coca-Cola, thermometer, bulb at right & over springtime view of Potomac river with Washington Monument beyond, framed, 8x10", NM, A **$210.00**

Coca-Cola, thermometer, dial, glass lens, 1950s, green with gold bottle outline & white Drink Coca-Cola on red dot, 12" dia, NM, A..**$450.00**

Coca-Cola, thermometer, dial, glass lens, 1950s, white Drink Coca-Cola on red, small-numbered border, 12" dia, NM, A..**$110.00**

Coca-Cola, thermometer, dial, glass lens, 1964, red Things Go Better With Coke, large-numbered border, glass missing, 18", VG, A **$65.00**

Coca-Cola, thermometer, masonite, 1944, button logo above bottle & tilted thermometer, rounded top & bottom, VG+, A **$310.00**

Coca-Cola, thermometer, metal, bulb above red Coca-Cola on white, attached brackets fit on building or wall, 7", MIB, A **$25.00**

Coca-Cola, thermometer, mirror, 1939, small thermometer at left, silhouette girl logo across bottom, gold frame, 14x10", EX, A.............................$450.00

Coca-Cola, thermometer, plastic, 1950s-60s, narrow body, button top, service-type to be printed with merchant's message, 7", MIB, A **$90.00**

Coca-Cola, thermometer, plastic, 1970s, black desktop-type lettered Piqua Coca-Cola Bottling Co, Piqua Ohio, 5x5", NMIB, A **$10.00**

Coca-Cola, thermometer, plastic, 1970s, Thirst Knows No Season, 12x4½", EX, D **$50.00**

Coca-Cola, thermometer, plastic, 1980, angled thermometer atop block base with Drink Coca-Cola/Coke contour logo, NM in package, A **$35.00**

Coca-Cola, thermometer, tin, bottle shape, ca 1930, 16½x5", VG, A **$150.00**

Coca-Cola, thermometer, tin, bottle shape, 1931, 1923 Christmas bottle, 17", EX+, A..............................**$210.00**

Coca-Cola, thermometer, tin, bottle shape, 1940s, 16", M, A **$65.00**

Coca-Cola, thermometer, tin, bottle shape, 1950s, 17", NM, D3 ....**$150.00**

Coca-Cola, thermometer, tin, bottle shape, 1950s, 17", VG+, A **$65.00**

Coca-Cola, thermometer, tin, bottle shape, 1956, gold, 7½x2¼", NM, A..**$45.00**

Coca-Cola, thermometer, tin, bottle shape, 1958, 17", VG+, A **$50.00**

Coca-Cola, thermometer, tin, bottle shape, 1958, 30", EX+, A **$80.00**

Coca-Cola, thermometer, tin, 1938, gold 1923 bottle on red, gold raised rolled rim, 16x7", NM, A **$250.00**

Coca-Cola, thermometer, tin, 1939, Drink..., Thirst Knows No Season on red above silhouette girl on yellow, Canadian, 18x6", NM, A................$1,450.00

Coca-Cola, thermometer, tin, 1939, rounded top & bottom with red disk logo above, silhouette girl below, 16x6½", VG, A **$210.00**

Coca-Cola, thermometer, tin, 1941, 2 Coke bottles flank thermometer atop Drink Coca-Cola logo, minor wear, 16x7", EX, A...**$375.00**

Coca-Cola, thermometer, tin, 1941, 2 Coke bottles flank thermometer atop Drink Coca-Cola logo, 16x7", NM, A **$475.00**

oca-Cola, thermometer, tin, 1948, red disk logo above, Drink Coca-Cola In Bottles, rounded top & bottom, 9", NM, A **$130.00**

oca-Cola, thermometer, tin, 1950, green, Refresh Yourself in diagonal script above, Drink... disk below, round ends, 17x3", NM, A **$1,250.00**

oca-Cola, thermometer, tin, 1950s, white Drink...In Bottles on red above bulb on white, Refresh Yourself, rounded ends, 30", G, A **$50.00**

oca-Cola, thermometer, tin, 1950s, white Drink...Sign Of Good..., on red above bulb on white, Refresh..., round ends, 30", NM, M3 .... **$180.00**

oca-Cola, thermometer, tin, 1950s, white with red button above vertical lines flanking bulb, Quality Refreshment..., 9", VG+, A **$120.00**

:oca-Cola, thermometer, tin, 1950s, white with red button above vertical lines flanking bulb, Quality Refreshment, 9", NM, A **$375.00**

:oca-Cola, thermometer, wood, 1905, Drink Coca-Cola 5¢ on rounded top, square bottom, 21x5", VG, A .. **$550.00**

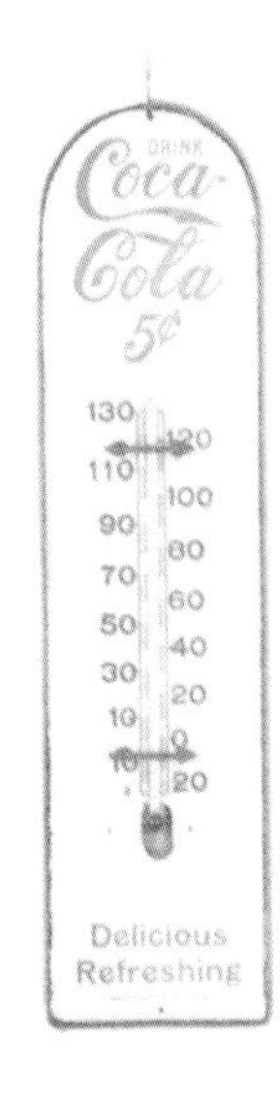

:oca-Cola, thermometer, wood, 1905, Drink Coca-Cola 5¢ on rounded top, Delicious Refreshing on squared bottom, 15x4", EX+, A $675.00

:oca-Cola, thermometer, wood, 1915, Drink Coca-Cola Delicious & Refreshing above bulb, arched top, squared bottom, 21x5", G+, A **$425.00**

:oca-Cola, thimble, 1920s, aluminum with red enamel inlay, EX, D **$30.00**

:oca-Cola, tip tray, features Lulu in Santa's suit with bag of toys, lettering on rim, Mexican, round, VG+, A ... **$50.00**

:oca-Cola, tip tray, 1901, Hilda Clark leaning over spray of roses, bean & leaf decorated rim, 6" dia, VG+, A . **$1,000.00**

:oca-Cola, tip tray, 1903, Hilda Clark lifting glass surrounded by decorative floral border, gold rim, 6" dia, VG+, A **$1,900.00**

Coca-Cola, tip tray, 1903, Hilda Clark lifting glass surrounded by decorative floral border, gold rim, 6" dia, NM, A **$3,300.00**

Coca-Cola, tip tray, 1906, Juanita tipping glass of Coke to mouth, Delicious & Refreshing on rim, some wear, 4" dia, G, A **$275.00**

Coca-Cola, tip tray, 1909, girl at table enjoying glass of Coke, St Louis Fair in the distance, oval, 6x4", EX+, A $2,300.00

Coca-Cola, tip tray, 1909, girl at table enjoying glass of Coke, St Louis Fair in the distance, oval, 6x4", VG, A **$900.00**

Coca-Cola, tip tray, 1910, Coca-Cola Girl in wide-brimmed hat & high collar, gold decoration on red rim, oval, 6x4", VG+, A **$300.00**

Coca-Cola, tip tray, 1913, smiling girl in wide-brimmed hat lifting Coke glass, Delicious & Refreshing, oval, 6x4", NM, A **$260.00**

Coca-Cola, tip tray, 1913, smiling girl in wide-brimmed hat lifting Coke glass, Delicious & Refreshing, oval, 6x4", VG+, A **$100.00**

Coca-Cola, tip tray, 1914, Betty in a bonnet, oval, 6x4", EX, A $260.00

Coca-Cola, tip tray, 1914, Betty in a bonnet, oval, 6x4", G, A **$120.00**

Coca-Cola, tip tray, 1916, Elaine leaning on arm looking over her shoulder holding bottle, edge chips, oval, 6x4", VG, A **$80.00**

Coca-Cola, tip tray, 1916, Elaine leaning on arm looking over her shoulder holding glass, oval, 6x4", EX+, A **$140.00**

Coca-Cola, tip tray, 1920, garden girl in yellow dress & floppy wide-brimmed hat holding glass, oval, 6x4", NM, A..**$400.00**

Coca-Cola, tire holder, 1950s-60s, round sign above wire rack, Enjoy...on red above While We Check Your Tires on white, NM, A..**$400.00**

Coca-Cola, token, Betty Says Atlanta Ga, oval top, A...**$130.00**

Coca-Cola, toy, 1920s-30s, Robin Hood Bo-Arro, complete with original card, NM, A..................................**$190.00**

Coca-Cola, toy, 1930s, red bottle-shaped machine-gun bubble blower, with original soap & instructions, some paint flecks, NM, A..**$250.00**

Coca-Cola, toy car, 1970s, tin, #22 on car, friction, NM, A **$140.00**

Coca-Cola, toy dishes, 1950s, My Dolly Loves A Party set, with original box, box EX+/dishes NM, A............**$80.00**

Coca-Cola, toy dispenser, 1950s, red plastic with slightly domed top, white Drink... logo, red ball-knob lever, 14", EX+, M2..**$60.00**

Coca-Cola, toy dispenser, 1960s, plastic, white flat top, Drink... on red side panels, images of 2 glasses above spigot, EX, M2 ....**$40.00**

Coca-Cola, toy race car, 1970s, tin, MIB, A **$85.00**

Coca-Cola, toy shopping cart, 1950s, masonite cart showing various products & a prominent Coca-Cola carton, rust on wheels, EX+, A $500.00

Coca-Cola, toy top, 1930s, wood, bright gold & red Drink Coca-Cola logo, rare, NM, A...............................**$803.00**

Coca-Cola, toy train, 1950s-60s, tin, windup, side of base features graphics of busy street scene, made in W Germany, EX+, A **$450.00**

Coca-Cola, toy train, 1980s, Thunderbolt Express, by Mehano, EX, D **$85.00**

Coca-Cola, toy truck, late model, white on red, enclosed cargo bed, contour logo with tilted bottle, battery operated, EX+, A...**$25.00**

Coca-Cola, toy truck, late model, yellow metal & plastic, square cab, open stair-step cargo bed, center red ad panel, 4", NM, M2..**$72.00**

Coca-Cola, toy truck, late model Buddy L enclosed cargo bed, contour logo on all sides, dolly attached to side, EX+, A **$30.00**

Coca-Cola, toy truck, Lincoln Toys, red with white Drir Coca-Cola on door, open bed holds 15 stamped block 16" long, EX, A **$355.0**

Coca-Cola, toy truck, 1930s, Metalcraft, flat roof, rubb wheels, 10 original bottles, Every Bottle Sterilize worn, G-, A...**$190.0**

Coca-Cola, toy truck, 1930s, Metalcraft A-frame with 1 bottles, metal wheels, very old repaint/craze decals, EX, M2 ....$550.0

Coca-Cola, toy truck, 1930s, Metalcraft A-frame with 1 bottles, rubber wheels, headlights, VG+, A........**$550.0**

Coca-Cola, toy truck, 1940s, red body with yellow carg area, Sprite boy logo on side panel, wheels have minc rusting, VG, A..**$250.0**

Coca-Cola, toy truck, 1949, yellow plastic, red panel wit yellow letters atop enclosed cargo bed, logoed sid panels, 11", VG, M2 ....**$110.0**

Coca-Cola, toy truck, 1950s, Marx, yellow with open bed Sprite boy on side ad panel, rubber wheels, #22, EX+ A...**$475.0**

Coca-Cola, toy truck, 1950s, metal, yellow with double decker cargo bed, center ad panel, EX+, A ..$220.00

Coca-Cola, toy truck, 1950s, red & white, enclosed cargc bed, box reads Route Truck for Coca-Cola, battery operated, EX+/VG+, M2 ....**$425.00**

Coca-Cola, toy truck, 1950s, Rosco, yellow cab with decaled cargo bed showing 4 tiers of cases, friction, 8" EX, M2...**$90.00**

Coca-Cola, toy truck, 1950s, tin litho, shows driver & several cartons of Coke, disk logo, rare, 8½" long, EX, A **$350.00**

Coca-Cola, toy truck, 1950s, white & yellow with red, battery operated, box lid only, EX+/G, M2 **$375.00**

Coca-Cola, toy truck, 1950s, yellow metal with red trim, decaled cargo bed showing 4 tiers of cases, EX, M2 **$85.00**

Coca-Cola, toy truck, 1954, Marx, yellow metal with red trim, double-decker open cargo bed, wheel-well covers, unused, 12", EX+, M2 **$270.00**

Coca-Cola, toy truck, 1956, yellow, double-decker cargo bed, Delicious....Refreshing red center panel, friction, Japan, 8", EX+, M2 **$250.00**

Coca-Cola, toy truck, 1960s, metal, Buddy L, yellow, double-decker bed with ad panel, Drink..., The Pause That Refreshes, VG, A **$45.00**

Coca-Cola, toy truck, 1960s, metal, Buddy L, yellow, double-decker bed with ad panel, Drink..., The Pause That Refreshes, EX+, M2 **$150.00**

Coca-Cola, toy truck, 1970s, tin & plastic, 2 bottle images & button logo on side panels, friction, Japan, EX+, A **$50.00**

Coca-Cola, toy van, 1950s, metal, Drink...Delicious Refreshing on sides, disk logo & bottle on top, friction, 4" long, NM, A **$140.00**

Coca-Cola, toy van, 1960, yellow metal with red trim, disk logo & bottle image on top, friction, 1 from set of 12, 4", EX+, M2 **$90.00**

Coca-Cola, toy van, 1970s-80s, plastic, Flip-O-Matic, bottle lever on rear, contour logo on sides, friction, NM, A **$45.00**

Coca-Cola, toy van, 1978, Corgi #437, Lieferwagen Camionnette, 4¾" long, van M/box VG, D $60.00

Coca-Cola, toy wagon, 1960, bottle-case body with wheels & handle, NM, A **$125.00**

Coca-Cola, transformer, 1980, can-shaped robot, MIB, D **$45.00**

Coca-Cola, travel clock, 1950s, brass, Be Really Refreshed, 3x3", EX, D **$225.00**

Coca-Cola, tray, TV, 1956, shows party spread with fondue pot & bottle of Coke, EX, D **$20.00**

Coca-Cola, tray, TV, 1958, pictures food cart, NM, A **$45.00**

Coca-Cola, tray, TV, 1961, shows harvest table with bucket of Cokes on ice & fiddle, EX, D **$10.00**

Coca-Cola, tray, 1900, Hilda Clark at table with Coke glass & letter, dark background, lettering above & below, 9¼", dia, G, A **$375.00**

Coca-Cola, tray, 1901, Hilda Clark leaning over spray of roses, bean & leaf decorated rim, minor paint loss, 9¼" dia, VG+, A **$1,400.00**

Coca-Cola, tray, 1903, Hilda Clark holding glass flanked by Delicious & Refreshing, floral & gold rim, 9¾" dia, VG, A **$1,100.00**

Coca-Cola, tray, 1905, Lillian Nordica with glass, oval, 13x10½", VG+, A **$1,350.00**

Coca-Cola, tray, 1906, Juanita with bouquet of violets & wearing large locket lifts glass to her mouth, oval, 13x10½", VG, A **$425.00**

Coca-Cola, tray, 1906, Juanita with bouquet of violets & wearing large locket lifts glass to her mouth, oval, 13x10½", EX+, A **$950.00**

Coca-Cola, tray, 1907, smiling girl with bare shoulders lifts glass, Relieves Fatigue 5¢, oval, 13x10½", NM+, A $3,900.00

Coca-Cola, tray, 1907, smiling girl with bare shoulders lifts glass, Relieves Fatigue 5¢, shows wear, oval, 13x10½", G-, A **$450.00**

Coca-Cola, tray, 1908, lettering around topless girl holding bottle in draped lap, decorative & logoed rim, 12½", G, A **$500.00**

Coca-Cola, tray, 1908, lettering around topless girl holding bottle on draped lap, decorative & logoed rim, 12½" dia, EX+, A **$4,300.00**

Coca-Cola, tray, 1909, girl at table enjoying a glass of Coke, St Louis Fair in the distance, oval, 16½x13½", VG, A **$885.00**

Coca-Cola, tray, 1909, lady at table enjoying a glass of Coke, St Louis Fair in the distance, oval, 16½x13½", EX+, A **$2,300.00**

Coca-Cola, tray, 1909, lady at table enjoying a glass of Coke, St Louis Fair in the distance, oval, 13¼x10½", G, A **$450.00**

Coca-Cola, tray, 1910, The Coca-Cola Girl in wide-brimmed hat & high collar, signed Hamilton King, 13¼x10½", NM, A **$2,600.00**

Coca-Cola, tray, 1910, The Coca-Cola girl in wide-brimmed hat & high collar, signed Hamilton King, 13¼x10½", VG, A **$950.00**

Coca-Cola, tray, 1913, smiling girl in wide-brimmed hat tipping glass, signed Hamilton King, oval, 15¼x12½", NM+, A **$1,900.00**

Coca-Cola, tray, 1913, smiling girl in wide-brimmed hat tipping glass, signed Hamilton King, 13¼x10½", EX, A.........**$575.00**

Coca-Cola, tray, 1913, smiling girl in wide-brimmed hat tipping glass, signed Hamilton King, 13¼x 10½", G, A.........**$210.00**

Coca-Cola, tray, 1914, Betty in a bonnet, oval, 15¼x12½", EX+, D **$495.00**

Coca-Cola, tray, 1914, Betty in a bonnet, oval, 15¼x12½", VG+, A **$210.00**

Coca-Cola, tray, 1914, Betty in a bonnet, 13¼x10½", EX+, A..**$1,000.00**

Coca-Cola, tray, 1916, Elaine leaning on hand looking over her shoulder holding a glass, 19x8½", EX+, A ...**$330.00**

Coca-Cola, tray, 1916, Elaine leaning on hand looking over her shoulder holding a glass, 19x8½", G, A **$150.00**

Coca-Cola, tray, 1920, garden girl in yellow dress & floppy wide-brimmed hat holding a glass, 13¼x10½", EX, A **$350.00**

Coca-Cola, tray, 1920, garden girl in yellow dress & floppy wide-brimmed hat holding a glass, 13¼x10½", G, A...**$150.00**

Coca-Cola, tray, 1921, autumn girl wearing a tam & holding a glass of Coca-Cola before a leafy background, 13¼x10½", G+, A..**$160.00**

Coca-Cola, tray, 1922, summer girl in wide-brimmed hat looking over shoulder while holding glass, 13¼x10½", EX, A...$725.00

Coca-Cola, tray, 1922, summer girl in wide-brimmed hat looking over shoulder holding glass, 13¼x10½", G+, A..**$575.00**

Coca-Cola, tray, 1923, smiling flapper girl wrapped in stole tipping glass, nice shine, 13¼x10½", EX, A........**$210.00**

Coca-Cola, tray, 1923, smiling flapper girl wrapped in stole tipping glass, heavy wear, 13¼x10½", G, A **$75.00**

Coca-Cola, tray, 1924, close-up of smiling girl holding a glass of Coca-Cola, overall wear, 13¼x10½", G+, A **$170.00**

Coca-Cola, tray, 1924, close-up of smiling girl holding glass of Coca-Cola, plain brown rim, 13¼x10½", EX, A......**$450.00**

Coca-Cola, tray, 1925, party girl in white fox stole looking at glass of Coca-Cola, 13x10½", G+, A................**$100.00**

Coca-Cola, tray, 1925, party girl in white fox stole looking at glass of Coca-Cola, minor rubs, 13¼x10½", NM, A..**$300.00**

Coca-Cola, tray, 1926, golf couple in white, he pourir her a glass of Coca-Cola, minor fading, 13¼x10½ VG+, A **$260.0**

Coca-Cola, tray, 1927, couple getting curb servic 10½x13¼", EX, D..**$650.0**

Coca-Cola, tray, 1927, couple getting curb servic 10½x13¼", G, A **$110.0**

Coca-Cola, tray, 1928, girl with bobbed hair drinking fro straw in bottle against black background, 13¼x10½ NM, A **$900.0**

Coca-Cola, tray, 1928, girl with bobbed hair drinking fro straw in bottle against black background, 13¼x10½ VG, A **$450.0**

Coca-Cola, tray, 1928, smiling soda jerk with 3 glasses Coca-Cola, paint loss/scratches/rubs/rim chip 13¼x10½", G, A...**$120.0**

Coca-Cola, tray, 1928, smiling soda jerk with 3 glasse of Coca-Cola, 13¼x10 1/2, EX+, D................$400.0

Coca-Cola, tray, 1929, seated girl in yellow swimsuit draped in towel holds glass, minor rubs/chips 13¼x10½", VG+, A **$150.0**

Coca-Cola, tray, 1929, seated girl in yellow swimsuit & drape in towel holds bottle, scarce, 13¼x10½", EX, D........**$325.0**

Coca-Cola, tray, 1930, girl in white swimsuit & red ca draped in white, black & red towel holds bottle 13¼x10½", VG, A **$180.0**

Coca-Cola, tray, 1930, girl on phone saying Meet Me At Th Soda Fountain, minor wear, 13¼x10½", EX, A **$250.0**

Coca-Cola, tray, 1930, girl on phone saying Meet Me A The Soda Fountain, heavy paint loss/scratches 13¼x10½", G, A **$80.0**

Coca-Cola, tray, 1931, boy in straw hat resting under tre enjoys a Coke & sandwich while dog watches, wea 13¼x10½", VG+, A **$225.0**

Coca-Cola, tray, 1931, boy in straw hat resting under tre enjoys a Coke & sandwich while dog watches 13¼x10½", EX, D...**$595.0**

Coca-Cola, tray, 1932, girl in yellow swimsuit posing on benc while holding a bottle, 13¼x10½", VG+, A................**$325.0**

Coca-Cola, tray, 1933, Francis Dee in swimsuit seated o ledge with bottle, 13¼x10½", VG+, A.................**$375.0**

Coca-Cola, tray, 1933, Francis Dee in swimsuit seated on ledge with bottle, 13¼x10½", NM, A **$750.00**

Coca-Cola, tray, 1934, Maureen O'Sullivan & Johnny Weissmuller posing with bottles, has been reproduced, 10½x13¼", NM, A **$900.00**

Coca-Cola, tray, 1934, Maureen O'Sullivan & Johnny Weissmuller posing with bottles, 10½x13¼", EX, D **$585.00**

Coca-Cola, tray, 1935, Madge Evans in gown with glass posing next to chair & table with bottles, 13¼x10½", EX+, A **$300.00**

Coca-Cola, tray, 1936, hostess in white silky gown leaning back on chair with glass in hand, 13¼x10½", VG+, A **$285.00**

Coca-Cola, tray, 1936, hostess in white silky gown leaning back on chair with glass in hand, 13¼x10½", NM, A $700.00

Coca-Cola, tray, 1937, girl in yellow swimsuit & white cape running on beach with 2 bottles, 13¼x10½", NM, A **$250.00**

Coca-Cola, tray, 1937, girl in yellow swimsuit & white cape running on beach with 2 bottles, 13¼x10½", EX, A **$140.00**

Coca-Cola, tray, 1938, girl in yellow dress & hat posed before Venetian blinds with Coke bottle on knee, G, A **$70.00**

Coca-Cola, tray, 1938, girl in yellow dress & hat posed before Venetian blinds with bottle on knee, 13¼x10½", NM, B1 .... **$210.00**

Coca-Cola, tray, 1939, girl in white swimsuit posed on diving board with bottle, 13¼x10½", EX+, A **$130.00**

Coca-Cola, tray, 1939, girl in white swimsuit posed on diving board with bottle, 13¼x10½", G+, A **$80.00**

Coca-Cola, tray, 1940, fishing girl on dock enjoying a bottle of Coke, 13¼x10½", G, A **$80.00**

Coca-Cola, tray, 1940, fishing girl on dock enjoying a bottle of Coke, 13¼x10½", NM, A **$190.00**

Coca-Cola, tray, 1941, smiling ice skater seated on log in snowy scene holding a bottle, minor wear, 13¼x10½", VG, A **$110.00**

Coca-Cola, tray, 1941, smiling ice skater seated on log in snowy scene holding bottle, 13¼x10½", NM, A. **$285.00**

Coca-Cola, tray, 1942, girl with bottle leaning against open car talking to friend in car with bottle, 13¼x10½", NM, A **$340.00**

Coca-Cola, tray, 1942, girl with bottle leaning against open car talking to friend in car with bottle, 13¼x10½", VG+, A **$190.00**

Coca-Cola, tray, 1950-52, smiling face with wind-blown hair & gloved hand with bottle on solid ground, 13¼x10½", NM, A **$170.00**

Coca-Cola, tray, 1950-52, smiling face with wind-blown hair & gloved hand with bottle on screened ground, 13¼x10½", VG, A **$60.00**

Coca-Cola, tray, 1950s-60, smiling girl with menu & bottle rests chin on hand, 13¼x10½", NM, A **$50.00**

Coca-Cola, tray, 1953, deep-dish, Coca-Cola in script over bottle, Mexican, round, VG+, A **$75.00**

Coca-Cola, tray, 1957, pictures birdhouse, French, NM, D **$135.00**

Coca-Cola, tray, 1957, sandwiches & bottles on individual trays with floral centerpiece, 10½x13¼", EX+, M2 ... **$80.00**

Coca-Cola, tray, 1957, smiling girl in raincoat holding bottle & red & white striped umbrella, Canadian, 13¼x10½", NM, A $180.00

Coca-Cola, tray, 1958, shows food cart, edges have not been turned under, NM, A **$75.00**

Coca-Cola, tray, 1958, shows food cart, fishtail logo on rim, NM, A **$20.00**

Coca-Cola, tray, 1959, deep-dish, lady in wide-brimmed hat & gloves holding bottle, Mexican, VG, A **$100.00**

Coca-Cola, tray, 1959, South African reproduction of 1910 Coca-Cola girl, scarce, M, D **$50.00**

Coca-Cola, tray, 1959, South African reproduction of 1926 golfers, M, D **$35.00**

Coca-Cola, tray, 1959, white with red fishtail logo & Goes Good With Food in center, Drive In For Coke on rim, NM, A **$425.00**

Coca-Cola, tray, 1961, hand pouring Coke in glass among pansies, Be Really Refreshed & fishtail logo on rim, EX, A **$15.00**

Coca-Cola, tray, 1961, hand pouring Coke in glass among pansies, Coke Refreshes You Best & rectangle logo on rim, NM, A **$30.00**

Coca-Cola, tray, 1966, deep-dish, center features pretty lady holding full Coke bottle next to face, Mexican, round, NM, A **$45.00**

Coca-Cola, tray, 1968, deep-dish, center features bottles on ice, Mexican, EX+, A **$50.00**

Coca-Cola, tray, 1969, deep-dish, girl reclining with bottle, Mexican, round, NM, A......................................**$189.00**

Coca-Cola, tray, 1970, deep-dish, center features food scene with glass & bottle of Coke, Mexican, round, NM, A **$8.00**

Coca-Cola, tray, 1971, deep-dish, Coke bottle with modern comma-shaped designs, Spanish lettering above, Mexican, round, NM, A **$17.00**

Coca-Cola, tray, 1973, Santa at fireplace, EX, D.........**$15.00**

Coca-Cola, tray, 1980, Vancouver 60th anniversary, harbor scene, EX, D **$5.00**

Coca-Cola, tray, 1980s, Houston Coca-Cola Bottling Co, pictures the factory, EX, D....................................**$20.00**

Coca-Cola, tray, 1981, pictures Santa with children, EX, D.**$6.00**

Coca-Cola, tray, 1983, close-up of wet Coke bottle, M, D **$30.00**

Coca-Cola, tray, 1984 Olympics, oval, EX, D **$20.00**

Coca-Cola, tray, 1985, Hoover Dam 50th anniversary, EX, D..**$5.50**

Coca-Cola, tray, 1986, 100th anniversary, Italy, rectangular, EX, D...**$25.00**

Coca-Cola, tray, 1988, Calgary Winter Olympic Games, EX, D..**$20.00**

Coca-Cola, tray, 1988, shows B&O Railroad Station, Zanesville Ohio, 3rd in series, EX, D...................**$10.00**

Coca-Cola, tray, 1990, pictures Santa with bunny, rectangular, EX, D **$6.00**

Coca-Cola, truck grill plate, die-cut cast aluminum, Drink Coca-Cola in bottles, 17" long, NM, A **$300.00**

Coca-Cola, umbrella, 1930s, 6 triangle-shaped panels in orange with Drink Coca-Cola & white with black bottle images, rare, VG, A..**$550.00**

Coca-Cola, vending machine, arched top, red with cream Drink Coca-Cola lettered at top, workings on side, missing rack, 54", VG, A.....................................**$400.00**

Coca-Cola, vending machine, 1955-?, 10¢, model CS72, red with hand holding Coke bottle, 57x24¾", EX, A...$1,500.00

Coca-Cola, vending machine, 1955-?, 10¢, model 44, red with logo atop on white, original working condition, 58x16, EX, A..**$1,600.00**

Coca-Cola, vendor, ballpark, 1930s, slight kidney shape with flat ends, insulated, divided, Drink Coca-Cola on front, EX, A...**$425.00**

Coca-Cola, vendor, ballpark, 1950s, metal, square with open & stationary handle, embossed logo on 2 sides, holds 20 bottles, VG, A.......................................**$130.00**

Coca-Cola, vendor, ballpark, 1950s-60s, masonite, red case with rounded corners, white Drink..., 3 sections, with strap, VG+, A..**$175.00**

Coca-Cola, vendor/cooler, airline, 1940s-50s, handled double-hinged lid, opener on end, stainless steel liner, 12x17x7", G, A..**$130.00**

Coca-Cola, vendor/cooler, airline, 1940s-50s, handled double-hinged lid, opener on end, stainless steel liner, 12x17x7", NM, A...**$600.00**

Coca-Cola, vest, corduroy, round Drink logo outlined in white, 6-button, VG, A..**$15.00**

Coca-Cola, Vienna Art Plate, seated nude with flowing hair holding glass in draped lap, decorative rim, unframed, VG+, A **$500.00**

Coca-Cola, Vienna Art Plate, 1905, girl holding rose, decorative filigree design around rim, without frame, EX+, A ...**$450.00**

Coca-Cola, Vienna Art Plate, 1908, tin, draped topless nude seated facing right, gold filigree & roses on black rim, 10" dia, G+, A **$400.00**

Coca-Cola, Vienna Art Plate, 1908-12, long-haired girl with scarf on head tied in back facing forward, unframed, NM, A $300.00

Coca-Cola, Vienna Art Plate, 1908-12, long-haired girl with scarf on head tied in back facing forward, unframed, VG+, A **$110.00**

Coca-Cola, Vienna Art Plate, 1908-12, long-haired topless girl in left profile, decorative rim, unframed, VG+, A ..**$130.00**

Coca-Cola, wall sconce, 1930s, fiberboard, gold with red & white football-shaped Coca-Cola emblem on front, 22" wide, NM, A **$1,000.00**

Coca-Cola, wallet, 1907, gold imprinted straight-sided bottle at left of When Thirsty Try A Bottle, overall wear, G-, A **$10.00**

Coca-Cola, wallet, 1907, leather, gold transfer of bottle at left of When Thirsty Try A Bottle on inside part, VG+, A......**$40.00**

Coca-Cola, wallet, 1912-15, leather, stamped Whenever You See An Arrow Think of Coca-Cola, oxidation to metal parts, worn, G-, A **$20.00**

Coca-Cola, watch fob, 1907, embossed sterling silver, Relieves Fatigue, NM, A **$330.00**

Coca-Cola, watch fob, 1907, silver wash, Relieves Fatigue, VG+, A **$110.00**

Coca-Cola, watch fob, 1911, metal with cel showing motor girl, Drink...In Bottles 5¢ on reverse, vertical rectangle, NM, A **$825.00**

Coca-Cola, watch fob, 1920s, embossed brass, Coke bottle flanked by 5¢, logo above, rare, 1¾", appears EX, A..**$95.00**

Coca-Cola, whistle, 1920s, wood, NM, A...................**$40.00**

Coca-Cola, whistle, 1950s, plastic, Merry Christmas, Coca-Cola Bottling Memphis Tenn, EX, D....................**$15.00**

Coca-Cola, window shade, reads Drink Coca-Cola, The Pause That Refreshes, In Bottles, rare, needs repair, 4 ft x 7 ft, VG, A **$3,100.00**

Coca-Cola, yo-yo, 1920s-30s, solid maroon color, by Bolo, NM, A **$60.00**

Coca-Cola, yo-yo, 1920s-30s, with multicolor inlay, NM, A **$40.00**

Coca-Cola, yo-yo, 1960s, bottle-cap shape, EX, D.....**$15.00**

Coca-Cola Chewing Gum, gum box, 1916, cardboard, holds 20 packages of Coca-Cola Chewing Gum 5¢, worn/dry, G-, A **$750.00**

Coca-Cola Chewing Gum, gum jar, 1903-05, glass, ...Chewing Gum embossed on front, ...Pepsin Gum embossed on finial, beveled corners, G+, A **$450.00**

Coca-Cola Chewing Gum, gum jar, 1903-05, glass, beaded finial, beveled corners, without paper label, NM, A .**$875.00**

Coca-Cola Chewing Gum, gum jar, 1905-11, glass, ...Pepsin Gum... embossed on front, Franklin Caro Co embossed on finial, beveled corners, NM, A **$424.00**

Coca-Cola Peppermint Pepsin Gum, sign, porcelain, 1912-16, package of Coca-Cola Peppermint Pepsin Gum, red & white, green border, rare, 4x10", EX, A........$7,500.00

Cockshutt Plow, sign, cardboard, panoramic factory scene with scrolled lettered inset lower right, original frame, 12x23", NM, M2 ....**$160.00**

Cocomalt, jigsaw puzzle, 1932, 'Faith,' full-color boy & dog, complete in original envelope, 6½x10", EX, P2 ....**$60.00**

Cognac Jacquet, sign, linen mounted stone litho by Bouchet, peacock & bottle on garden wall, Vercasson Paris 1896, 62x47", EX, A..................................**$425.00**

Coiner Cigars, box label, outer, pictures an eagle perched atop the earth, 4½x4½", M, D **$8.00**

Cokins Red Wing Beer, label, 1933-36, Red Wing Brewing Co, U-type permit number, 12-oz, EX, A.............**$23.00**

Col JJ Astor 5¢ Cigar, cigar cutter, cast metal, white lettering on round top sitting on fancy 4-footed base, 13½", EX, A **$130.00**

Colburn's Mustard, recipe book, ca 1930, 32 pages, G, D **$3.00**

Coleman Furnace, salesman's sample, miniature furnace, 10x8x5", EX, A **$150.00**

Coleman's Beverages, bottle topper, cardboard, head portrait of smiling girl, Ask For Coleman's Beverages, NM, B1 ....**$5.00**

Coleman's Ginger Ale, sign, embossed tin, red Noted For It's Flavor above Coleman's in green script, red Ginger Ale below, 10x28", EX, M3 ....**$55.00**

Coleman's Pale Dry Ginger Ale, bottle topper, die-cut cardboard, waiter with oversized tray & glass jumping over sign, multicolored, 9", NM, B1 ....**$10.00**

Coleman's Pale Dry Ginger Ale, bottle topper, Good With Coleman's... above open-face ham sandwich, 8½x6", NM, A...**$6.00**

Coles Peruvian Bark & Wild Cherry Bitters, sign, porcelain, white lettering on blue, No More Malaria...Best Nerve & Blood Tonic, edge chips, 6x16¼", VG, A..................**$450.00**

Colgan's Gum, tin, pre-1900, McAfee & Colgan, EX, G2.**$495.00**

Colgate & Co's Harness & Stable Soaps, sign, paper, horse-drawn carriage with figures in circular inset, 21x16½", EX, A...**$450.00**

Colgate Dental Cream, display, 1950, die-cut cardboard image of Howdy Doody waving & holding product box with white ad card, 7x4", VG+, A **$50.00**

Colgate's Action Soap, sign, cardboard, product name lettered above fast moving battle ship, Does It's Bit Well on inset below, 16x23", G, A................................**$30.00**

Colgate's Baby Talc, tin, green with Colgate's Baby Talc arched above baby's portrait in oval, gold shaker top, EX, M2 ....**$165.00**

Colgate's Borated Baby Powder, tin, white flat oval shape with illustrated baby leaning on pillow, lettering above, shaker top, VG+, M2...**$95.00**

Colgate's Cashmere Bouquet, sample tin, 3¼", EX, D...**$20.00**

Colgate's Cold Cream, sign, In Summer arched above woman in canoe, ...After Exposure To The Sun The Year Round below, framed, 30x23", VG+, A........**$70.00**

Colgate Tooth Powder, tin, with contents, red & cream, plastic lid, 4x2½", NM, D **$10.00**

College Club Beverages, bottle topper, die-cut cardboard, boy with glass & hot dog above hat & diploma at left of product name, 10x6½", NM, A **$4.00**

College Heights, crate label, 1930s, California orange, orange blossoms with packing house & railroad beyond, Claremont, 10x11", M, C1 ....**$3.00**

Collins Axes, sign, 1910s, embossed cardboard, pictures an ax on 2 world globes, 20x10", EX, D..............**$60.00**

Collins Baking Co, calendar, 1911, child in chair with dog & puppy, embossed floral design on edges, full pad, EX, A **$130.00**

Collins Celebrated Bread, calendar, 1909, diagonal version with product name above girl in bonnet with holly leaves, full pad, 8x8", EX+, A **$25.00**

Colman's DSF Mustard, sign, paper, small children peering into large can of Colman's Mustard, framed, image: 22x16½", G, A **$105.00**

Colman's Mustard, sign, paper, product name above & below bull's head in circular inset, overall soiling/minor tears, 22x16", VG, A **$150.00**

Colonial Bread, door push bar, embossed metal, Is Good lettered between Colonial & Bread in white, 31½" long, EX, A **$110.00**

Colonial Club 5¢ Cigars, sign, tin flange, 2-sided, yellow & red lettering on blue, overall wear, 9x23¾", G+, A .**$35.00**

Colonial Coffee, tin, pictures colonial infantryman above lettering, screw lid, 1-lb, EX, A............................**$80.00**

Colonial Dame Coffee, sign, embossed tin, product name lettered above Distinctively Different, lined edge, 10x28", EX, A **$30.00**

Colonial Furniture Co, catalog, 1918, classy collection of upholstering frames for fancy chairs & couches, 40 pages, EX, D **$10.00**

Colonial Lubrication, sign, porcelain, 2-sided, tan lettering on green ribbon, colonial soldiers in blue at lower corners, 30x30", EX, D **$400.00**

Colt, ad, ca 1920, paper, Revolvers Y Pistola Automaticas lettered above Texas lawman on horseback, 33x20", G, A...**$1,760.00**

Colt Automatic .45, pin, pistol shape, VG, A...........**$35.00**

Colt Firearms Co, postcard, 1953, printed photo of the Colt Museum, VG, A **$16.00**

Columbia Beer, sign, Vitrolite, product name above & below Lady Liberty holding patriotic shield, 23x18", VG, A...$6,500.00

Columbia Beer, tray, stock image of Bavarian gentleman holding flagon of beer, decorative rim, oval, 16¾x13½", G-, A **$220.00**

Columbia Belle, crate label, Washington apple, symbolic lady in stars & stripes holding sword, 9x11", EX, G1.........**$5.00**

Columbia Bicycles, ad, 1890s, pictures girl carrying the 'Light' bicycle across a creek, ...$100, Pope Manufacturing Co, 10x7½", VG, A.......................................**$20.00**

Columbia Bicycles, catalog, 1950, 34 pages, VG, D.**$35.00**

Columbia Bicycles, trade card, night cycling scene, lights shine gold, prices on reverse, EX, A...................**$42.00**

Columbia Flour, pocket mirror, pictures lady among flowers bordered by Columbia Flour, A Perfect Product, 2⅛" dia, EX, A..**$190.00**

Columbia Graphophone, pin-back button, pictures a graphophone with Columbia in graduated letters, black & white, round, EX, A..**$41.00**

Columbia Ignitor Dry Cells, sign & 1912 calendar, devil in waterfalls with dry cells trying to speed up auto, boat & plane, framed, 43x32", EX, D3 ....$5,500.00

Columbia Mill Co, match holder, die-cut tin, blue rectangular holder with flour sack graphics attached to patriotic lady, 5½x2", EX, A **$850.00**

Columbia Motor Oil, can, 1960s, Columbia superimposed over eagle atop lettered shield, pour spout & handle, 2-gal, EX+, A...**$44.00**

Columbia Records, catalog, 1920, June, 28 pages, VG, D.**$7.50**

Columbia Records, catalog, 1946, 499 pages, VG+, H2...**$40.00**

Columbian Brewing Co, pocket mirror, celluloid, factory image, ...The Beer That Makes Milwaukee Jealous, rectangular, 2¾x1¾", VG, A....................................**$150.00**

Columbian Extra Pale Bottled Beer, sign, embossed tin hanger, labeled bottle flanked by logo, Tennesee Brewing Co below, HD Beach litho, 14x10", VG, A.....**$85.00**

Columbian Pure Manila Rope, sign, 1940s-50s, plastic, pictures different sizes of ropes, product name above, black on white, 17x11½", EX, A **$35.00**

Columbian Rope, sign, early 1900s, man in raincoat holding rope on black ground, Buy Red, White, Blue... upper corner, VG, A **$950.00**

Columbus Buggy Co, sign, paper, Australian scene with 4 ostriches pulling couple in buggy with help of 2 aborigines, framed, 31x44", NM, D3 ....**$5,800.00**

Columbus Buggy Co, sign, paper, Christopher Columbus presenting trophies to the King & Queen of Spain, framed, image: 25x38", G, A...............................**$400.00**

Columbus Dispatch Newspaper, thermometer, porcelain, ...Ohio's Greatest Home Daily... above & below, orange & black, rare, 27x7", EX+, A...............................**$200.00**

Comfort Powder, tin, canister-type featuring happy child & nursemaid, 4x2 1 /2" dia, EX, A **$110.00**

Comfytalc Baby Powder, tin, white with blue lettering & crawling baby, shaker top, tall round shape, EX+, M2 ....**$135.00**

Common Sense Engine Co, sign, paper, vignettes of various farm equipment & factory, ...Champion Corn Planters..., framed, image: 37x25", EX, A....**$500.00**

Common Sense Exterminator, sign, well-dressed rat reading paper lower right of Kills Rats & Roaches, Common Sense Exterminator above, 8x7", VG, A **$150.00**

Commoner Cigars, box label, outer, Commoner arched over portrait of Oliver Cromwell, 4x4", EX, D **$10.00**

Commonwealth Title Insurance & Trust Co, thermometer, paper face, degrees arched above company name & logo, pitting, 9¼" dia, G+, A....**$15.00**

Compania General Cigars, box label, outer, tobacco leaf emblem & snakes, 4½x4½", M, C3 ....**$3.00**

Conboy's Buggy or Carriage Tops, pocket mirror, pictures backside of amorous couple in buggy surrounded by lettering, 2⅛" dia, EX, A **$600.00**

Concord Axles, postcard, logo flanked by product name above 2 wagon axles, text below, black & white, VG+, P3 ....**$75.00**

Concord Cigars, sign, cardboard, Concord on large cluster of purple grapes, 5¢ Cigars above, FR Knowlton... below, 28x20", VG, A....**$125.00**

Conestoga Western Vegetables, crate label, 1940s, covered wagon in the prairie, Watsonville Cal, 9x6", M, C3....**$3.00**

Congress Beer, match holder, tin, features open case of beer with capitol building logo on back plate, some wear, 5½x5", VG, A....**$165.00**

Congress Beer, pocket mirror, product name arched above large bottle, Haberle Brewing Co lettered below, blemishes, oval, 2¾", G+, A....**$30.00**

Congress Beer, see also Haberle Brewing Co

Congress Playing Cards, sign, paper, elegant woman, horse race scene & harem dancer on 1903 cards, ...Quality, framed, image: 18x12", NM, A **$700.00**

Congress Playing Cards, sign, paper, 3 pictorial images of elegant women on backs of 1903 cards, ...None Better, framed, image: 18x12", EX+, A....**$600.00**

Conkeys First Aid Products, sign, die-cut tin flange, 2-sided, homely large-beaked bird standing on 1 leg right of product name, 20x14", EX, A....**$160.00**

Conkeys Y-O Feeds, sign, die-cut tin in shape of bag of feed, navy & red lettering on yellow, Poultry, Mashes..., 29½x17½", G, A....**$50.00**

Conn Band & Orchestra Instruments, catalog, 1940, 56 pages, VG+, H2 ....**$50.00**

Connecticut General Fire Insurance Co, calendar, 1906, general on horseback carrying document, full pad, stains & creases, matted & framed, 19½x13½", A....**$70.00**

Connecticut State-Leased Waters, sign, 1930s, die-cut porcelain, yellow lettering on green field, Fishing Permitted..., edge flaking, 12x9½", VG, A....**$130.00**

Conoco, pocket lighter, embossed gold & silver with cowboy holding Conoco branding iron, Hottest Brand Going..., 1¾x2", EX, A **$20.00**

Conoco, presentation book, ca 1936, 12 posters demonstrating good work habits & products, scarce, 60x48", EX, A....**$500.00**

Conoco, pump sign, porcelain, green triangle shape, 9½x8½", EX, D **$100.00**

Conoco Gasoline, sign, porcelain, colonial soldier with rifle, product name arched above & below, minor chips/fading, 25" dia, G+, A **$850.00**

Conoco Outboard Motor Oil, can, 1930-40, green & red lettering above triangular logo on white, pour chart on front, screw lid, 1-qt, 7½", EX, A....**$35.00**

Conrad & Jones Co, catalog, 1912, features flowers, 98 pages, VG, D **$12.00**

Conrad Meyer & Sons Piano Manufacturers, trade card, pictures Oriental lady with parasol, brown lettering on gray, EX, A....**$26.00**

Consolidated Ice Co, hand mirror, back shows polar bear, hunter, ships & iceburgs, gold ornamental handle, VG+, A **$80.00**

Consumers Ale, label, 1933-36, U-type permit number, 12-oz, EX, A....**$20.00**

Consumers Brewing Co, calendar, 1895, elegant woman in blue dress & hat, full pad, water staining/soiling, framed, image: 19x14½", G, A....**$400.00**

Consumers Brewing Co, display mug, glass with reverse-painted image of man holding American flag & glass of beer, 10x6" dia, G, A....$4,500.00

Continental Baking Co, lapel pin, 1930s, For Safe Driving One Year, blue & white enameled brass, EX, D....**$8.00**

Continental Brewing Co, sign, paper, soldier & colonists drinking steins of beer, lettering above, framed, image: 19½x15", VG, A **$200.00**

Continental Brewing Co Burton Ale, label, pre-1920, product & company name arched above logo, 11-oz, EX, A **$5.00**

Continental Brewing Co Extra Brown Stout, label, pre-1920, Continental arched above product name, 11-oz, EX, A **$5.00**

Continental Brewing Co Gardiner's Special Beer, label, pre-1900, product name in script above company name, 13-oz, EX, A....**$5.00**

Continental Cubes, pocket tin, 'kidney' shape featuring soldier in landscape, 3½x2½", VG, A....**$200.00**

Continental Cubes Pipe Tobacco, pocket mirror, Latest & Best Process arched above lady in red seated on tobacco tin, 2¾x1¾", EX, A **$270.00**

Continental Insurance Co, sign, self-framed tin, trademark image of Continental soldier, Cash Capital Ten Million Dollars, 30x20", VG, A **$500.00**

Continental Insurance Co, trade card, 2-sided, beach scene on front, fire insurance advertising on reverse, VG, A **$16.00**

Continental Motor Oil, can, 1935-45, product name above soldier & stars, red, white & blue, pour spout & handle, 2-gal, 10½", EX, A **$100.00**

Continental Rubber Heels, postcard, pictures dog smelling footprints, The Footprint Of A Gentleman, German, EX, D **$45.00**

Continental Tailoring Co, sign, company name upper left of pretty girl wearing crown & holding lilacs, fancy border, matted, vertical, EX, A **$110.00**

Continental Tires, figure, 1980s, PVC, features the Continental Tire man, 2", EX, D $35.00

Continental Tires, postcard, comical image of posed dogs around sausage vendor, German, EX, D **$40.00**

Continental Trailways, calendar, 1960, pictures old buses, complete, D **$20.00**

Converse Shoes, display, cardboard stand-up, man & woman with tennis rackets beside touring car, Big C-Outing Shoes..., 26x30", VG, A..........................**$300.00**

Cook's Goldblume Beer, sign, self-framed tin on cardboard, policeman holding skidish horse back from early auto on busy street, 13x21", G, A **$90.00**

Cook's Goldblume Beer, sign, tin, lady in red gown & wide-brim straw hat holding glass of beer, signed Irene Patten, framed, 26½x20", G, A **$200.00**

Cook's Goldblume Beer, sign, tin, riverboat with dock scene loading crates of beer, Quality Cargo In 1853, framed, image: 21½x27½", G-, A..........................**$115.00**

Cook's Goldblume Beer & Ale, sign, tin, tilted bottles flank product name, Now Try..., 8x19", NM, A....**$55.00**

Cook Seed Co, pocket mirror, large pansy pictured on center square with all-around advertising, horizontal oval, 2¾" long, NM, A **$22.00**

Cooke's Special, label, product name in script above Cooke Brewing Co, pre-1920, G, A **$40.00**

Cooks Water, pocket mirror, red, black & white, shows man before & after drinking product, Ring Bros SF Agents, 1⅞" dia, NM, A **$50.00**

Cooks Water, sign, embossed cardboard, alluring woman in red dress, She Drinks..., matted & framed, image: 23½x11½", NM, A..........................**$2,750.00**

Cooley's Globe Corset, trade card, unhappy woman opens to woman with great figure, Dressing For The Ball..., EX, A..........................**$13.00**

Coolidge Near Beer, bottle, white ceramic with red & blue lettering, Keep Cool & Keep Coolidge With Near Beer, 7", EX, A..........................**$65.00**

Coon Chicken Inn, ashtray, 4" dia, M, D **$35.00**

Coon Chicken Inn, glass, 4¼", G, D **$35.00**

Coon Chicken Inn, matchbook cover, front shows smiling Black porter with red lips wearing cap, 3 addresses on back, 20 strike, NM, R1 ....**$12.50**

Coon's Ice Cream, sign, 1918, cardboard, pictures sundaes, G, D..........................**$285.00**

Cooper Tires, sign, embossed tin, shield & tire graphic left of Bond Cooper Tires, Go As Far As You Like! below, 12x33", VG, A **$200.00**

Cooper Tires, sign, tin, white knight's helmet in profile above Cooper Tires on blue, cream & orange border, oval, 15x23", EX+, A **$100.00**

Cooper Underwear Co, pocket mirror, Buy White Cat Union Suits arched above smiling feline, company name below, oval, 2¾", VG+, A **$35.00**

Coors, ashtray, white porcelain with logo, 6" dia, EX, P4 ....**$4.00**

Coors, chaser glasses, clear with red logo, set of 6, 6-oz, D **$60.00**

Coors, door sign, 2-sided, Open, Closed, Thank You & Coors logo, VG+, P4 ....**$8.00**

Coors, mug, pottery with Coors logo, 2¼", D **$15.00**

Coors, playing cards, logo on back, M in G box, D..**$12.00**

Coors, sign, neon, Coors in script over mountain image on crosshatch backing, 2 colors, EX, A **$45.00**

Coors, stein, 1988 Holiday, pictures the brewery, 7", M, D **$18.00**

Coors, tray, red with white lettering, 13⅛" dia, EX, D **$25.00**

Coors Bock Beer, label, 1933-36, ram's head in center, A Coors Co, U-type permit number, 12-oz, EX, A...**$42.00**

Coors Golden Malted Milk, container, pottery with tin lid, rare, glaze loss around bottom edge, otherwise EX, A **$250.00**

Coors Pure Malted Milk, container, pottery, product name lettered in square, knob on slip lid, rare, EX, A **$170.00**

Coors Silver Bullet, tray, deep-dish, plastic, 12" dia, EX, P4..........................**$7.00**

Copenhagen Tobacco, dispenser, metal cylinder with bottom opening, red with Copenhagen arched above The Best Chew Ever Made, 9", NM, A..........................**$85.00**

Copenhagen Tobacco, thermometer, tin, black on white, Chew Copenhagen Summer, Winter, Spring & Fall, It's A Pleasure above, 12", VG, A **$10.00**

Copper Clad Ranges, pocket mirror, Copper Clad over World's Greatest Ranges in oval flanked by figures, oval, 2¾" long, EX, A **$15.00**

Corbett's Extra Old Stock Ale, radio, Bakelite bottle on round base, not original label, 24", EX, M2........**$300.00**

Corby's 'Special Selected' Canadian Whiskey, sign, paper, 'A Little Touch,' hobo eyeing bottle through open window while man reads paper, framed, 40x28", EX, M2 .... **$850.00**

Corby's Old Rye Whiskey, tip tray, scene with man & dog, EX, D **$70.00**

Cordove Cigar Co's Class Cigars, tin, product name above In Workmanship & Quality, slip lid, horizontal rectangle, VG+, A **$35.00**

Coreco Gasoline, drinking glass, Gasoline & Motor Oil in red on yellow above & below yellow Coreco on black, 4¾", EX, A **$25.00**

Coreco Gasoline, sign, porcelain, 2-sided, black shield logo on yellow with red Coreco arched above & red Gasoline below, 24" dia, G-, A **$275.00**

Coreco Motor Oil, can, 1920-30, logo & product name above 100% Pure logo & company name on yellow, screw lid & handle, 1-gal, 11", VG, A **$120.00**

Coreco Motor Oil, container, 1940s, glass jar with paper label, product name above & below logo, screw lid, 1-qt, EX, A **$20.00**

Cork Distilleries Co Ltd Pure Pot Still Whisky (sic), sign, self-framed tin, company & product name above bottle & box of corks, ribbed frame border, 13x17", EX, D3 .... $150.00

Cornelius & Baker Engraving, print, paper, depicts their 2 Philadelphia manufacturing buildings, matted & framed, 4¼x7¼", VG, A **$70.00**

Cornell University Cigar, box label, inner lid, bronze & black, 6x9", EX, C3 .... **$10.00**

Cornell Wood Board, tin, porcelain flange, black & white on red, white border, silhouetted workmen around product name, 8x18", EX, D3 .... **$325.00**

Corona Beer, glass, embossed barrel shape, 8-oz, D.. **$10.00**

Corona Extra, sign, die-cut tin, bottle form in yellow & white outlined in blue, cap is blue & yellow, 20x5¼", EX, A **$40.00**

Corticelli Silk, display, mechanical, cat caught in thread while batting spool of thread with paws, Makes A Rip Proof Seam, 21x16", EX, A **$3,000.00**

Corticelli Spool Silk, display cabinet, wood with curved glass front, gold leaf drawers, several slide drawers missing, 18½x21x16", EX, A **$600.00**

Corvette, sign, 1953, metal, ...Sales & Service, white Corvette on blue background, 12x18", EX, D....... **$6.50**

Cosmopolitan Hotel, trade card, black on gray stock with vignette of hotel & street scene, ...Rooms $1 Per Day & Upwards, EX, A **$38.00**

Cosmos Tobacco, tin, square corners, scarce, VG, D..... **$300.00**

Cott, sign, 1950s, tin, It's Cott To Be Good! above bottle in bowl of fruit, True Fruit & Terrific!, 23x17", NM, M3 .... **$80.00**

Cottolene Pie Shortening, trade card, die-cut folder, woman making pie & boy eating it, The Best Way To Shorten Pie..., advertising inside, EX, A **$34.00**

Cottolene Shortening, tip tray, Black woman & child picking cotton, Source Of Cottolene, Best For Shortening-Best For Frying, 4" dia, EX, A **$220.00**

Cottons Witch Hazel, bottle, clear glass with long neck & cork top, CL Cotton Co, Earlville NY, label missing, 7", EX+, P4 .... **$15.00**

Country Club Beer, clock, wood case, horse & rider on glass dial, Famous Since The Days Of The Pony Express below, 19" long, EX, A **$80.00**

Country Club Sweet Apple Cider, sign, cardboard, red lettering on white background, Drink...For Sale Here, 8½x11", EX, D **$15.00**

Court House Baking Powder, can label, 1923, pictures a court house, EX, C3 .... **$25.00**

Cow Brand Baking Soda, advertisment, features large copy of card inserted in boxes of product, shows cedar waxwing bird on branch, 15x11", EX, A **$80.00**

Cow Brand Soda, sign, paper, pictures a spaniel running through a pasture, box of product lower right, framed, image: 25x16½", EX, A **$320.00**

CPW Motor Car Enamel, display, cardboard, man painting car at garage, product name & Durable-Lustrous-Economical below, 22x18", EX+, A **$170.00**

CR Quarton Hardware Dealer, pocket mirror, pictures nude standing on rock by water's edge, lettering arched above, 2⅛" dia, EX, A **$100.00**

Crack Shot Cigars, box label, inner lid sample, 1901, lady's head coming from target with coins, rifles & arrows, American Litho Co, EX, A **$72.00**

Crack-A-Jack Clothes, sign, tin flange, man with long stride in top hat carrying box, I've Got My..., 13½x18", EX, A **$1,950.00**

Cracker Jack, baseball card, 1915, prize, Pratt #93, VG, B2 .... **$75.00**

Cracker Jack, drawing book, 1930s, front cover pictures the Cracker Jack boy with lettering around, 2¼x1¼", VG, G **$25.00**

Cracker Jack, figure, 1950-60, 3-D plastic collie or other dogs, prize, EX, B2 .... **$4.00**

Cracker Jack, fortune wheel, 1933, premium, tin litho, VG, B2 .... **$60.00**

Cracker Jack, handkerchief, cotton, red, white & blue, shows rows of the Cracker Jack boy & dog, 30x12", EX, S5 .... **$85.00**

Cracker Jack, periscope, MIB, D2 .... **$35.00**

Cracker Jack, tin, bowl of Cocoanut Corn Crisp with product name lettered in red & black on yellow background, pry lid, 6¼", G+, A **$40.00**

Cracker Jack, tin, 1980, white, 8¼x5" dia, EX, D **$10.00**

Cracker Jack, window decal, large Cracker Jack boy, scarce, D2 .... **$25.00**

Craddock-Terry Long Wear Shoes, sign, porcelain, 2-sided, bell shape, white lettering on red background, 17x16", G, A **$250.00**

Craftsman Model Power Tools, catalog, 1937, 41 pages, EX, D **$18.00**

Crane's Havana Smokers, cigar cutter, glass pyramid-shaped key-wind cutter with labels under glass dome, 4½x8¼", VG, A **$175.00**

Crane's Imported Cigars, box label, inner lid, 1920s, Now 2 For 5¢ & Formerly 5¢ around scene with crane in oval on hanging sign, 6x9", EX, D **$5.00**

Cranepenn Motor Oil, pocket mirror & paperweight, Pennsylvania Oil logo above product name, Crane & Oil flank 2 cranes, 3½" dia, EX, A........................ **$65.00**

Craven 'A' Cigarettes, sign, paperboard, woman rests left hand with cigarette on right shoulder, Will Not Affect..., framed, 26x17½", EX, A **$30.00**

Craven Mixture Tobacco, tin, pictures a cat, unopened, round, EX, D.. **$35.00**

Crawford Shoes, trade card, 'Fishing,' pictures man fishing in stream, advertising on reverse, VG, A **$35.00**

Crawford Shoes, trade card, 'Hunting,' colorful hunt scene with man aiming rifle, advertising on reverse, VG, A.......... **$26.00**

Crayola Crayons, necklace, green crayon on plastic cord, EX, D **$4.50**

Crayola Crayons, store display, 1950s, cardboard stand-up, in original mailer, 12x7½", EX, D **$25.00**

Cream Dove Shortening & Peanut Butter, pocket mirror, pictures farm boy holding up can of product, Look Into...& other lettering around rim, 2⅛" dia, VG+, A.. $475.00

Cream of Wheat, doll, 1920, Rastus, print on cotton, lacking his chef's hat, some soil, VG+, P2 .... **$85.00**

Cream of Wheat, sign, 1906, Pony Express rider putting mail in box reading Cream Of Wheat, signed NC Wyeth, framed, 34x23 1/2, VG+, A..................... **$300.00**

Credo Peanut Butter, pail, white on red, horizontal oval logo, slip lid & bail handle, 1-lb, EX, D3............. **$75.00**

Crema Beer, label, 1933-50, Crema in script, Garden City Brewing Co, Internal Revenue Tax Paid statement, 1-qt, EX, A **$23.00**

Creme de Menthe Asparagus, label, dark green with white & red lettering, San Francisco, EX, G1 .... **$2.00**

Cremo Cigars, store bin, cigar & lettering on simulated wood-grain front with product name inside lid, 6x14", VG+, D $110.00

Crescent Beer, label, 1933-36, crescent moon logo, Overland Beverage Co Inc, U-type permit number, 1/2-gal, EX, A **$37.00**

Crescent Beverages, sign, 1940s, embossed tin, crescent moon & star flanked by Since 1893, red, white, black & gold, 13½x19½", EX, D **$50.00**

Crescent Bottling Co, sign, embossed tin, moon & star shining down on lady with bottle, Crescent -- Shines Over Them All, 10x13½", VG, A........................... **$30.00**

Crescent City, crate label, 1930s, Florida citrus, woman seated on crescent moon, 9x9", M, C3................... **$5.00**

Crescent Macaroni & Cracker, pocket mirror, lady in flowing dress seated on crescent moon, company name below, oval, 2¾", EX, A...................................... **$280.00**

Crescent Salted Peanuts, tin, pictures 2 girls carrying large crescent, red, white & blue, pry lid, 10-lb, 9¾x8½" dia, VG, A **$175.00**

Crescent Sewing Machine Co, trade card, ca 1880, pictures a happy group of Black men & women dancing on a floating barge, 2½x4½", EX, P1.................... **$20.00**

Crest Sauerkraut, can label, pictures head of cabbage, EX, C3 .... **$6.00**

Crest Toothpaste, telephone, 1980s, Crest man holding tube of toothepaste, blue with silver specks, 10½", EX, D.. **$35.00**

Cretors Pop Corn, box, 1929, cardboard, smiling girl ready to eat some popcorn from box, lettering below, 7x5", NM, A.. **$10.00**

Crisco, recipe book, 1937, 'Cooking Hints & Tested Recipes,' 32 pages, EX, D **$2.50**

Crisco, recipe book, 1948, 'New Recipes for Good Eating,' 112 pages, EX, D **$6.00**

Crisco, sign, ca 1905-15, die-cut porcelain, features large can with lettered panels above & below, 10x14", EX, A... **$1,600.00**

Crosley Appliances, pin-back button, 1940s, red, white & blue, EX, D **$8.00**

Crosley Radio, globe sign, red, black & white reverse-painted lenses, ...You're There With A Crosley, 12" dia, VG, A **$525.00**

Crosman Bros Choice Flower Seeds, sign, copyright 1887, shows girl with spray of flowers in arched inset surrounded by flowers & advertising, EX, A **$225.00**

Crosman Bros Seeds, sign, paperboard, shows happy Black couple in stride, she being pregnant, Sowing The Seed, framed, 23½x16½", G+, A **$625.00**

Cross Department Store, sign, 1910s, waxed cardboard, Visit Cross & Save..., black on yellow, 5x14", EX, D . **$8.50**

Crown Beer, calendar, 1915, paper roll-down, girl holding rose, crown logo in each corner, full pad, 34x10", EX, A.. **$305.00**

Crown Brewing Co, sign, embossed die-cut cardboard, ram in goggles driving car made of beer barrels, hops & poppy above, 14x14", EX, A **$1,100.00**

Crown Diamond Paints, sign, porcelain flange, product name lettered around crown & diamond logo in circular inset, 16x17", EX, M2 .... **$125.00**

Crown Gas, globe, milk glass, crown shape, 15½", VG+, A **$110.00**

Crown Gasoline, sign, porcelain, 2-sided, red, white & blue, product name on fancy crown, 26x26", EX, D **$350.00**

Crown Premium Motor Oil, bank, oil can shape, Crown lettered on stylized wing emblem above Premium Motor Oil, 3", EX, A **$18.00**

Crown Quality Ice Cream, sign, embossed tin, features lettered bucket of ice cream, Anderson & Patterson Mfgrs, Worcester Mass, 28x20", VG, A **$85.00**

Crustene Shortening, pin-back button, 1920s, pictures product in yellow with white lettering on red background, EX, D **$5.00**

Cruz Blanca Cerveza, tray, deep-dish, blond woman holding glass of beer, Mexican, 13¼" dia, D **$16.00**

Cruz Blanca Cerveza, tray, deep-dish, matador with passing bull, Mexican, some rust spots on bottom, 13¼" dia, D **$20.00**

Crystal Export Beer, label, pre-1920, Crystal in script above logo flanked by Export Beer, National Brewing Co, G, A **$43.00**

Crystal Spring Brewing Co, match striker, stoneware, overall soiling/minor chips to underside of foot, 6¼x5" dia, EX, A **$300.00**

Crystal Spring Brewing Co, tray, porcelain with brass rim, company name arched above, Superior Stock Lager below, 12" dia, EX, A **$400.00**

Crystal-Flash Line, sign, die-cut porcelain, lettered blue & white tank car on tracks with Just A Little Better in red below, 47x99", VG, A **$850.00**

Cub Tobacco, shelf marker, tin, white Smoke in blue oval at left of Cub Best Tobacco 10¢ Can Buy, bear in blue oval at right, NM, A **$30.00**

Cuban Winner Cigars, label, Cuban Winner arched above Cuban girl, tobacco field beyond, lettered ribbon intertwines round seals, 6x9", EX, D **$10.00**

Cuesta, Rey & Co Tobacco, sign, embossed tin, woman surrounded by medallions & tobacco leaves, framed, image: 13x19½", VG, A **$350.00**

Cuesta-Rey Habana Cigars, tip tray, lady in profile looking downward, lettering above & below, rust spot on rim, EX, A.. $66.00

Culter & Proctor Stove Co, pin-back button, white company name & Peoria Ill lettered on blue band around early stove graphic on white, EX, A..................... **$25.00**

Culture Crush Cut Smoking Tobacco, pocket tin, upright, product name on white design on striped background, EX+/VG, A **$35.00**

Cumberland Brewing Co's Old Export Beer, sign, tin, 3 men in fishing boat, It's All In The Bait lettered below, self-framed, 15½x19½", G, A **$195.00**

Cunard, sign, ca 1872, paper, frontal view of oncoming ship, logo upper left, Major & Knapp litho, 29x25¾", EX, A **$3,350.00**

Cunningham Pianos, pocket mirror, Cunningham in delicate script above baby grand piano, The Matchless, oval, 2¾", EX, A **$90.00**

Cunningham Pianos, pocket mirror, 2 colonial gents on either side of piano with company name, oval, 2¾" long, EX, A **$80.00**

Cunningham Radio Tubes, sign, embossed die-cut tin, emblem, raised border & mottled background, cutout center, Complete With..., 5x5", NM, M2 .... **$120.00**

Cupid Bouquet Little Cigars, pocket tin, flat, Little Cigars encircled at left of cupid, Cupid Bouquet above, company name below, slip lid, VG, A **$33.00**

Cupid Sliced Plug Smoking Tobacco, tin, square with rounded corners, black with red heart motif & gold filigree accents, EX, M2 .... **$68.00**

Cupids Best Cigars, box label, inner lid, pictures cupid offering cigar box to a woman, 6x9", EX, D **$25.00**

Curad Bandages, figure, Curad Kid, 7", M, D............ **$25.00**

Cure-All Malt Bitters, trade card, The House That Jack Built, colorful bottle, EX, D **$4.00**

Curity Medical Bandages & Supplies, store display, 1950s, plastic figure of Miss Curity, Kendall Co, 19", M, D... **$125.00**

Curtiss, see also Baby Ruth

Curtiss Spearmint Gum, complete package, G2...... **$20.00**

Cushman Motor Vehicles, sign, porcelain flange, gold, white & blue on red, Cushman logo above Sales, Service, 14x20x1½", M, D3 .... **$500.00**

Cutter Ventura County Lemons, crate label, 1937, cutter going full speed through choppy seas, Seaboard Lemon Assoc, Oxnard Ca, 9x12½", M, C1 .... **$3.00**

CW & Co Cough Drops, tin, Cough Drops lettered diagonally with CW & Co above, slip lid, 5-lb, square, A **$50.00**

CW Parker, sign, paper, vignettes in the sky above double-horsed carousel, minor soiling, 20½x27½", NM, A .. **$225.00**

CWL Meadow Cream Toffees, store bin, tin, CWL above Meadow Cream emblem, Toffees below, green & orange, slant top, half round, 15x11", G, A **$35.00**

CY Young Cigars, tin, portrait above baseball bats & glove flanked by baseball players & signatures, slip lid, rare, 5x5" dia, EX+, A **$6,590.00**

Cycle Cigarettes, box, 1910 stamp, Cycle Cigarettes above man riding bicycle, The American Tobacco Co below, held 15 cigarettes, EX, A..................................... **$150.00**

Cyclone Twister Cigar, sign, 1928, cardboard, Cyclone embossed in a tornado with product name & Five Cents above & below, 11x9", EX, A...................... **$80.00**

Cyrus Noble & WA Lacey Whiskies, sign, ca 1910, paper, pictures gentlemen at roulette table, 26x40", G, A........ **$715.00**

D

D Buchner & Co Tobacco, sign, paper, policeman with night stick surrounded by insets of policemen & firefighters, 27x20½", VG, A................................. **$2,000.00**

D&M Sporting Goods, trade card, die-cut, pointer flanked by The Best Made & The Strongest Made, baseball glove on back, VG, A... **$60.00**

Dad's Root Beer, bottle, 1940s, enameled label, with cap, 7-oz, EX, D **$14.00**

Dad's Root Beer, bottle, 1967, clear, pictures boy on bottle, yellow & red label, 10-oz, EX, D **$9.50**

Dad's Root Beer, bottle topper with bottle, cardboard, man in blue lounging jacket promoting Dad's Draft Root Beer, 1/2 Gal 18¢, EX, M3 .... **$75.00**

Dad's Root Beer, sign, embossed tin, Have A above Dad's Old Fashioned Root Beer on diagonal band, ...It's Delicious below, 20x28", EX+, A **$140.00**

Dad's Root Beer, sign, 1950s, die-cut cardboard, features 1/2-gal bottle, EX +, D.. **$45.00**

Dad's Root Beer, sign, 1950s, die-cut metal, bottle cap above panel reading The Old Fashioned Root Beer, 28x20", NM, D **$130.00**

Dad's Root Beer, teddy bear, 8½", EX, D **$12.50**

Daeuber's, display light, embossed glass, Daeuber's in script superimposed over foaming glass of beer, 15" dia, G, A **$100.00**

Daeufer's Peerless Beer, sign, porcelain, logo above product name surrounded by lettering, Quality's First, Allentown's Favorite, 19" dia, EX+, A.......................... **$225.00**

Dahlia, crate label, 1940s, California orange, 3 salmon-pink dahlias on black ground, Redlands, 10x11", M, C1 .... **$2.00**

Daily Double Beer, label, 1933-50, Wagner Brewing Co, Internal Revenue Tax Paid statement, 12-oz, EX, A........... **$21.00**

Daily Habit Cigars, box label, inner lid, pictures parrot on a perch, 6x9", M, D **$15.00**

Dairy Queen, salt & pepper shakers, 1960s, Dairy Queen girls, rare, M, P2 .... **$225.00**

Daisee Coffee, tin, pictures daisies on sides, red & gold, key-wind lid, EX+, A.. **$60.00**

Daisirosa Cigars, box label, inner lid, 1901, side view of buxom woman in plumed hat, 6x9", VG, C3 .... **$25.00**

Daisy & Sentinel Air Rifles, calendar, 1901, paper, child holding rifle, full pad, rare, framed, image: 22½x15½", VG, A **$3,200.00**

Daisy Air Rifle, pin-back button, Shoot Safe Buddy surrounded by other lettering, red, white & blue, round, EX, A **$16.00**

Daisy Hair Tonic, sign, tin, Daisy emblem over burst of rays, 4 round logos in each corner, A Daisy For Your Hair..., 10x9", EX, A **$150.00**

Dalecarlia Cigars, box label, outer, 1896, woman in Swedish costume, M, C3 .... **$6.00**

Dalley's Prime Coffee, tin, lettering over scenic background, slip lid with knob, round, 1-lb, EX, A .. **$120.00**

Dalton Adding Machine, pin-back button, ca 1900, red, black & white, EX, D **$5.00**

Damasco Cigars, box label, outer, pictures man in plumed hat, 4½x4½", M, D **$1.50**

Damascus Ice Cream, sign, 1920s-30s, die-cut porcelain, product lettering & ice cream sundae on red & white, yellow border, 18x17", M, A........$1,300.00

Damrow Brothers Co, watch fob, brass with blue border, DB in vat on front, lettering on back, EX, D........ **$22.00**

Dan Patch Cut Plug, tin, black & red logo on yellow, rounded corners, slip lid, 3x4x6", EX, A.............. **$65.00**

Dan Patch Roasted Coffee, tin, encircled image of horse & driver on front & back, Tennessee Coffee Co below, wire handle, 10½", G, A..................................... **$800.00**

Dandelion Stout, sign, reverse-painted glass, Drink...For Health 5¢ lettered in silver on red, scalloped silver border, 5x8", NM, A **$200.00**

Daniel Bermes Brewery, calendar, paper, King & henchmen riding to local tavern, calendar pad missing, framed, image: 29½x19½", EX, A...................... **$1,100.00**

Daniel Bermes Brewery, calendar, 1908, comical image of serving girl with kneeling fellow proposing to empty chair, pad missing, 18x13", NM, A **$500.00**

Daniel Webster Flour, sign, tin, Daniel Webster in red lettering above Flour in black on cream, wood frame, 15x48", EX, D3..................................$225.00

Danielson's Bartletts, crate label, 1920s, large orchard with Victorian ranch house beyond, Suisun Cal, 7½x11", M, C3..**$10.00**

Danne Miller's Coffee, tin, stenciled lettering & logo, CC Prouty Co, Des Moines Iowa, round with dome top & slip lid, 2-lb, EX, A...**$110.00**

Darby & Joan Cigars, label, Darby & Joan above & below English couple sitting at table before fireplace, diagonal corners, 4x4", EX, D...**$10.00**

Darkie Toothpaste, fan, die-cut paper, minor soiling, framed, 21x14", D...**$70.00**

Daufuski Brand Oysters, tin, paper label featuring Indian chief in profile with product name above & below, no lid, 1-gal, NM, A **$31.00**

Daufuski Brand Oysters, tin, paper label featuring Indian chief in profile with product name above & below, no bottom, 1-pt, NM, A **$16.00**

Dauntless Coffee, sign, cardboard, Roman boy with horses, ...& All Food Products Challenge The World For Quality, 8x16", NM, B1...**$8.00**

Davenport Ladders, sign, cardboard, blue & orange, product name lettered diagonally above For Sale Here, 7x15", NM, B1..**$8.00**

David Bradley Plows & Cultivators, tape measure, pictures a plow, red, yellow, blue & white, measures to 4 feet, EX, D **$85.00**

David Brewster Cigars, box label, inner lid, pictures David Brewster (inventor of the kaleidoscope), 6x9", M, D...**$10.00**

David's Electrochemical Products, case, dovetailed wood box containing 12 pints of fluid, round logo on front, lettering on sides, unopened, 15", EX, A..**$100.00**

David's Prize Soap, sign, paper, comical image of Chinese laundryman finding gold coin in soap, There's Money..., framed, 21x16", G, A.......................**$3,000.00**

David's Prize Soap, trade card, 3-dimensional product box opens to scene with woman using product, scarce, EX, A..**$80.00**

David Stevenson Brewing Co, calendar, 1904, Uncle Sam toasting residents of New York above factory inset, framed, image: 28x19½", EX, A.......................**$2,300.00**

Davidson's Breads, sign, porcelain, Ask For upper left of Davidson's in diagonal script left of Breads, They're Different, 4x16", EX+, D1......................................**$70.00**

Davis' Pain Killer, sign, tin, large bottle with portrait label in center of large crowd of people, soiled, framed, image: 18x24", G, A.......................................**$5,000.00**

Davis Baking Powder, recipe book, 1904, 'Davis' OK Cookbook,' colorful covers & illustrations, 64 pages, EX, H1...**$16.00**

Davis Baking Powder, recipe book, 1922, 48 pages, EX, D...**$12.00**

Davis Baking Powder, recipe book, 1940, 'Davis Master Pattern Baking Formulas,' 80 pages, EX, D **$8.00**

Davis Carriage M'F'G Co, sign, embossed tin, couple in carriage on inset lower left, red company name across top on yellow, 6¾x20", EX, A **$130.00**

Davis Sewing Machine Co, catalog, 1893, 24 pages, VG, D...**$40.00**

Davis Vertical Feed Sewing Machine, trade card, people in old clothing, opens up to people in nice clothing, scarce, EX, A..**$35.00**

Dawes Imported Black Horse Ale, display, glass trapezoid on wood base, shadowed product lettering over black horse image, 4½x7¼", EX, A **$110.00**

Dawn Typewriter Ribbon, tin, girl reaching for stars, EX, D...**$20.00**

Dawson's Ale & Beer, clock, glass front, metal frame, king's portrait encircled below Time Out For Dawsons in larger circle, round, VG, A **$65.00**

Days of 49 Whiskey, sign, ca 1900, canvas, icon of the west depicting the westward movement to California gold fields, framed, 24x36", G, A...................**$2,530.00**

Dazey Churn & Merger, display, die-cut cardboard, woman using butter churn, You Can Make In 5 Minutes..., framed, image: 22x27", VG, A **$185.00**

De Kalb, display, die-cut tin, winged corn cob, 8x18", G, A..**$210.00**

De Laval, display, die-cut tin cow family with advertising on sides, American Art Sign Co, VG+, A, set of 4..........**$100.00**

De Laval, sign, black on yellow, We Use De Laval, Better Farm Living & Better Farm Income, 12x16", EX, A **$20.00**

De Laval, sign, die-cut tin, We & Use flank blue logo above De Laval on yellow, Drink More Milk on blue below, 12x18", NM, M3 ....**$70.00**

De Laval Cream Separator, banner, cloth, oval image of woman using separator, Sooner Or Later..., More Than 1,625,000 In Use, 3x10", G+, A..........................**$300.00**

De Laval Cream Separator, banner, cloth, oval image of woman using separator, Sooner Or Later..., Nearly 2,000,000 In Use, 8x36", G-, A **$170.00**

De Laval Cream Separator Co, print, 1940, cardboard, 'Wild Horse Catcher,' pictures Indian with lasso chasing wild horses, scarce, 16x9", EX, D.........................**$60.00**

De Laval Cream Separators, calendar, 1908, oval image of girl & cow, yellow lettering above, calendar never opened, framed, 24½x17½", EX, A **$650.00**

De Laval Cream Separators, calendar, 1915, product name above boy giving calf pan of milk, scrolled courtesy panel below, full pad, EX, A **$1,500.00**

De Laval Cream Separators, calendar, 1918, product name above girl standing with horse, courtesy panel at right, full pad, framed, 24x12", NM, A **$695.00**

De Laval Cream Separators, calendar, 1938, pictures a lady, full pad, G, D **$35.00**

De Laval Cream Separators, calendar top, 1919, pictures boy with fish, G, D **$75.00**

De Laval Cream Separators, display, embossed tin stand-up, pictures a separator, ...The World's Standard, 19½x13½", VG, A **$500.00**

De Laval Cream Separators, Junior separator, cast iron, 40x32x16", VG, A **$325.00**

De Laval Cream Separators, pocket mirror, pictures milkmaid next to separator, some wear, 1¾" dia, VG, A..........**$275.00**

De Laval Cream Separators, sign, ca 1890, tin, Farm & Dairy Separator above separator image at left of other advertising, framed, 14x20", VG+, A..................**$160.00**

De Laval Cream Separators, sign, paper with metal strips, little girl in feathered hat holding miniature separator, 18x13½", VG, A **$625.00**

De Laval Cream Separators, sign, porcelain flange, 2-sided, pictures cream separator, Local Agent lettered below, 26½x18", VG, A....................................**$350.00**

De Laval Cream Separators, sign, tin, milkmaid with cow surrounded by vignettes of cows & separators, original frame, 40½x29½", G, A.................................**$1,750.00**

De Laval Cream Separators, sign, tin, milkmaid with cow surrounded by vignettes of cows & separators, original frame, 40½x29½", EX, A **$3,250.00**

De Laval Cream Separators, sign, tin, woman using separator & child carrying cream into barnyard, embossed letters on rolled border, 26" dia, VG, A..........**$1,850.00**

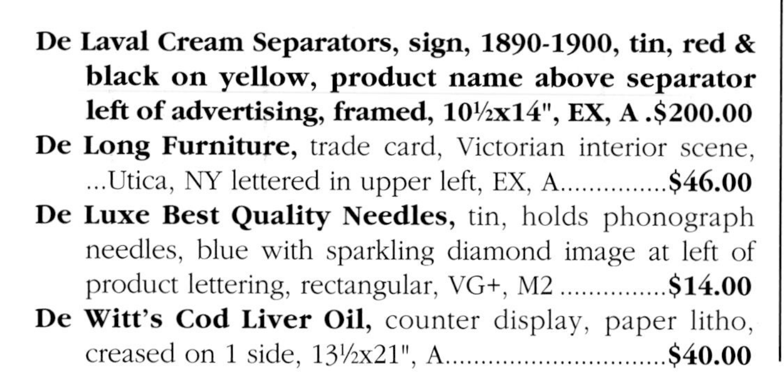

De Laval Cream Separators, sign, 1890-1900, tin, red & black on yellow, product name above separator left of advertising, framed, 10½x14", EX, A .$200.00

De Long Furniture, trade card, Victorian interior scene, ...Utica, NY lettered in upper left, EX, A..............**$46.00**

De Luxe Best Quality Needles, tin, holds phonograph needles, blue with sparkling diamond image at left of product lettering, rectangular, VG+, M2 ....**$14.00**

De Witt's Cod Liver Oil, counter display, paper litho, creased on 1 side, 13½x21", A.............................**$40.00**

De Vilbiss Atomizers, display, cardboard trifold, boy on knees sprays dog on octagon-shaped field flanked by advertising panels, 31x42", NM, A............$225.00

Deacon Brown, tip tray, 1911, patriotic lady lifting glass, decorative patriotic border, The King Of Phosphates, wear, 5" dia, G, A..**$190.00**

Dead Shot Smokeless Powder, watch fob, brass & celluloid, wounded duck in flight on front, product & company name on back, rare, EX, D........................**$210.00**

Dead Shot Sporting Powder, tin, 1920s, hunter & dogs on red background, bird in flight on reverse, black lettering, minor rust, 4", A $165.00

Dead Shot Tobacco, tin, paper transfer on front picturing dog lying beside hunter's gun, red background, paint wear/soiling, 4", A..**$20.00**

Decker Brothers Pianos, trade card, pictures little girl reading sheet music, EX, A..................................**$18.00**

Dee-Light Beverage, sign, embossed tin, Drink Dee-Light (underlined) above bottle, It's Dee-licious! lettered diagonally below, 18x6", EX, A **$5.00**

Deep Rock Gasoline & Motor Oil, sign, porcelain, 2-sided, red, white & blue, 32x24", EX, D............**$150.00**

Deep-Rock Gasoline & Motor Oil, matchbook, red, white, black & silver, EX, D **$5.00**

Deer Creek Ice Cream, tray, pictures elves & ice cream, NM, D **$125.00**

Deere & Co Automatic Trip Cultivator, trade card, 3-panel folder, pictures 12-point buck & cultivators within floral border, EX, A **$115.00**

Deere Hay Loader, sign, 3-fold flyer, equipment & 12-point buck with pastoral farm scene beyond, testimonials on reverse, 11x14", G, A **$125.00**

Deering Harvesting Machines, calendar, 1908, shows hunter & 2 bird dogs, 1908 stamped over 2 rows of 6 months each at bottom, no pad, EX, A **$160.00**

Deering Harvesting Machines, sign, paper, hunter with spaniel & game, minor creasing/soiling, matted & framed, image: 15½x12", EX, A **$55.00**

Deering Twine Binder, trade card, pictures colorful farm scene, orange background, advertising on reverse, EX, A **$13.00**

Defender Motor Oil, can, 1940-50, soldier with campsite in background & 100% Pure logo, pour spout & handle, 2-gal, 10½", EX, A **$45.00**

Defiance Tick Mitton Co, pocket mirror, 1920s, celluloid, colorful image of the factory, World's Most Modern... in red, 2¾x1¾", VG, D **$16.50**

DeKuyper Blueberry Schnapps, mirror, plastic frame, 16½x25", EX, D..**$20.00**

Del Monte, bank, clown figure, EX, D **$28.00**

Del Monte, doll, 1983, Pineapple, stuffed plush, M, D..**$10.00**

Del Monte, doll, 1984, Reddy Tomato, Country Yumpkins series, red plush with felt eyes, mouth & leaves on head, 11", M, N1 ....**$8.00**

Del Monte, doll, 1991, Sweety Pea, green figure shaped like a pea pod, M, N1 ....**$8.00**

Del Monte, pin-back button, early 1900s, black & white with red logo, EX, D **$5.00**

Del Monte, recipe book, 1930s, 'Del Monte Recipes of Flavor,' 62 pages, G, D **$9.50**

Del Monte Hominy, can label, pictures hominy in floral-designed pottery bowl, EX, G1 ....**$3.00**

Del Monte Mixture, pocket tin, upright, brown with yellow lid, gold lettering, very rare, less than 24 known, 4½x3x3/4", EX, H3 ....$400.00

Del Monte Pumpkin, can label, pictures a pumpkin with green leaves on green background, red logo, G1..**$3.00**

Delaware Punch, bottle, 1956, clear with red & white label, EX, D...**$6.50**

Delco Batteries, sign, 1940s-50s, Delco lettered vertically above encircled battery, orange background, minor dents, framed, 70x19", A.......................................**$35.00**

Delco Battery Service, sign, tin, 2-sided, Battery above & service below Delco on diagonal band, shows battery & seal, 22x30", EX/VG+, A **$160.00**

Della Rocca Cigars, can label, bust portrait of a young woman with long golden hair, M, D....................**$12.00**

Delta Power Tools, catalog, 1939, 63 pages, VG+, H2 ...**$25.00**

Delta Sugar Corn, can label, embossed ears of corn, M, C3 ....**$6.00**

Deluth Imperial Flour, pocket mirror, Black chef displaying a sack of flour & loaf of bread with lettering around rim, 1¾" dia, EX, A..**$800.00**

Denman Handcrafted Tires, sign, embossed tin, Handcrafted in diagonal script between Denman upper left & Tires lower right, 17x60", VG, A........................**$75.00**

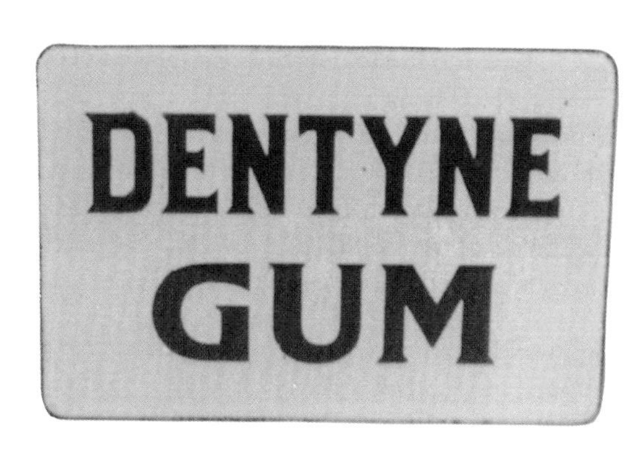

Dentyne Gum, sign, porcelain, Dentyne Gum lettered in green on white, horizontal with rounded corners, EX, M1 ....$120.00

Denver Dry Goods, pocket mirror, factory scene viewed through double doorway, lettering around, 2⅛" dia, EX, A **$65.00**

Denver Dry Goods, pocket mirror, features factory with busy street scene, 400 Feet Long lettered below, oval, 2¾" long, EX, A **$60.00**

Deppen Brewing Co, sign, reverse-painted glass, elk logo above ...Reading Pa, original copper frame, 25x13¼", EX+, A..**$800.00**

Deppen Brewing Co, sign, wood, factory scene with train & wagons in foreground, elk logo in upper corners, 20x28", G, A **$750.00**

Deppen Brewing Co's Extra Pale Muenchener, tip tray, elk head in center surrounded by lettering, good sheen, minor chips to image, 4¼", VG, A........................**$85.00**

Deppen Brewing Co's Queen Quality Beer, sign, reverse-painted glass, elk logo above labeled bottle, original copper frame, 25¼x13", NM, A **$800.00**

Der 3 Mann, crate label, Spanish citrus, pictures man with X-ray vision, M, C3...**$15.00**

Derby Boot & Shoe Polish, sign, 1859, paper, costumed merchant looking at his reflection in boot, A Substitute For Blacking, 10x8", VG, A................................**$300.00**

Derby Club Beer, label, ca 1933-36, horse race scene, Bismarck Brewing Co, U-type permit number, 12-oz, G, A........**$20.00**

Derby Paint, sign, tin flange, 2-sided, We Sell above paint can, blue & white, 19½x12½", G, A....................**$50.00**

Derby Pale Ale, label, 1933-50, horse's head above, Haberle Congress Brewing Co, Internal Revenue Tax Paid statement, 32-oz, EX, A **$15.00**

Derby Smoking Tobacco, sign, embossed cardboard, horse & jockey in oval center, black ground, matted & framed, image: 22½x17½", EX, A $4,500.00

Derby Tobacco, pocket tin, flat, pictures horse's head flanked by lettered banners, slip lid, VG+, A **$25.00**

Desert Bloom, crate label, California grapefruit, yucca plants blooming in high desert landscape, Redlands, G1.....**$6.00**

Deviled Crabs, sign, paper, fishing scene with crab in the foreground, encircled crabs above, Fresh...McMenamin & Co, 13x9", VG, A...**$1,500.00**

Devoe Paint, sign, 1930-40, porcelain, pictures gallon of paint, Ed Hartz & Sons Deposit below, yellow & orange ground, 29x19", EX, A..**$75.00**

Devoe Paint & Varnish Products, sign, ca 1925, cardboard, black cloud pouring water on an auto, ...Prevent Destruction, 34½x23½", EX, A...........................**$300.00**

Devoe's Brilliant Oil, sign, paper, night scene with lamp surrounded by lighthouse & train, several figures above, 13x17", VG, A...**$700.00**

Devoe Watercolors, tin, pictures kneeling Indian, EX, D **$35.00**

Dewars Scotch, display bottle, glass, 20", EX, D.......**$18.00**

Dewars Scotch, mirror clock, beveled glass, 12x12", EX, D..**$25.00**

Dexter Cement, sign, porcelain, hand within triangle on circle in center, yellow & red on black, Nazareth Pa, 28x12", EX, D **$150.00**

Dexter's Mothers Bread, sign, embossed tin, white lettering on red, Buy To-Day above Dexter's, Mothers Bread below, white border, 5x14", VG, A......................**$45.00**

DF Foley & Co Gold Pens, display case, gold-painted wood frame with company name on curved glass front, 8x21x15", EX, A..**$850.00**

DG Yuengling, see also Yuengling's

DG Yuengling & Son Brewers & Bottlers, sign, paper, multiple factory scenes & vignettes of how it works, lettering at top, framed, 26¼x19½", VG+, A...........**$300.00**

DG Yuengling & Son's Porter, pitcher, china, mauve & gold leaf over white, decorative design on spout, 9¾x6½", VG, A **$75.00**

Dial Smoking Tobacco, pocket tin, upright, pictures a dial with product name & 100% Burley above & below, slip lid, EX+, A..**$54.00**

Dial Smoking Tobacco, sign, cardboard, lettering above pack at left with 1¾-oz tin & 10¢ at right, framed, approx: 20x14", EX, A..**$75.00**

Diamond Black Leather Oil, clock, tin with embossed lettering, ...Best Leather Preservative, Baird Clock Mfg Co, chips/scratches, 18" dia, G, A............................**$100.00**

Diamond Crystal Salt, pencil clip, 1930s, multicolored, EX, D **$28.00**

Diamond Crystal Salt, watch fob, celluloid, black & white with crystal in center on front, salt being poured on back, EX, D...**$28.00**

Diamond Dyes, cabinet, tin with simulated wood-grain finish, 2 doors with lettered diamonds, HD Beach, 18½" long, G, A **$60.00**

Diamond Dyes, cabinet, wood, embossed tin front pictures children & lady playing with ball & ribbons in landscape, 30x22½", NM, M2 ....**$1,895.00**

Diamond Dyes, cabinet, wood, embossed tin front pictures children playing with balloon, Standard Package Dyes..., 24½x15", VG, A.....................................**$650.00**

Diamond Dyes, cabinet, wood, embossed tin front pictures children skipping rope, case restored, 24x15", G, A..**$550.00**

Diamond Dyes, cabinet, wood, embossed tin front pictures kids jumping rope, Diamond Dyes across top, 24x15", NM, A $1,225.00

Diamond Dyes, cabinet, wood, embossed tin front pictures lady & children playing with ball & ribbons in landscape, 30x22½", EX, A.............................**$1,100.00**

Diamond Dyes, cabinet, wood, embossed tin front pictures lady dyeing clothes, It's Easy To Dye With..., no back doors, 30x22", G, M2 ....**$600.00**

Diamond Dyes, cabinet, wood, tin front pictures baby in framed inset surrounded by feathers & flowers, 19x15½", G, A..**$750.00**

Diamond Dyes, cabinet, wood, tin front pictures fairy in garden with birds surrounded by lettering & vignettes, 30½x24", NM, A **$2,300.00**

Diamond Dyes, cabinet, wood, tin front portrays the evolution of women, Fast Colors For Domestic & Fancy Dyeing, 30x22½", VG, A....................................**$850.00**

Diamond Dyes, paper doll, ca 1880, chromolitho, blond-haired girl with pink party dress, 5¼", EX, D.........**$8.00**

Diamond Dyes, sample card, folder type with 32 different cloth patch add-ons inside, EX, A........................**$46.00**

Diamond Dyes, sign, die-cut cardboard hanger, parrot perched in circular logo, Use Diamond Dyes, 14", VG, A...**$1,100.00**

Diamond Dyes, sign, 1911, self-framed tin over cardboard, Bessie Pease Gutman illustration of girl dyeing doll clothes, 11x17", G, A **$1,050.00**

Diamond Dyes, trade card, little girl dipping cat into dye, It's Easy To Dye With Diamond Dyes lettered below, EX, A **$14.00**

Diamond Edge Scissors, cabinet, wood & glass with reverse-painted logo, 24", VG, A........................**$500.00**

Diamond Gloss Starch, poster, girl wearing lace scarf with product name, Favorite below, 22x17", G-, A......**$30.00**

Diamond Jim's Beer, bottle, long neck, paper label, Cold Spring Brewing Co, VG, D **$10.00**

Diamond Tailoring Co, pocket mirror, It Pays To Dress Well above elongated diamond with company name, Chicago Ill below, 2½" dia, NM, A.......................**$18.00**

Diamond Tool & Horseshoe Co, paperweight, figural horseshoe, G, D **$28.00**

Diamond Wine Co Champagne, sign, 1896, paper, 3 women sharing bottle of champagne with factory view out window, framed, image: 27x19", EX, A....**$1,500.00**

Diamond-34x4, sign, ca 1910, paper, cherubic couple at wheel of daddy's car encircled by lettered tire, framed, scarce, 37x34", EX, D3.................$2,800.00

Diaparene Baby Products, doll, 1980, Diaparene baby, molded vinyl, Sterling Drug Inc, 5", M, D **$35.00**

Dick & Bros Quincy Beer, tray, factory scene with busy street scene in foreground, lettering on decorative rim, 10½x13¾", G, A...**$350.00**

Dick Custer Cigars, box label, inner lid, pictures cowboy with pistol, Holds You Up, 6x9", M, D **$8.50**

Dick Grave's Nugget Hotel & Casino, squeeze toy, 1950s, Nugget Sam, rubber, 12", VG+, D **$35.00**

Dick's Pilsener Select Beer, label, 1933-50, product name on ribbon, Dick Bros Brewing Co, Internal Revenue Tax Paid statement, 12-oz, EX, A **$6.00**

Dick's Quincy Beer, label, 1933-36, Quincy Beer in script on diagonal center band, U-type permit number, 12-oz, G, A...**$23.00**

Dickenson's Witch Hazel, puzzle, in original envelope measuring 4½x3", EX, P2.....................................**$25.00**

Dickinson Big Buster Yellow Popcorn, tin, product name above & below drum major beating drum, top missing, #10, 6" dia, VG, A................................**$125.00**

Dickinson's Ace Clover, cup, 1880s-90s, porcelain, product advertising on side, handled, rim chips/staining, G-, A...**$20.00**

Diet-Rite Cola, bottle, 1962, aqua with red & white label, 10-oz, EX, D..**$4.00**

Diet-Rite Cola, sign, embossed tin, red Sugar-Free above black product name by bottle on light green, dark green border, 18x54", NM, M3 ....**$85.00**

Diet-Rite Cola, sign, mother pouring Diet-Rite into glasses for her little girl & boy, minor wear, 32x20", D ...**$25.00**

Diet-Rite Cola, sign, 1950s, embossed tin, pictures a bottle, Enjoy Sugar Free...Less Than 1 Calorie Per Bottle, 12x32", EX, D **$45.00**

Dignity Cigar, sign, paper, portrait of a woman wearing full-length gown, Smoke The Great..., matted & framed, image: 23x12", G, A **$175.00**

Dill's, see also JG Dill Co.

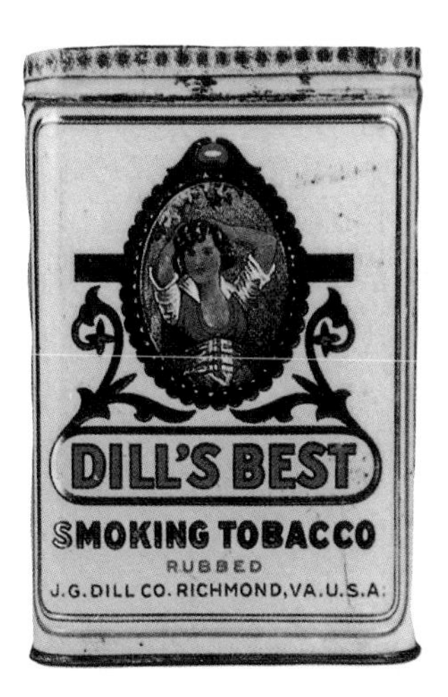

Dill's Best Smoking Tobacco, tin, pictures girl in fancy oval above product & company name, JG Dill Co, Richmond Va, USA, slip lid, VG, A $5.00

Dill's Cube Cut Tobacco, pocket tin, upright, VG+, H3 ..**$45.00**

Dilling's Marshmallows, tin, Dilling's lettered diagonally in script, slip lid, some wear, round, A................**$20.00**

Dipper, crate label, Florida citrus, half orange draining into an antique dipper, black background, 9x9", M, C1..**$3.00**

Diving Girl, crate label, California apple, 1920s bathing beauty diving in lake, 9x11", EX, G1 ....**$15.00**

Dixi-Cola, mirror, Enjoy Dixi-Cola... on panel below mirror, edge wear/flaking, 14x6", VG+, A..................**$38.00**

Dixie, can label, Washington salmon, 2 salmons in the ocean with flowers & leaves in background, M, C1 ....**$2.00**

Dixie Beer, label, 1933-34, Merz Products Co Inc, U-type permit number, VG, A **$22.00**

Dixie Boy Shoes, pin-back button, product name above little boy admiring his shoes, Geo D Witt Shoe Co below, round, EX, A **$20.00**

Dixie Brand Jumbo Salted Peanuts, tin, Black boy with large lettered peanut in mouth & other lettering on shield, no lid, 9½x8¼" dia, G-, A **$10.00**

Dixie Cups, dispenser, 1¢, iron & glass, coin operated, original condition with keys, 31x4", VG, A **$225.00**

Dixie Delite, crate label, 1930s, Florida Citrus Fruits, romantic couple dancing, Marion County Citrus Co, 9x9", M, C3 ....$5.00

Dixie Gasoline, pump sign, 1970s, porcelain, blue & red on yellow, crossed Confederate flags above Dixie, red border, round, EX+, A **$170.00**

Dixie Kid Cut Plug, lunch pail, pictures a Black baby flanked by product name, Nall & Williams Tobacco Co, hinged lid & wire handle, EX+, A.......................**$330.00**

Dixie Motor Oil, sign, counter-top, illuminated reverse-painted glass lens in metal case, pictures can of oil, 14", EX, A...**$250.00**

Dixie Peanut Butter, pail, tin, red with Dixie in red on white circular logo, Peanut Butter on gold banner, slip lid & bail, 1-lb, VG, A **$110.00**

Dixie Pride Grits, can label, 1929, woman holding can of grits, G, C3 ....**$6.00**

Dixie Queen Plug Cut, lunch pail, product name on red & white basketweave background, rectangular, EX+, A.**$35.00**

Dixie Queen Plug Cut, tin, Dixie Queen lettered above portrait of lady in plumed hat, Plug Cut below, slip lid, round, 7", VG, A..**$195.00**

Dixie Springs Beverages, sign, 1940s, die-cut cardboard stand-up, pictures bottle & 2 glasses, 24x18", EX, D .**$25.00**

Dixie Super Motor Oil, sign, reverse-painted glass in illuminated metal case, pictures product, Drain Your Crankcase Now!..., 11x23", EX, A........................**$300.00**

Dixie Sweet Brand Watermelon, label, 1940s, classic pickaninny eating slice of watermelon, 1½x2¼", M, D.....**$3.50**

Dixieland Machine Needles, display card with 20 packs of sewing needles, 1930s, 8x6", EX, D..................**$20.00**

Dixon's Carburet of Iron Stove Polish, trade card, pictures Black woman cleaning child, advertising on reverse, EX, A...**$19.00**

Dixon's Pencils, display, oversized sharpened pencil, yellow, 70" long, NM, A **$130.00**

Dixon's Pencils, sign, paper, Victorian scene with woman doing child's portrait, American Graphite Pencils, framed, image: 29x13", VG, A **$300.00**

Dixon's Stove Polish, ad, copyright 1886, paper, group of Black men at meeting, Lime, Kiln, Club lettered by stove pipe, matted, 5x6", EX+, A..........................**$70.00**

Dixon's Stove Polish, sign, paper roll-down, girl in green dress & paper hat with lettering, framed with metal strips, image: 30x12½", G, A...............................**$150.00**

Dixon's Stove Polish, sign, paper roll-down, woman in red, white & blue dress holding fishing net, framed, image: 28½x13", EX, A.......................................**$400.00**

DM Ferry & Co's Standard Seeds, sign, 1900s, little girl holding vegetables with dog beside her, product name above & below, framed, 29x19", EX, A **$210.00**

Doan's Kidney Pills, thermometer, die-cut wood, man with bad back above lettering, Is Your Back Bad Today..., tube missing, 21x5", G-, A.....................**$95.00**

Doan's Kidney Pills, thermometer, die-cut wood, man with bad back above lettering, Is Your Back Bad Today..., 21x5", VG+, D **$225.00**

Dobler Brewing Co, tray, deep-dish, demure long-haired girl in right profile, 13¼" dia, A...........................**$25.00**

Dobler Brewing Co, tray, horse-drawn beer wagons with logo & lettering above, decorative rim, oval, 15¼x18½", G-, A...**$70.00**

Dobson the Mover, sign, 1950s, tin, pictures moving van with Call Collect Bay City TW3-6562 lettered below, black & gold, 24x30", M, A.................................**$125.00**

Dockash Stove Factory, match holder, tin, product name above factory image, blemishes, 5", G-, A............**$25.00**

Dockash Stoves, pocket mirror, stove with Dochash Stoves Are The Best at top, Mfg By Scranton Stove Works... below, 2¼" dia, G, A...**$18.00**

Dodge, booklet, 1967, dealer stamp center front, 24 pages, D ...**$5.00**

Dodge, key chain, enameled logo on leather background, EX, D **$12.00**

Dodge Brothers, trunk emblem, 6-point star logo, black, gold & silver, 8" wide, EX, D...............................**$40.00**

Dodge Trucks, postcard, 1951, 7½x4", EX, D **$4.00**

Dodge Trucks, sign, porcelain, Dodge above 'Job-Rated' above Trucks, Sales & Service, round corners, 42x42", VG, A **$500.00**

Dodge Trucks, sign, 1920s, paper, red & black on white, The Choice Of National Users above fleets of commercial trucks, 38x49", EX, D3 ....**$850.00**

Dodge Trucks, table lighter, oil drum shape, M, D...**$25.00**

Dodge/Plymouth sign, neon, Dodge on blue band above Plymouth on white band, 35x65", G, D **$1,200.00**

Dold Foods, pin-back button, 1920s, blue & white with red highlights, EX, D...**$5.00**

Dole Pineapple Juice, sign, cardboard, 3-part, S2..**$185.00**

Dolly Madison Cigars, trade card, mechanical, man peeking through keyhole into room where woman's leg kicks up, scarce, VG, A..**$75.00**

Domino's Pizza, doll, The Noid, stuffed cloth, 12", EX, D **$15.00**

Don Carlos Cigars, box label, inner lid, medieval man with sword, 6x9", M, C3......................................**$35.00**

Don Max-Ze Cigars, box label, inner lid, bust portrait of a man with medallions & coat-of-arms, 6x9", M, D **$4.00**

Don Nieto Cigars, box label, outer, 1923, image of 1923 scholar, 4½x4½", EX, C3 ....**$10.00**

Donald Duck Lime Cola, 6-pack carton, cardboard, multiple images of Donald Duck, unused, B1.............**$15.00**

Donald Duck Orange Juice, bank, cardboard with metal ends, Donald saying Start Your Day The OJ Way, Drink Donald Duck Orange Juice, 4", NM, A **$5.00**

Donald Duck Pop Corn, can, product name above & right of Donald salting his pan of popcorn, unopened, 10-oz, EX, A **$250.00**

Donaldson Cigar, sign, 1910s, embossed die-cut cardboard stand-up, open box of cigars, 11x9", EX, D **$20.00**

Donner, crate label, 1930s, California pear, snow scene at Lake Tahoe, Placer County Mountain Bartletts, 7¼x11", M, C1 ....**$2.00**

Donniford Tobacco, pocket tin, upright, pictures a small pipe above Donniford in diagonal script lettering, VG+, A **$20.00**

Donovan's Red Diamond Coffee, thermometer, tin, bag of coffee above can of coffee at left of thermometer, product name above, rounded top, 15", G+, A....**$85.00**

Doring's Reliable Shoe Store, trade card, oval image of the store, Established 1868, 270 River Street, Troy NY above & below, EX, A **$26.00**

Dot Coffee, tin, front label on dotted can pictures large red dot with product name above & below, Dot's Good, pry lid, EX, A **$70.00**

Double Cola, bottle, 1971, clear with red & white label, 10-oz, EX, D **$5.00**

Double Cola, calendar, 1950, girl holding beach ball in front of clouds, July/Aug/Sept shown below, framed, 15½x21½", G, A **$10.00**

Double Cola, menu board, Drink Double Cola on red oval over 3 yellow stripes on green panel above chalk board, round corners, EX+, M2 ....**$42.00**

Double Cola, menu board, Drink Double Cola on red oval with star bursts on blue band above chalk board, 28x20", NM, M3 ....**$75.00**

Double Cola, sign, cardboard, mother kangaroo & 3 babies enjoying Double Cola, Get More When You Pour..., 10x12", NM, M3 ....**$18.00**

Double Cola, sign, tin, white Drink Double Cola on red with white & green border, oval, 24x36", NM, M3.........**$165.00**

Double Cola, sign, 1946, metal, Drink Double Cola in oval right of bottle pouring into 2 glasses, Double Measure..., 11x28", VG+, D **$80.00**

Double Cola, sign, 1950s, die-cut cardboard hanger, 2-sided, 2 happy kids in hot-air balloon, Get A Big Lift..., 22x11", NM, B1 ....**$15.00**

Double Cola, thermometer, dial, metal frame, glass lens, red numbers around red dot with Drink Double Cola in white, 12" dia, NM, M2 ....**$80.00**

Double Cola, thermometer, tin, red & white on blue, Drink Double Cola in top oval, You'll Like It Better in bottom oval, 17", NM, M3 ....**$75.00**

Dougherty's New England Mince Meat, sign, Uncle Sam standing atop boxes of product with other political figures fighting for them, black & white, framed, 33x26", NM, D.....**$1,200.00**

Douglas Corn Gluten Feed & Meal, sign, 1920s-40s, tin, cow's head in center & feed sacks in bottom corners, red & black lettering, 23½x35½", VG, A.............**$225.00**

Doutrich's Clothes, sign, wood, black on orange-brown, diagonal Doutrich's with Always Reliable & Clothes above & below, 12x59", G, A **$60.00**

Dover Egg Beater, sign, 1870s, paper, wistful maid whisking eggs beside large egg beater, For Sale Here, minor soiling, 12x9", EX, A **$1,400.00**

Dow Bathroom Cleaner, squeeze toy, 1989, Scrubbing Bubble, molded vinyl, 3½", M, D......................$5.00

Dowagiac Drills & Seeders, pocket mirror, banner over sheath of wheat encircled by band of lettering, ...Are The Leaders, 2⅛" dia, EX, A **$90.00**

Doyle Derby Bread, pin-back button, 1930s, orange & black, EX, D **$8.00**

Doyle Gulf, pin-back button, 1930s, orange with blue lettering, EX, D **$20.00**

Dr AC Daniels' Horse, Cat & Dog Medicines, sign, embossed tin, Use Dr AC Daniels Horse Cat Dog Medicines For Home Treatment in white on black, 17½x28", EX, A...**$110.00**

Dr AC Daniels' Horse Medicines, pocket mirror, woman, horse & dog viewed between gate posts lettered with product name, scratching, 2⅛" dia, EX, A **$110.00**

Dr AC Daniels' Veterinary Medicines, cabinet, wood, embossed tin front pictures Dr Daniels with products below, 28½x21½x7½", VG, A..........................**$1,550.00**

Dr Brown's Celery Syrup, dispenser, pattern-glass bowl with milk-glass base, no lid, 10½x7" square base, EX, A....**$65.00**

Dr Brown's Cream Soda, can, steel, EX, D **$4.00**

Dr Brown's Patent Baby Tender, sign, paper, interior view of children in highchairs, baby seats & cribs with adults at table, framed, 18x22", VG, A............**$4,000.00**

Dr Caldwell's Syrup, sign, cardboard, product bottle displayed before child in pageboy hairdo being given spoonful of syrup, 17x15", NM, M3 ....**$185.00**

Dr Caldwell's Syrup Pepsin, display, counter-top cardboard stand-up, Dr Caldwell holding product behind sign, ...Family Laxative, NM, D...........................**$175.00**

Dr Caldwell's Syrup Pepsin, door push plate, porcelain, You Can Depend On...The Family Laxative, yellow & black, 6½x3¾", VG, A **$95.00**

Dr Caldwell's Syrup Pepsin, thermometer/barometer, wood, black on white, lettering above & below, rounded top, minor scratches, 24", G+, A **$190.00**

Dr Calvin Cranes Remedies, display case, wood with slanted glass lid, crane graphic at left of advertising on front panel, 10x15½x10", EX, A..........................**$650.00**

Dr Clark's Life Balsam, sign, paper, crowned lady in yellow dress with spray of roses promoting medicinal cure-all, framed, image: 13x9", VG, A................**$425.00**

Dr D Jayne's Expectorant & Tonic Vermifuge, sign, paper roll-down, woman in red hood, For Coughs & Colds Use... above & below, framed, image: 29x13½", VG, A **$500.00**

Dr D Jayne's Family Medicines, sign, glass with embossed silver & gold foil lettering with gold border, wood frame, 11½x21¾", EX+, A **$110.00**

Dr D Jayne's Sanative Pills, sign, tin, advertising on fence behind boy holding cat while fending off dog with stick, framed, image: 15x11", EX, A................**$1,300.00**

Dr D Jayne's Sanative Pills, trade card, 1880s, pictures Little Red Riding Hood, 4x4½", EX, P1 ....**$11.00**

Dr Drake's Glessco Cough & Croup Remedy, sign, shows couple looking over child in crib, ...For Young & Old below, crazing/faded, 14¼x11½", G-, A..**$200.00**

Dr EL Graves Tooth Powder, sign, foil-backed with reverse-painted black ground, mirrored back, ...Beautiful Teeth, framed, 30x11", EX, A........................**$325.00**

Dr Frost's Homeopathic Remedies, cabinet, wood with tin door panel listing remedies for 38 ailments, surface rust, 19", G, A **$375.00**

Dr Greene's Nervura, thermometer, green-painted wood with rounded top & squared bottom, Dr Greene's Nervura For The Nerves, 14", EX, A.....................**$30.00**

Dr Haile's Ole Injun System Tonic, sign, paperboard, Indian chief in full headdress, ...For The Kidneys, Liver & Stomach, 13½x20½", EX, A..............................**$10.00**

Dr Harter Medicine Co, almanac, 'Dr Harter's Almanac & Weather Forecasts for 98', shows cute little girl with finger in her mouth, EX, H1 ....**$14.00**

Dr Hess Medicated Powder, tin, Dr Hess lettered above horse collar logo flanked by Medicated Powder lettered diagonally & 4-oz 25¢, VG, A...............................**$20.00**

Dr Jaeger's Sanitary Woolen, sign, tin, Agency For The Celebrated..., black, silver, & gold stencil, Tuchfarber, framed, image, 13½x20", VG, A **$185.00**

Dr Johnson's Educator Crackers, tin, product name surrounded by decorative border, lift lid, 6x5½" square, VG+, A **$30.00**

Dr Kellogg's Asthma Remedy, tin, slip lid, tall square shape with rounded corners, EX, A......................**$15.00**

Dr Lesure's Veterinary Medicines, cabinet, wood with glass door, 4 shelves, lettered marquee, 28x16x6", NM, A...$2,000.00

Dr Lions Celebrated Stomach Bitters, calendar, 1907, die-cut cardboard, advertising above 3 ladies enjoying product, small pad attached below, 17x13", VG, A.........**$15.00**

Dr McMunn's Kinute of Quinine & Cinchonine, sign, 1850s, paper, pictures sick woman in interior scene with men hard at work outside, framed, image: 10x14", EX, A **$1,000.00**

Dr Melvins Vegetable Pills, trade card, dapper Black man with big hat, VG, D **$8.00**

Dr Miles Medical Co, almanac with 1925 calendar, forecast & lots of medical cures, 32 pages, tear at top corner, G, D...**$3.00**

Dr Miles Nervine, almanac, 1937, 32 pages, EX, D **$6.00**

Dr Miles Remedies, calendar, 1908, child holding a rose, HH Alley & Co, Druggists..., calendar never opened, minor edge wear, A..........................$50.00

Dr Morse's Indian Root Pills, display, die-cut cardboard trifold, product packs flank Indian & village scene, product name above, 27x40", EX, M3................**$150.00**

Dr Morse's Indian Root Pills, trade card, image of the bottling plant with workers, green & black on white, EX, A..**$30.00**

Dr Morse's Indian Root Pills, trade card, Indian on horseback fighting a bear, Comstock's Dead Shot Worm Pellets lettered below, EX, A......................................**$16.00**

Dr Nebbs Baby Powder, tin, pictures baby with blocks, EX, D..**$50.00**

Dr O'Neill's Vegetable Remedy, tin, 1919, oval portrait of Dr O'Neill, red, white & blue, slip lid, full, 1½x2", EX, D..**$10.00**

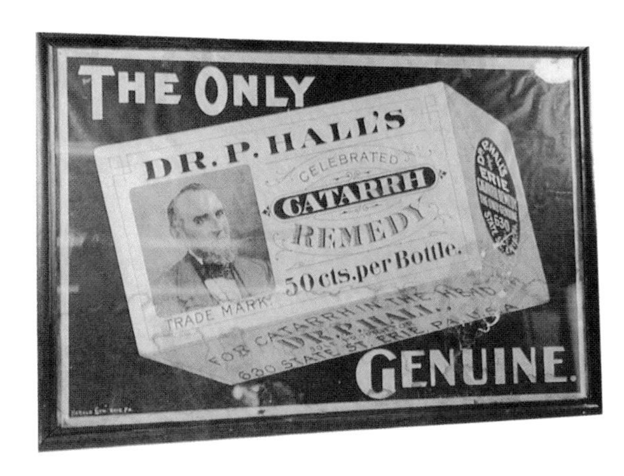

Dr P Hall's Catarrh Remedy, sign, 1880s, Dr Hall on product box, blue background, The Only Genuine lettered above & below, framed, 30½x45", G, A...$35.00

Dr Pepper, awning, porcelain, Drink...Good For Life on checked ground above clock logo, lime-green background, 46", EX, A..**$4,000.00**

Dr Pepper, bottle, aqua with embossed label, 6 1/2-oz, EX, D..**$8.50**

Dr Pepper, bottle, 1940s, Victoria Texas, rare, 6 1/2-oz, EX, D..**$25.00**

Dr Pepper, bottle, 1976, clear with red & white label, 10-oz, EX, D..**$4.50**

Dr Pepper, bottle, 1985, 100th anniversary, EX, D....**$10.00**

Dr Pepper, calendar, 1951, smiling girl wearing pageboy hairdo & pearls, 4 months & 10-2-4 bottle-cap logo below, A Lift For Life, EX, A................................**$40.00**

Dr Pepper, calendar, 1960, 75th anniversary, EX, D.**$35.00**

Dr Pepper, calendar, 1965, features Donna Loren, complete, EX, D..**$15.00**

Dr Pepper, calendar, 1965, lady standing at oval mirror with 3 months showing below, Distinctively Different, NM, A..**$25.00**

Dr Pepper, calendar, 1977, January & February months feature girl in raincoat standing at edge of Niagara Falls, complete, NM, A...**$18.00**

Dr Pepper, calendar, 1983, Be A Pepper, complete, EX, D..**$7.50**

Dr Pepper, can, cone top, rare, 6-ox, EX, A...........**$150.00**

Dr Pepper, character glass, 1976, Star Trek collector series, Mr Spock, M, D..**$25.00**

Dr Pepper, clock, neon, Dr Pepper logo below hands, numbered with emphasis on 10-2-4, square, EX, D......**$250.00**

Dr Pepper, clock, plastic, white Dr Pepper on red band across white bottle cap numbered in blue with 10-2-4 in red, 14" dia, VG, M3..**$55.00**

Dr Pepper, display, die-cut cardboard, lady in hat ready to drink from bottle, Drink... & 10-2-4 logo below, VG+, A...**$486.00**

Dr Pepper, door pull, 1940s, aluminum, red, gray & white bottle shape with Dr Pepper logo on top bracket, 10x3½", VG, A..**$210.00**

Dr Pepper, drinking glass, flared rim, Dr Pepper in script on front, extremely rare, 6", EX, A..................**$1,700.00**

Dr Pepper, emergency card, tin, bottle & clock logo above name & address card, 8x4", VG, A.......................**$90.00**

Dr Pepper, fan, paper, 2-sided, elegant girl with bottle, man in top hat on reverse, 14", VG, A.................**$60.00**

Dr Pepper, menu board, tin, Dr Pepper oval above green board, white border, rounded corners, 28x20", EX+, M2...**$30.00**

Dr Pepper, menu board, tin, Dr Pepper oval above green board, white border, rounded corners, 28x20", NM, M3..**$55.00**

Dr Pepper, name badge, celluloid, Junior Chamber Of Commerce above blank name plate, Winston-Salem, Dr Pepper below, round, EX, A.............................**$102.00**

Dr Pepper, pencil clip, 1930s, orange, black & white, EX, D..**$28.00**

Dr Pepper, pin tray, Black boy in straw hat eating watermelon, vertical oval with scalloped rim, G, A.......................**$275.00**

Dr Pepper, radio, wood-cased cooler form with logo, working, 8½x12x8", EX, A..............................**$1,200.00**

Dr Pepper, recipe book, 1965, 'Cookin' with Dr Pepper,' 15 pages, EX, D..**$5.00**

Dr Pepper, shot glass, 1985, 100th anniversary, EX, D...**$3.50**

Dr Pepper, shot glass, 1989, America's Oldest Soft Drink, EX, D..**$3.00**

Dr Pepper, sign, cardboard, die-cut, hanger, 1940s, Dr Pepper logo above smiling brunette opening bottle, 7x5", NM, D..**$45.00**

Dr Pepper, sign, cardboard, self-framed, Dr Pepper above 2 ladies watching chef barbecuing next to large bottle, vertical, EX, M1 ....**$320.00**

Dr Pepper, sign, cardboard, 1940s, Certainly & Drink... logo above lady in hat & stole with bottle before NY skyline, 25x15", NM, A.......................................**$140.00**

Dr Pepper, sign, cardboard, 1940s, girl in open car at drive-in enjoys hamburger & Dr Pepper, Join Me!, horizontal, NM, A..**$180.00**

Dr Pepper, sign, paper, BC character water skiing on bottle guided by dinosaur, It's Different...I Like It!, 15x25", NM, M3 ....**$24.00**

Dr Pepper, sign, paper, diagonal shadowed logo behind bottle & 10-2-4 clock, Drink A Bite To Eat, 9x11½", G+, A..**$55.00**

Dr Pepper, sign, paper, hands putting ice cream & pouring Dr Pepper into glass, Try A Frosty Pepper..., 15x25", NM, M3 ....**$15.00**

Dr Pepper, sign, porcelain, Dr Pepper Bottling Co lettered on triangle with rounded corners, 12x21½", EX+, A...**$200.00**

Dr Pepper, sign, porcelain, Drink Dr Pepper, Good For Life in white & black on red, green & white, 10½x26½", VG, A **$150.00**

Dr Pepper, sign, porcelain, Drink Dr Pepper in red on white center band, 10-2-4 in white on red above & below, 10" dia, NM, A.................................$675.00

Dr Pepper, sign, tin, die-cut, 1950s, white & red 10-2-4 bottle cap, 24" dia, EX+, D **$230.00**

Dr Pepper, sign, tin, Dr Pepper lettered in white on red, white border, 8x18", NM, M3 ....**$45.00**

Dr Pepper, sign, tin, Drink above Dr Pepper in script, For The Good Life on tail, red & white checked background, 13x34", G+, M3......................................**$75.00**

Dr Pepper, sign, tin, embossed, pictures 6-pack of bottles, Take Home A Carton, 27x19", EX, A **$350.00**

Dr Pepper, sign, tin, Enjoy above red Drink Dr Pepper logo, Distinctively Different below, grid background, 20x28", EX, A..**$75.00**

Dr Pepper, sign, tin, white rectangle with Drink Dr Pepper on red horizontal oval, red border, round corners, 12x30", NM, M3 ....**$135.00**

Dr Pepper, straw holder, glass with chrome top & holder, 11½", EX, D **$25.00**

Dr Pepper, syrup dispenser, ceramic urn shape, glass pedestal, ...An Ideal Beverage, 5¢, ring handle on lid, 18x9" dia, G, A...**$7,500.00**

Dr Pepper, thermometer, bottle cap shape, G, D **$95.00**

Dr Pepper, thermometer, tin, shaped 10-2-4 logo above Drink Dr Pepper panel above bottle displaying bulb & 10-2-4 clock, EX, M1 ....**$290.00**

Dr Pepper, thermometer, tin, 1939, Drink...Good For Life above thermometer flanked by At 10, 2 & 4, bottle below, 17x5", EX, A **$400.00**

Dr Pepper, tray, pretty girl holding 2 bottles, You'll Like It Too!, Dr Pepper & Drink A Bite To Eat on rim, vertical, EX, A **$180.00**

Dr Pierce's Anuric Tablets, sign, cardboard, hand holding product before man complaining about back, Oh My Back!, The Newest Discovery..., VG+, A **$120.00**

Dr Pierce's Medical Discovery, sign, ca 1915, paper, product name & other lettering around nurse with soldier on battle field, 16x20", VG+, A...................**$210.00**

Dr Pierce's Pleasant Purgative Pellets, sign, paper, giant overlooking squire trumpeting arrival of pellets in oval inset, framed, image: 27½x21½", VG, A **$3,100.00**

Dr Price's Phosphate Baking Powder, recipe book, copyright 1921, 'The New Dr Price Cook Book,' pictures girl carrying cake plate, 49 pages, 8x5", EX, D................**$4.00**

Dr Roberts Dental Powder, canister, cardboard & metal, EX, A **$17.00**

Dr Russell's Pepsin Calisaya Bitters, sign, paper, nymph with cornucopia above product name, flag-draped bottle on 2 globes below, framed, 21½x15", EX, A...$1,750.00

Dr Scholls Foot Eazer, box, copyright 1935, cardboard, with used supports & instructions, original price $3.50, 7½x3½", EX+, P4 ....**$20.00**

Dr Scholls Foot Soap, tin, with contents, shaker top, round, 5", EX, P4 ....**$9.00**

Dr Schoop's Health Coffee Imitation, match holder, tin, product name above & below circular portrait of Dr Schoop, minor scratches, 4¾", EX, A **$185.00**

Dr Seth Arnolds Cough Killer, trade card, little girl holding puppy, It Works Like Magic, Price 25 Cents lettered below, EX, A...**$19.00**

Dr Strong's Tricora Corset, trade card, 1880s, woman in bustle dress, Affords Great Relief & Comfort, 2½x5½", EX, P1 ....**$20.00**

Dr Swett's Original Root Beer, pin-back button, girl hugging horse's head surrounded by stars & stripes border, red, white & blue, round, EX, A..........................**$40.00**

Dr Swett's Root Beer, mug, stoneware, Dr Swett's, The Original Root Beer, chip near handle, 4¾", VG, A...........**$35.00**

Dr Swett's Root Beer, sign, tin, bust-length portrait of girl with portrait mug, The Great Health..., curled corners, 14½x14½", VG, A **$500.00**

Dr Warner's Coraline Corsets, trade card, die-cut folder picturing flowers & leaves, advertising inside, EX, A ...**$16.00**

Dr Wells, menu board, blue Dr Wells on diagonal white & red bands above green menu panel, The Cooler Doctor below, 27x19", VG, M3 ....**$40.00**

Dr Wells, sign, tin, The Cooler Doctor & other text at left of yellow-haired boy on skis, Dr Wells sign at right, 12x31", EX, M3 ....**$55.00**

Dr Wells, thermometer, tin, red & blue on white, Dr Wells, The Cooler Doctor, rounded ends, 15x6", NM, M3 .**$35.00**

Dr Wernet's Powder, sample tin, 2¼", EX, D **$25.00**

Dr White's Cough Drops, tin, pink, slip lid, rectangular, tall, EX, A **$75.00**

Dr Willis A Myers & Co Veterinary Medicines, sign, printed paperboard, white on blue, list of products flanked by horse's head & lettering, 7x20", G, A .**$80.00**

Drako Coffee, tin, pictures duck on water with product name above, Coffee below, gold screw lid, 1-lb, EX, A..**$1,600.00**

Dreadnaught Tire Chains, box, heavy cardboard, pictures battle ship sailing through tire & factory scene, 7x7x5", EX, D **$35.00**

Dreikorn's Bread, mirror with thermometer & barometer, 23x15", VG+, A **$25.00**

Driver Sliced Plug Smoke or Chew, box, 1898 stamp, cardboard, J Wright Co... & Driver above racing surrey, Sliced Plug Smoke Or Chew below, 1 2/3-oz, G, A **$31.00**

Droste's Cocoa, tin, square shape with product name above seated Dutch boy & girl, 1-lb, 6x4x4", EX, A **$5.00**

Droste's Dutch Process Cocoa, tin, 4 sides with different graphics, 2 showing crown logo on light blue & seated Dutch kids on red, 8-oz, EX, A **$17.50**

Drum Major Marshmallows, tin, slip lid, some scratches & dents, A **$75.00**

Drummond Tobacco Company, sign, 1895, paper, woman in regal gown holding bouquet, Forbes Litho Co, framed, image: 26¾x19", G, A **$90.00**

DS Brown & Co Toilet Soaps, sign, paper, outdoor scene of women washing in stream with insets of bedroom & bathroom scenes above, 13x20", EX, A $2,600.00

DS Morgan & Co, trade card, vignettes of various farm implements, EX, A..**$46.00**

Du Barry Cigars, box label, inner lid, bride holding roses, 6x9", M, C3 ....**$14.00**

Du Belle Grape Juice, pocket mirror, demure lady lifts glass of grape juice, None Better lettered below, lettered border, oval, 2¾", EX, A............................**$194.00**

Du Bois Budweiser, clock, metal case with reverse-painted glass front, product name on white face with black numbers, 15" dia, VG, A **$200.00**

Du Bois Budweiser, sign, embossed tin, Try The Original... above bottle flanked by Truly Different & Always Good, 19¼x13¼", VG, A **$33.00**

Du Bois Budweiser, sign, light-up, metal back, curved glass front, red, white & black lettering on divided red & white field, 10x11", EX, A **$125.00**

Du Pont, calendar, 1900, battle scene of Santiago, full pad, matted & framed, 28x14", VG, A **$495.00**

Du Pont, pin-back button, pictures dogs on multicolored background, round, EX, A **$65.00**

Du Pont, pin-back button, red, white & blue, oval, EX, A **$20.00**

Du Pont, sign, 'Hunters Inspiration,' 2 side-by-side pointers in profile, advertising on back, framed, 8x13", VG, A .**$150.00**

Du Pont, sign, self-framed tin, elderly man showing young boy how to shoot, Generations Have Used Dupont Powder, VG, A **$400.00**

Du Pont, sign, 1904, paper, shows dog retrieving downed mallard, Shoot Dupont in lower right, framed, 26x18", VG, A **$450.00**

Du Pont, sign, 1907, paper, pictures a dog (Joe Cumming), winner of 1899 National Field Trial Championship, 31x20", EX, D **$550.00**

Du Pont, stickpin, brass bird, VG, A.......................**$140.00**

Du Pont, stickpin, silver dog, EX, A..........................**$55.00**

Du Pont Duco-Dulux, sign, 1940s, 2-sided cardboard light-up on bracket, Automobile... on yellow above Du Pont... on green, 12x15", EX, A **$240.00**

Du Pont Powders, postcard, 'Canvas Backs,' unused, VG, A **$60.00**

Du Pont Powders, postcard, pictures a large Canada Goose, 1 from a series of 12, VG+, P3 ....**$30.00**

Du Pont Powders, postcard, 1921, 'Prairie Chicken,' used, VG, A **$40.00**

Du Pont Powders for Firearms, booklet, 1924, pictures dog barking at leopard in tree, well illustrated, 28 pages, EX, A **$25.00**

Du Pont's Gun Powder, sign, 1869, paper, hunting scene, EI Dupont De Nemours & Co, Wilmington Del, framed, image: 22x27½", EX+, A $19,000.00

Du Pont Shot Shells, ad cover with insert, 1920, image of a mallard in flight, Canadian, scarce, VG, A....................**$95.00**

Du Pont Sporting Powders, sign, 1917, paper, pictures 5 generations of hunters, metal strips top & bottom, 31x20", G, A **$200.00**

Du Pont Sporting Powders, sign, 1919, paper, wintry hunt scene of elderly man & boy seated on a log, metal strips top & bottom, 26x17", VG, A **$800.00**

Du Pont Superfine Gunpowder, can, product name in center with vignettes of various game in each corner, 1-lb, VG, A **$35.00**

Duckwall, crate label, apple, wood duck by stone wall on blue background, 10½x9", M, C1 ....**$10.00**

Duesseldorfer Beer, tray, bald baby with beer bottle beside beaming bird, lettering on rim, crazing/chipping/fading, 21" dia, G-, A **$100.00**

Duffee's Fifty-Fifty Laxative Tonic Tablets, sign, embossed tin, banded edge, 9½x13⅝", G, A........**$50.00**

Duffy's Pure Malt Whiskey, pocket mirror, profile of elderly gent seated lifting glass, Makes The Weak Strong, horizontal oval, 2¾", EX, A **$45.00**

Duffy's Pure Malted Milk, container, porcelain, product name above little girl with product, lid missing, otherwise EX, A **$200.00**

Duffy Trowbridge Co Stoves, sign, embossed tin, pictures a pig & lettering on sunray design, ...From Selected Pig Iron, Shonk litho, 17x24", VG, A........................**$550.00**

Duke Beer, clock, metal back & frame with painted glass front, gold backgound with red & gold lettering, diagonal, 15x15", VG, A **$30.00**

Duke of Wellington Cigars, box label, inner lid sample, the duke before domed building flanked by large coins, George S Harris litho, 1880s, VG, A...........**$30.00**

Duke's Cameo Cigarettes, folding chair, wood, chair back lettered on both sides with girl pictured on 1 side & couple on other, EX, A **$1,400.00**

Duke's Cameo Cigarettes, portrait, paper, half-length Victorian woman in ornate gilt frame with plaque denoting brand, 24¼x20½", VG, A **$140.00**

Duke's Cigarettes, sign, paper, elegant woman in plumed hat, black ground, ...The Best In The World, original frame, 33x25", EX, A **$400.00**

Duke's Mixture, cigarette papers, pictures bag of tobacco with Special Duke's Mixture Papers lettered above, brown, NM, A **$6.00**

Duke's Mixture, door push plate, We Sell above Duke's Mixture pouch, It Pleases below, bottom edge chips, vertical, EX, M1 ....**$270.00**

Duke's Mixture, sign, porcelain, Duke's Mixture in script above hand pouring tobacco into other hand, The Roll Of Fame, 8x5", EX, M1 ....**$675.00**

Duke's Mixture, sign, 1899, paper, 2 military comrades sharing pack of tobacco, Best In War..., framed with metal strips, 31x20", G, A **$200.00**

Duke's Tobacco, display, die-cut cardboard, man putting tobacco pouch in hat, Headquarters For Rolling Duke's, 34x21½", VG, A **$10.00**

Duke's Tobacco, pack, full, H3 ....**$15.00**

Dunbar's Pitcher Syrup, tin, pitcher form with pour spout & handle, rare, some wear, A..............................**$60.00**

Dundee Marmalade, crock container, glazed with emblem & lettering, top missing, round, 4½", EX, P4........**$10.00**

Dunham's Cocoanut, pocket mirror, shows girl in open coconut shell lettered with product name, 2⅛" dia, VG+, A **$90.00**

Dunkin' Donuts, child's tea set, 1970s, plastic, MIB, P2..**$90.00**

Dunkin' Donuts, figure, wood, Dunkie holding tray of donuts, coffee cup at center of torso, surface scratches/scuffs, 30", VG, A...............................**$240.00**

Dunlap's Seeds, poster, paper, child holding large cabbage with various vegetables at her feet, matted & framed, image: 24x16", EX, A...**$550.00**

Dunlop Gold Seal, ashtray, rubber, tire shape with clear insert, D **$16.00**

Dunlop Tires, sign, embossed metal, cream Dunlop lettered vertically above Tires on black panel on red, 2-tone border, 60x14", G, A....................................**$50.00**

Duplex Marine Engine Oil, sign, 1950, tin, red Authorized Dealer above blue product name on green, Use Kasson...Grease below, 10x20", VG, A **$80.00**

Duplex Motor Oil, can, 1915-25, product name above woman in a Pierce-Arrow, yellow with black lettering, pour spout, 1-gal, 15½", EX, A **$180.00**

Duplex Outboard Gear Oil, can, 1940-50, 2 fisherman in boat with lettering above & below, blue background, screw lid, 1-qt, 7½", EX, A **$35.00**

Duplex Outboard Gear Oil, can, 1940-50, 2 fishermen in boat with lettering above & below, white background, screw lid, 1-qt, 7½", EX, A **$25.00**

Duquesne Pilsner, sign, neon, metal box with hard plastic raised letters, green neon on black, minor rust/water spots, 6x24½", EX, A **$85.00**

Duralin Linoleum, display rack, wood with 2-sectioned tin sign on crossbar at top, pictures use in every room, approx: 80x75x7", G, A......................................**$300.00**

Durham Smoking Tobacco, label, woman on rearing stallion, Smoke The Only Genuine Favorite..., decorative border, 12½x10", EX, A......................................**$300.00**

Durham Tobacco, cigarette papers, pictures bag of tobacco with New Size above & 5 Cents below, NM, A..........**$6.00**

Dust-Puff, tin, 1915-25, woman cleaning touring car on blue inset, blue & white checked ground, slip lid, 6x3", NM, A **$80.00**

Dustbane Mfg Co, pin-back button, Dustbane arched above leaping black cat, orange, black & white, round, EX, A **$62.00**

Dutch Boy Marine Finishes, sign, 1930s-40s, tin, 2-sided, Dutch Boy with ship's wheel, product name below in black & white, 27½x17½", VG, A.......................**$200.00**

Dutch Boy Paints, booklet, copyright 1914, 'Adventures of the Dutch Boy & the Color Spirits,' John T Lewis & Bros, 20-pages, 6x5", EX, D **$12.00**

Dutch Boy Paints, booklet, 1923, colorful images of Dutch Boy with matching black & white line drawings, 12 pages, 5½x4½", VG, D **$22.00**

Dutch Boy Paints, display, copper-clad plaster figure of the Dutch Boy, 20" EX, A **$440.00**

Dutch Boy Paints, figure, embossed die-cut tin figure of the Dutch Boy with paint can, rust on bucket, 6½", VG, A...**$250.00**

Dutch Boy Paints, hand puppet, 1956, cloth body with soft vinyl head, felt hands missing some fingers, VG+, D....................$24.00

Dutch Boy Paints, hand puppet, 1956, cloth body with soft vinyl head, replaced felt hands, EX, D..........$45.00

Dutch Boy Paints, match holder, embossed die-cut tin, Dutch Boy in black shading with black bucket that holds matches, 6¼x3¼", NM, A.................$1,000.00

Dutch Boy Paints, sample case, ca 1910, black leather with impressed logo, contains several paint samples, 2½x3½", VG+, D....................$12.00

Dutch Boy Paints, sign, porcelain flange, 2-sided, Dutch Boy with brush & paint can, Pure White Lead... below, 21x14", G, A....................$200.00

Dutch Boy Paints, sign, tin flange, 2-sided, Dutch Boy in light blue oval above red Dutch Boy Paints lettered on white, 27x18", VG, A....................$300.00

Dutch Boy Paints, see also Anchor White Lead Paint

Dutch Boy Paints, see also Atlantic White Lead Paint

Dutch Boy White Lead Paint, display, papier-mache, Dutch Boy holding can of paint, overall chips/wear, 30x12", G, A....................$500.00

Dutch Boy White Lead Paint, sign, embossed tin, Dutch Boy & White Lead logo on red panel at right of advertising on yellow, 9¾x27¾", NM, A....................$135.00

Dutch Java, pocket mirror, kissing Dutch couple standing on pier next to large coffee tin, Secret Of Happiness, 2⅛" dia, VG+, A....................$55.00

Dutch Java Blend Coffee, display, die-cut cardboard, comical scene of livestock fleeing oncoming open touring car, framed, 8¾x7", EX, A....................$120.00

Dutch Lager Tap Beer, label, 1933-36, St Cloud Brewing Co, U-type permit number, 64-oz, VG, A............$12.00

Dutch Master Beer, label, 1933-50, Bruckman Co, Internal Revenue Tax Paid statement, 12-oz, EX, A..........$66.00

Dutch Masters, tin, pictures Dutchmen seated around table, product name on red band above, logo on slip lid, 5½x5¼" dia, EX, D....................$30.00

Dutchess Trousers, sign, porcelain, 2-sided flange, ...10 Cents A Button, $1.00 A Rip, 9¼x15¼", VG+, A...$125.00

Dutchess Trousers, sign, tin, factory image, Largest Factory In The World..., original frame, 24½x34½", G, A...$100.00

Duxbak & Kamp-it, sign, 1920-40, self-framed tin, man fishing in stream while woman prepares supper, minor scuffs overall, 12x17", A....................$250.00

DW Hoegg & Co Canned Goods, poster, paper, pictures canned products surrounded by raw products, ...Favorite Brands, matted & framed, image: 27½x22", EX, A.$1,100.00

Dwight's Saleratus, trade card, pictures a cow flanked by circular logos, product name above & below, EX, A...$21.00

Dwinell & Wright Boston Coffees, crate, wood, 1 good label with Fresh Roasted logo, lettering above & below, 14½x20½" square, G, A....................$55.00

Dybala's Beverages, sign, embossed tin, pictures colorful bottle, orange, black & white, 20x9", EX, D.........$45.00

Dybala's Spring Ginger Ale, sign, cardboard, Dybala's lettered diagonally above list of other flavors, 20x8½", NM, A....................$60.00

Dybala's Spring Ginger Ale, sign, cardboard, Spring lettered on tail of S in Dybala's in diagonal script above Ginger Ale & list of flavors, 20x10", NM, M3........$30.00

Dyer's Pork & Beans, sign, self-framed tin, large hand holding can of product, lady in pink seated in large D on Dyer's, 11x8", VG, A....................$225.00

Dynafuel, pump sign, 1940s, die-cut porcelain, diamond shape, blue lettering on yellow background, minor edge wear, 8x12", A **$205.00**

Dynamo Detergent, doll, 1990, dinosaur, green with yellow lid from detergent bottle, 11", M, N1 .... **$15.00**

E

E Robinson's Sons Old Stock Pilsener, pocket mirror, large bottle of Old Stock Pilsener flanked by lettering, small crack/some wear, oval, 2¾x1¾", G+, A **$35.00**

E Robinson's Sons Pilsener, calendar, 1910, oval image of girl with roses above product & factory insets, matted & framed, image: 22x11", VG, A **$350.00**

E Robinson's Sons Pilsener Bottled Beer, tray, factory image flanked by logo, lettering on rim, minor chips, 13½" dia, NM, A **$450.00**

E Turner Shoes, pocket mirror, sexy Victorian lady in a smug pose, oval, 2¾", EX, A **$140.00**

E&W Collars, display, oak base with glass sides, shows 12 white collars, some rounded & some pointed, 25½x19¾x8½", EX, A **$350.00**

Eagle Brand Condensed Milk, sign, cardboard, little girl standing behind fence points finger upward, product image & lettering on fence, EX, M1 .... **$475.00**

Eagle Brand Dry Cleaner, tin, suburban neighborhood scene above product lettering & eagle logo, The American Shoe Polish Co, 5x2½" dia, EX+, D **$35.00**

Eagle Mikado Pencils, matchbook cover, The Yellow Pencil With The Red Band, 20 strike, front strike, NM, R1 .... **$7.00**

Eagle Oil, can, 1925-45, eagle logo & 100% Pure Pennsylvania... on white center, black background, screw lid & handle, 2-gal, VG, A **$30.00**

Eagle Pencil Co's Colored Crayons, trade card, pictures a crayon over floral design & a paint palette, ...Made In Over Fifty Shades, EX, A **$22.00**

Eagle Pencil Leads, display box with 12 tubes of pencil leads, 1930s, eagle logo, 4x3", EX, D **$8.50**

Eagle Run Beer, tip tray, boy with bottle & glass riding eagle, Pure & Aged, Fuhrmann & Schmidt, Shamokin Pa, 4¼" dia, VG, A **$150.00**

Eagle Seed Sower, sign, paper, features eagle & shield promoting a variety of farm-seed sowers, framed, image: 19½x16", M, A **$50.00**

Early Times Distillery, sign, embossed painted plaster, pictures a log still with oxen-drawn wagon laden with barrels, 28x23", VG+, A **$100.00**

Eastern Clay Goods Co, postcard, 1909, mechanical, #655, pull fishing line to open, ad text inside, by Livermore & Knight, EX, D **$75.00**

Eau Claire Book & Stationery Co, catalog, 1939, features school equipment & supplies, 160 pages, VG+, H2 .... **$35.00**

EB Lamme Clothing, sign, tin, man dressed in suit at left of product name, Boxeman lettered below, 6½x14", EX+, D1 .... **$49.00**

Ebbert Wagons, sign, tin, 'In the Shade of the Old Apple Tree,' farmer helping girl with apples, framed, 25½x37½", VG, A **$800.00**

Ebbert Wagons, sign, tin, 'In the Shade of the Old Apple Tree,' farmer helping girl with apples, framed, 25½x37½", NM, A **$1,700.00**

Eberhardt & Ober Beer, sign, neon, E&O above & Beer below center panel reading Early & Often in blue on red, rectangular border, 16x26", EX, A **$425.00**

Eberhardt & Ober Beer, sign, tin over cardboard, product name lettered above factory flanked by vertically lined graphics, 9¼x11¼", VG, A **$33.00**

Eberhardt & Ober Brewing Co, sign, paper, aerial factory view, eagle logo in center of company name below, wood frame, 26x41", EX, A **$350.00**

Eberhardt & Ober Brewing Co, sign, paper, colorful factory image with multiple buildings & busy street scene, framed, image: 44x50", EX+, A **$450.00**

Eberhardt & Ober Pilsener & Lager Beer, sign, embossed tin, Drink left of E&O above rest of product name, Early & Often with company seal below, 12x24", VG+, A **$55.00**

Ebling Brewing Co, calendar, 1913, paper, factory scene with casino & restaurant in foreground, full pad, framed, image: 28½x21", VG, A **$500.00**

Ebling Brewing Co, sign, tin, script logo in center, ...Ales & Porter, embossed design on border, ornate frame, 26" dia, EX, A **$350.00**

Ebling Brewing Co, tray, factory scene with casino & restaurant in foreground, lettering on fancy rim, Shonk litho, oval, 15x19", EX, A $1,150.00

EC & Schultz, pin-back button, orange & blue lettering on buff, round, VG, A **$35.00**

Echo Plug Cut, tin, deer hunt scene & lettering on paper label, slip lid, 4x6", EX+, A **$105.00**

Eckart Bro's Lager Beer, sign, embossed & reverse-painted, eagle surmounting world globe flanked by Eagle Brewery, framed, 27½x21½", EX, A **$750.00**

Eckstein White Lead Co, sign, paper, factory & street scene with horse-drawn wagons & trains flanked by interior scenes, 33¾x21¾", VG+, A **$450.00**

Eclipse Coffee, tin, encircled scenic view with Eclipse Coffee lettered in diagonal script at top left & lower right, 1-lb, EX, A **$160.00**

Eclipse Milling Co, sign, company name above 1888 coin flanked by 196 & lbs, Gold Dust Half Patent below, decorative border, 16" dia, M, D **$75.00**

Eclipse Yeast Cakes, can, cardboard with tin lid, red, gold, black & white, Eclipse in diagonal script above Yeast Cakes, EX, M2 .... **$5.00**

Eddy's Plows, sign, wood, Eddy Plows lettered at right of Mr Eddy's portrait & logo, framed, 24x60", EX .. **$475.00**

Edelweiss Beer, stained glass window, cabin in mountains surrounded by grapes & leaves, hyacinth plant each side, framed, 34x37", EX, A **$3,500.00**

Edelweiss Beer, tray, 1913, shoulder-length frontal view of smiling girl, Edelweiss lettered diagonally, floral rim, 13½" dia, VG, A **$110.00**

Edelweiss Lime Rickey, label, 1920s, pictures limes, Lime Rickey in script, Schoenofen Co, G, A **$7.00**

Edgar P Lewis Boston Hard Candy, tin, nonpictorial, round screw lid, 9½x5x5", NM, A **$10.00**

Edgeworth Extra High Grade Plug Slice, pocket tin, ornate graphics, Manufactured By Larus & Bro Co, Richmond Va, USA, hinged lid, 2¼x3¼", VG, D ..$5.00

Edgeworth Extra High Grade Ready-Rubbed, tin, light-blue square shape with concave sides, blue lettering with blue & gold fancy graphics, slip lid, 6x4", EX, A **$33.00**

Edgeworth Ready Rubbed Tobacco, sample tin, product name above other lettering, EX+, A **$60.00**

Edgeworth Smoking Tobacco, sign, painted tin, yellow product name on blue scrolled emblem, Mild, Slow-Burning, Cool, horizontal rectangle, G, A **$25.00**

Edison Battery Oil, bottle, signature in high relief on right side, EX, D **$4.00**

Edison Mazda Lamps, display, metal & glass, 2-sided, bellboys carrying light bulbs on front, large GE bulb on reverse, 13x20½x7", VG, A **$375.00**

Edison Mazda Lamps, display, tin, bulb shape with light bulbs surrounding the circumference, 24x15½x11½", VG, A **$1,550.00**

Edison Mazda Lamps, tape measure, celluloid, G, D... **$55.00**

Edison Mazda Lamps, tin, pictures a lamp, For Your Car, 3x2x1½", EX, D **$28.00**

Edison Phonographs, trade card, boys looking over stone wall, opens up to lawn party scene with phonograph, EX, A **$38.00**

Edison Star Metal Polish, tin, 1920s, star logo, screw lid, unused, 5x2" dia, D **$10.00**

Edouard Dubonnet & Labussiere, thermometer, wood, blue on white, bottle of product above, lettering below, rounded top, square bottom, 24", VG, A **$40.00**

Edw K Tryon Co Fire Arms, catalog, 1907, 3 setters in oval vignette & fancy scrolls on front in orange & brown, 160 pages, VG+, A **$90.00**

Edward Heuer Bottler, calendar, 1895, waitress beside large bottle surrounded by flowers, full pad, matted & framed, image: 19x12", VG, A **$975.00**

Edward Parkinson Factory Sewing Machines, trade card, pictures sewing machine at left, ...131 Dorrauce Street, Cor Dyer, Providence RI, EX, A **$20.00**

Edward's Coffee, tin, nonpictorial, Regular Grind on band below product name, 1/2-lb, EX+, A **$35.00**

Edwards India & Ceylon, bin, stenciled tin, slanted top, bold white lettering with white trim, scratches/damaged bottom, 18" long, G, A **$50.00**

Edwin C Burt & Co Fine Shoes, trade card, colorful image of little girl picking wildflowers, medals won from various expositions on reverse, EX, A **$12.00**

Edwin C Burt & Co Fine Shoes, trade card, 1881, boy on skates pushing girl in a shoe skate-shaped sleigh, 2¾x4¾", EX, P1 .... **$12.50**

Ee-Dah-How Beer, label, 1933-50, pictures snow-capped mountains, Overland Beverage Co, Internal Revenue Tax Paid statement, 12-oz, EX, A **$35.00**

Effinger Beer, label, 1933-50, Internal Revenue Tax Paid statement, 12-oz, EX, A **$10.00**

Egg Baking Powder, pocket mirror, features young baker holding cake, crazing, 2⅛", G-, A **$60.00**

Egyptian Deities Cigarettes, sign, copyright 1908, paper, draped Egyptian girl facing mirror holding cigarette pack, framed, 14x9½", VG+, A **$90.00**

Egyptienne Luxury Cigarettes, sign, paperboard, girl standing before draped background, lettering above, product flanking girl, framed, 28x20", G+, A **$140.00**

Egyptienne Straights Cigarettes, sign, paper, girl's face in black bonnet on red background, pack of cigarettes & lettering below, framed, 20x18", VG, A **$160.00**

EH Barney Ice Skates, trade card, blue & white, pictures ice skate surrounded by text, VG, A **$26.00**

Ehlers Coffee, tin, 1938, key-wind lid, 1-lb, VG, D .. **$40.00**

Ehricks' Scrap Book, trade card, 1882, The Child's Dream, little girl in bed opens up to Santa with toys & scrapbook, rare, EX, A **$170.00**

Eight O'Clock Coffee, bank, metal, tall red rectangular shape with gold Eight O'Clock logo, 4", NM, A... **$10.00**

Eisemann's Klondike Head Rub, sign, hanging, embossed cardboard, colorful image of the product, 8½x11", EX, A **$60.00**

Eisenlohr's Cinco Cigars, sign, tin, red, blue & orange, Cinco in diagonal script, Eisenlohr's above, Cigars below, 9x19½", NM, B1 .... **$40.00**

El Belmont Havana Cigars, thermometer, dial, paper face, degrees above product lettering, 9" dia, G+, A **$10.00**

El Galope Cigars, box label, inner lid, 1900, angel in chariot pulled by 4 horses, 6x9", G, C3 .... **$45.00**

El Garcia Cigars, box label, inner lid, pictures 3 women with Indian squaw, 6x9", M, D $3.00
El Guardo Cigars, box label, outer, bulldog guarding box of cigars, 4½x4½", M, D $4.00
El Maestro Cigars, box label, outer, pictures musical instruments, 4½x4½", M, C3 ....$10.00
El Minero Tobacco, bucket label, underground miner at work with candle on his hat, 13x7", EX, D $55.00
El Parmela Cigars, tin, head portrait of girl in profile surrounded by flowers, product name above, slip lid, VG, A $50.00
El Poeta Cigars, box label, inner lid, El Poeta lettered above 8 portraits of various poets, 6x9", EX, D $15.00
El Symphonie Havana Cigars, tray, deep-dish, portrait of composer flanked by Havana Cigars, FA Kline & Co Makers, oval, 18x15", EX, A $250.00
El Traficante Cigars, box label, inner lid, 1880s, draped nude at left of views of port city, OL Schwencke & Co litho, EX, A $90.00
El Universo Cigars, fan, paper, pictures flamboyantly dressed Black man blowing cigar smoke, lettering around, 17" with handle, G, A $225.00
El Veedor Cigars, box label, inner lid, ancient lovers in garden, 6x9", M, C3 ....$12.00
El Verso Cigar, sign, embossed tin, red & white, 3x14", VG, D $26.00
Eldred Motor Oil, can, 1920-30, triangular logo on black, 100% Pure logo in bottom corners, screw lid & handle, 1-gal, 9½", G-, A $130.00

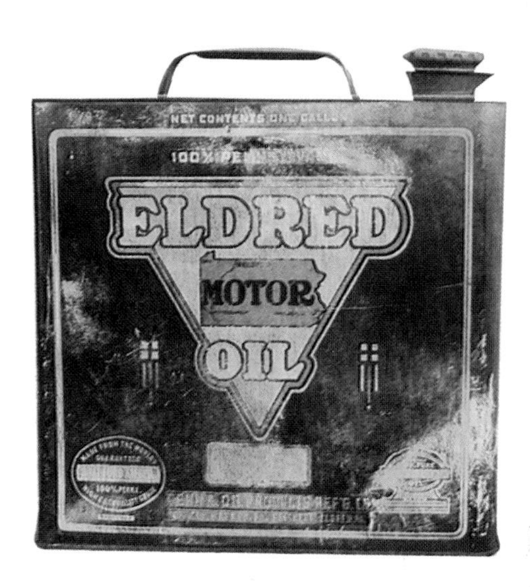

Electric Brand Spinach, can label, colorful image of woman with light, M, C3 ....$6.00
Electric Brand Succotash, can label, black & white image of woman with light, M, C3 ....$4.50
Electric City Lager Beer, label, 1933-36, Electric Brewing Co, U-type permit number, 12-oz, EX, A $35.00
Electric Cutlery Co, cabinet, oak & glass with high top & curved front, incised geometric patterns in upper section, 29", VG, A $600.00
Electric Lustre Starch, thermometer, stenciled & lacquered wood, blue product name & product above, beveled edges, rounded top, 21", G, A $70.00
Electrolux, ashtray, 1950s, ceramic, Electrolux sweeper in soft blues & chrome silver on edge of base, 5½x6½", EX, A $121.00
Electrolux, bank, 1950s, light-blue hard plastic Model G vacuum cleaner, spring action, missing 1 wheel, EX, D ..$25.00

Elgin Coal & Ice, playing cards, pictures an eagle on black & yellow background, complete, M, D...$6.50
Elgin Watches, clock, light-up, metal case with glass front, large numbers around edge, Elgin Watches above hands, 15" dia, EX, A $50.00
Elgin Watches, sign, decal on wood, boy in tattered clothes with pocket watch, worn at bottom, 22x15", VG, A $20.00
Eli Bridge Co, pocket mirror, pictures large Ferris wheel bordered by I Love My Dime, But Oh! You Big Eli Wheel, 2⅛" dia, VG+, A $500.00
Elie Sheets-Martha Washington Candies, box, pictures George & Martha Washington, Mother Of American Candies, Baltimore Md, white background, 2x7x4" dia, EX, P4 ....$15.00
Elite Cigars, box label, inner lid, woman in opera attire, 6x9", EX, C3 ....$12.00
Elk Brand Prunes, can label, elk head & prunes on red background, San Jose Ca, EX, G1 ....$6.00
Elk Speed Pure Rye, sign, self-framed tin, pictures running elk, overall darkening/soiling/dents, 25½x37½", G-, A $45.00
Ellet Kendall Shoe Co, charm, early 1900s, black composition, pictures high-top shoe with brass loop embedded at top rear, EX, D $9.00
Ellis & Helfer HH Tablets Confections, tin, 1930s-40s, log cabin on red ground, red & black lettering, slip lid & bail, minor paint chips, 6½x6" dia, A $15.00
Ellwood Steel Fences, match holder, tin, pictures a fence, The Old Reliable... letter above, red, white & blue, rust spots, 5", G-, A $30.00
Elmer's Glue-All, container, 1960s, plastic Elmer figure in blue bib overalls, Borden Chemical Co, 6½", NM, D....$55.00
EM Lyman & Son Garden Seeds, sign, colorful image of man steeling radishes from garden, colorful graphics below, rare, gold frame, 26x22", EX, A $950.00

Emerson Radio, clock, glass, metal frame, Emerson Radio below G-clef image surrounded by E-M-E-R-S-O-N R-A-D-I-O, round, EX, D **$260.00**

Emery Apricots, can label, apricots on a branch, EX, C3 .. **$7.00**

Emilia Garcia Cigars, label, oval with Emilia Garcia arched above lady rising from smoke, island beyond, Mild Blend below, 6x9", EX, D **$5.00**

Emilia Garcia Tobacco, tin, round, NM, H3 .... **$35.00**

Emmerling's Grossvader Beer, sign, ca 1913, tin, Bavarian couple eating & drinking flagons of beer, Kaufmann & Strauss, framed, image: 19x27", EX, A **$400.00**

Empire Anti-Freeze, thermometer, wood, The Right Anti-Freeze on the diagonal above Empire logo, Never Rusts Your Radiator below, 36", VG, A **$35.00**

Empire Beer, label, 1933-34, AB Bechaud, U-type permit number, 12-oz, EX, A **$35.00**

Empire Cream Separator, pocket mirror, milkmaid in innocent pose with lettering arched above & below, cracked mirror, oval, 2¾", EX, A **$95.00**

Empire Drill Co Seeding Machinery, trade card, farm scene with children feeding horse, lettering above & below, VG, A **$16.00**

Empire Mills Coffee, tin, pictures Santa with reindeer, black on red, Ginna litho, small round top, 8x4" dia, VG, A **$225.00**

Empire State Motor Oil, can, airplane flying in front of Empire State building, cars surround bottom, pour spout & handle, 2-gal, EX+, A **$105.00**

Empress Cayenne, tin, Empress arched above horizontal oval inset of steamship, Cayenne lettered below, vertical rectangle, NM, M2 .... **$28.00**

En-Ar-Co Motor Oil, sign, copyright 1917, die-cut metal, boy in checked nickers holding sign, ...Miles To White Rose..., 59x39", NM, A....$2,750.00

En-Ar-Co Road Maps, sign, 1937, painted tin, 2-sided, boy in checked nickers holds map of US reading Free En-Ar-Co Road Maps, 16x12", VG+, A **$400.00**

English Lad Beer, label, 1933-50, horseshoe surrounds horse & rider, Prima-Bismark Co, Internal Revenue Tax Paid statement, 12-oz, EX, A **$15.00**

Ensign, crate label, Oregon apple, Ensign in light blue above green flag with apple in center, Portland, 9x11", G1 .... **$10.00**

Ensign Mixture, tin, pictures flag on front & back, Indian on sides & ship on slip lid, EX, A **$65.00**

Enterprise Brewing Co, match safe, nickel-plated brass, embossed lettering & ornate graphics, 2¾x1½", G, A **$115.00**

Enterprise Brewing Co, tray, bust-length portrait of a woman with red flower flanked by logo, lettering on rim, 13¼" dia, VG, A **$150.00**

Enterprise Brewing Co, tray, girl sitting by vase of flowers, lettering on rim, overall fading/chips/scratches, 13½" dia, G-, A **$75.00**

Enterprise Brewing Co, tray, portly Bavarian gentleman with glass of beer, ...San Francisco, Cal on rim, oval, 13½x16½", EX, A **$300.00**

Enterprise Brewing Co's Lager Beer, sign, 1901, embossed tin, gold lettering on black background, Tuchfarber Co, contemporary frame, 16x20", EX, A **$440.00**

Enterprise Lager Beer, mug, glass with reverse-painted lettering on flag motif background, red, white & blue, 10x6" dia, G, A.......... $3,150.00

Enterprise Raisin Seeder, trade card, shows product in use, product name above, Ottmann litho, EX, A . **$190.00**

Enterprise Stoves & Ranges, sign, embossed tin, white lettering on dark blue background, We Sell..., minor scratches, 6½", VG, A **$40.00**

EO Webber Lumber & Building Material, match holder, stenciled tin, diamond shape, ...Glass A Specialty, Marysville, Kansas, minor creases, 6½", VG, A..... **$45.00**

EP Waite & Co Crayons, trade card, Victorian parlor scene with couple watching child sleep, EX, A **$25.00**

Epco Cigars, box label, inner lid, Egyptian lady with harp in seaside garden, M, C1 .... **$3.00**

Erickson's Pure Rye Whiskey, sign, self-framed tin, early submarine under attack surrounded by floating whiskey bottles, 22x32", G, A **$600.00**

Eshelman Red Rose Dog & Puppy Food, sign, tin, colorful bag of dog food & pointer, blue & red lettering, dents/paint loss, 18x36", A **$35.00**

Eskimo Pie, decal, 1964, peel & stick, Eskimo boy holding sign, Enjoy An Eskimo Pie, 16x9", EX, D **$12.00**

Eskimo Pie, dispenser, glass-lined with 3 nickel-plated cast-iron Eskimo figures as feet, The Magic Jar..., 15½", EX, A **$1,000.00**

Eskimo Pie, sign, 1922, red & blue image of Eskimo & bear in front of igloo on textured imitation-foil ground, 9½x19½", EX, A $160.00

Eskimo Pie Ice Cream, sign, heavy metal, 24x36", EX, D1 ....$185.00

Eskimo Smoking Tobacco, tin, Alaskan Malamute with igloos in the background, gold lettering, brown background, slip lid, rare, worn, 6", A $75.00

Esquire Beer, label, 1933-50, top hat logo in center, Binzel Brewing Co, Internal Revenue Tax Paid statement, 12-oz, EX, A $9.00

Esquire Magazine, statuette, 1940s, Esky in navy suit & black hat on 3" dia base, composition, You Saw It In Esquire in red, 8½", VG, A $400.00

Esso, bank, glass block with embossed Esso emblem & Watch Your Savings Grow With..., 4¾x4¾", EX+, A $55.00

Esso, bank, plastic, red Esso man saluting on round base, Esso emblem in center of chest, 6½", EX, A $110.00

Esso, bank, 1950s or 60s, red plastic tanker truck with coin slot on top, Save At Your Esso Dealer, VG+, A ...$40.00

Esso, coloring book, 1963, 'Happy Motoring,' features the oil-drop boys & girls through US landmarks, 24 pages, NM, D $28.00

Esso, gas globe, 1930-40, glass, white with blue border, Esso lettered in red, oval, EX, A $275.00

Esso, gas pump display, 1960s, plastic, colorful embossed image of tiger head & paws, minor edge splits, 18x16x4", EX, D $28.00

Esso, lubrication guide for cars & trucks, cardboard, spiral-bound top, lettered arrow points down to 1940, 16x11", VG, A $10.00

Esso, mug, 1970s, milk glass with tiger's face in orange, white & brown, Anchor Hocking, 3½", VG+, A $8.00

Esso, pitcher, 1969, clear glass with 3 tiger heads & Put A Tiger In Your Tank lettered in 8 foreign languages, 9", EX, A $36.00

Esso, salt & pepper shakers, plastic gas pumps, pepper is red & white, salt is blue & white, decaled, 2¾x1x3/4", EX, A $20.00

Esso, toy tiger, hard plastic windup, EX, P2..............$65.00

Esso, waste can, 1970s, metal, round with large embossed portrait of tiger in orange, white & brown, 10x7" dia, EX, A $43.00

Esso, see also Golden Esso Extra

Esso Handy Oil, can, red, white & blue, full, 3-oz, D...$15.00

Essoline, gas globe, 2-sided, glass with inserted metal band, Essolene lettered over circular band, 21x18x6", VG, A $115.00

Essolube Motor Oil, jigsaw puzzle, 1926, family drive auto through forest inhabited by 'auto-ailing' creatures by Dr Seuss, 11x17, EX, F1 ....$100.00

Estabrook & Eaton's Slice, pocket tin, large decorative in upper left, ...Fine Virginia Smoking..., squared corners, slip lid, 4½", EX+, A $65.00

Estabrook's Red Rose Coffee, sign, tin, pictures large can of product on green background, 16x18", M, D1 ....$160.00

Esterbrook Writing Sets, blotter, pictures ink sets & pen tips, multicolored, unused, 8x3½", D $8.00

Estey Organ Co, trade card, parlor scene with 2 women dancing to organ music, EX, A $8.00

Estey Organ Co, trade card, 1890, pictures boy with tennis racket singing to girl in window, EX, D $5.00

Estey Organs & Pianos, trade card, factory vignette with lettering above & below, 1880 calendar on reverse, EX, A $20.00

Estrella De Habana Cigars, box label, outer, 1889, woman holding Cuban flag, 4½x4½", M, C3....................$25.00

Ethan Allen Clothier, sign, die-cut, man in suit & lettered shirt with hands in pockets atop box reading Ethan Allen Clothier, 36x12", VG, A $300.00

Ethyl, pump sign, ca 1940, porcelain, lettered triangle on gold sunrays, black & yellow, minor scratches, 7" dia, EX, A $75.00

Ethyl Corporation, money clip, sterling silver, EX, D..$25.00

Ethyl Gasoline, globe, milk glass body, pictures an Olympic runner, Best In The Long Run, 16½x15", VG+, A $300.00

Ethyl Gasoline Corp, see also Wilcox Gasoline

Ethyl Super 100, pump sign, ca 1940, die-cut porcelain, Ethyl lettered in black above 100 in orange circle, edge flaking, 11½x11", A $95.00

Eulberg's Brew, label, 1933-50, Internal Revenue Tax Paid statement, 12-oz, EX, A $22.00

Eureka, crate label, 1930s, Florida Citrus Fruit, Turner Fruit Co, Ocala Fla, 9x9", M, C3 ....$5.00

Eureka Harness Oil, sign, tin, oval image of 2 work horses, Standard Oil Co, Ind, red, blue & white, minor rust, 13x19", G, A **$40.00**

Eureka Silk, cabinet, wood case with 8 glass front drawers & 2 wood drawers, mirrored panel sides, 25x23x16½", VG, A **$775.00**

Eureka Spool Silks, cabinet, wood case with 3 glass front drawers & 1 lettered wood drawer, fancy lettered marquee atop, 18x22x16", EX, A **$578.00**

Evaporated Milk Association, ad, pictures mother holding infant, framed, EX, A **$25.00**

Eve Cube Cut Tobacco, pocket tin, upright, pictures Eve beside apple tree, EX+, A **$295.00**

Ever-Ready, clock, man shaving on clock face, Ever-Ready lettered below, pendulum missing, 22x18", G, A .. **$400.00**

Ever-Ready Safety Razor, clock, man shaving on clock face, Ever-Ready Safety Razor lettered below, 12 Bladed... on pendulum, 28x18", EX+, A **$2,900.00**

Eveready Batteries, bank, 1981, black cat, vinyl, premium, NM, D **$22.00**

Eveready Batteries, jigsaw puzzle, 1931, boy using flashlight in bedroom, Is That You Santa Claus?, by Frances Tipton Hunter, 9x12", EX, F1 .... $50.00

Eveready Flashlight Batteries, display case, embossed batteries on tin door with battery displays on sides, Extra Long Life..., 16x11½x9½", VG, A **$110.00**

Eveready Flashlight Batteries, sign, die-cut cardboard, logo atop scene with man shining light on family of skunks, ad panel below, 26x14", VG, M2 .... **$45.00**

Eveready Flashlight Batteries & Mazda Lamps, display case, 1930s-40s, tin with glass top, Let Us Reload... in cream on blue, red & green, 11x9", VG, A **$75.00**

Everett Piano, trade card, 1893, recital scene, EX, A.... **$19.00**

Evinrude, catalog, 1929, features outboard motors, 32 pages, EX, D **$28.00**

Evinrude, sign, embossed tin, white, yellow & blue, shows large motor & 2 men fishing in boat against rising sun, 15x26", EX, D3 .... **$475.00**

Evinrude Motor Co, crate lid, pictures a motor, ...Milwaukee Wis, Detachable Motors & Boats, 16x43", VG, A..... **$25.00**

Evinrude Rowboat & Canoe Motors, tip tray, deep-dish, figure in motorboat, On The Crest Of The Wave, rim wear, 4" dia, VG+, A **$375.00**

Ex-Lax, door push plate, porcelain, Tirez lettered above tilted product box, En Vente Ici lettered below, Canadian, 8x4", NM, M2 .... **$98.00**

Ex-Lax, matchbook covers, 1935-36, features various cartoons with jingles, 20 strike, front strike, set of 12, NM, R1 .... **$20.00**

Ex-Lax, sample tin, contains 2 tablets, Brooklyn NY,¼x1¾", EX, P4 .... **$8.00**

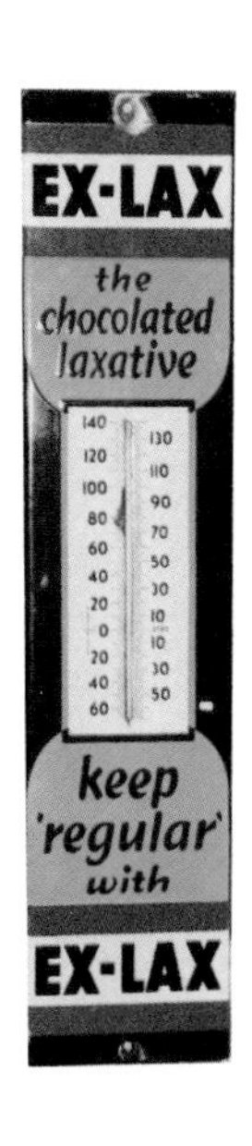

Ex-Lax, thermometer, porcelain, red, white, blue & black on black, logos above & below, squared corners, 36x8", EX, M2 .... $130.00

Ex-Lax, thermometer, wood, Ex-Lax tin at bottom, The Sweet Chocolate Laxative, round top & squared bottom, 15x4", VG, A **$100.00**

Excelsior Carbonate Ammonia, tin, flag logo at left, baker at right, product name in green, yellow background, pry lid, 5-lb, VG, A **$10.00**

Excelsior Malt Syrup, can label, 1930, dried barley on yellow background, EX, C3 .... **$4.00**

Excelsior Metal Polish, trade card, pictures Dumbo leaving England on a steamship, EX, A **$15.00**

Exclusive, crate label, 1930s, California lemon, lemon meringue pie on pink checked table cloth, Ivanhoe, 9x12½", M, C1 .... **$3.00**

Exeter Beer, can, flat top, blue & white logo on striped background, great sheen, rare, unopened & empty, minor scratches/wear, A **$200.00**

Exide Batteries, display stand, metal with 2-sided tin panel featuring a battery, When Its An Exide You Start, 40", VG+, A **$185.00**

Exide Batteries, sign, embossed tin, Exide lettered vertically above Batteries, 40x14", EX+, A **$35.00**

Exide Batteries, sign, metal, 2-sided, When Its An above Exide battery graphic, car & receding You Start below, 15x12", EX/VG, A **$130.00**

Export 'A' Filter Tip Cigarettes, sign, light-up, green, red & white, Enjoy Export 'A' Filter Tip Cigarettes, 15" dia, NM, M2 .... **$70.00**

Export Beer, label, pre-1920, product name above logo, Birk Bros Brewing Co, G, A **$40.00**

Export Cigarettes, change mat, green heel shape with Export Cigarettes lettered in white above nubby surface, 7x6", NM, M2 .... **$10.00**

Export Lager Beer, label, 1933-50, Stenson Brewing Co, Internal Revenue Tax Paid statement, 1/2-gal, EX, A **$18.00**

Express Cigars, box label, inner lid, 1890s, train with mountains in distance, elaborate border, Witsch & Schmidt litho, EX, A **$148.00**

Express Fine Cut Tobacco, tin, railroad engine & cars, Globe logo at right, Globe Tobacco Co lettered below, slip lid, rare, 1-lb, 8" dia, G, A **$350.00**

Exquisite Canned Goods, sign, porcelain, fruit compote on 2-tone ground, Exquisite Canned Goods, There Is A Difference! below, 30x24", VG, D1 .... **$140.00**

Extra Fine Cigars, box label, inner lid, woman flanked by Spanish village scenes, 6x9", M, C3 .... **$8.00**

Exxon, letter opener, Employee Safety Award with Attendance Award on reverse, metal, red, white & blue, EX, D **$10.00**

Eye-Fix, tip tray, features bust portrait of pretty lady looking up at cherub, The Great Eye Remedy, crazing, 4⅛" dia, EX, A $300.00

Eze-Grape, sign, paper, product name on yellow diagonal banner with bottle & grape cluster, 5¢ dot, 8x20", NM, M3 .... **$22.00**

Eze-Orange, sign, paper, product name on white diagonal banner with bottle & group of oranges, 5¢ dot, 8x20", NM, M3 .... **$22.00**

F

F O'Neill Cheese, thermometer, wood, black on yellow, company name & address above, Kraft Cheese below, rounded top, 12", VG+, A **$15.00**

F&M Herbs Cigars, sign, ca 1880, paper, woman in Victorian-style interior, Black Prince..., matted & framed, image: 25x16½", VG, A **$200.00**

F&M Schaefer Brewing Co's Bock Beer, sign, factory seen through open-end of barrel with drinking gnomes and resting rams, matted & framed, image: 34x23", G-, A **$1,000.00**

FA Poth & Son Brewers, calendar, 1898, paper, hunter & dog pausing to look at billboard, full calendar, framed, image: 30x20½", EX, A **$800.00**

Fab, sample box with contents, features stylized ocean waves, Colgate's Fab lettered below, 4x3x1", NM, A **$8.00**

Fabrica De Tabacos, box label, inner lid, Black man's face through US banner, 6x9", VG, C3 .... **$65.00**

Facit Adding Machines & Calculators, statuette, 1960s, rubber, Facit man in red uniform, 4", M, D $25.00

FAD Cigars, sign, tin, red & black stenciled lettering on white background, Always Good, some scratches, wood frame, 11x46", G, A **$85.00**

Fagg's Wire Cut Liniment, sign, paper, For Wire Cuts, Sore Shoulders, Saddle Sores..., IN Fagg Co, Elgin Tx, framed, image: 6x5", EX, D **$50.00**

Fairbank's Cottolene, trade card, Black woman picking cotton, recipes for making donuts on reverse, EX, A **$18.00**

Fairbank's Gold Dust, see also Gold Dust

Fairbank's Gold Dust, trade card, Gold Dust twins in skirts, 1 playing banjo, 1 dancing on product box, ...Cleans Everything..., 4x3", EX, D **$100.00**

Fairbank's Gold Dust Scouring Cleanser, can, metal with paper label featuring famous logo, full, 14-oz, EX, A **$50.00**

Fairbank's Gold Dust Scouring Cleanser, sign, paper, Uncle Sam & Roosevelt welcoming the Gold Dust twins, Roosevelt Scoured..., framed, image: 11x20", VG, A **$1,250.00**

Fairbank's Gold Dust Scouring Cleanser, trolley sign, bathroom scene flanked by advertising, product name below, framed, 11x21", EX, A **$285.00**

Fairbank's Gold Dust Washing Powder, box, cardboard, features Gold Dust twins logo, open top, 2-lb 4-oz, VG, A **$20.00**

Fairbank's Gold Dust Washing Powder, box, cardboard, free home sample with Gold Dust twins logo, NM, A **$35.00**

Fairbank's Gold Dust Washing Powder, sign, cardboard, octagon shape with Gold Dust twins scrubbing the word Home, product box between feet, EX, M1 .... **$360.00**

Fairbank's Gold Dust Washing Powder, store hanger, die-cut cardboard, 2-sided, letters on top of boxes spelling product name, 1 of 3, 7¾x15½", VG, A..............**$5,500.00**

Fairbank's Gold Dust Washing Powder, watch fob, enameled & embossed round metal piece with 2 natives holding pans, embossed advertising in middle, EX, A..............**$40.00**

Fairbank's Standard Scales, sign, wood with relief-carved letters, overall wear, 18¾x40½x1½", VG, A..............**$450.00**

Fairbank's Washing Powder, sign, paperboard, full-color image of little girl & baby boy in front of box, Knapp litho, framed, 16½x14", G, A..............**$250.00**

Fairbanks-Morse Scales, sign, porcelain, white product name on blue, 9x50", EX, D3..............**$175.00**

Fairchild's Flour, watch fob, celluloid, boy hawking newspapers reading Extra-Fine Quality, reverse says Remember Fairchild's..., EX, D..............**$25.00**

Fairies Starch, banner, 1910s, canvas, Makes Ironing Easy, Once Tried--Always Used, red, white & green, 14x30", EX, D..............**$30.00**

Fairies Starch, sign, cloth, Fairies lettered diagonally with Makes Ironing Easy above, Once Tried -- Always Used below, 14x30", G, A..............**$55.00**

Fairies Starch, sign, paper, Makes Ironing Easy, Fairies Starch, Once Tried--Always Used, red, white & green, 10x15", NM, B1..............**$6.00**

Fairway Marshmallows, tin, pictures 2 children facing each other with lettering above & below, slip lid, round, A..............**$65.00**

Fairy Soap, print, dated 1895, paper, lady seated watching girl blow bubbles with children in them, framed, 24x18", EX+, D..............**$235.00**

Fairy Soap, tip tray, ca 1936, little girl sitting atop bar of soap, Have You A Little Fairy In Your Home? on rim, 4" dia, EX, A..............$75.00

Fairy Soap, tip tray, ca 1936, little girl sitting atop bar of soap, Have You A Little Fairy In Your Home? on rim, 4" dia, G, A..............**$15.00**

Falcon Motor Oil, can, pictures a falcon with product name above & below, 1-qt, NM, A..............**$15.00**

Fall River Line, sign, paper, oval image of the Bristol steamer, New York & Boston lettered below, 10½x13", EX, A..............**$575.00**

Falls City Beer, nodder, 1970, composition, Falls City Bottleman on rectangular base with product name in red oval, 14", EX+, D..............**$150.00**

Falstaff, charger, tin, trademark image of Shakespearean man at table admiring friends with glass of Lemp beer, 24" dia, G, A..............**$150.00**

Falstaff, stein, 1971, with lid, 10½", M, D..............**$125.00**

Falstaff Beer, sign, ca 1912, self-framed tin, portly man with flagon & bottle in front of window with factory view, 30x24", EX, A..............**$1,450.00**

Falstaff Bottled Beer, sign, tin, driver of open touring car offering farmer a beer, Peacemaker lettered on frame, 22½x30½", EX, A..............**$2,000.00**

Famous Amos Cookies, cookie jar, ceramic, brown paper bag shape with Famous Amos in script above large cookie, Treasure Craft, NM, D..............**$50.00**

Famous Brands, sign, cattle drive campfire scene, wood frame with various cattle brands, Famous Brands & title, 27x42", VG, A..............**$35.00**

Famous Dukes Smoking Tobacco, sign, 1920s, paper, 2 midgets carrying product & umbrellas, lettering above & below, matted & framed, 17½x13", EX, A..............**$210.00**

Famous Pineapples, can label, large roses & pineapple, VG, C3..............**$9.00**

Fan Tan Gum, tray, geisha girl with gum pack & Fan Tan Gum lettered above Japanese landscape, basket-weave border, 10x13", NM, D..............**$285.00**

Farmer Boy Pop Corn, box, light cardboard, Farmer Boy lettered above boy's image in circle, Pop Corn None Better below, 7x4½", NM, A..............**$7.00**

Farmer's Pride Brand Coffee, tin, product name arched over elderly gent & child in wreathed oval on paper label, slip lid, 1-lb, G, A..............**$41.00**

Farmer's Pride Food Products, banner, canvas, tilted can of product left of advertising, Hulman & Company, Terre Haute Ind below, horizontal, EX, M1..............**$220.00**

Farmers Ice Cream, display, metal & cardboard, electric, ice cream cone atop panel featuring product name & flavors, 31½", EX, A..............**$300.00**

Farmiloe's Hard Gloss Paint, display, 1930s, gallon of paint form with wooden arms, legs & base, contains 5 stir sticks, 7x6½" dia, VG, A..............**$202.00**

Farmway Barn Cleaner, sign, 1930s, die-cut tin, red lettering on yellow, 11x28", EX, D..............**$40.00**

Farmwells Feeds, salt & pepper shakers, ceramic, farmers smoking pipes with logo on back, EX, P2..............**$175.00**

Fashion Cut Plug Tobacco, lunch box, metal, fashionable couple with car beyond, hindged lid & wire handle, fading/scratches, 8x5¼x4½", G, A..............**$150.00**

Fast Mail Tobacco, pocket tin, shows speeding train, flat with rounded corners, EX, S5..............**$350.00**

Fatima Turkish Blend Cigarettes, sign, cardboard, tilted open pack of cigarettes over Turkish city, 20 For 15¢, text above, Fatima below, 34x21", EX, A..............**$45.00**

Fatima Turkish Blend Cigarettes, sign, paperboard, product name above & below portrait of veiled woman flanked by symbols, framed, 30x21", EX, A..$300.00

Fatima Turkish Blend Cigarettes, sign, reverse-painted glass, chain hanger, Fatima lettered behind leaning cigarette pack, thin metal frame, 6x14", VG, A **$10.00**

Fatima Turkish Blend Cigarettes, sign, tin, Turkish girl on simulated wood-grained background, A Sensible Cigarette...20 For 15¢, 37½x25½", VG, A...........**$500.00**

Fatima Turkish Blend Cigarettes, thermometer, porcelain, with barometer, blue & black on white & yellow, product & name above, lettering below, 27", G, A...............**$25.00**

Fauerbach Beer, sign, porcelain, 2-sided, shield & Since 1848 above Fauerbach in diagonal script above Beer, 36x48", G+, D1...**$110.00**

Faultless Dry Shrimp, can label, pictures shrimp on lettuce, EX, C3...**$15.00**

Faultless Spray Starch, sample box, early, unopened, NM, D2...**$20.00**

Faust Blend Blanke's Drip Coffee, coffeepot, stoneware, tan knobby texture with embossed knight, black lettering on side & lid, 9", NM, A................................**$550.00**

Fawn Beverages, sign, tin, Fawn in black diagonal script letters with red shadow lines above Beverages in black on white, 14x28", EX, M3 ....**$35.00**

FE Myers & Bro Equipment, catalog, ca 1910, equipment for spraying, painting, & disinfecting, engraved illustrations, scarce, 64 pages, EX, D **$17.50**

Fecker Beer, tray, stock image of beer maid holding large growler of beer, lettering on rim, minor dents/fading, 13¼x10½", G, A...**$45.00**

Federal Cartridge Sample Shells, box, red with 5 cutout shells, 3x5", VG, A **$100.00**

Federal Tires, sign, porcelain, Authorized Sales Agency...Extra Service, 18x36", NM, S2 ....**$400.00**

Feen-A-Mint Laxative, dispenser, tin, pictures woman & product, oval mirror atop, 16", EX, A **$325.00**

Feen-A-Mint Laxative, sign, tin, porcelain, Feen-A-Mint For Constipation in blue outlined in white on orange, product at right, 7x29, G, A.................................**$55.00**

Fehr's Ambrosia Non-Alcoholic Beverage tray, image of Greek maiden presenting beverage to gods at Mt Olympus, decorative rim with lettering, 13¼" dia, EX, A..........**$155.00**

Fehr's Famous FFXL Beers, tray, colorful image of classical figures in romantic embrace, ...None Purer, None Better on rim, 13" dia, VG, A **$215.00**

Fehr's Malt-Tonic, sign, self-framed tin, bare-chested maid holding bottle, cherubs reaching for glass, oval, 28x22", EX, A...**$1,500.00**

Fehr's Malt-Tonic, tray, woman holds bottle & glass surrounded by cherubs, oversized bottle on table, rust spots/faded, oval, 29x22", G-, A.........................**$175.00**

Feifer's Quaker Cigars, box label, 1900s, lithographer's proof, Quaker man surrounded by early Quaker life, EX, A **$45.00**

Feigenspan's Amber Ale, label, pre-1920, PON in center with product name arched above & below, VG, A **$12.00**

Fell Brewing Co, sign, 1905, paper, girl in fur-trimmed apparel & feathered hat in oval, Season's Greetings, framed, image: 22x16", G, A **$1,000.00**

Fell Brewing Co Dark Beer, label, 1933-36, logo above product & company name, U-type permit number, 12-oz, EX, A **$8.00**

Fellow Citizens Cigars, sign, reverse-painted glass with silver leaf glue chip letters, inset of Grant & Lee, Belmont Cigar Co, 7x16", EX, A **$770.00**

Fenwick Cranberries, label, early 1900s, pictures spray of red berries & green leaves, 7x10", M, C1 ....**$2.00**

Fern Glen Rye, sign, self-framed tin, Black man with watermelon & chicken looking at bottle in the road, 33x23", VG, A..**$1,800.00**

Ferris Woolens, display, foldout cardboard box, inner lid litho shows early airport scene with people in Ferris clothing, 19", EX, A **$200.00**

Ferry's Seeds, sign, 1901, cherub boy tying hands of clock, Don't Tie Your Hands... above, Buy Ferry's below, framed, 34x25", M, A **$220.00**

Festival, crate label, 1920s, California lemon, ladies riding in carriage, Red Ball logo, Santa Barbara, 9x12", M, C3...**$4.00**

Festival Bartlett Pears, can label, pictures a bear, M, C3...**$8.00**

FF Lewis Groceries & General Merchandise, sign, cardboard cutout, boy in blue with boat stands at steps of park gazebo, advertising on roof of gazebo, 9x5", EX, A....**$25.00**

FH Ohaus Grocer, match holder, die-cut tin arrowhead shape, embossed image of Indian in full headdress, 5½", VG, A **$140.00**

Fi-Na-St Peanut Butter, pail, tin, red with man in white coat in circle logo, lettering above & below, slip lid & bail, 1-lb, EX, A **$65.00**

Fidel Ganahl Lumber Co, paperweight/mirror, features early truck lettered with company name at factory, lettering below, 4" dia, EX, A **$120.00**

Fidelio Beer, label, pre-1920, Fidelio in script on diagonal center band, H Koehler & Co, EX, A **$20.00**

Fidelity & Casualty Co, trade card, allover vignettes of reasons for insurance, EX, A....................................**$27.00**

Fidelity-Phenix Insurance, sign, company name & eagle logo left of Insurance above Fire-Automobile-Rents-Tornado, agent's name below, 12x23", EX, A **$80.00**

Fig Newtons, doll, copyright 1983, vinyl with movable arms & head, yellow dress with orange apron & shoes, 4½", VG, A $42.00

Finck's 'Detroit Special' Overalls, pocket mirror, white pig with blue lettering on blue, ...Wear Like A Pig's Nose, oval, 2¾", EX, A $120.00

Fink Brewing Co, tray, 1913, man pouring beer into glass, black background, oval, scratching/soiling, 16x12½", G, A **$65.00**

Finotti Beverage Co, calendar, 1961, pinup girl in sundress posed with globe & maps scattered about, full pad, creasing/edge wear, 33x16", A **$25.00**

Fireman's Fund Insurance Co, sign, paper, company name in gold around oval showing fireman rescuing girl from fire, framed, 29x22", EX, M2 .... **$525.00**

Firestone, ashtray, rubber & cast iron, tire shape, G, D ... **$35.00**

Firestone, catalog, 1960, VG, D **$35.00**

Firestone Battery Cables, display, tin, red with white Firestone above white Battery Cable, hangs on wall, 8 hooks to hold cables, 8x20", EX+, M2 .... **$38.00**

Firestone Cycle Tires, sign, painted metal, Firestone Cycle Tires in red outlined in white, For Sale Here in white above, 12x22", VG, A **$300.00**

Firestone Deluxe Champion, ashtray, soft rubber, tire shape, clear insert, D **$18.00**

Firestone Gum-Dipped Tires, calendar, 1928, product name above mountains & tall pines looming over car on road, proprietor & full pad below, VG, A **$175.00**

Firestone Rims, sign, paper, people in open touring car cruising west, Quick, Detachable, Demountable..., framed, image: 40x21", VG, A **$850.00**

Firestone Spark Plugs, cabinet, 1940-50, painted tin, large spark plug graphic & advertising, minor scratches/rust, 15¼x20⅛", EX, A **$325.00**

Firestone Steel Radial 500, ashtray, tire shape, clear insert, D **$12.00**

Firestone Tires, sign, 1930s-40s, embossed tin, ...Most Miles Per Dollar, Butternut Valley Hdwe..., orange, cream & black, 12x36", NM, A **$10.00**

Firestone Tires, sign, 1930s-40s, porcelain flange, 2-sided, orange Firestone Tires outlined in white on blue, oval, 16x21", VG, A **$25.00**

Firestone Tires, Batteries..., clock, wood case, glass front, numbered 1-12 in square around advertising, ...Sparkplugs, Brakelining..., 15x15", G, A **$100.00**

Firestone Tractor, ashtray, hard rubber, tire shape, clear insert with embossed Firestone, D **$15.00**

Firestone Tractor, ashtray, soft rubber, clear insert with scratched company imprint, D **$13.50**

First Aid, sign, paper, For Your Health's Sake Drink First Aid, Orange Fruity Flavor, red, white & blue, 5½x9", NM, B1 .... **$3.50**

First Aid, sign, paper, In Real Hot Weather Ask Your Doctor...Lime, It's Pure Flavor, green & white, 5½x9", NM, B1 .... **$3.00**

First Aid, sign, 1920s, embossed tin, Thirsty?...Drink Plenty Because It's A Food, red, white & blue, 10x28", EX, D **$55.00**

First Banner Cigars, box label, inner lid, Geo Washington in oval, patriotic emblem & eagle flank striped First Banner emblem, 6x9", EX, D **$25.00**

First Cabinet Cigars, box label, inner lid, pictures Washington, Jefferson & Adams, 6x9", M, D **$6.50**

First National Bank, calendar, 1899, pictures sailing ship, First National Bank, Moravia NY in red, full pad, EX, A $230.00

First National Cigars, box label, inner lid, street scene with bank building, car & trolley, 6x9", M, D **$16.50**

Fischer's Coffees, bin, tin, gold & cream on seagreen & blue, product & company name on fancy emblem, 20¼x19¼x13", EX, A **$140.00**

Fischer's Vitamin D Bread, jigsaw puzzle, pictures mother serving soup & bread to 4 seated children, 7x9½", EX, F1 .... **$25.00**

Fisher's Blend Flour, pin-back button, pictures flour sack surrounded by lettering, America's Finest Flouring Mill's..., round, EX, A **$26.00**

Fisher Scientific Co, catalog, 1958, features modern laboratory appliances, 1,028 pages, VG+, H2 .... **$60.00**

Fisk, sign, 1926, paper, boy watches friend walk on sign reading Time To Re-Tire..., bees flying about, framed, 14x11", EX, A **$50.00**

Fisk Tires, display, cardboard, circus theme backdrop with die-cut pieces, instructions & game sheets, never used, 35x62", M, D3 .... **$650.00**

Fisk Tires, pen holder, 1940s, glass & metal, brass Fisk boy holding tire & candle in center, glass base, 4x7x1", VG+, A **$326.00**

Fisk Tires, tumblers, Libby Safedge, boy in pajamas holding candle leaning on tire, original box, set of 6, 5", VG, A **$50.00**

Fisk Tires & Tubes, sign, wood with sand-blasted finish, 2-sided, Fisk above sleepy boy & tire, framed with wrought bottom, 47x31", VG/G, A.................. **$425.00**

Fitch's Dandruff Remover/Shampoo, sign, 1939, die-cut cardboard, lettered banner above band wagon with photo images of band members, 38x24", EX, A.**$110.00**

Fitwell Hats, light, metal 4-sided pyramid-shaped frame with 2 sides of milk glass lettered Wear Fitwell Hats, 2 sides jeweled, EX, A **$1,300.00**

Fitzgerald's Porter, label, 1933-36, Fitzgerald Bros Brewing Co, U-type permit number, 12-oz, EX, A **$25.00**

Five Roses Flour, menu board, cardboard, Indian with flour bag at left, Specials Today at top, product name below, 16x20", EX, M1........................$650.00

Five Roses Flour, sign, tin, Five Roses in red above The All-Purpose in black script underlined in red, 9x28", EX, M2 .... **$25.00**

Five Roses Flour, sign, 1910-20s, porcelain, The World's Best arched above circular image of Indian with flour bag, 40x24", VG+, M1 ....$2,000.00

FL Ober Brewing Co, calendar, 1896, die-cut, dogs hold ing monthly calendar sheets in front of palm trees framed, image: 9½x17", G, A.............................**$350.0**

Flag Tobacco, pillow cover, felt, A **$5.0**

Flamingo Special, label, 1933-36, pictures a flamingo Flamingo Brewing Co, U-type permit number, 12-oz EX, A **$47.0**

Flanagan, Nay & Co XXX Special Brew, label, pre-1920 company name arched above logo, G, A **$13.0**

Flanagan-Nay Beer, sign, tin, man in overalls holding bee glass in circular inset, It's A Man's Beer, framed, image 16½" dia, VG, A.. **$225.0**

Flanagan-Nay Light Beer, label, 1933-36, U-type permi number, 12-oz, EX, A **$10.0**

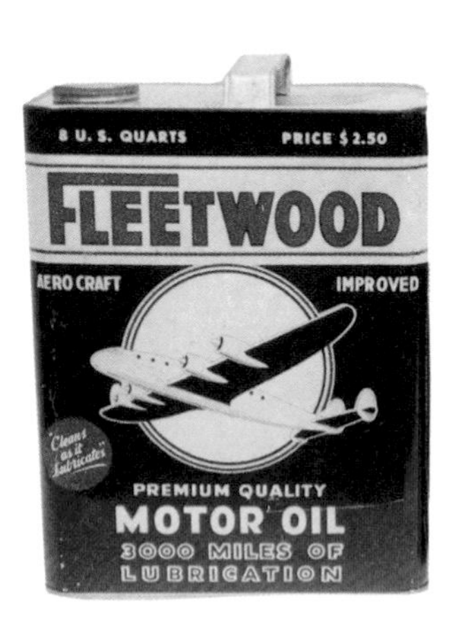

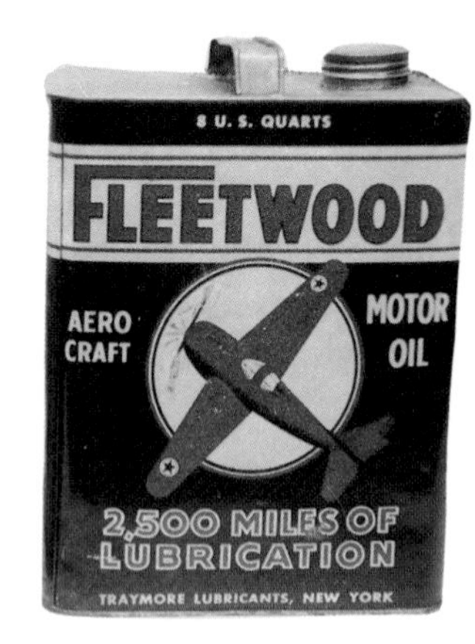

Fleetwood Aero Craft Motor Oil, can, red & white on navy, features single engine plane, 2,500 Miles Of Lubrication, screw lid & handle, 2-gal, VG D3 .... $225.00

Fleetwood Motor Oil, can, red & white on navy, features 4-engine plane, 3,000 Miles Of Lubrication screw lid & handle, 2-gal, EX, D3.................$335.00

Fleetwood Motor Oil, can, 1925-45, airplane on white circle in center, Premium Quality... below, pour spout & handle, 2-gal, 10½", NM, A...............................**$135.00**

Fleischmann Preferred Whiskey, rug, wood frame 14x12", EX, D **$10.00**

Fleischmann's, napkin & swizzle-stick holder, beige with black & red lettering, D **$4.00**

Fleischmann's, pitcher, clear glass with blue lettering, no handle, D **$4.00**

Fleischmann's Yeast, pocket calendar, 1911, celluloid cover, pictures lady in long hair, calendar & product name on reverse, 3x2", VG+, A **$26.00**

Fleischmann's Yeast, pocket mirror, horse-drawn buggy with product name lettered above & below, ad text left of horse, 1¾" dia, EX, A...................................**$120.00**

Fleischmann's Yeast, pocket note pad, 1908, celluloid cover, shows lady in floral hat, Good Yeast Makes Good Bread, with pencil, 3x2", VG+, A...............**$29.00**

Fleischmann's Yeast, recipe book, 1910, 52 pages, G, D.**$7.50**

Fleischmann's Yeast, recipe book, 1945, 'Healthy Cooking,' 40 pages, EX, D.. **$3.50**

Fleischmann's Yeast, sign, embossed tin, yellow with package of yeast encircled in black lower left of product name, black edge, 6x9", VG, A $40.00

Fleischmann's Yeast, wall pocket, black with yellow lettering & graphics on front & side panels, 8x6¼x3", VG+, A **$40.00**

Fli-Hi, crate label, California orange, wild duck flying into dark sky to join flock, Tustin, 10x11", EX, G1...... **$20.00**

Flock's Fine Stock & Pale Lager, sign, embossed paper, 3 women in rowboat in need of assistance, floral border, matted & framed, image: 23x17", G, A **$800.00**

Flor de Salon Cigars, box label, outer, moonlit face of a woman, Art Nouveau style, 4½x4½", M, C3 .... **$10.00**

Flor de Scotia Cigars, box label, outer, Flor de Scotia above portrait of Mary Queen of Scots in filigree frame with crown atop, 4x4", EX, D.............................. **$15.00**

Floral Gem Little Cigars, pocket tin, flat, product name lettered on flowers, slip lid, EX, A **$40.00**

Floressence Violette Talcum, tin, Art Nouveau design, EX, D.......... **$16.50**

Florida Water Perfume, sign, paper, fountain & figures in tropical setting, Genuine Murray & Lanman..., decorative border, 14x10", EX, A **$450.00**

Florsheim Shoes, display, man's oxford, 5" long, EX, D **$37.50**

Flyer Sleds, display, flexible paper die-cut sled, 6x3¼", G, A **$10.00**

Flyer 5¢ Cigar, sign, paper, plane above globe flanked by the cities of New York & Paris, World's Greatest..., framed, 10x9", EX, A.. **$200.00**

Flying A Credit Service, credit card machine, red, silver letters, serial #067348, filling station stamp & note pads included, 6x14x12", VG, A.................................. **$75.00**

Flying A Service, sign, 1962-70, embossed die-cut porcelain, Flying Service above & below winged A, red, black & white, NM, A **$400.00**

Flying Wheel Firecrackers, package, 1930s, pictures winged wheel, 3x2", EX, D.................................... **$8.00**

FO Pierce & Co Bricks, sign, paper, 3 cats on roof with chimney, Brick Red lettered on roof, 169 & 170 Fulton St..., 11x9", EX, A **$350.00**

Foley Kidney Pills, door push plate, porcelain, black lettering on yellow, oval, 6½x3", G, A....................................... **$70.00**

Folger's Coffee, jigsaw puzzle, pictures sailing ships, Free When You Buy Folger's Flaked Or Vacuum Coffee on lid label, unopened, D.. **$20.00**

Folger's Coffee, thermometer, dial type, painted tin, pictures coffee can, Served Here Exclusively, red & black on white, 6" dia, EX, A **$200.00**

Folger's Golden Gate Steel Cut Coffee, tin, view in horizontal oval with product name above & below, slip lid, 1-lb, appears EX, A **$150.00**

Folsom Sporting Goods & Fishing Tackle, catalog, No 45, great image of a dog's face on front, 245 pages, EX, A **$30.00**

Fontana & Co California Canned Fruits, sign, embossed tin, boy on crate eating peaches from can, San Francisco Cal below, framed, image: 15½x11½", G, A $1,900.00

Ford, booklet, 1934, 'Ford At The Fair,' 28 pages, EX, D..**$20.00**

Ford, calendar, 1929, lady posed with stole over arm, Albertus Motor Sales, 3 rows of 4 months each, no pad, 16x10", EX, A **$25.00**

Ford, display, 1960s, plastic, Ford logo atop light bulb on black base, ...See The Light on top of base, 26x11", NM, A **$110.00**

Ford, key chain, tubular, blue & white with oval script logo, EX, D **$20.00**

Ford, mechanical pencil, script logo in black oval, EX, D .**$20.00**

Ford, money clip, heavy metal, green & black, 2¼x2½", EX, D **$15.00**

Ford, pin-back button, tin litho, 1932 above Ford logo, A Ford Year lettered below, ¾" dia, NM, A............. **$16.00**

Ford, pin-back button, 1972, Have A Good Ford Summer, EX, D **$3.50**

Ford, pin-back button, 1984, Mustang 20th anniversary, 3", EX, D **$5.00**

Ford, service bulletin, December 1932, EX, D **$10.00**

Ford, sign, neon, Ford in white script with red neon tubing on blue oval bordered by white tubing, restored, 48", EX, D **$1,200.00**

Ford, sign, porcelain, blue script on white oval on blue rectangle, 25x39", EX, D **$800.00**

Ford, sign, porcelain, 2-sided, Genuine Parts arched above & below Ford in script, oval, 16x24", EX+, S2 ...**$595.00**

Ford, soup cup, Shenango China, Ford logo in script & single green band, M, D **$20.00**

Ford Economy Trucks, banner, 1953, silk with fringed bottom & hanger top, shows colored & lettered circles connected by lines, 48x39", VG+, A....................**$35.00**

Ford Genuine Parts, clock, neon, white lettering & numbers on black, green border with gold trim, octagon, 18" dia, EX+, A.............................$700.00

Ford Motor Co, blotter, Ford Trucks Last Longer lettered on logs protruding from back of truck, unused, 6x3", H1 ....**$4.00**

Ford Motor Co, spoon, 1930s, Royal Stainless, Ford logo in script on handle, EX, D...**$7.50**

Ford Motor Oil, display stand, wire with metal advertising panel featuring the Ford emblem, blue & white on white, 25x18", VG, A...**$65.00**

Ford Service Station, stationary sheet, ca 1920, from William A Lewis Service Station, pictures a convertible, unused, VG, D...**$12.00**

Ford Studebaker & Maxwell, screwdriver, chrome-plated with metal handle, $8\frac{1}{2}$" long, EX, D....................**$45.00**

Ford Used Cars, sign, stenciled sheet metal mounted to folding steel frame, 2-sided, attached label: Pat August 29, 1933, 36", EX, A..**$425.00**

Ford V-8 Deluxe Sedan Coupe, display, cardboard insert framed with orange neon, pictures a car, A New 1947...Tickets On Sale Here, 19x16x6", G, A......**$225.00**

Ford V8, pin-back button, 1934, Ford V8 arched above America's Choice For '34 superimposed over Ford grill close-up, round, EX, A..**$79.00**

Ford 300-500 Club, cigarette lighter, Zippo, in original box, EX, D **$35.00**

Fordson Tractor, booklet, Nov 1923, 'The Fordson,' monthly journal with many articles & photos, 22 pages, EX, D...**$10.00**

Fore 'n' Aft High Grade Sliced Plug, sign, Fore 'n' Aft flanked by anchors on diagonal band, sailboat top left, product lettering lower right, 23x20", EX, A.........**$75.00**

Foremost Milk, sign, die-cut tin milk carton with embossed lettering, orange, brown & white, minor paint loss/bending, 22x11", D **$65.00**

Foremost Strawberry Ice Cream, sign, embossed die-cut tin, shaped like square of ice cream, pictures 2 dishes of ice cream, 18x24", M, D1 ....**$125.00**

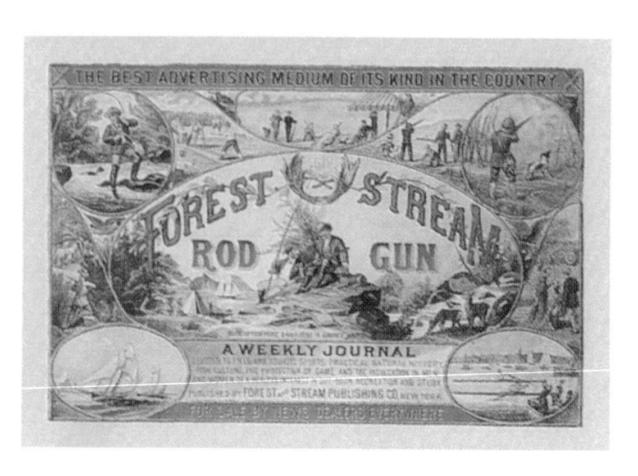

Forest & Stream Rod Gun, sign, paper, oval image of 2 men seated on rock surrounded by vignettes of hunters & fishermen, 10x15$\frac{1}{2}$", EX, A.........$900.00

Forest & Stream Tobacco, pocket tin, Forest & Stream arched above circular inset picturing fisherman in stream, Tobacco below, EX+, M2.........................**$85.00**

Forest & Stream Tobacco, pocket tin, upright, pictures 2 men in canoe, product name above & below, NM, A **$565.00**

Forest Rose Bock Beer, label, 1933-36, Lancaster Brewing Co arched above logo & product name, U-type permit number, 12-oz, EX, A..**$11.00**

Formosa Tea, banner, cloth with hand-painted velour, Japanese girl in floral kimono, Delano, Potter & Co, 34x23", G, A **$250.00**

Fort Bedford Peanut Butter, pocket mirror, pictures jar of product, flaking on mirror, $1\frac{3}{4}$" dia, EX, A.........**$110.00**

Fort Cumberland Brew, sign, litho transfer on board, 2 men in open touring car being served by Black waiter, 24x16", VG, A **$700.00**

Fort Garry Brand Pure Coffee, tin, Indian campsite on square inset, lettering above & below, Hudson's Bay Co, slip lid & bail, EX, M1 ....**$500.00**

Fort Pitt Special Beer, sign, illuminated, green & frosted glass, 7x25x$2\frac{3}{4}$", EX, A......................................**$205.00**

Fort Western Coffee, tin, pictures fort on horizontal oval with lettering arched above & below, pry lid, 1-lb, EX, A..**$220.00**

Foster Hose Supporters, sign, celluloid, woman superimposed over corset with supporters, The Name Is On The Buckles, 17x9", EX, A **$275.00**

Foster Pianos, trade card, die-cut girl with jump rope, when head is pulled up hands holding jump rope move, EX, A...**$12.00**

Foster Rubber Co, swivel stick pin, black cat with arched back featured on shoe heel, Cat's Paw lettered below, I Like Rubber..., EX, A...**$33.00**

Fostoria Products, postcard, black & white photo image of girl with rifle, Hunt As Hard As You Please..., VG, P3......**$35.00**

Fountain Club Beer, bottle, long neck, Old Heidelberg Style on paper label, VG, D..................................**$10.00**

Fountain Oysters, can label, 1933, pictures a fountain & basket of oysters, M, C3..**$20.00**

Fountain Tobacco, store bin, pictures a fountain on ornate design flanked by bands of medallions, 8½x7¼" dia, EX, A..**$220.00**

Four Roses, clock, plastic, square with white face numbered 12-3-6-9 around 4 red roses atop base with product name, 13x12", NM, M3....................................**$95.00**

Four Roses Smoking Tobacco, pocket tin, embossed green lettering & red roses on front panel on red, fold-over lid, some rust, 4x3½", G, A.............$17.50

Four Roses Whiskey, sign, copyright 1912, self-framed tin with oval center showing 2 men with cock fighters, gold lettering, 24x20", EX, A..............................**$300.00**

Four Roses Whiskey, sign, 1910-30, tin, various game animals hanging on cabin wall, elaborate gold & black plaster frame, 57x43", NM, A.............................**$800.00**

Fowler's Cherry Smash, see Cherry Smash

Fox, crate label, peach, orchard scene, large peach & red fox, 7x8", M, C3..**$25.00**

Fox Guns, catalog, hunter aiming at mallards in flight on cover, 24 pages, EX, A..**$125.00**

Fox Guns, catalog, 1931, with wholesale price list, well illustrated, 8 pages, EX, A....................................**$55.00**

Fox Guns, pocket catalog, 1923 price list laid in, fox scene on front, well illustrated, 38 pages, scarce, EX, A.......**$120.00**

Fox Lake Beer, label, 1933-37, Internal Revenue Tax Paid statement, 12-oz, EX, A...**$20.00**

Fox Valley Brewing Co, pocket watch, lettering on front, enameled back, working, 2 1/2" dia, VG, A.......**$250.00**

Fragrant Mixture, tin, pictures elegant woman at left of product name surrounded by fancy graphics, slip lid, 4x6", EX+, A..**$73.00**

Fram Filter Service, thermometer, product name above & product shown below, rounded top & bottom, 39x8", EX...**$35.00**

Francisco Auto Heater, sign, self-framed tin, product name above winter scene with family in cutaway view of car, 18x40", EX, A..**$1,000.00**

Francisco Auto Heater, sign, self-framed tin, product name above winter scene with family in cutaway view of car, 18x40", NM, D3......................$1,475.00

Franco American, bowl/2 vinyl space figures, 1983, hard plastic, UFO logo on side, alien creatures inside rim, 8" dia, EX, A..**$34.00**

Franco American, recipe book, '30 Tempting Spaghetti Meals,' 18 pages, EX, D..**$7.50**

Franco American, spoon, silverplated, Oh Oh Spaghettios inscribed on handle, 3 smiling figures on end, 6" long, EX, A...**$20.00**

Franco American Food, trade card, pictures boys painting sign, ...French Soups, Game & Chicken Pates..., EX, A.........**$32.00**

Franco American Teddy O's, doll, 1990, teddy bear with tan fur, logo on chest, 12", M, N1........................**$15.00**

Frank Coe's Fertilizer Co, calendar, 1906, pictures 3 lads at field's edge with plow & fence, full pad, 13x9", EX, A...**$35.00**

Frank E Davis Fish Co, pocket mirror, pictures hand displaying fish & lobster with lettering all around, oval, 1¾x2¾", EX, A..**$375.00**

Frank Fehr Brewing Co, sign, self-framed tin, elderly man sleeping in chair with maiden beside him holding large bottle, 28¼x22¼", G, A.......................................**$500.00**

Frank Fehr Brewing Co's Bock Beer, sign, paper, girl with 3 goblets of beer & leering goat looking on, framed, image: 29½x21½", G+, A.......................**$500.00**

Frank Jones Brewing Co, sign, paper, large factory image, lettering below, soiling/minor edge tears, framed, image: 30x40", G, A **$700.00**

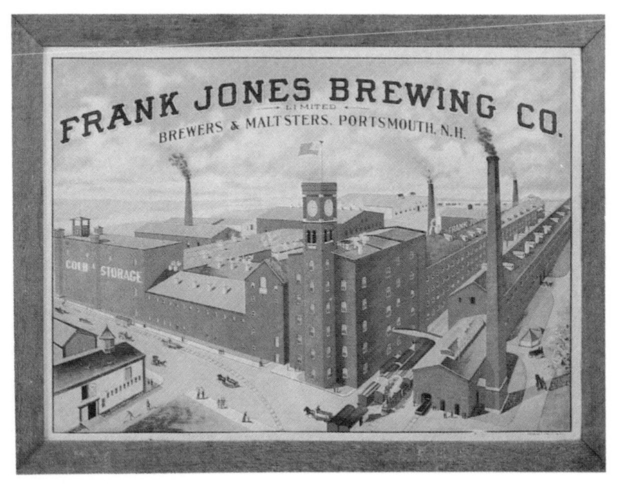

Frank Jones Brewing Co, sign, tin, factory & busy street scene, ...Brewers & Maltsters, Portsmouth, NH above, framed, 35½x47", VG, A...........$2,050.00

Frank Mayo Cigars, box label, inner lid, man in profile & theatrical symbols, 6x9", M, D **$5.00**

Frank Miller's Bright Leather Dressing, tin, 1910-25, black & beige with product name above early touring car on oval inset, 32-oz, 5", VG, A........................**$20.00**

Frank's Old Fashioned Beer, label, 1933-40, M Frank & Son Brewery, Internal Revenue Tax Paid statement, 12-oz, VG, A **$21.00**

Frank's Orange Nectar, bottle topper, cardboard, logo above plate of hot dogs, 8x5", NM, A **$3.00**

Frank's Pale Ale, tray, Frank's in script over top of large bottle, Pale Ale, 5 Full Glasses, Since 1895 & A Good Mixer on rim, EX+, A **$55.00**

Frank X Schwab Co, tray, boy carrying large barrel, From The Distiller Direct To Your Home below, Wholesale & Retail on rim, 13x11", EX, A **$130.00**

Frankenberry Cereal, see General Mills

Frankenmuth Munchner Beer, label, 1933-36, pictures dachshund in center, Frankenmuth Brewing Co, U-type permit number, 12-oz, EX, A **$10.00**

Franklin Glass & Mirror Co, pocket mirror, advertising above & below logo, some cracking to advertisement, 3⅜" dia, EX, A..**$10.00**

Franklin Insurance, pin-back button, ca 1900, sepia bust portrait of Benjamin Franklin with red border, white lettering, EX, D **$8.00**

Franklin Mills Flour & Wheatlet, sign, cardboard stand-up, little girl in pink dress & plumed hat holds 2 boxes, advertising on skirt, 9", EX, A $300.00

Franklin Mills Wheatlet, sign, cardboard stand-up, Uncle Sam promoting Wheatlet to an eager crowd, Eaten & Enjoyed By All Nations, 6¼", EX+, A.................**$100.00**

Fred'k Gamash Automobiles, sign, tin, Fred'k Gamash above Automobiles arched over frontal view of early car, ...Supplies, Ford Parts, 14x20", G, A **$145.00**

Fred Krug Brewing Co, plate, 1859-1909, 50th anniversary, portrait of the founder with banner above, hops & wheat below, rare, 10" dia, EX, A **$500.00**

Fred Sehring Brewing Co, miniature mug, ceramic, features factory scene, gold band around rim, 2¼", EX, S5...**$150.00**

Fredericksburg Bottled Beer, tip tray, portrays close-up of hooded girl, lettered rim, Always Good, 4⅛" dia, G, A **$120.00**

Fredericksburg Bottled Beer, tray, hooded girl with flowers flanked by circular logos, lettering on rim, Kaufmann & Strauss litho, 13" dia, VG, A **$250.00**

Freedom Perfect Motor Oil, can, 1935-45, watchdog atop product name, 100% Pure logo in bottom corner, yellow & blue background, 1-qt, 5½", VG, A...........**$55.00**

Freeway Nevr-Nox Ethyl, pump sign, 1930s-40s, porcelain, red, white & blue with product name in bold letters, minor flaking, 13½x12", A **$100.00**

Freightliner Trucks, key chain, 1970s, enameled, EX, P1 ...**$5.00**

Fremlins Family Ale & Stout Depot, sign, metal, 2-sided, die-cut elephant atop emblem shape with curled corners, gold lettering on black, 45x43", VG, A **$725.00**

French Auto Oil, sign, tin flange, orange & tan lettering on green, ...Keeps Your Motor Young, 9x18", VG, A .**$175.00**

French's Mustard, spoon, hard yellow plastic, Hot Dan holding mustard jar on end, French's Mustard on reverse handle, 4½" long, EX, A...........................**$11.00**

Fresh Bond Bread, broom display, metal, brooms hang from green panel with red & white round Fresh Bond Bread logo, 41x19", EX, A **$375.00**

Fresno Bohemian Export Beer, label, 1933-50, Fresno Brewing Co, Internal Revenue Tax Paid statement, 11-oz, G, A **$5.00**

Fresno Lager Beer, label, 1933-50, Fresno Brewing Co, Internal Revenue Tax Paid statement, 11-oz, EX, A **$25.00**

Friedman, Keiler & Co Distillers, sign, paper, woman relaxing on divan while looking in hand mirror, minor soiling, framed, image: 14x20", EX, A **$1,700.00**

Friendly Five Shoes, sign, die-cut porcelain, The Friendly Five above 2 colonial gents shaking hands next to $5 above shoe, 24x18", VG, A.................................**$315.00**

Friends Tobacco, print, 1895-1900, Remember Friends & product above the Dark Town Fire Brigade, Tobacco below, Currier, 19x23", VG, D............................**$350.00**

Friends Tobacco, tin, pictures man & dog, EX, D **$35.00**

Friendship Cut Plug Chewing Tobacco, clock, footed round case, animated paper face with moving mouth which chews tobacco, lettered & numbered, 4x4", EX, A..**$2,090.00**

Frigidaire, pin-back button, 1941, yellow & brown, EX, D.**$3.00**

Frigidaire, recipe book, 1938, 'Your Frigidaire Recipes,' 36 pages, VG, D **$6.00**

Frigidaire, still bank, pot metal, refrigerator shape, National Products Corp, Chicago USA, minor paint chips, 4x2", H1 ....**$36.00**

Frigidtest Anti-Freeze, can, 1945, red, white & blue artic scene with airplane flying before red sun above 2 polar bears, 1-gal, 7¾", EX, A..**$15.00**

Frisch's Big Boy, bank, 1973, Big Boy figure, soft vinyl, red & white checked outfit, 9", EX, D **$28.50**

Frisch's Big Boy, pocket lighter, 1960s, flat with metal top, gray body pictures Big Boy, restaurant & product name, 1¾x2", EX, A **$250.00**

Frisco Line Railroad, pocket mirror, train speeding through scenic landscape, There Is Something To See lettered on rim, 2⅛" dia, VG+, A........................**$160.00**

Friskies, clock, light-up, winking dog, N2..............**$145.00**
Fritos, eraser, 1960s, Frito Bandito, pink, 2", EX, D.....**$7.50**
Fritz Brew, label, 1933-36, pictures a castle, Fritz Brewing Co, U-type permit number, 12-oz, EX, A.............**$15.00**
Front Rank Steel Furnaces, sign, embossed painted tin, product lettering right of devil images around furnace, Good Bye!..., framed, 9x20", EX, A....................**$110.00**
Frontenac Peanut Butter, pail, tin, white with Frontenac... in red with gold outline, red & gold square border, sealed lid & bail, 12-oz, NM, A............................**$25.00**
Frontier Ultra Lube Motor Oil, can, 1935-45, man on horse above product name, red & white striped background, pry lid, 1-qt, 5½", EX, A..........................**$10.00**
Frostene Frosting, sign, embossed tin, girl in white robe, jewels & crown displays frosted cake, For Perfect Frosting..., 27x19", VG, A **$1,000.00**
Frostie Root Beer, bottle, 1967, clear with cream & red label, 10-oz, EX, D **$5.00**
Frostie Root Beer, can, steel, EX, D............................**$4.00**
Frostie Root Beer, fan pull, 1950s, 2-sided, You'll Love It!, EX, D...**$5.00**
Frostie Root Beer, sign, die-cut cardboard, billboard with silhouetted people behind man with Everybody Loves... banner, 13x21", NM, M2 ....**$24.00**
Frostie Root Beer, thermometer, dial, red & blue Frostie logo & blue numbers on white, 12" dia, NM, M3..........**$125.00**
Frostie Root Beer, thermometer, Frostie boy with lettered bottle cap above, bottle & A Real Taste Treat below, round ends, 36x8", VG, A....................................**$90.00**
Fruehauf Trailers, cigarette lighter, in original box, EX, D **$25.00**
Fruit Bowl Soda, sign, tin flange, tilted bottle & Drink Fruit Bowl on yellow with black wavy border, 14x18", NM, M3 ....**$180.00**
Fruit of the Loom, mannequin, painted 3-D hard rubber figure wearing girdle, mounted on wood rods connected to base, 29", VG, A **$230.00**
Fruitfield Apricots, can label, large apricots & row of trees, M, C3..**$15.00**
Full Dress Pipe & Cigarette Tobacco, tin, pictures man in tuxedo with wheel designs on sides, domed slip lid, 6x5" dia, EX+, A **$150.00**
Full O' Juice, crate label, 1930s, California orange, partially peeled orange & glass of juice on lavender, Redlands, 10x11", M, C1...**$2.00**
Full Weight 5 Cent Cigar, sign, tin, oval image of lady on 5¢ scale, ...Hand Made, Gumpert Bros Makers Phila, framed, image: 28x20", VG, A.......................**$13,500.00**
Fuller Brush, letter opener, clear or brown, G, D.......**$5.00**
Fun-To-Wash Washing Powder, product box, features black face with head scarf, product name above & below, Hygienic Lab, unused, 7x5x2½", EX, A **$30.00**
Funk-G Hybrid, pencil clip, 1930s, multicolored ear of corn on white background, EX, D **$12.00**
Funkes Chocolate Creams, pin-back button, colorful image of boy with wheelbarrow, slight edge foxing, round, EX, A..**$33.00**
Funsten Bros & Co, booklet, 1907-08, 'A Trapper's Guide,' shows winners of Funstens trapping contest inside, 80 pages, EX, A **$35.00**
FW Cook Brewing Co, sign, 1907, self-framed tin, elderly couple enjoying glass of beer, Kauffman & Strauss litho, 27x19", G, A...**$280.00**
FW Cough Tablets, tin, blue, slip lid, heavily worn, rectagular, A...**$5.00**

G

G Heileman Brewing Co's Old Style Lager, sign, wood, litho transfer of man toasting woman at table & woman in bed with cherubs above her, 20x30", G, A....**$150.00**
G Washington Coffee, display case, tin, slanted glass front, white letters on red below, Better Coffee...An Easier Way, 13x12", EX, A **$50.00**
Gail's Best Snuff, trade card, die-cut, full-color image of 2 puppies, 3½x5", EX, D **$6.00**
Gainer Cigar, sign, waxed cardboard, large Gainer cigar on the diagonal, A Burning Success above, ...Havana Filler below, 7x11", NM, A...................................**$10.00**
Gale Manufacturing Co, match holder, tin, oval factory image above lettering, ...Means Good, 5", G, A.**$300.00**
Galleon, crate label, 1937, California lemon, galleon sailing on high seas, Seaboard Lemon Assoc, Oxnard, 9x12½", M, C1 ....**$5.00**
Galliker's Ice Cream, display, tin on cardboard, features tilted 1/2 gal of ice cream above flavor slots, 24x10", EX, A...**$30.00**
Galt Teas, tin, very colorful graphics, Rich Strong Flavor, slip lid, VG, M2 ....**$75.00**
Gambrinus Lager Beer, label, 1933-36, Gambrinus Brewing Co, U-type permit number, 12-oz, EX, A **$15.00**
Game Cock Smoking Tobacco, tin, pat 1858, round with paper label featuring image of cock, lettering & border, Lone Jack Tobacco Works, G, A **$80.00**

Game Fine Cut Tobacco, tin, grouse in brush flanked by lettering, 48 5¢ Pkgs & Game Fine Cut lettered on side, slip lid, 7x12", EX, A.......................$285.00
Gander Cigars, box label, 1927, lithographer's proof, oval close-up of goose in landscape with house beyond, VG, A **$26.00**

Garbro Orchard, crate label, California apple, photo image of 6 Gravenstein apples on a branch, blue background, 9x11", EX, G1 ....**$8.00**

Garcia Grande Cigar, sign, metal, product name in bold letters, It's Mild lettered diagonally in script at right, 3¼x22", NM, B1 ....**$12.00**

Garcia Mystery Mild Rum Cured 5¢ Cigar, dispenser, metal, yellow drum with black lettering on stand, yellow lettering on black lid, The Wonder Cigar, VG, A **$85.00**

Gard Gum, package, complete, G2 ....**$20.00**

Garden City Tailoring, pocket mirror, 'Spirit of 76' scene encircled by lettered border, 2¼" dia, EX, A **$50.00**

Garden Court Talc, tin, 1930s, embossed irises, green, yellow & blue, shaker top, 6x3", EX, D **$28.00**

Gardenia Talcum, tin, gardenia decor above product name, Richard Hudnut, New York -- Paris below, shaker top, oval, 2¼x1¼", EX, D..........................**$40.00**

Garfield Manor Cigars, box label, outer, 1934, cluster of houses, 4½x4½", M, C3 ....**$25.00**

Garfield Tea, ruler, wood, Cures Constipation & Sick Headache, small piece missing each end, 12", D...**$3.00**

Garland Stoves & Ranges, match holder, tin, red, yellow & white, ...The World's Best, minor crazing, 5", G, A .**$30.00**

Garland Stoves & Ranges, pocket mirror, distant factory with logo & lettering above & below, The World's Best, horizontal oval, 2¾", VG+, A **$30.00**

Garland Stoves & Ranges, sign, cardboard, woman carries bucket of roses & stool, inset of stove, Barstow's Garland Oil Stove 1886, 16x11", EX, A **$65.00**

Garrett's XXXX Baker Rye, pocket mirror, celluloid, nude girl at water's edge, Oldest Brand In Baltimore at left, oval, 2¾x1¾", VG, A **$300.00**

Garretts Tobacco, sign, tin, red & blue lettering on gold background, paint scuffs, 11x15", A.....................**$10.00**

Gateway Sporting Goods, catalog, 1957, 68 pages, VG, D **$12.00**

Gatley Clothing, match safe, celluloid, pictures nymphs, G, D **$80.00**

Gatordredge, sign, tin, Gatordredge lettered across center of alligator, Florida Dredge Industries arched above, square, VG, D1 ....$285.00

Gay-Ola, pocket mirror, lady in shawl collar holding up bottle, Drink lettered above, Gay-Ola below, 1¾" dia, VG, A **$200.00**

GBS Co Eigenbrot Brewery, sign, embossed tin, ...Baltimore, Md, black & gold, original wood backing, scratches/minor chips, 20x14", G, A **$550.00**

Geisha Brand Crab, sign, die-cut cardboard, Oriental girl with umbrella pointing at can of crab meat, minor scratches, 14½x10", VG, A **$200.00**

Gem Damaskeene Razor, clock, die-cut wood, pictures man holding angry baby while shaving, 27½x23", EX, A **$2,500.00**

Gem Freezer, trade card, 1890, little girl feeding her doll ice cream, 5x3", EX, P1 ....**$16.00**

Gem Wringer, salesman's sample, cast iron & wood, American Wringer Co, 16" long, VG, A **$80.00**

Gems of Columbia Cigars, box label, inner lid sample, early 1900s, white lady trading with Indian lady, John's & Co litho, M, A **$42.00**

General Accident Insurance, pocket mirror, shows sow feeding piglets encircled by lettering, foxing around edge, 2¼" dia, EX, A **$42.00**

General Arthur Cigar, sign, paper, bust-portrait of General Arthur in mosaic-like setting, matted & framed, image: 14x11", EX, A..**$75.00**

General Arthur Cigar, sign, reverse-painted glass oval in wood frame, pictures the general in center, red with gold, 34½x27", EX, A **$125.00**

General Cigar Co, sign, early 1900s, A Few of the 67... surrounded by 16 factory vignettes, minor flaking, framed, 35x23½", A..**$200.00**

General Cord Tires, sign, 1900-20, oleograph, family in car greeting Chinese family, Sign Of Friendship..., rare, framed, 24x23", EX, A......................................**$1,600.00**

General Dual-8 Tires, medallion, aluminum, The World's Quickest Stopping Tire, EX, D **$15.00**

General Electric, display, 1927, plastic light-up with metal cylinder at bottom, Clocks, Irons, Heaters..., 8½x14", EX, A **$130.00**

General Electric, kite, 1960s, Topflite, red, yellow & black graphics on white paper, Spring Specials On GE Appliances..., 32x27", EX, D **$15.00**

General Electric, paperweight, 1980s, embossed brass, GE symbol upper left of early lightbulb, raised border, 3x2¼x1/4", EX, A **$18.00**

General Electric Edison Mazda Lamps, display, cardboard stand-up, Eyestrain Days... above 2 girls doing homework, 15¢ bulb & advertising below, 50x40", EX, A **$176.00**

General Electric Home-Freezer Refrigerator, salesman's sample, black & white plastic refrigerator in cardboard box, card announcing Your...Will Be Along Soon, EX, A...**$35.00**

General Electric Refrigerators, recipe/refrigerator-freezer instruction book, 48 pages, G, D **$3.00**

General Electric Refrigerators, salt & pepper shakers & sugar bowl, shaped like refrigerators, M, D2 .....**$150.00**

General Electric Refrigerators, sugar bowl, milk glass, shaped like coil top refrigerator, M, D.................**$65.00**

General Electric Refrigerators, tape measure, plastic, product name on front, Remember Me on back, tab missing, D **$15.00**

General Foods Corp, recipe book, 1940, 'Calendar of Desserts,' 48 pages, EX, D **$4.00**

General Foods Corp, recipe book, 1943, 'Recipes for Today,' 40 pages, G, D **$3.00**

General Insurance Co, pin-back button, 1930s, black & white with serial number in red, EX, D **$4.00**

General Mills Cinnamon Toast Crunch Cereal, bank, 1988, plastic, musical, 6", NM, D..........................**$10.00**

General Mills Frankenberry Cereal, doll, Frankenberry, soft vinyl, 8", EX, D...**$35.00**

General Mills/Five Star Hour, figurine, 1938, plaster caricature figure with NBC microphone, 6 radio soap operas inscribed on base, 5x6" dia, VG+, A....**$1,200.00**

General Steel Wares Limited, sign, porcelain, Slow Dipt Galvanized Ware above trash can marked GSW Quality Goods, company below, 25x20", EX, M2 ....**$175.00**

General Streamline Jumbo, ashtray, tire shape with embossed insert, The General Tire Goes A Long Way To Make Friends, D **$25.00**

General Tire & Rubber, ashtray, tire shape with glass insert, 5" dia, G, D..**$25.00**

Genesee Beer & Ale, clock, light-up, logo & lettering on white background, working, 16x16x3", EX, P4....**$13.00**

Genesee Brewing Co, tray, Indian maidens in canoe with panoramic view of teepees & waterfall beyond, decorative rim, 12" dia, G, A **$135.00**

Geo A Schmidt's Nut-Oil-Soaps/Toilet Preparations, soap dispenser, ca 1900, white bell shape with metal spigot, red & blue lettering, age cracks/faded lettering, rare, M2 ....$1,200.00

Geo Esslinger & Son Brewing Co, sign, 1903, sunset scene with fishermen coming home to chalet, framed, image: 15x20", EX, A..**$525.00**

Geo Haas & Sons Fine Candies, trade card, ca 1900, pictures a violin & flowers, 2½x4½", EX, P1 ....**$16.00**

Geo Ringler & Co Brewers, calendar, 1899, paper, girl wrapping herself in American flag, 12 calendar sheets below, framed, image: 24x16", EX, A **$2,500.00**

Geo Ringler & Co Brewers, calendar, 1916, factory image with bottle insets below, store inset above, March pad, framed, image: 19x13½", NM, A.........................**$650.00**

Geo Ringler & Co Brewers, tray, foaming glass flanked by lettered banners, Extra Pilsener & Real German... on rim, oval, 13¾x16½", EX, A **$425.00**

Geo Zett Brewery, calendar, 1909, embossed die-cut cardboard, 2 children in hay surrounded by puppies, framed, 20x20", VG, A **$1,000.00**

George E Mitchell's Perforated Belladona Plasters, box with drawer, Pat Sept 12 1871, wood, features 7 paper labels of interior & exterior factory scenes, 2x10x7", VG, A...**$180.00**

George W Childs Cigars, box label, inner lid, pictures man at cluttered desk, 6x9", M, C3 ....**$12.00**

George W Smith Dealer In Dry Goods & Groceries, broadside, paper, cherubs in store carrying & testing goods, black lettering on white, early, VG, A **$250.00**

George Washington Cut Plug, lunch pail, oval portrait of George Washington flanked by Greatest American, wood handle, EX+, A..**$75.00**

George WM Hoffman Co, pocket mirror, draped nude leans on bar lettered The Barkeeper's Friend, black lettering on gold rim, 2⅛" dia, EX, A..$425.00

Georgia Peaches, crate label, pictures 2 large peaches, 7x8", M, C3 ....**$20.00**

Gerber, cup, embossed image of Gerber Baby & emblem, pink, aqua or yellow, marked Gerber Prod Co, 3¼", EX, D...**$5.00**

Gerber, doll, 1955, rubber, sculpted hair, Sun Rubber Co, letters worn on bib, 12", D **$45.00**

Gerber, doll, 1988, teddy bear, light-tan plush with logo at neck, 22", M, N1 ....**$25.00**

German American Brewing Co's Maltosia, tip tray, Maltosia logo shield in center, Our Beer Is Sterilized, Not Pasteurized lettered below, 5" dia, EX+, A **$55.00**

Gerst Dark Beer, label, 1933-36, G logo above product name with decorative border, U-type permit number, 12-oz, EX, A **$6.00**

Get Up, sign, tin, Get Up lettered on yellow vertical ovals on black band, Drink on yellow above, It's King-Size, 14x24", NM, M3 ....**$55.00**

Geyserite Soap, sign, paper, nude bathing beauties in hot springs, pictures product below, 19x13½", G-, A...**$50.00**

GF Burkhardt's Lager Beer, sign, tin, large frothy mug & wreath of hops & wheat, For Sale Here! below, minor flakes, framed, image: 17x13½", A **$550.00**

GF Hueblein & Bro, sign, ca 1894, tin, satisfied gentleman in wicker chair holding cocktail glass, 36½x27½", G, A.**$350.00**

Ghirardelli's Chocolate & Cocoa, clock, regulator, wood, glass front, company name above product names with San Francisco below, Roman numerals, EX, A...**$700.00**

Ghirardelli Chocolate, tin, pictures an eagle, lid missing, otherwise EX, 6x3¼" dia, D **$12.50**

Giant Brand Roasted Coffee, tin, lettering above & below shield logo, slip lid & bail, 5-lb, round, appears EX, A...........**$75.00**

Giant Power Gasoline, banner, cloth, muscular figure with winged 'A' in hand looming over service station & car, text at right, 34x79", EX, A...................................**$70.00**

Giant Salted Peanuts, tin, pictures Giant with club, seaside castle in distance, press lid, 10-lb, 11¼", G, A......**$60.00**

Gibbs Imperial Plows, sign, embossed tin, farmer promoting plow to another man, I Tell You Sir..., 1 of 2 known, framed, 10x14", G, A....................$600.00

Gibbs Mew, tray, man's hands pour beer at table with tray, bottles, glasses, ashtray & cigarettes, square, rounded corners, EX, A...**$30.00**

Gibley's Gin, thermometer, brass bound with glass face, die-cut bottle on pointer, various flags on background, 9" dia, EX, A **$55.00**

Giblin's Liniment, display case, wood with glass front, multiple shelves, 26x24x7½", EX, A...................**$750.00**

Gibson Furniture Co, pocket mirror, company name arched above exterior view of factory, horizontal oval, 2¾", EX, A...**$185.00**

Gibson Refrigerator, jigsaw puzzle, ca 1931, man delivering ice finds that lady of the house purchased refrigerator, 9x12", EX, F1...**$45.00**

Gilbert Mfg Co, trade card, 1886, President & Mrs Garfield selecting cloth, EX, A..**$26.00**

Gilbert Rae's Aerated Waters, sign, embossed tin, 3 labeled bottles above factory scene, rolled edges, 28x20", EX+, A..**$600.00**

Gilbert's Gloss Starch, trade card, 1870s, pictures little girl with package, black background, 3x4¼", EX, P1....**$10.00**

Gilby's Gin & Vodka, thermometer, tin face, numbers surround Gilby's in bold print, Gin & Vodka lettered on wavey banner, 9" dia, G-, A **$7.00**

Gilda, crate label, Spanish citrus, woman dressed in white, M, C3..**$15.00**

Gillett's Lye, pin-back button, Black man seated on stack of soap boxes holding sign reading Gillett's Lye Eats Dirt, 1¼" dia, EX, A...**$120.00**

Gillette Safety Razor, pocket mirror, pictures baby encircled by 1909 calendar, 2¼" dia, EX, A...............**$100.00**

Gillette Safety Razor, sign, die-cut tin, 2-sided, man shaving surrounded by ...Shaves Perfectly With Either Hand, 15x13½", EX, A..**$2,750.00**

Gillette Tech Razor, box with original razor, pictures King Gillette, red, white & blue, slide-off top, razor: 3", box: 4½x2", VG, D..........................$16.00

Gillette Tires, sign, embossed metal, A Bear For Wear lettered below image of bear's head at left of Gillette Tires, 19x73", VG+, A...**$50.00**

Gillies Coffee Co, tin, company name lettered in diamond with bowed sides over decorative bands, round screw lid, tall square, 5-lb, VG, A **$40.00**

Gilmore Gasoline, calendar, 1947, red lion logo, 17x7", EX, D...**$18.50**

Gilt Edge Lager Beer, sign, cardboard, photo offset image of paddle wheeler at dock & harbor scene, matted & framed, image: 15x18", EX, A............................**$250.00**

Gilt Edge Whiskey, sign, paper, young girl reclining on chaise lounge, ...A Treat That Can't Be Beat, original frame, 26x30", EX, A......................................**$4,250.00**

Gilt Top Cream Ale, label, 1933-50, Spokane Brewery Inc, Internal Revenue Tax Paid, 11-oz, EX, A **$20.00**

Gin Seng, tray, Oriental lady in rickshaw beneath Gin Seng banner, Beverage Of Purity sign at right, rectangular, 13¼", VG, A **$80.00**

Ginger-Mint Julip, dispenser, stoneware, barrel shape, Drink Ginger-Mint Julip lettered in horizontal oval, no pump, 10x7" dia, VG, A **$50.00**

Girl of the Pingree Shoe, pocket mirror, pictures woman in left profile, lettering below, oval, 2¾", VG+, A........**$35.00**

Gisela Cigars, box label, outer, woman with long flowing hair, 4½x4½", M, C3 .... **$14.00**

Glad Tidings Cigars, box label, inner lid sample, 1880s, pictures old seaman at the helm, George Schlegel litho, VG, A **$47.00**

Glattolin, display box, cardboard, with samples, M, A . **$15.00**

Glen-Lube Motor Oil, can, 1930-40, red & blue lettering on cream background, blue & red stripes top & bottom, 1-qt, 5½", EX, A **$20.00**

Glendale Yellow American Cheese, box, wood, green & red farmhouse scene & lettering, ...Pauly & Pauly Cheese Co, Manitowoc Wis, 4x11½", EX, D **$10.00**

Glendora Coffee, sample tin, EX, D **$45.00**

Glendora Coffee, sign, tin, features large image of coffee tin meeting all 4 edges, dark blue with gold & white, 14x8½", EX, A **$50.00**

Glenwood & Elm Ranges, sign, dated 1906, paper, Black man by range shooing away cat, 'Cat Hab Kittens In De Ubben...,' framed, EX, A **$350.00**

Glenwood Ranges & Heaters, trade card, pictures little girl holding cat in a tree, ...Perfect With A Faultless Record lettered below, EX, A **$12.00**

GLF Quality, gas globe, 1920s-30s, red metal body with red on white panel, product name surrounded by scroll design, EX, A **$155.00**

Glick's Cabaret Mints, tin, 1906-10, dancing cabaret girl on red & black stripes, gold highlights, press lid, 10-lb, 9x8½" dia, G, A **$25.00**

Glider, crate label, 1930s, California orange, airplane in colorful sky, Fillmore Citrus Assn, 10x11¾", M, C3... **$27.50**

Globe Brewing Co, sign, paper, bare-chested nymph looking over rock with 3 ogling faces looking up at her, framed, image: 25x18", G, A..........$1,250.00

Globe Feeds, calendar, 1920, pictures children & chicks, full pad, G, D **$110.00**

Globe Machinery & Supplies, catalog, 1949, 1,424 pages, VG+, H2 .... **$75.00**

Globe Polish, trade card, die-cut cat wearing tag, Ask For..., 2-piece hinged body so front legs bend & cats sit up, EX, A **$36.00**

Globe Ranges, sign, tin, pictures a stove, Globe Ranges Make Happy Homes, E Wangler Hdw..., soiling/fading, framed, 49x29", G-, A **$50.00**

Globe Scratch Feed, pin-back button, egg shape, Something To Crow About above rooster atop globe, laying hen below, Makes 'Em Lay, EX, A **$33.00**

Globe Wernicke Bookcases, tip tray, pictures 1930s couple, G, D **$65.00**

Globe-Seal Motor Oil, sign, painted tin, product emblem with man checking car engine above Seals The Pistons & company name, 14x10", EX, A **$275.00**

Gloria Jean Golden Mushroom Pop Corn, can, photo image of girl with bowl of popcorn in geometric fan-shaped graphic, product name above, no top, 10-oz, EX, A **$110.00**

Glory Cocoanut Soap, container, glass ball shape with metal lid, 10", EX, A **$120.00**

Glostora, sign, 1930s, die-cut cardboard, pictures man & product bottle, Keeps Hair Neat, A Scalp Massage..., EX, A **$15.00**

Gluek Brewing Co Beer, sign, Vitrolite with copper-clad corners, star logo with lettering above & below, 23½x18", NM, A **$850.00**

GM Buick Cadillac, playing cards, double deck, MIB, D. **$25.00**

GM Parts Division, decanter, for Jim Beam Whiskey, 1978, Mr Goodwrench, 13", M, D **$75.00**

GM Trucks, sign, ca 1924, porcelain, 2-sided, orange, navy & white with GMC logo surrounded by product name, rare, 30" dia, EX, A **$250.00**

GMAC National Credit Service, sign, porcelain, 2-sided, yellow & white eagle & globe logo left of yellow & white lettering on blue, 12x24", NM, D3 ......$335.00

GMC Trucks, sign, 1930s-40s, neon, GMC logo in center, continuous moving green light, mirrored background, working, 18" dia, EX, A **$400.00**

Goebel Beer, tip tray, pictures Dutch girls, G, D **$95.00**

Goebel Beer, tray, Bavarian man with glass & bottle flanked by Goebel Beer in script, hops & grain on rim, 12" dia, G, A **$200.00**

Goebel's Malt Extract, tip tray, pictures girl with doll, G, D **$42.00**

Goebel 22 Beer, sign, tin, product name with rooster & foaming glass above If It's Goebel...It's Good on band below, 21x25", VG, D3 .... **$375.00**

Goetz Country Club Bock Beer, label, 1933-50, product name above ram's head, Internal Revenue Tax Paid statement, 12-oz, G, A **$8.00**

Goetze Niemer Surgical Instruments, catalog, 1922, 416 pages, VG+, H2 .... **$100.00**

Goff's Best Braid, display, early 1900s, wood with product name lettered on 3 drawers, 11¼x17", VG, A **$145.00**

Gold Band Pineapple, can label, vista of Napa Valley on blue background, G1 .... **$6.00**

Gold Bond Tobacco, pocket tin, upright, Gold Bond Cross Cut lettered on bow in center, Old Reliable above, slip lid, EX+, A **$237.00**

Gold Brand Apricots, can label, vista of Napa Valley on blue background, San Francisco Ca, EX, G1 .... **$8.00**

Gold Coin & Gold Medal Stoves & Ranges, trade card, North Pole scene with product surrounded by sunrays, Bussey & McLeod Stove Co, EX, A **$15.00**

Gold Coin Stoves, trade card, 1880s, sepia image of elegant girl on front, stove engraved on back, 3½x5½", EX, P1 .... **$15.00**

Gold Dust, see also Fairbank's

Gold Dust Washing Powder, trade card, die-cut, the Gold Dust twins in tub, EX, A............ $28.00

Gold Flake Peanut Butter, pail, product name & other lettering in oval center, numerous stars on background, slip lid & bail, 1-lb, EX+, A **$85.00**

Gold Flake Peanut Butter, pail, tin, black with black & gold horizontal oval logo, random gold-star design, gold slip lid & bail, 1-lb, VG, A **$170.00**

Gold Hunter Cigars, box label, outer, 1890s, gold hunter with equipment, The Independent Gold Hunter On His Way To Klondike, 5x4½", M, C3 .... **$22.00**

Gold Lager Beer, label, 1933-36, Ambassador Brewing Co, U-type permit number, 11-oz, EX, A **$20.00**

Gold Medal Beer, label, 1933-50, Time Brewing Co, Internal Revenue Tax Paid statement, 12-oz, EX, A **$26.00**

Gold Medal Bock Beer, label, 1933-50, Indianapolis Brewing Co Inc, Internal Revenue Tax Paid statement, EX, A..**$30.00**

Gold Medal Cotton Netting, trade card, die-cut of Gold Metal kid holding fish & hat, coins & lettering below, EX, A **$19.00**

Gold Medal Flour, cookie jar, tin, white round canister with Gold Medal logo above Cookies lettered in blue, EX, D **$30.00**

Gold Medal Lubricant Grease, can, 1930s, product name & car on green trees, Best For The North below, pry lid & bail, 10-lb, 9", G, A **$30.00**

Gold Nugget, crate label, California pear, Gold Nugget lettered in yellow on blue background, pears at right, Lodi, 8x11", G1 .... **$2.00**

Gold Prize Cigars, box label, inner lid, embossed Gold Prize above portrait of lady in fancy embossed gold oval, 2 seals below, 6x9", EX, D **$25.00**

Gold Shield Coffee, tin, shield flanked by Vacuum Packed with product name above & below, brick-like background, key-wind lid, 1-lb, EX+, A **$43.00**

Gold Soap, sign, paper, oval images of man seated on a stump & woman with children using product, 18x22", G-, A **$900.00**

Gold Tint for Frying & Shortening, box, waxed cardboard, yellow, orange & blue, Baltimore Butterine Co, 1-lb, EX, D $8.50

Gold Tone Razor Blades, sign, cardboard, 5x13", G, D...**$25.00**

Goldeck Beer, label, pre-1920, logo above Goldeck in script, Birk Bros Brewing Co, G, A **$30.00**

Golden Bear Cookies, tin, features product name arched above white bear graphic, Bridge assortment, no lid, VG, A **$20.00**

Golden Bear Oil Co, sign, 1920-30, tin, 2-sided, yellow bear highlighted in black, ...Petroleum Products on white border, 15" dia, EX, A **$200.00**

Golden Bosc Pears, crate label, 1930s, yellow train on blue & black background, Medford Oregon, 7¼x11", M, C1 .... **$2.00**

Golden Bridge Root Beer, door push plate, 1930s, embossed tin, pictures a bottle, red, yellow & brown, 12x3½", EX, D **$50.00**

Golden Circle, crate label, 1930s, California orange, big wreath of oranges, Redlands Co-operative Fruit Ass'n, 10x11", M, C1 .... **$2.00**

Golden Crown Marshmallow Drops, tin, rectangular with rounded corners, A **$15.00**

Golden Dome Whiskey, pocket mirror, pictures whiskey bottle, round, EX, D **$55.00**

Golden Eagle Tobacco, bucket label, eagle on American shield & flag, 13x7", EX, D **$35.00**

Golden Esso Extra, banner, canvas, large graphic of gas pump reading Golden Esso Extra above The Gold Pump Is Here!, 83x36", VG, A **$20.00**

Golden Glow Margarine, pin-back button, 1950s, multi-colored, EX, D **$4.00**

Golden Grain Bread, rolling pin, stoneware, G, D ..**$85.00**

Golden Grain Coffee, bin, tin, product flanked by Steel Cut, Roasted Coffee on slant top, Packed For Gateway Grocery Co, 9x8x6½", G, A **$185.00**

Golden Grain Tobacco, bag, cloth with paper label featuring sheaf of Golden Grain, with contents, 7/8-oz, EX, A **$15.00**

Golden Lager Beer, label, 1933-36, Ambassador Brewing Co, U-type permit number 1158, 11-oz, G, A.......**$23.00**

Golden Lights, playing cards, looks like pack of cigarettes, MIB, P4 ....**$7.00**

Golden Pheasant Sebewaing Beer, bottle, long neck, paper label, G, D..**$6.00**

Golden Rain Tobacco, tin, Golden Rain arched above WJ Yarbrough & Sons, Richmond Va, Ginna litho, 3x5x2½", VG+, A **$15.00**

Golden Rod, crate label, Washington pear, flowers on black 1920s design, Yakima, 8x11", EX, G1 ....**$4.00**

Golden Rod Coffee, tin, paper litho on tin, yellow & cream letters on blue, warehouse on reverse, key-wind lid, minor wear, 1-lb, 5", G, A **$65.00**

Golden's Blue Ribbon Cigars, sign, cardboard hanger, 2-sided, product name in white on 3 blue fields on green background, 6½" dia, M, H1 ....**$6.00**

Golden's Blue Ribbon Cigars, sign, 1930s, We Recommend Golden's Blue Ribbon Cigars, blue & white, 5x10", EX, D...**$8.50**

Golden Scepture, crate label, 1920s, California orange, crowned woman pointing to orchard, Rialto Orange Co, 10x11¾", M, C3...**$16.00**

Golden Shell Motor Oil, can, 1935-45, Golden Shell in white outlined in red on orange & red seashell, minor dents, 5-qt, 9½", EX, A **$45.00**

Golden Spike Beer, label, 1933-50, Fontenelle Brewing Co, 12-oz, EX, A...**$15.00**

Golden Square Mixture, pocket tin, shows carpenter squares, squared corners, slip lid, 4½", VG+, A.........................**$55.00**

Golden Veil Cigars, box label, inner lid, woman in gold veil, 6x9", M, D **$6.00**

Goleta Lemons, label, 1940s, Goleta in bold yellow letters, sailing ship above, Sunkist lemon in lower left, 8½x11", NM, C3 ....**$2.00**

Golf Girl Talcum, tin, pictures caddie placing ball for lady golfer on paper label, 5½x2¼" dia, EX+, A **$1,375.00**

Gollam's Ice Cream, sidewalk sign, Gollam's in script & Lebanon printed on tail above Ice Cream, The Cream Of Matchless Merit, 32x20", EX, A........................**$75.00**

Good Gulf Gasoline, gas globe, 1920s, embossed porcelain, That Good Gulf Gasoline lettered in brown on white ground, 16" dia, EX, A...............................**$750.00**

Good Humor Ice Cream, squeeze toy, 1975, molded vinyl, Good Humor Bar with bite missing, 8", M, D....**$250.00**

Good Luck Bread, watch fob, ca 1910, oval celluloid insert on nickel with scrolled border, original leather strap, 5½" long, EX+, A **$190.00**

Good Morning, crate label, apple, crowing rooster at sunrise, 9x10½", M, C3...**$35.00**

Good Pickens, crate label, Washington apple, laughing boy holding up apple with bite missing, blue background, Cashmere, 9x11", G1 ....**$4.00**

Good Taste Cigars, box labels, inner & outer sample set, 1877, 1 lettered oval, lady under arch stirs bowl, Heppenheimer & Maurer, EX/M, A.............................**$85.00**

Good-Will Soap, sign, embossed tin, Good-Will Soap lettered in black on yellow with black outline, 2½x20", NM, A............**$35.00**

Goodell Auto Oil, can, early 1900s, round logo on green tree, green letters outlined in silver, screw lid & handle, 1/2-gal, 6", EX, A.....................$190.00

Goodman's Toyland, pin-back button, pictures Santa reading a book titled Good Girls & Good Boys, Meet Santa At... above & below, EX, A.........................**$38.00**

Goodrich, see also BF Goodrich

Goodrich Advantage Radial, ashtray, tire shape, clear insert, D **$15.00**

Goodrich Batteries, Tires, Accessories, sign, porcelain, Goodrich arched above G between 2 diamonds, Batteries-Tires-Accessories lettered across bottom, 21x60", VG+, A **$100.00**

Goodrich Black Safety Tread Tires, sign, embossed tin, proprietor's name & address above Goodrich & product, tire shown at left, 12x33", VG, A **$350.00**

Goodrich Hot Water Heater, sign, paper, large product image at right of ad text, Heat Condition Your Car This Winter on band below, 34x57", VG, A **$10.00**

Goodrich Silvertown Heavy Duty Cord, ashtray, tire shape, Goodrich Silvertown embossed on green insert, D ..**$20.00**

Goodrich Silvertowns, sign, embossed porcelain flange, 2-sided, white Goodrich Silvertowns above 2 red diamonds on blue, 19x23", VG/G, A **$300.00**

Goodrich Silvertowns Tires & Tubes, sign, porcelain, Goodrich Silvertowns in white flanked by elongated diamonds lettered Tires, Tubes, 18x58", G, A **$60.00**

Goodrich Sport Shoes, sign, die-cut cardboard stand-up, boy in white shirt, blue pants & red tie promoting product, 23¼x16", VG, A **$25.00**

Goodrich Tires, calendar, 1926, Thompson print, full pad, G, D **$26.00**

Goodrich Tires, sign, porcelain, Goodrich arched above logo, Tires below, white on royal blue with green border, 60" long, G-, A **$210.00**

Goody Goody Peas, can label, 1927, young boy & girl dancing, VG, C3 .... **$25.00**

Goody Orange Drink, bottle topper, die-cut cardboard bottle cap, pictures the Goody boy above product name & lettering, NM, B1 .... **$5.00**

Goody Root Beer, bottle topper, pilot with airplanes behind promoting Sky High Goodness, A Taste Lifter Upper 5¢, 7x5⅜", NM, A **$15.00**

Goody's Headache Powders, sign, 1940s, cardboard, pictures smiling girl with product, Why Pay More?, blue, yellow & white, 9x14½", EX, D **$15.00**

Goodyear, display, die-cut metal, black winged-foot logo outlined in white, 62", VG, D **$175.00**

Goodyear, plaque, 1930s, cast iron painted gold, busy factory scene in relief, Ten Years of Friendly... below, 17x12", EX, A **$120.00**

Goodyear, sign, die-cut porcelain flange, Goodyear panel over large image of tire in gray with dark gray & black, 43x21", G, A **$600.00**

Goodyear, sign, porcelain, yellow vertical Good Year with winged foot lettered above Tires on blue, white line border, 96x24", EX, D3 .... **$575.00**

Goodyear, window display, paper, 3-piece with end tape-up sheets of auto & motorcycle scenes, Goodyear on banner in center, EX, A **$120.00**

Goodyear Batteries, sign, porcelain, elongated diamond, flag logo above product lettering & winged foot logo, NM, D **$275.00**

Goodyear Pathfinder, sign, 1930s, cardboard, product name above Indian in canoe, A Dependable Tire At A Low Price below, 18" dia, NM, M1 .... $450.00

Goodyear Rubber Heels, sign, porcelain hanger, 2-sided, yellow & white on blue, Goodyear above Rubber Heels Applied Here, 10x18", EX, M2 .... **$40.00**

Goodyear Tires, ashtray, 1950s, black rubber tire with glass insert, marked Super Cushion, minor surface wear, 6" dia, EX, D **$25.00**

Goodyear Tires, display rack, 1950s-60s, elongated diamond shape, flag above winged foot flanked by Good & Year, Tires below, 25", NM, A **$80.00**

Goodyear Tires, sign, light-up, reverse-painted glass in wood frame with metal back, yellow & silver lettering on blue, 8x25", VG, A **$55.00**

Goodyear Tires, sign, paper, elegant girl in tire tube encircled by vehicles, They All Roll Best..., framed, image 38x31", G-, A **$200.00**

Goodyear Tires, sign, porcelain, yellow on blue with white lined border, Good & Year flank winged foot, Tires below, 24x66", EX, D3 .... $475.00

Goodyear Tires, sign, tin, elongated die-cut diamond with product name & logo above Tire & Battery Service, EX, D **$175.00**

Goodyear Tires, thermometer, wood, blue letters & highlights on yellow, tire around globe above, round top, square bottom, 12x3", VG, A **$50.00**

Googh's Sarsaparilla, sign, paper, winged child in fur-trimmed coat holding basket of flowers, matted & framed, 14x11", EX, A **$110.00**

Gordon's Fresh Potato Chips, tin, cream with red band & lid, early van above product name, company name on red band, slip lid, 11¼", 1-lb, VG+, A **$55.00**

Gordon's London Dry Gin, pitcher, clear glass with white lettering, D **$6.00**

Gordon-Van Tine Farm Buildings, catalog, 1935, 12 pages, VG, D **$8.00**

Gorton Seafoods, recipe book, 1930, colorful ads throughout, 40 pages, EX, D **$7.00**

Goshen Sweeper Co, trade card, interior scene with 2 women admiring a sweeper, A Christmas Gift lettered above, EX, A **$15.00**

Goudy & Kent's Fine Biscuits & Confectionary, trade card, picnic scene, Childrens Picnic engraved in bottom, EX, A **$22.00**

Grads Cigarettes, thermometer, porcelain, silhouette of man in cap & gown in profile above advertising & bulb, rounded ends, 39x8", VG, M2 .... **$90.00**

Graham's Ale, label, 1933-36, product name above logo, Burton Products Inc, U-type permit number, 12-oz, EX, A **$11.00**

Graham's Bock Beer, label, 1933-36, ram's head at bottom, Burton Products Inc, U-type permit number, 12-oz, EX, A **$30.00**

Graham's Vitabrew Beer, label, 1933-36, Burton Products Inc, U-type permit number, 1/2-gal, EX, A **$52.00**

Grain Belt Beer, label, pre-1920, features product name on diamond-shaped center, Minneapolis Brewing Co, G, A **$42.00**

Grain Belt Beer, sign, 1947, cardboard, pictures guns & wildlife, 23x27", G, D **$115.00**

Grand Coulee, crate label, 1940s, Washington pear, encircled dam, Columbian Basin Orchard, Coulee, 7¼x11", NM, C1 .... **$5.00**

Grand Council Cigars, box label, outer, 3 men in front of lake smoking cigars, 4½x4½", M, D **$4.00**

Grand Lion Cigars, box label, inner lid, lion atop world globe, 6x9", M, C3 .... **$4.00**

Grand Prize, crate label, 1915, California pears, shows California mission & 2 large pears, Chicago Park, 7½x11", M, C3 .... **$15.00**

Grand Rapids Brewing Co, calendar, 1906, paper, little girl in red shawl & bonnet with open book, pad missing, framed, image: 14½x9½", G, A **$550.00**

Grand Rapids Brewing Co, tray, pictures Victorian girl, NM, D **$550.00**

Grand Union Hard Candies, tin, 1920s-40s, red with blue bands top & bottom, cream & blue lettering, press lid, 5-lb, 8⅝x6", VG, A $25.00

Grandstand, crate label, Texas citrus, cartoon bass drummer in tall hat on orange background, white logo, 9x9", G1 .... **$3.00**

Granger Tobacco, display, die-cut cardboard, features Sam De George (champion fly & bass fisherman), 40", VG, A **$25.00**

Granger Tobacco, sign, die-cut cardboard, Granger Says Merry Christmas above Billy Werber Jr in Reds uniform with man smoking pipe, VG, A **$35.00**

Granger Tobacco, sign, paper, The Right Ammunition For All Pipes at left of pipe-smoking soldier holding Mild Cool Granger, 12x17", NM, A **$15.00**

Granger Tobacco, sign, paperboard, colorful image of Ace Golfer (Sam Snead), Keeps The Smoker Happy, nail holes, framed, 19x15", VG, A **$150.00**

Granite Iron Ware, sign, paper, country girl holding bucket beside cow, For Kitchen & Table Use below, framed, image: 28x12", EX, A **$1,450.00**

Grant Batteries, mechanical pencil, red & gray, EX, D **$6.50**

Grant's Hygienic Breakfast Food, box, ca 1915, A Hearty Breakfast For A Few Cents above bowl of cereal with strawberries, green & gold, 4x8x2", EX, P1 .... **$17.50**

Grant's Tobacco, label, Civil War image of General Grant with soldiers in the background, slightly trimmed, 14x7", EX, A **$725.00**

Grants Hygienic Crackers, thimble, 1920, aluminum with green enamel band, EX, P1 .... **$10.00**

Granulated 54 Sliced Plug, pocket tin, upright, Granulated Sliced Plug lettered above 54 on leaf, company name below, slip lid, VG+, A **$45.00**

Grape Kola, syrup dispenser, porcelain, figure-8 shape with 5¢ script logo above & colorful grape cluster below, 20x9", EX, A **$800.00**

Grape Sparkle Soda, bottle topper, die-cut cardboard, small man pointing to large round image reading Enjoy Grape..., 8½x5¼", NM, A **$8.00**

Grape-Julep, sign, 1940s, tin, Drink Grape-Julep In Bottles, white on navy background, 8x20", VG, A **$90.00**

Grape-Nuts, sign, embossed self-framed tin, girl & St Bernard, To School Well Fed On Grape-Nuts, There's A Reason, 30x20", VG, A **$800.00**

Grape-Nuts, sign, embossed self-framed tin, girl & St Bernard, To School Well Fed On Grape Nuts, There's A Reason, 30x20", M, A **$2,150.00**

Grape-Nuts, sign, pictures George Burns & Gracie Allen, EX, D **$300.00**

Grape-Ola, sign, tin, basket of grapes & bottle, Drink Grape-Ola, It's Real Grape, 20x28", NM, D **$225.00**

Grapette, bottle, 1959, aqua with red & white label, 8-oz, EX, D **$6.50**

Grapette, clock, glass, metal frame, 1-12 surround horizontal oval, Enjoy Grapette Soda, round, EX, D **$260.00**

Grapette, door push bar, aluminum, features Thirsty & Or Not lettered on either side of oval Grapette logo, EX, M3 .... **$125.00**

Grapette, sign, cardboard, pretty girl holding bottle & bouquet of tulips with oval Grapette logo below, 26x20", NM, M3 .... **$125.00**

Grapette, sign, porcelain, red & white lettering on blue, white & red border, Grapette in script, oval, 10x17", EX, A **$140.00**

Grapette, sign, 1930s, tin, Drink on 3-banded partial circle upper left corner, Contains 6-oz on same lower right corner, M, A **$165.00**

Grapette, thermometer, tin, bottle with oval Grapette label above Thirsty Or Not!, square corners, EX, A **$100.00**

Grapette Soda, sign, porcelain, Grapette in script above Soda, 2-lined border, 10½x26½", NM, A **$250.00**

Grapette Soda, sign, 1930s-40s, neon counter-top, glass & metal, Grapette oval on pin-stripe ground, The Reasons In The Bottle, NM, A **$700.00**

Gray Line Bus Lines, sign, porcelain, 1930s, Sight Seeing Everywhere lettered around globe with The Gray Line on diamond, 20" dia, EX, D3............................**$535.00**

Gray's Paint Store, thimble, ca 1910, aluminum with blue band, ...3rd St, VG, D............................**$7.50**

Great American Tea Co, tin, building with decorative top & bottom border, slip lid on bottle-neck top, Ginna & Co, 8x4" dia, EX, A............................**$165.00**

Great American Tea Co, tin, pictures a cockatoo on red ground, A............................**$110.00**

Great American Tea Co, tin, pictures store in New York on front, text on sides, black on red, slip lid, dents & chips, 2-lb, 7½x6" dia, G, A............................**$50.00**

Great American Tea Co, trade card, pictures tired Santa leaning on chimney, advertising on reverse, green & brown, EX, A............................**$10.00**

Great Atlantic & Pacific Tea Co, print, paper litho applied to glass with pressed tin embellishments at corners, boy with rifle & sword, 22x12", G, A............................**$65.00**

Great Atlantic & Pacific Tea Co, sign, copyright 1884, cardboard cutout, 2-sided, man pushing 2 children in wheelbarrow, 8½x5½", EX, A............................**$25.00**

Great Majestic Ranges, pocket mirror, features lady at range surrounded by lettering, 2⅛" dia, EX, A............................**$100.00**

Great Northern Railroad, playing cards, pictures Indian chief & women, double deck, MD............................**$45.00**

Great Northwest, crate label, Washington apple, primitive mountain goat in red circle on summit, blue background, 9x11", EX, G1............................**$5.00**

Great Puff Tobacco, bag, 1903 stamp, cloth with paper label featuring man blowing smoke, with contents, Bleidersdorf & Co, EX, A............................**$66.00**

Great Victorian Troupe, sign, 1890-1900, paper, 14 vignettes of people swallowing swords, ...Originators & Presenters..., framed, 44x30", EX, A............................**$160.00**

Great Western Champagne, sign, tin, pictures hanging bottle of champagne surrounded by a glass & grapes, framed, image: 19x13", EX+, A............................**$300.00**

Gree Soff Automobile Soap, can, 1930s, early touring car with yellow lettering above & below, slip lid & bail, scuffs/scratches, 5", A............................**$100.00**

Green Bluff, crate label, apple, orchard scene, 9x10½", M, C3............................**$15.00**

Green Giant, bank, 1980s, composition figure of Little Sprout, plays musical melody of Valley Of The Jolly Green Giant, 8½", EX, A............................**$52.00**

Green Mountain Distillery, shot glass, etched letters, ...Makes Of The Celebrated Green Mountain Rye & Bourbon..., gold rim, EX, D............................**$18.00**

Green River, dispenser, milk glass, incised & painted circular design, metal base, pump missing, 14", G, A.........**$200.00**

Green River, sign, 1919, embossed tin, Green River lettered above sun setting over river, In Bottles below, 12x20", EX, M1............................**$130.00**

Green River Sour Mash Whiskey, sign, reverse-painted glass, JW McCulloch above, product name above & below horseshoe, framed, round, A............................**$350.00**

Green River Tobacco, box, pictures man beside horse, The Tobacco Without A Bite, 6x5" dia, EX, D...**$175.00**

Green River Whiskey, blotter, cardboard, Black man beside horse, She Was Bred In Old Kentucky, 4x9½", NM, D............................**$3.00**

Green River Whiskey, charger, tin, Black man beside horse, She Was Bred In Old Kentucky below, minor fading/inpainting, 24" dia, G, A............................**$250.00**

Green River Whiskey, print, Black man beside horse standing before brick wall, brand name plaque on frame, 22½x17½", G-, A............................**$25.00**

Green River Whiskey, sign, tin, Black man beside horse, She Was Bred In Old Kentucky below, fading, filigree Victorian frame, 31x40", A............................**$175.00**

Green River Whiskey, token, M, D............................**$10.00**

Green's Seed Corn, sign, tin, proud farmer wearing yellow ribbon promoting product on yellow & blue ground, Plant Green's, 12x36", NM, M3............................**$75.00**

Green Spot Beverages, sign, tin, white with Green Spot lettered on green spot above tilted orange bottle, 36x14", NM, M3............................**$145.00**

Green Spot Orange Drink, menu board, tin, Take Home.. left of drink being poured in several glasses above black menu area, 27x17", NM, M3............................**$75.00**

Green-Wheeler Shoe Co, pin-back button, ca 1900, green wheel design with company name in red, EX, D..**$4.00**

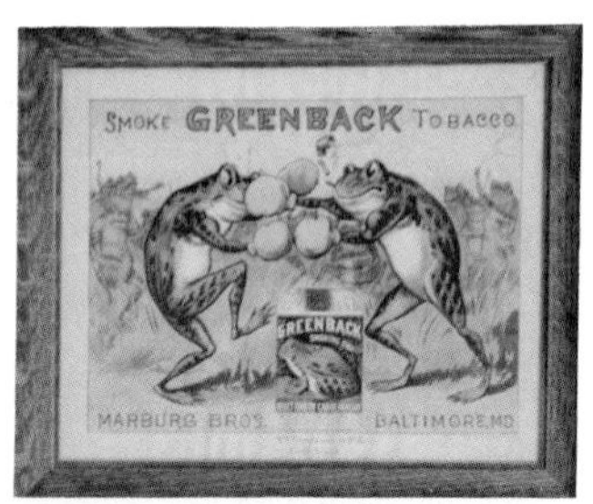

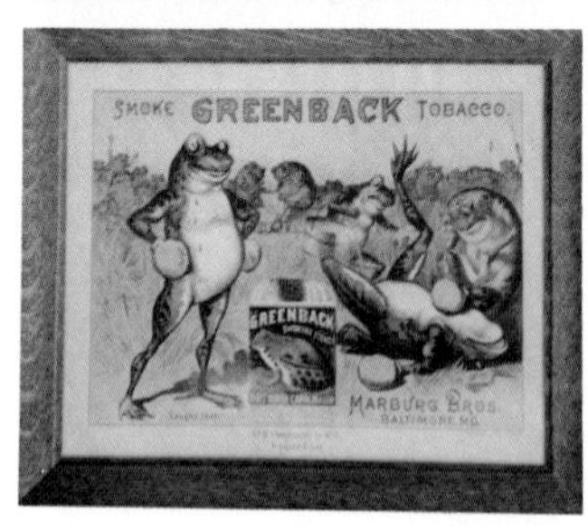

Greenback Tobacco, sign, paper, comical images of frogs & product, 1 of 2 sets known, framed, pair, 17x20", NM, M1............................$3,800.00

Greenbrier Coffee, tin, paper label, key-wind lid, 1-lb, VG, D............................**$25.00**

Greenway's Brewery, sign, embossed cardboard, woman with wreath in her hair & 4 girls in corner vignettes, framed, image: 20x15", EX, A............................**$300.00**

Greer's California Perfumes, trade card, ca 1885, lady carrying fruit, scenic background, 3x5½", EX, P1............................**$22.50**

Greer's OVH Vatted Highland Whisky (sic), mirror, late 1800s, framed, horizontal rectangle, A............................**$450.00**

Gregertsen Brothers Co, scrub brush/mirror, cartoon images of Min & Andy, blue & red lettering, average wear, 3½" dia, D............................**$70.00**

reyhound Package Express, sign, 1941, painted metal, 2-sided, Greyhound & Package above & below outlined image of greyhound dog, 18x21", EX, A.....**$80.00**

reyhound, sign, porcelain flange, 2-sided, white image of greyhound dog, above Greyhound lettered in white on blue, 9x15", NM, A...**$350.00**

reyhound Bus, first aid kit, 1940, embossed steel, Greyhound Lines, no contents, D **$40.00**

reyhound Bus, plaque, 1960s, lettered See The USA, Go Greyhound & Leave The Driving To Us, 13x16", EX, D......**$15.00**

reyhound Lines, sign, porcelain flange, 2-sided, navy oval with white dog & orange lettering, white border, 21x25", NM, D3.....................................$700.00

reyhound Lines, sign, 1940s-50s, porcelain, 2-sided, Greyhound lettered above dog image, Lines lettered below, 21x36", EX, D1.......................................**$575.00**

reyhound Lines Bus Depot, sign, porcelain, 2-sided, burst of rays in red, white & blue around emblem with dog & lettering, 21x25", EX, D3 ....**$450.00**

riesedieck Bros Light Lager Beer, sign, paper, Griesedieck Bros in script above lady holding up bottle, matted & framed, 29½x22½", VG+, A...........**$425.00**

riffith & Boyd Fertilizers, sign, stenciled sheet metal, fish in logo, 14x20", G, A.....................................**$20.00**

rimes Drinks, sign, 1920s, embossed tin, labeled bottle at left, For Your Health's Sake...12 Other Popular Flavors, 20x28", EX, A...**$150.00**

rimes 5 Cent Cigar, box label, inner lid, pictures eagle & banner, 6x9", M, C3..**$8.00**

rinnell Bros Victor Victrolas, pocket mirror, Nipper the dog facing Victrola encircled by 2 bands of lettering, Easy Payments, 2⅛" dia, VG+, A........................**$250.00**

ross Brothers ABC Soap, trade card, girl painting a picture by a lake, 3x4½", EX, D **$4.00**

roub's Belle Coffee, tin, shows bust of lady in wide-brimmed hat with lettering above & below, screw lid, 1-lb, A..**$1,700.00**

round Chocolate, can label, floral design, M, C3 ..**$15.00**

uarantee Tire & Rubber Co, catalog, 1926, featuring auto supplies, 104 pages, VG+, H2......................**$35.00**

uarantee Tire & Rubber Co, catalog, 1938, 66 pages, VG, D **$14.00**

uaranteed Red Ball Service, gas globe, 1950s, plastic light-up, product name in black & white on red, 18" dia, EX, A..**$300.00**

Guardian Assurance Co of London, ledger marker, ca 1890, tin, guardian atop world with lettering above & below, US Branch Of NY, 12x3", VG, A..................**$85.00**

Guardian Service Cleaner, can, with contents, pictures knight in armour on red circular inset above lettering, silver ground, 5½", EX, D $7.00

Guide Pipe & Cigarette Tobacco, pocket tin, mountain guide with backpack & canoe, Roto Cut logo, hinged lid, minor soiling/scratches, 4¼x3x1", VG, A **$140.00**

Guion Line, sign, paper, shows steamship on rough sea, ...United States Mail Steamer Arizona, Hatch litho, 21x31", G-, A..**$100.00**

Gulf, clock, glass, metal frame, 12-3-6-9 surround Gulf logo, diagonal square, EX, D **$240.00**

Gulf, display stand, wire with 2-sided tin Gulf panel, overall wear, G, A **$60.00**

Gulf, gas pump & globe, 1935-45, Good Gulf logo on pump, brass nozzle, orange, white & blue globe, total repaint, 86", EX, A $650.00

Gulf Authorized Dealer, sign, 1935-45, porcelain, Authorized Dealer in blue flanked by Gulf in blue & white rings, white ground, 9x40", EX, A......................**$150.00**

Gulf Gasoline, sign, 1935-45, porcelain, pictures early touring car, That Good...At The Sign Of The Orange Disc, 60x28", VG, A **$550.00**

Gulf Insect Bomb Aerosol Spray, banner, paper, pictures a bomb with Gulf logo, blue, orange, yellow & white, 10x21", EX, D **$10.00**

Gulf No-Nox Motor Fuel, sign, porcelain flange, 2-sided, No-Nox Motor Fuel lettered around Gulf, Gulf Refining Company below, 18x18", VG, A **$200.00**

Gulf No-Nox Motor Oil, sign, ca 1930, linen, product text above pump attendant with touring car & plane, Now Aviation Grade, 34x28", EX, D3 ....$1,650.00

Gulf Oil Lubricate & Polish, display, tin, horse's head on round orange Gulf Oil emblem on rectangular base with advertising, 12x10x5", VG, A **$155.00**

Gulf Refining Co, sign, porcelain, pictures early touring car, Supreme Motor Oil, G, D **$530.00**

Gulf Registered Lubrication Service, display rack, embossed porcelainized metal, white with blue border, 2 rows of hooks & product listings below logo, 50x32", VG+, A **$150.00**

Gulf Supreme Motor Oil, sign, porcelain, pictures early touring car, That Good...At The Sign Of The Orange Disc, 60x28", G, A **$440.00**

Gulf Tourguide Service, map holder, metal, 3-tier with orange Gulf lower left above Tourguide Service in white, with Gulf maps, 18x9", VG, A...................**$50.00**

Gulf 3% Club, pocket knife, blue & orange Gulf logo left of Member 3% Club, Spring 1949 below, 2 blades, EX, A...**$40.00**

Gulfpride Motor Oil, sign, embossed tin, Gulfpride above Gulf logo, text below, 3 lines divide 2-tone background, 24x48", VG, A **$50.00**

Gulfpride Oil, can, 1935-45, product name in script above company name & text, blue ground, pour spout & handle, 1-gal, 11", VG, A **$80.00**

Gulfspray, sign, paper, pictures a large fly, ...Quick Action Against Household Enemy No 1, Quick-Safe-Sure, 9x12", NM, B1 ....**$6.00**

Gund's Pioneer Beer, sign, cardboard, pioneer family su rounded by vignettes of other families crossing plain framed, image: 14x28", G, A..............................**$300.0**

Gund's Pioneer Beer, see also John Gund Brewing Co

Gunk S-C Degreaser, can, pictures airplane flying ove product name in circle, screw top & handle, 1-ga VG+, A **$15.0**

Gunther's Beer, globe, clear glass with reverse-painte glass inserts picturing beer logo, red, yellow & blac 17x15" dia, EX, A **$1,800.0**

Gurd's Ginger Beer, display bottle, stoneware, white bo tom with large black oval logo, brown top, hairlin crack on bottom, M2..**$875.0**

Gustav A Mayer Champagne Wafers, tin, 1920s-40s, pic tures champagne bottle, glasses & wafers on orang with black highlights, slip lid, 3x5", G-, A.........$10.0

Gutermann's Sewing Silk, cabinet, stenciled wood wit hinged glass doors, contains 120 spring-loaded sil spool slots, 19" long, EX, A **$325.0**

Gypsy, can label, Washington salmon, dancing gypsy lad & salmon, Chinook, M, C1......................................**$3.0**

H

H Clausen & Son Brewers, sign, paper, Teutonic Kin drinking flagon of beer flanked by Gothic structure overall soiling, 22x18", VG, A.............................**$200.0**

H Kleber & Bros Pianos, pocket mirror, pictures gi seated at upright piano bordered by company name address, 2⅛ " dia, VG+, A **$55.0**

H Koehler & Co Brewers, calendar, 1911, paper, elegar girl in profile sampling glass of Fidelio beer, Marc pad, framed, image: 18x11", EX, A **$225.0**

H&K Coffee, tin, man in turban, flat, 1-lb, EX, D...............**$20.0**

H&R Arms Co, sign, felt, features trademark logo in cen ter, company name in script above, framed, 9x12½ " VG, A **$75.0**

Haberle Brewing Co, match striker, stoneware, blue & gra decoration, 6½ x4¾" dia, G-, A **$150.0**

Haberle Brewing Co, see also Congress Beer

Haberle's Beer, tray, eagle logo at top, Haberle-Congress Brewing Co, green, red & white, VG, D **$45.00**

Haffen Brewing Co, sign, paper, driver with 3 bonneted beauties in open touring car, matted & framed, image: 20x15½ ", VG, A **$500.00**

Hage's Ice Cream, sign, embossed die-cut tin, shaped like square of ice cream with product advertising, Chocolate, 8x9", M, D1 .... $85.00

Hagearty's Porter, label, 1933-50, product name in ornate border, New England Brewing Co, Internal Revenue Tax Paid statement, 12-oz, VG, A **$5.00**

Hagerstown Brewing Co, tray, 1900, pictures girl holding vase of chrysanthemums, lettering on rim, overall chips/scratches, 13¼ x10½ ", G-, A **$40.00**

Hales Midget Popcorn, tin, midget in tails & top hat in oval with product lettering above & below, missing pry lid, 4½ " dia, EX, A **$5.00**

Half & Half Buckingham Bright Cut Plug Smoking Tobacco, pocket tin, multicolored lettering on green, cream & black, text on back, hinged lid, heavy wear, 3½ x3", D $20.00

Hall & Hayward Crackers, print, paper, parents & children at play in turn-of-the-century parlor, gilt frame with raised letters, 6x12", G, A **$280.00**

Hall's Distemper, sign, porcelain, 2 men carrying buckets & white board reading Hall's Distemper before red-roofed house, 18x48", VG+, M2 .... **$700.00**

Hall's Ice Cream, tray, children gathered around lady carrying tray of ice cream, decorative & lettered rim, rectangular, 13¼ ", EX, A **$700.00**

Hall's Vegetable Hair Renewer, trade card, 1880s, panel of 5 women, 8x3", EX+, P1 .... **$37.50**

Hall's Vegetable Sicilian Hair Renewer, trade card, portraits of 5 women from different countries, One Of These Five Attractive Faces..., EX, A **$26.00**

Hallpryd Bread, pin-back button, 1900, gold on white picturing award medals, red lettering on rim, EX, D **$7.00**

Hamburger Helper, transistor radio, 1980s, plastic, Helping Hand, 6½ ", M, D **$35.00**

Hamilton, Brown Shoe Co, catalog, 1929, 69 pages, VG+, H2 .... **$50.00**

Hamilton, Brown Shoe Co, sign, girl holding fruit on green ground, Compliments Of... in upper left corner, black & gold frame, 30x26", EX, A **$160.00**

Hamilton, Brown Shoe Co, sign, paper, shows company name above George & Martha Washington dancing on checked floor with company emblem, 40x30", EX, A **$210.00**

Hamilton, Brown Shoe Co, sign, paper, pictures elegant woman, Largest Shoe House In The World, framed with metal strips, 30x21½ ", VG, A **$100.00**

Hamilton, Brown Shoe Co, sign, tin flange, 2-sided, black & white lettering on red oval with lettered appendages top & bottom, 14x20", VG, A **$25.00**

Hamilton Watch, notebook, 1909-10, celluloid, cover shows 940 pocket watch on front of steam engine, Rail Road Time Keeper, 5x3", EX, A **$32.00**

Hamilton Watch, sign, paper, conductor waving locomotive on, ...The Railroad Timekeeper Of America..., framed, image: 11x21", G, A **$275.00**

Hamlins Wizard Oil, thermometer, wood with impressed lettering, lacquered finish, Great For Pain..., blemishes/wear, 21", G, A **$70.00**

Hamm's Beer, bank, 1980s, ceramic, Hamm's bear, 11", M, D **$25.00**

Hamm's Beer, decanter, 1973, Hamm's bear standing at bar with mug of beer, head is top of decanter, 11", M, D **$75.00**

Hamm's Beer, ice bucket, chrome finish with red lettering, few minor dents, 5", EX, D **$18.00**

Hamm's Beer, matchbook cover, red, white & blue, features Hamm's bear rolling log on front & back, 20 strike, front strike, NM, R1 .... **$3.00**

Hamm's Beer, mug, Krug-Klub by Red Wing Pottery, M, P2 .... **$45.00**

Hamm's Beer, sign, lighted beer keg, G, D **$45.00**

Hamm's Beer, sign, roofed panel with lighted picture on right changing from waterfalls to camping, ad text at left, 18x31", EX, M2 .... **$495.00**

Hamm's Beer, stein, 1974, St Patrick's Day, M, D **$30.00**

Hamm's Beer, stein, 1987 Holiday, pictures bear, dog & rabbit on a sled, 6", M, D **$20.00**

Hamm's Beer, tray, deep-dish, lake scene with bears, some paint peeling/rust on bottom, 12" dia, D....**$12.00**

Hampden Beer, sign, tin, stock image of the Handsome Waiter, overall chips, 11" dia, VG, A....................**$70.00**

Hampden Brewing Co, tray, deep-dish, stock image of the Handsome Waiter, Who Wants The Handsome Waiter?, 13" dia, G, A **$40.00**

Hand Made Tobacco, pocket tin, upright, pictures hand on world globe, Globe Tobacco Co, EX, A **$215.00**

Hando Hand Cleanser, tin, 1920s, lettering on front, 6 vintage scenes on sides, 4x2" dia, EX, D **$16.00**

Handsum, crate label, 1930s, California orange, hand holding orange on gold & yellow rays, Strathmore, 10x11", NM, C1 ....**$2.00**

Handy Package Dyes, sign, paper, cherubs hanging clothes on line & laying fabric in yard to spell Handy Package Dyes, 13½ x17¼ ", EX, A.......................**$90.00**

Hanes Merrichild Sleepers, store display, composition figure of sleepy little boy & his dog on lettered base, 23x12", EX, A...**$105.00**

Hanlen's 98 Whiskey, tray, stock image of bulldog, Ask For...WC Hanlen on rim, minor spots/scratches, 13¼ x13¼ ", EX, A..**$200.00**

Hanley Brewing Co, photograph, horse-drawn beer wagon, overall fading/soiling, matted & framed, image: 12x20", G, A...**$85.00**

Hanley's Ale & Lager, pin-back button, pictures a bulldog at top, Everyone's Saying: Hand Me Hanley's..., red, white & blue, round, EX, A **$37.00**

Hanley's Peerless Beer, matchbook cover, white, features bull dog, Providence RI, front strike, NM, R1....................**$10.00**

Hanline Paints, sign, neon, reverse-painted glass with logo in center, working, 20" long, EX, A...........**$200.00**

Hannum's Prevento, tin, 1910-25, blue, black & white with product name above early touring car, fancy graphics below, 4½ ", EX, A **$40.00**

Hanover Brewing Co, sign, paper, shows elegant girl with green silk scarf, logo upper left, framed, 19½ x14½ ", VG, A...**$250.00**

Hanover Whiskey, sign, self-framed tin, shows racehorse looking out of stall, product emblem below, wavy border, 28x39", EX, A **$300.00**

Happiness Candy Stores, tin, 1930s-40s, animals in sporting events on all sides, slip lid & movable tin handle, signed H Cady, 3x6", EX, A **$65.00**

Happy Farmer Tractor Co, pin-back button, Happy Farmer Tractor Co lettered on band around smiling farmer in hat, round, EX, A **$29.00**

Happy Home Needles, package, 1930s, pictures 3 smiling women, 6x3", EX, P1 ....**$10.00**

Happy Jim Chewing Tobacco, thermometer, tin, blue & red on yellow, Happy Jim pictured above, lettering below, mount tabs above & below, 13", G+, A ...**$15.00**

Happy Jim Chewing Tobacco, thermometer, tin, red & blue on white, Biggest & Best above, Happy Jim pictured below, rounded top & bottom, 17", EX, A **$65.00**

Happy Thought Cigars, box labels, 1878, inner & outer sample set, man on man's back lights cigar from lamppost, Heppenheimer & Maurer, EX/M, A **$73.00**

Happy Thought Plug Tobacco, sign, paper, product name above sailor holding plug of tobacco encircled by rope & tobacco, vertical, EX, M1 ....**$775.00**

Hardees, doll, Gilbert Giddy-Up, 1971, printed cloth, minor soiling, 15½ ", N1 ....**$10.00**

Hardin Lavin Plumbing & Heating Supplies, catalog, 1924, 240 pages, VG+, H2 ....**$50.00**

Hardware Shoe, sign, stenciled steel, flanged, red & black lettering on white, ...Wears Like An Anvil, 7¼ x19¼ ", G+, A...**$150.00**

Hardy's Salt, thermometer, tin, white & yellow on red above blue, white rim, thermometer at left of lettering, 10" dia, G+, A **$35.00**

Harley-Davidson, catalog, 1925, VG, D **$80.00**

Harley-Davidson, display, light-up, glass panel on tin base with casters, H-D logo on panel, Genuine Parts &... on base, 11x14", EX, A...............$2,800.00

Harley-Davidson, fender emblem, 1950s, brass, commemorating 50 Years, minor scuffs/wear, A **$200.00**

Harley-Davidson, lapel stud, 1930s, embossed silvered brass, shows motor with company name across bottom, scarce, ¾", EX, A **$67.00**

Harley-Davidson, magazine, April 1950, EX, D........**$12.00**

Harley-Davidson, sign, paper on canvas, man riding New-Type motorcycle, ...Schaber's Bicycle Shop, 210 First Street, 8 ft 9"x19 ft 9", EX, A **$9,500.00**

Harley-Davidson, stein, 1983, high relief with pewter eagle on lid, MIB, D...**$225.00**

Harpers Whiskey, sign, ca 1904, reverse-painted glass, girl reaches for bottle, old man & 2 kids watch, signed TH Keifer, 36x24", NM, A **$6,500.00**

Harrington & Richardson Arms Co, calendar, 1907, wintry scene with running mountain man, full pad, framed, 27x14", VG, A...**$2,000.00**

Harrington & Richardson Arms Co, calendar top, embossed paper, lady standing before screen flanked by firearms, framed, image: 19½ x14", EX, A..**$1,500.00**

Harrington & Richardson Arms Co, pocket catalog, 1905, pictures a revolver & target on front, 16 pages, EX, A **$24.00**

Harris Oils, sign, porcelain flange, features Oils lettered on barrel below Harris, other lettering below, 18x19", G, A **$750.00**

Harrison's Heart O'Orange, thermometer, round metal case with porcelain face & glass lens, thermometer arched above advertising, 18" dia, G, A **$125.00**

Harrison's Ice Cream, sign, tin, rolled edge, rare, EX, D **$495.00**

Harry Horne Marshmallows, tin, monkey in jacket, vest, bow tie & green hat, tall round shape, EX+, M2..**$210.00**

Harry Mitchell's Quality Lager Beer, label, 1933-50, Internal Revenue Tax Paid, 12-oz, VG, A **$11.00**

Hart Hardware Co, billhead, 1892, Parker Gun Vignette at left, red & black on buff, VG, A **$40.00**

Hartford Bicycle Tires, sign, paper, features 3 famous cyclists for Columbia Bicycles, names above, framed, image: 21½ x27½ ", G, A **$350.00**

Hartford Fire Insurance Co, bookends, 1935, bronze, G, D **$75.00**

Hartford Fire Insurance Co, letterhead, 1890, 1-page handwritten letter dealing with insurance business, deer logo at top, EX, D **$6.50**

Hartford Fire Insurance Co, sign, ca 1923, tin, 2-sided, elk in a mountain scene with text on reverse, oval, framed, 23½ x19½ ", G, A **$25.00**

Hartshorn Shade Roller, trade card, 1880s, shows baby that has been pulled out of window by a shade roller, 2¾x4¼ ", EX, P1 ....**$16.00**

Hartz Mountain Flea Powder, tin, pictures girl with terrier, EX, D **$15.00**

Harvard Beer, display, die-cut tin, 3-D, labeled bottle, ...In The Hall Of Fame, minor chips/soiling, 21x15x4½ ", EX, A **$500.00**

Harvard Brewing Co, calendar plate, 1907, Vienna Art, tin, girl surrounded by months, minor chips, 10" dia, EX, A **$135.00**

Harvard Brewing Co, calendar plate, 1907, Vienna Art, tin, elegant girl surrounded by months, 10" dia, G-, A ..**$55.00**

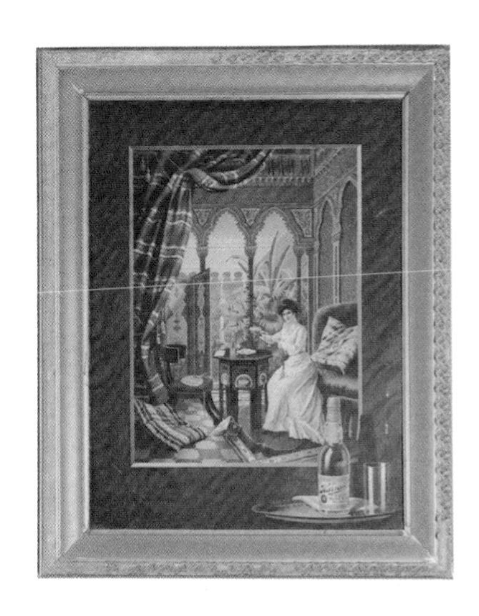

Harvard Brewing Co, sign, tin, woman in Turkish-style room that opens up to courtyard, bottle on tray in foreground, framed, 45x36", EX, A............$2,500.00

Harvard Cigar, sign, tin, man in red sweater with Harvard Cigar lettered in his hair, Highest Grade... on collar, 36x24", G, A **$200.00**

Harvard Jumbo Peanuts, tin, gold with Harvard fellow holding flag with Harvard lettered in gold, Millard Supply Co, Chicago, 10-lb, EX, A **$110.00**

Harvard Pure Rye, sign, tin litho, pictures Harvard graduates celebrating, few chips/scratches, framed, image: 17½ x23½ ", VG, A **$400.00**

Hash-Brown Tri Cut Blend, pocket tin, pictures a water pipe flanked by Tri Cut, Hash-Brown arched above, slip lid, EX+, A **$44.00**

Hassan Cork Tip Cigarettes, sign, early 1900s, shows man in uniform flanked by product & lettering, product name etched in frame, 29x22", EX, A $235.00

Hassan Cork Tip Cigarettes, sign, paper, elegant girl seated in profile with Japanese lantern, minor creases, framed, image: 22½ x16½ ", EX, A **$225.00**

Hastings Piston Rings, clock, 1935-45, reverse-painted glass in tin case, Made in USA on face, ...Stop Oil Pumping below, 17½ x12", G, A **$90.00**

Hastings Piston Rings, clock, 1940-50s, electric, man with product & product name on face, Engineered... on border, 16" dia, EX, A **$145.00**

Hastings Piston Rings, sign, painted tin, Hastings with arrow above Sherlock Holmes-type piston graphic, Free...Test Station, 28x20", VG+, A **$85.00**

Hastings Piston Rings, sign, 1935-45, light-up, reverse-painted glass, yellow & white lettering on black, paint loss/cracking, 11x26½ ", A **$35.00**

Hathaway's Shirts, sign, ca 1874, paper, little girl showing her folks a boxed shirt, decorative border, image: 24x18", VG, A **$1,500.00**

Hauenstein's Special, label, 1928-33, shows product name in script above logo, L-type permit number, 12-oz, VG, A **$5.00**

Hauswald's Bread, end label, Hauswald's lettered above spotted leopard, Color For Fun lettered below, 2¾x2¾", EX, S1 ....**$3.00**

Havana Cigars, cutter, oval mirror with decorative border at top, ...Excellent Quality, 8½ x8", G, A **$225.00**

Havana Flavor Cigars, box label, inner lid, tropical scene in soft gold pastels, EX, C3 ....**$18.00**

Havana Rope Cigars, box label, outer, Havana Bay filled with ships, 4½ x4½ ", M, C3....................................$2.00

Havoline Motor Oil, bank, porcelain, football shape, NM, D2...$50.00

Havoline Motor Oil, sign, porcelain flange, oil-can shape, Havoline lettered vertically along left edge of can, bull's-eye logo, EX, M1.......................................$625.00

Hawaiian Punch, beach raft, 1970s, yellow canvas with white roping, colorful image of Punchy, Let's Get Together..., 34x19", EX, D $15.00

Hawaiian Punch, board game, 1970s, Mattel, EX, D ..$25.00

Hawaiian Punch, transistor radio, 1970s, plastic, Punchy figure, 6", M, D..$35.00

Hawthorne Asparagus, can label, pink blossoms & asparagus on blue background, San Francisco Ca, EX, G1...$2.00

Hayes Fashions, catalog, 1954, Spring/Summer, ladies fashions for half-sizes, 50 pages, VG+, H2...........$15.00

Hazle Club Cream Soda, sign, tin, Hazle Club on band arched above foaming mug with On Tap tag, Cream Soda below, 9" dia, EX, A....................................$30.00

Hazle Club Sparkling Beverages, sign, tin, product name & bottle with bubbles on red, white & blue background, 12x30", EX+, M3.....................................$55.00

Hazle Club Tru-Orange, thermometer, tin, black & red on yellow, That's Your Drink..., Contains Pure Orange Juice, rounded ends, 27", EX+, M3 ....$125.00

He-No Tea, pocket mirror, Victorian lady holding box of tea to cheek, I Love It, It's Absolutley Pure, oval, 2¾", VG+, A...$230.00

Headlight Overalls, sign, neon, Headlight in graduated letters on light beam from locomotive, Overalls below, in case, rare, 14x28x8", EX, A................................$715.00

Heath & Milligan Paints, tip tray, pictures 2 girls & dog, lettered rim trimmed in black, Sunshine Finishes, loss to top edge, 4⅜ " dia, EX, A..............................$175.00

Heaven Hill Bourbon, display, painted chalk, thermometer at right of mounted glass bottle, lettering above & below, beveled frame, 20", EX, A...........................$7.00

Heckers Buckwheat, trade card, 1893, die-cut stand-up of the Buckwheat baby in highchair, EX, A.............$20.00

Heckers Flour, pin-back button, ca 1900, red & white with serial number in blue, EX, D $9.00

Heckers Flour, sign, tin, Hecker boy seated on bench slicing bread, Heckers Flour in red above, Always The Same below, 6¾x5", VG, A...............................$425.00

Heckers Flour, trade card, young boy & girl carrying large box of flour overhead, If You Want Muffins, Fritters, Waffles..., EX, A..$12.00

Heide's Candy Co, store jar, glass, embossed lid, 10¾x4¾" square, EX, A...$10.00

Heide's None Finer Marshmallows, tin, slip lid, round, A...$70.00

Heide's Silver Frost Marshmallows, tin, bold lettering on front, slip lid, round, EX, A $70.00

Heileman's Old Style Lager Beer, recipe book, 1945, '300 New Ways of Making Delicious Sandwiches,' 96 pages, EX, D...$5.00

Heileman's Old Style Lager Beer, stein, 1982 Holiday, Chicagoland, You've Got Style, 7½ ", M, D $40.00

Heileman's Old Style Lager Beer, stein, 1985 Holiday, Brewed With Water From When The Earth Was Pure, 7½ ", M, D...$30.00

Heilemann's Ice Cream, sign, die-cut cardboard stand-up, boy with Stop For Heilemann's Ice Cream flag points to ice cream cone, 41", EX, A $50.00

Heineken Beer, bottle, green glass with white & green paper labels, white, red & black lettering, soiling to label, 18", EX, A..$5.00

Heinz, charm bracelet, 1940s, silvered brass links hold 5 product charms including a green pickle, EX, A................$47.00

Heinz, figurine, 1940s, painted hard rubber tomato head in black top hat & wearing monocal, Heinz embossed on base, 6", EX, A..$374.00

Heinz, pin-back button, pickle shape with embossed Heinz, EX, A $70.00

Heinz, recipe book, 1930, 'Heinz Book of Salads,' 92 pages, VG, D $4.00

Heinz, string holder, 2 die-cut tin pickles flank spool of string, Pure Foods & 57 Varieties on panel above, 17x14x7", EX, A..$7,500.00

Heinz, talking alarm clock, 1980s, plastic, Aristocrat Tomato man behind clock on round base, 9½ ", M, D.......$150.00

Heinz, treasure chest, 1933, tin, interior colonial scenes on all sides, made for Century of Progress Expo, 8x11x9", EX+, A.................................$225.00

Heinz, see also HJ Heinz

Heinz Baby Food, ink blotter, 1950s, shows doctor with baby, Friends Your Baby Can Count On!, products lower right, 3¾x9", EX, A $18.00

Heinz Baked Beans, recipe book, 1932, 'Thrifty New Tips on a Grand Old Favorite,' 20 pages, EX, D..........$10.00

Heinz Baked Beans, trade card, ca 1890, mechanical, opens to dinner table with family & all Heinz products, open: 3½ x8", EX, P1..$65.00

Heinz Home-Style Soups, sign, tin, product name on red band above 5 diagonal bowls flanked by lists of flavors, Large Bowl 15¢, 11x27", NM, M3.......................$185.00

Heinz Ketchup, bottle topper, features dinosaur figure, EX, D2..$10.00

Heinz Ketchup, display, 1940s, die-cut cardboard stand-up, red, yellow & green with NRA decal, folds out to hold bottle, 15x12", VG, D $65.00

Heinz Peanut Butter, trade card, 1910, front shows girl leaning on park bench with basket EX, A....................**$18.00**
Heinz Pickles, watch fob, brass pickle shape, 57 Varieties, 1¾x1½ ", NM, A....................**$50.00**
Heinz Pickling Vinegar, jar, 6-sided, embossed logo on stopper & H on sides, label on neck & front, 12x5½ ", EX, A....................**$225.00**
Heinz Pure Food Products, tin, pictures a pickle, lid missing, 12x6" dia, EX, D....................**$65.00**
Heinz Selected Queen Olives, jar, clear with paper label, stopper top, 9", EX, A....................**$55.00**
Heinz Soups, cup, 1970s, plastic, white & orange, 4-oz, NM, D....................**$3.00**

Heinz Soups, menu board, tin, 2-sided, yellow with red border, black base, logo above list of soups, Try A New One Today, 14x9", EX A $400.00
Heinz Soups, timer, 1940s, round plastic case with metal bell-shaped covering on back, Heinz Soups lettered on front, 3" dia, VG, A....................**$22.00**
Heinz Strained Foods, store display, tin sign above rack pictures baby with arms out flanked by Babies Need..., 18x18", EX, A....................**$250.00**
Heinz 57, Ertl bank, late 1970s, metal 1913 Model T Van, NMIB, A....................**$75.00**
Heinz 57, watch fob, metal, round with scalloped edges, 57 embossed in center, EX, A....................**$102.00**
Heinz 57, watch fob, silver, features 57 logo on front, This Charm Entitles The Wearer To 57 Varieties... lettered on back, EX, D....................**$28.00**
Heinz 57 Varieties, jigsaw puzzle, children playing grocery store with an array of Heinz products on shelves, 12x10", EX, F1....................**$35.00**
Heiple Insurance, calendar, 1941, cardboard, pictures girl in nautical attire, Hammel litho, full pad, 14x8½ ", EX, D....................**$25.00**
Helderberg Cement, sign, porcelain, pictures eagle with wings spread, blue & white, 20x12", EX, D....................**$75.00**
Hellman Brewing Co's Bock Beer, sign, paper, pictures ram bursting through barrel, black & white, Kaufmann & Strauss, framed, image: 24x17½ ", VG, A....................**$135.00**

Hellmann's Mayonnaise, recipe book, 1929, 'Salad Ideas,' 14 pages, VG, D....................**$3.50**

Helmar Turkish Cigarettes, sign, ca 1907, pictures Turkish woman in straw hat, signed AH Sonn Oz, product name etched in frame, 29½ x22", EX, A $425.00
Helmar Turkish Cigarettes, sign, cardboard, Quality Superb & product left of Helmar, Turkish Cigarettes at right, wood frame, 4x22", EX, A....................**$5.00**
Hembold's Jelly of Glycerine & Roses, sign, tin, product surrounded by lettering on patterned ground, ...Toilet Preparation, framed, image: 12x16", G, A....................**$175.00**
Hennessy, sign, tin, 23x23", EX, D....................**$20.00**
Henrietta Cigars, sign, embossed tin, man enjoying cigar, It Surely Is A Masterpiece, American Art Works litho, 13x9¼ ", EX, A....................**$300.00**
Henry Boker's Phonograph Needles, tin, green with black product lettering, rectangular with rounded corners, NM, M2....................**$22.00**
Henry Claus Brewing Co Extra Beer, label, pre-1920, company name arched above logo, G, A....................**$5.00**
Henry Draper Cigars, box label, inner lid sample, 1907, oval portrait of Mr Draper, The Moehle Lithographic Co, EX, A....................**$22.00**
Henry Field Seed Co, pin-back button, 1930s, red, white & blue, EX, D....................**$8.00**
Henry George 5¢ Cigar, sign, embossed tin, shows profile portrait of Henry George, Hirsghhorn Mack & Co Makers NY, framed, 23x17", VG+, A....................**$900.00**
Henry Prentiss Music Umbrella Store, trade card, coated stock, ...33 Street Boston, black & white, EX, A...**$105.00**
Hensler's Sparkling Ale, label, 1933-50, product name above & below logo, Internal Revenue Tax Paid statement, 32-oz, VG, A....................**$5.00**
Heptol Splits Laxative, tip tray, 1904, pictures bronco rider with gold lettering & trim on black rim, crazing, 4¼ " dia, VG+, A....................**$325.00**
Herald Square Typewriter Ribbon, tin, EX, A....................**$10.00**
Herbert A Strong Tailoring Co, fabrics case, inside of lid features advertising panel, Finest Quality Fabrics..., factory lower left, 16½ ", VG, A....................**$55.00**

Herco Cigar, sign, cardboard with string hanger, blue & white, M, D $12.00

Hercules EC & Infallible Smokeless Shotgun Powders, sign, 1924, paper, 2 Black hunters in snow lamenting 'Dah He Goes!,' advertising below, metal strips, 24x16", NM, D3..$950.00

Hercules Explosives, calendar, 1927, 'Pals,' pictures man & his dog, full pad, metal strips top & bottom, 20x13", VG, A $200.00

Hercules Explosives, calendar top, 1921, 'Outnumbered,' hunt scene, framed, VG, A $80.00

Hercules Infallible Smokeless Shotgun Powder, sign, paper, pictures mallards flying over stream, green, blue & yellow, metal strips top & bottom, 24½ x15", VG, A............$450.00

Hercules Powder Co, ad cover, 1890, image of Hercules, black & white, VG, A $35.00

Hercules Powder Co, badge, embossed metal, oval shape with image of Hercules above company name, 0000 below, 2x1½ ", NM, A $56.00

Hercules Powder Co, pin-back button, Hercules flanked by Hercules Powder Co, Keep 'Em Shooting above & below, red, white & blue, EX, A $55.00

Hercules Pure Coffee, tin, red, tall square shape, lid missing, A...$40.00

Hercules Sporting Powders, catalog, pictures elderly man & his dog on front cover, several powder cans illustrated inside, 28 pages, EX, A..............................$35.00

Hereford Brothers Clothes & Shoes, display, die-cut tin figure of man in red tuxedo attached to wood panel, Delighted With..., 36", VG, A.............................$220.00

Herman Cortez Cigars, sign, ca 1915, die-cut tin, girl holding open box of cigars, Hausermann litho, 16½ x12", EX, A...$500.00

Hero Coffee, tin, pictures General Shafter, Admiral Dewey & others, wooden knob on slip lid, octagonal, 1-lb, 7x4" dia, VG, A...$170.00

Herold's Smoked Sardines, tin, book shape, EX, D..$90.00

Heronia Cigars, box label, outer, Egyptian woman holding hand over her breast, 4½ x4½ ", M, D...................$5.00

Hershey's, recipe book, 1930, 'The Hershey Recipe Book,' VG, D $10.00

Hershey's, recipe book, 1937, 'Favorite Recipes,' 30 pages, EX, D..$10.00

Hershey's Chocolate, calculator, looks, feels & smells chocolaty, M, D2 ....$25.00

Hershey's Chocolate, tin, pictures boy cutting cake & girl eating on lid, matte finish, EX, D $7.50

Hershey's Chocolate Bar, candy bar wrapper, early 1900s, pictures cherub in coco bean, More Sustaining Than Meat, A Sweet To Eat!, framed, EX, D2 ....$50.00

Hershey's Cocoa, pocket mirror, lady preparing cocoa in circle flanked by Trade/Mark with product name above & below, 1¾" dia, EX, A....................................$950.00

Hershey's Cocoa, tin, 1984, pictures boy crying, matte finish, rectangular with rounded edges, 5½ x3¾x2", EX, D $7.50

Hershey's Kisses, doll, stuffed plush candy shape with embroidered face, 8", EX, D $8.00

Hershey's Kisses, tin, 1982, girl feeding candy to boy on lid, matte finish, 2x5" dia, EX, D $7.50

Hershey's Kisses, tin, 1990, rocking horse on front, red or green background, 6x4" dia, EX, D........................$3.50

Hershey's Mr Goodbar, pillow, 1989, candy bar shape, 4x6", NM, P4 ....$8.00

Hershey's Syrup, bank, pottery, can shape with silver & brown decor, P2..$35.00

HH Carr & Co, sign, wood, farmer pointing at train, Farmers! The Best Way To Sell Your Grain & Seeds..., 12x28", G-, A $100.00

HH Debolt's Workman's Friend, pocket mirror, man from behind surrounded by lettering holds mirror reflecting his eye, 65¢, 2½ " dia, VG+, A $30.00

Hi-Gloss Auto Enamel, can label, 1927, man painting antique car, gold & blue, VG, C3 ....$15.00

Hi-Klas Orange, sign, 1930s, embossed tin, Enjoy in script left of Hi-Klas Orange, bottle at right, black, red & yellow, 8x27", EX, M3 ....$75.00

Hi-Plane Smooth Cut Tobacco, pocket tin, white single-prop plane on red, lettering above & below, For Pipe & Cigarettes, lid wear, 4½ x3", EX, A.........................$55.00

Hi-Plane Tobacco, cigarette papers, pictures 2-engine plane with Hi-Plane above & Smooth Cut Tobacco For Pipe & Cigarettes below, NM, A..........................$35.00

Hi-Plane Tobacco, sign, 1930s, embossed tin, pictures a tobacco tin, black, white & green, 12x35", EX, D ..$90.00

Hiawatha, crate label, 1930s, California orange, stern-faced Indian & Red Ball logo, Strathmore, 10x11¾", M, C3....$50.00

Hick's Capudine Liquid, product bottle, amber glass with blue & white label under glass, For Headaches, Gripp, Etc, 8½ ", EX, A $175.00

Hickok's Lily White Marshmallows, tin, lettering surrounds encircled logo, slip lid, EX, A $40.00

Hickory Children's Garters, display, wood cutout, features boy & girl under lettered umbrella on beveled base, 19½ x13x5½ ", EX, A $315.00

Hickory Farms, playing cards, shows farm scene with red barn, Hickory Farms lettered on mailbox, complete, M, D..$6.50

High Admiral Cigarettes, lapel stud, ca 1896, Puritan lady portrait under Pure & Sweet slogan, multicolored, EX, D $8.00

High Grade Beer, label, pre-Prohibition, Franz Bartl Brewing Co, 14-oz, EX, A...$15.00

High Grade Pears, can label, early train climbing Sierra at Cape Horn, G1 ....**$10.00**

High Seal & Gold Drop Cigars, postcard, 1905-10, mechanical, beach umbrella lifts up from 2 bathers, Eilenberger Co, Troy Pa, VG, D **$8.50**

Highlander Pilsner Brew, sign, tin, Quality Beer above Highlander in diagonal script above glass & 2 bottles, Pilsner Brew below, 14x19", EX+, M2 ....**$275.00**

Hildreth Varnish Co, sign, cardboard, pictures Brooklyn Bridge with factory scene in upper corner, Whitehead & Hoag Co, 20x15", EX, D.................................**$650.00**

Hill Brand, crate label, California apple, ornate vignette of wagons, orchard & 3 gravensteins, 9x11", EX, G1...**$30.00**

Hill's Bros Coffee, tin, Hills Bros man drinking coffee, product name above & below, 2-lb, EX, A **$190.00**

Hinks, Wells & Co Selected Pens, tin for pen nibs, Hinks, Wells & Co arched above graphics atop panel reading Selected Pens, small rectangle, VG+, M2 ....**$9.00**

Hires, ashtray, glass, shows bottle shape with orange & white logos, EX, S3 ....**$12.00**

Hires, banner, cloth, R-J logo flanked by It's So Good & In Bottles, With Real Root Juices, blue background, 36x57", NM, M3 ....**$125.00**

Hires, banner, paper, bottle & glass lower left & lady with glass upper right, Confidence In It's Purity..., EX+, A........**$300.00**

Hires, banner, paper, Hires R-J logo left of elegant lady with glass, So Good With Food & tray at right, 60" long, VG, A **$100.00**

Hires, banner, vertical paper pennant in white, blue & yellow striped ground, Enjoy A Hires Float above boy & girl, 16", M, S3 ....**$17.00**

Hires, bottle, 1948, clear with orange & white label, 8-oz, EX, D...**$8.50**

Hires, bottle carrier, cardboard, pictures mugs of root beer, Try 10-oz Bottles, Draft, NM, B1 ....**$5.00**

Hires, bottle dispenser, tin, dark blue with white product lettering, round top, bottles dispense at bottom, 19", VG, A...$125.00

Hires, bottle topper, features carnation logo with Hires So Good With Food 5¢ above, 6x3½ ", NM, A **$25.00**

Hires, bottle topper, Hires For Finer Flavors 5¢ fanned out over flowers, 3¾x6", NM, A **$17.00**

Hires, bottle topper, Hires Healthful & Delicious 5¢, 6⅛ x3½ ", NM, A..**$25.00**

Hires, bottle topper, 1940s, die-cut cardboard, features woman holding glass, A Toast To Better Taste, 10x8", NM, D..**$40.00**

Hires, box, 1889, wood, Hires Improved Root Beer Liquid, Price 25 Cents stamped on side of box, 6x7", VG, S3..........**$85.00**

Hires, calendar, 1893, 2 girls with kitten, rare, S3 ....**$175.00**

Hires, calendar, 1975, Number One In More Ways Than One, 8-bottle carton & hand with mug above full pad on backing, M, S3...**$24.00**

Hires, checkerboard, images of Hires boy, black & yellow checkerboard on reverse, 12x12" open, VG, A..**$350.00**

Hires, clock, glass, metal frame, 1-12 surround Drink Hires Root Beer on dot, round, EX, D.........................**$240.00**

Hires, decal, bottle cap in brown, orange & white, Drink Hires Root Beer, EX, S3 ....**$10.00**

Hires, dixie cup, 1960s, waxed paper, 4x3" dia, EX, D .**$2.00**

Hires, door push bar, bottle cap at left of It's High Time For Hires Root Beer, 30" long, G, A.....................**$15.00**

Hires, door push bar, metal, shows bottle cap at left of It's High Time For Hires Root Beer, white ground, 2x24", G, S3 ....$45.00

Hires, door push plate, tin, white with R-J logo above tilted bottle, Hires To You, 2 Glass Size, It's So Good, 14x4", EX+, M2 ....**$70.00**

Hires, door push plate, 1940s, tin, shows Finer Flavor above tilted bottle, Real Root Juices left side, Ice Cold below, 11½ x3½ ", NM, D..**$125.00**

Hires, globe, milk glass with brown lettering, Drink Hires, 8½ ", EX, A...**$185.00**

Hires, ice cream scoop, plastic, white with black lettering on handle, EX, S3...**$10.00**

Hires, magazine ad, 1901, Saturday Evening Post, boy & girl enjoys Hires on bench, caged owl & bird above, framed, rare, EX, S3 ....**$45.00**

Hires, menu board, tin, blue & white stripe with black board, Drink Hires left of tilted bottle above, 29x16", NM, M3 ....**$125.00**

Hires, mug, ceramic, barrel shape with flared base, pointing Hires boy & Drink Hires Root Beer above, reproduction, NM, M2...**$45.00**

Hires, mug, ceramic, tapering, pointing Hires boy, Join Health & Cheer, Drink..., small rim chips, 5x4x3", VG, A..**$225.00**

Hires, mug, ceramic, white hour-glass shape, pointing Hires boy, handled, scarce, NM, M2..................**$225.00**

Hires, pocket knife, 1915, features Josh Slinger in white jacket and tie, EX+, S3 ....**$245.00**

Hires, pocket mirror, owl & parrot sharing tree branch on blue, Hires lettered in white, Who-o! You, 1¾" dia, G, A...**$600.00**

Hires, pocket mirror, woman holding mug & roses, gold border, Put Roses In Your Cheeks, oval, 2¾", EX, A ..**$265.00**
Hires, punch bowl, Mettlach, multiple images of boy with flowered lapel holding mug, Drink Hires..., 12x18" dia, VG, A **$20,000.00**
Hires, puzzle book, shows dressed elephant, EX, S3 ....**$32.00**
Hires, salesman's note pad & calendar, 1891, trifold, rare, EX, S3 ....**$138.00**
Hires, salesman's presentation display case, features 2 bottles & cans, a mug & 5 bottles of spices, Hires colors, EX+, S3 ....**$40.00**
Hires, sign, aluminum, Genuine in script on blue ribbon atop label with Hires in white & Root Beer in orange, 9x15", EX, S3 ....**$37.00**
Hires, sign, cardboard, Give Hospitality... & bottle over frosty window with pane wiped away for interior view, 12x18", NM, M3 ....**$40.00**
Hires, sign, cardboard, lady with glass in oval inset, bottle lower right & Drink Hires In Bottles lower left, vertical, EX, M1 ....**$1,050.00**
Hires, sign, cardboard, Say! above Drink Hires..., youth in straw hat, diagonal, 6x6", VG, S3 ....**$140.00**
Hires, sign, cardboard, self-framed, 1880-90, Say above pointing Hires boy with frothy mug, Hires below, oval, 24x20", VG, M2 ....**$1,100.00**
Hires, sign, cardboard, 1900s, girl with flared glass in oval, bottle lower right, Drink...In Bottles lower left, 21x15", EX, A **$575.00**
Hires, sign, cardboard, 1940s-50s, Top It Off With Hires left of lady in chefs hat with hot dog & 6-pack, 29x20", EX+, D **$40.00**
Hires, sign, cardboard die-cut, baby with bib reading Just One More leans on box, Hires' Improved Root Beer 25¢, 14x11", EX, D **$750.00**
Hires, sign, cardboard hanger, Enjoy in script left of lady with glass on yellow striped ground, blue Hires panel below, EX, M3 ....**$95.00**
Hires, sign, cardboard stand-up, shows bottle & fireplace, Give Hospitality That Old Time Flavor..., 18x12", EX, D....**$40.00**
Hires, sign, cardboard stand-up, Hires To You! on yellow above bottle & Tuned To... on blue with musical notes, 18x12", NM, M3 ....**$55.00**
Hires, sign, metal over cardboard, Drink Hires In Bottles lower left of lady's portrait facing forward, 9x6", VG, S3 ....**$235.00**
Hires, sign, paper, girl holding glass in oval with bottle in foreground, ...In Bottles, signed Haskell Coffin, 11x15", VG, A **$600.00**
Hires, sign, paper, icy scene with Drink Real Oldtime Hires Root Beer above full mug & price dot, blue ground, 14x11", M, S3 ....**$28.00**
Hires, sign, paper, pictures blue & white striped 6-pack, Special Sale! 15¢ Off Regular Price, 16x14", NM, M3.....**$25.00**
Hires, sign, paper, Refreshing & full glass of Hires above Ice Cold Hires on icy background, 12x17", EX, S3...........**$26.00**
Hires, sign, paper, round 5¢ symbols flank Drink Hires in white on red background with black border, 9x21", EX, S3 ....**$38.00**
Hires, sign, paper, woman in wicker chair upper right, glass & bottle lower left, text in between, framed, image: 11x20", VG, A **$110.00**
Hires, sign, tin, embossed, beige & brown with white highlights, Ask For Hires In Bottles, edge chips, 10x28", EX, A **$310.00**
Hires, sign, tin, embossed, black, red & white check-mark logo above So Refreshing in black on blue, 12x14", EX, S3 ....**$65.00**
Hires, sign, tin, embossed, Josh Slinger in white suit with bottle on yellow & blue, ...It Hits The Spot..., 7x17", VG+, S3 ....**$320.00**
Hires, sign, tin, embossed, Josh Slinger in white suit with bottle on yellow & blue, Drink...It Hits The Spot..., 9x16", EX, M3 ....**$375.00**
Hires, sign, tin, embossed, pointing Hires boy with frothy mug, Say Hires, oval, matted & framed, image: 20x14", VG, A **$500.00**
Hires, sign, tin, embossed, smiling girl wearing hat at right, Enjoy Hires, It's Always Pure, 9½ x27½ ", EX, A ..**$600.00**
Hires, sign, tin, embossed, 1920s, Drink Hires In Bottles on elongated diamond, Bracing Delicious below, 10x30", NM, D **$145.00**
Hires, sign, tin, orange & white on blue, Hires lettered at left of In Bottles lettered over tilted bottle, 10x28", G, M2 ....**$36.00**
Hires, sign, tin, round red, black & white R-J logo surrounded by raised blue border, 12" dia, M, S3 ....**$88.00**
Hires, sign, tin, white Hires on black panel bordered by yellow & red, Drink above & In Bottles below, 5x14", NM, M3 ....**$95.00**
Hires, syrup bottle, label under glass, metal cap, 11½ ", EX, A **$375.00**
Hires, syrup bottle, 1900, chip on label, rare, S3.....**$278.00**
Hires, syrup dispenser, blue porcelainized bracket, stainless steel tank with logo plaque front & back, top missing, 20", VG, A **$80.00**
Hires, syrup dispenser, counter clamp-on style, metallic with Hires R-J Root Beer label, 22", EX, A **$200.00**

Hires, syrup dispenser, Mettlach, urn shape, multiple images of Hires boy pointing, Drink Hires 5¢..., 19x10½ " dia, VG, A $22,500.00

Hires, syrup dispenser, porcelain hourglass shape, Drink Hires, It Is Pure, with original pump, 14x7½ " dia, VG, A...**$325.00**

Hires, thermometer, tin, panel in Hires colors on white with Hires above, Root Beer below bulb, rounded ends, 17x5", EX+, M2 .... **$30.00**

Hires, trade card, portrait of lady holding roses, Put Rose In Your Cheeks, EX+, S3 .... **$18.00**

Hires, trade card, 1888, girl sitting on barrel, S3 .... **$20.00**

Hires, trade card, 1888, girl standing in pink dress & blue stockings, It Cured My Colds, rare, S3 .... **$20.00**

Hires, trade card, 1889, Ruth & Naomi, VG, S3 .... **$8.00**

Hires, trade card, 1890, lady seated in black dress, EX, S3 .... **$15.00**

Hires, trade card, 1890, little girl in pink dress & yellow floral bonnet, rare, EX, S3 .... **$28.00**

Hires, trade card, 1895, boy in black wide-brimmed hat holding glass, All Gone, G, S3 .... **$14.00**

Hires, tray, 1915, Things Is Getting Higher, ...Still A Nickel A Trickle on rim around Hires 5¢ & Josh Slinger, round, VG+, S3 .... **$390.00**

Hires, tray, 1930s-40s, shows pointing Hires boy with frothy mug flanked by lettering, C Shonk litho, 13½ " dia, VG, A $450.00

Hires Condensed Milk, needle holder, copyright 1899, die-cut cardboard with paper cover each side, minor wear at bottom, 1½ x2½ ", VG, D **$12.00**

Hitchner Biscuit Co, barrel, tin, features blue with red lettering in horizontal oval, slip lid & bail, some wear, 27x15", G, A **$25.00**

HJ Heinz Co, sign, 1930s, for Heinz Foods International Trucks, paper, truck above green & black lettering, framed, 38x28", EX, A **$190.00**

HJ Heinz Co Pure Pickling Vinegar, display, die-cut cardboard, woman seated on barrel holding product, rare, small holes & overall soiling, 57x40", A **$700.00**

HJ Stone, sign, 1930s, painted & sanded wood, 2-sided, white lettering on black, ...Expert Auto Repairing, 9½ x42", VG, A **$160.00**

HO Stanley & Son Rangely Spinner, trade card, 1900-1910, shows bait, black & white, scarce, EX, A **$75.00**

Hobart Baking Machines, catalog, 1941, 16 pages, EX, D **$10.00**

Hochschild, Kohn & Co, postcard, pictures a horse-drawn buggy, Baltimore's Best Store, VG+, P3 .... **$35.00**

Hoerber Beer, label, 1933-50, logo above product name, Internal Revenue Tax Paid, 12-oz, VG, A **$5.00**

Hoffman House Cigar, sign, cardboard, nudes playfully tugging on Satyr by stream, The New...5 Cents, framed, image: 26x18", VG, A **$600.00**

Hoffman's Ice Cream, sign, hanging, porcelain, 2-sided, red & green on white emblem, product name above Sealtest logo, 22x26", EX, A **$140.00**

Hofmann Brew, label, 1933-50, Hofmann encircling world globe, Peter Fox Brewing Co, 12-oz, EX, A **$14.00**

Hohenadel Beer, sign, tin, John L Sullivan in boxing ring, minor chips/scratches/rust spots, framed, image: 23x17", G, A **$200.00**

Holdz Dental Plate Holder, sample tin, 3¼ ", EX, D **$25.00**

Holeproof Hosiery, pocket mirror, Are Your Hose Insured arched above crown logo, Charles H Anthony... across bottom, 2¼ " dia, EX, A **$15.00**

Holiday Special Beer, label, 1933-50, Santa with beer mug at top, Sebewaing Brewing Co, Internal Revenue Tax Paid statement, 12-oz, EX, A **$10.00**

Holland Furnaces, tape measure, aluminum, Make Warm Friends, color missing, G, D **$3.00**

Hollandina Cigars, box label, inner lid, woman dressed in Dutch costume, 6x9", M, C3 .... **$9.00**

Hollingshead Carriage Top Dressing, tin, 1900-10, pictures carriage top & fancy graphics, white background, text on reverse, 3¼ ", VG, A **$20.00**

Holly Plums, can label, 3 purple plums on a branch & embossed logo, San Francisco Ca, EX, G1 .... **$10.00**

Hollywood Bread, end label, shows Mamie Van Doren above product name & Special Formula, No Fats Added, EX, S1 .... **$15.00**

Hollywood Glo, display, paperboard, trifold, Hollywood Glo above movie star in center flanked by cameraman & light man, 12x18", VG, A **$20.00**

Holsum Bread, pin-back button, 1930s, pictures 2 parrots, yellow & black, EX, D **$12.00**

Holsum Bread, thermometer, tin, black on yellow, Ask For above Holsum lettered vertically at left of thermometer, 18½ ", G+, A **$200.00**

Holt & Morrill Taxidermists, ad cover, 1891, pictures a large buck, EX, A **$40.00**

Holt Combined Harvester, sign, shield shape, red & black lettering on yellow, dented in center/paint loss/rubs, 16x21", A **$10.00**

Holtons Band Instruments, sign, cardboard, pictures the O'Brien Minstrels with various brass horns & drums, 27x41", VG, A **$100.00**

Home Brewing Co, sign, paper, demure girl in oval surrounded by flowers, Brewers of Fine Lager Beer..., framed, image: 29x23", G-, A **$350.00**

Home Brewing Co's Eureka Beer, Ale & Porter, sign, embossed tin with curved glass front, black & gold, 21¼ x16", EX, A **$800.00**

Home Brewing Co's Monogram Ale, label, pre-1920, Home in arched letters above logo, Monogram Ale below, G, A **$19.00**

Home Ice Cream & Protected Milk, sign, porcelain, white lettering on royal blue background, minor edge chips, 32x42", VG, A **$100.00**

Home Investment & Savings Association, sign, porcelain, white on blue, Agency Of above Home Investment arched over ...Head Office Winnipeg..., 12x18", VG, M2..**$125.00**

Home Run Cigarettes, sign, early 1900s, tin, cigarettes flanked by 15 For 5¢, product name above & below, red ground, rare, 12" dia, VG, A **$5,050.00**

Home Run Razor Blades, original box with contents, pictures baseball player hitting a home run, EX, A ..**$31.00**

Home Town Bread, pencil clip, 1930s, red, white & blue, EX, D **$14.00**

Home-Run Stogie, tin, pictures baseball field with players in action, 6 holes in slip lid, A **$1,800.00**

Homer Brand, label, 1940s, Homer Brand above bird in flight, Sunkist orange lower left, Orange Heights Orange Ass'n, 10x11", NM, C3...............................**$4.00**

Honda Motorcycle, playing cards, 1980s, MIB, P4 .....**$5.00**

Honer's Silver Foam Draft Beer, label, 1933-50, Internal Revenue Tax Paid statement, 1/2-gal, VG, A........**$12.00**

Honest Scotch Snuff, fan, features men at moonlit campsite, vertical rectangle with loop handle, NM, A ..**$15.00**

Honest Scotch Snuff, fan, 1932, features colonial couple beyond modern couple among flowers & cans of product, vertical rectangle, NM, A **$24.00**

Honest Scrap Tobacco, sign, cardboard, cat & dog with tobacco pouch between them, An Everyday Scrap, framed, 24½ x32", EX, A **$600.00**

Honest Scrap Tobacco, sign, porcelain, Honest above image of arm & hand holding hammer, Scrap below, Trade Mark under arm, vertical, EX, M1............**$525.00**

Honest Scrap Tobacco, store bin, metal, red with feisty cat & dog looking at product in landscape on front panel, slant lid, 12x18x14", EX, A.............$1,650.00

Honest Weight Tobacco, sign, baby pictured with product name above & below, Weyman & Bro, Pittsburgh Pa, matted & framed, EX, A......................................**$200.00**

Honey & Sonny Bread, pin-back button, 1930s, multicolored on white background, blue lettering, EX, D **$12.00**

Honey Bear Pure Honey, can, paper label pictures 2 bears on a branch with Honey Bear in script above & below, lid missing, 5-lbs, EX, A............................**$35.00**

Honey Moon Rum-Flavored Tobacco, tin, man on the moon on front, cigarette & pipe on back, red ground, hinged lid, minor scrathes, 4½ x3x1", VG, A......**$200.00**

Honeysuckle Beans, can label, dish of beans & bouquet of flowers, M, C3 ....**$5.00**

Honker Brand Cranberries, crate label, flying geese on orange & black background, M, C3 ....**$8.00**

Honor Pork & Beans, can label, pictures George Washington & bowl of beans, EX, C3................................**$25.00**

Hood's Ice Cream, sign, enameled tin, It's Hoods... on panel above ice cream cone & cow's head, The Flavor's There, 28x20", VG+, A **$280.00**

Hood's Ice Cream, sign, metal, wrought-iron hanger, It's Hoods (underlined) on octagon shape with Ice Cream on lower panel, 42x36", EX, A **$400.00**

Hood's Milk, blotter, delivery man in horse-drawn wagon with case of milk, logo on side of wagon, multicolored, unused, 6x3½ ", D **$20.00**

Hood's Milk, calendar, 1940, pictures happy baby face with bottle, October pad, 14x10", G, D **$35.00**

Hood's Royal Oak Rubber Boots, sign, embossed tin, large boot on yellow ground with green band, red & white lettering, stylized border, 13x9", EX, A.....**$110.00**

Hood's Rubber Footwear, catalog, 1926, VG, D......**$25.00**

Hood's Sarsaparilla, calendar, 1888, die-cut paperboard, young girl's head portrait wearing blue bonnet, full pad, 9¾", EX, A **$180.00**

Hood's Sarsaparilla, calendar, 1892, 8 kids with various sewing projects surround complete calendar pad, round, 7¾" dia, EX, A **$85.00**

Hood's Sarsaparilla, calendar, 1897, die-cut paper, pretty child in lilac hat, October pad, top corner bent/facial creasing, 7x4½ ", P1 ....**$37.50**

Hood's Sarsaparilla, calendar, 1900, die-cut, pictures 2 little girls, complete, D..**$60.00**

Hood's Sarsaparilla, coupon calendar, 1898, embossed image of little girl in circular inset surrounded by flowers, 7½ x5", EX, A....................................$65.00

Hood's Sarsaparilla, jigsaw puzzle, cardboard, horse-drawn buggy carrying doctor away from laboratory & factory, 10x15", VG, A $95.00

Hood's Sarsaparilla Pansy, booklet, die-cut pansy, several illustrations, EX, A $8.00

Hood Shoe Rebuilding, sign, tin, Hood man pointing to ...Authorized Dealer, Heels & Soles flank Hood arrow logo, 7x31", VG+, D3 ....$300.00

Hood Tire Tube, box, cardboard, Hood Tire man in cream & red, lettering in cream, rare, creasing/soiling/tears, 13x5x5", G+, A $185.00

Hood Tires, sign, 1930-40, die-cut porcelain, red, black & white with Hood Tire man signaling to stop, 35½ x10", EX, A $1,100.00

Hood Tires, sign, 1930-40, tin, Hood Tire man at side, lettering on cream & blue background, Hiatt & Roosa Garage..., 12x24", VG, A $175.00

Hoody's Peanut Butter, pail, pictures kids on teeter-totter with product name above & below, slip lid & bail, straight sides, 1-lb, EX+, A $650.00

Hoop-La Cigars, box label, inner lid sample, 1880, circus scene with girl trying to mount horse, Schumacher & Ettlinger litho, EX, A $72.00

Hoosier Cement, sign, porcelain, white on blue with red logo in center, minor chips, 20x12", D $75.00

Hoot-mon Talcum, tin, bagpipe player, EX, D $35.00

Hoover, tape measure, 1950s, hard plastic Global vacuum, taupe & beige with red logo, 2" dia, EX, D $18.00

Hop Ointment, trade card, pictures little girl flanked by lettering, rectangular vignettes of dog & horse below, EX, A $30.00

Hopalong Cassidy's Favorite Pop Corn, can, photo image of Hopalong at left of popping corn, product name above & below, 10-oz, EX, A $110.00

Hopkins & Allens Arms Co, mug, Mettlach, made for 1911 Police Chief's Convention in Rochester, scarce, M, D $335.00

Hopkins & Allens Arms Co, print, 1906, 'A Modern William Tell,' boy aiming rifle at dog with an apple on his head, matted & framed, 14x20", VG, A $400.00

Horlacher Brewing Co's Perfection Beer, sign, 1940s, cardboard, shows 2 gnomes hauling beer barrel, Aged Nine Months In Dark Clean..., framed, image: 24x19", EX, A $135.00

Horlick's Malted Milk, jar, clear with blue enameled lettering, original top missing, EX, A $40.00

Horlick's Malted Milk, pocket mirror, milkmaid with product & cow encircled by lettering on gold border, 2⅛" dia, EX, A $100.00

Horne's Sun-Dried Coffee, tin, features sun graphic with Sun-Dried arched above Coffee, pry lid, Canadian, VG+, A $50.00

Hornell Crystal Ale, label, 1933-50, Hornell Brewing Co Inc, Internal Revenue Tax Paid, 12-oz, EX, A $15.00

Horner Harmonicas, display, die-cut cardboard, pictures boy holding instrument with display rack below, chips/scratches, 31x15¼", VG, A $300.00

Horse Shoe (Cut Plug Tobacco), sign, embossed tin litho, 3 gunboats with hulls made of Horse Shoe Cut Plug, Best Navy On Earth, framed, 24x36", G, A $850.00

Horsford's Bread Preparation, sign, paper, little girl in white dress & bonnet holding basket of flowers, several creases, framed, 22¾x17", A $65.00

Horsford's Bread Preparation Baking Powder, sign, paper, double image of little girl in bonnet resting on plinth, Major & Knapp litho, 23½ x32½", EX, A ..$700.00

Horsman's, sign, paper, elegant woman in plumed hat shooting bow & arrow, minor edge tears/overall soiling, 22x17½", G, A $1,000.00

Horton Brewing Co, bar sign, reverse-painted glass, lettering & logo on shield, squared top & rounded bottom, 10½ x10", G, A $65.00

Hoster's Beer, sign, tin, shows 2 monks looking at man passed out on a barrel, oval, framed, image: 16½ x19½", EX, A $290.00

Hoster's Famous Beer, charger, tin, pictures a crow in graduation cap & gown at the bar, Something To Crow About, 24" dia, G, A $375.00

Hoster's Famous Columbus Bottled Beers, sign, cardboard hanger, pictures bottle at left of lettering, matted & framed, image: 10½ x13½ ", VG, A $110.00

Hostetter's Stomach Bitters, postcard, pictures Panama Canal, G, D $28.00

Hostetter's Stomach Bitters, sign, mother-of-pearl & reverse-painted glass, gold image of St Anthony sleighing dragon, framed, image: 29x22", G-, A $100.00

Hot Brand Vegetables, label, features desert scene & mountains with cowboys branding calf, Guadalupe, 7x9", EX, G1 ....$5.00

Hot Spur Mixture, pocket tin, pictures a rooster on diagonal center band, product name above & below, squared corners, slip lid, EX, A $50.00

Hotel Alpine San Francisco, trade card, dog with lettering above & below, green on white, EX, A $28.00

Hotel Ardmore, paperweight/mirror, pictures hotel in Ardmore, Oklahoma, JC Clopton Manager, decorative border, 3½ " dia, VG, A $30.00

Hotel Pemberton, trade card, 2-sided, busy Victorian scene, Japanese pattern table wear advertising on reverse, EX, A $18.00

Hotel Statler, pocket mirror, 1906, exterior view of hotel with lettering above & below, Buffalo NY, oval, 2¾", VG+, A $45.00

Hotel Tuller, pocket mirror, large deer head superimposed over building, Souvenir Of..., Detroit, lettered rim, oval, 2¾", EX, A $110.00

House of Morrison Tailors, pocket mirror, It Fits Well Around The Neck arched above elegant couple, company name below, oval, 2¾", EX, A $170.00

Household Sewing Machine, sign, paper, woman at sewing machine with child & kittens at play, factory view out window, 19x26", EX, A $700.00

Howard, Clark & Co Household Ranges, trade card, die-cut border, pictures elegant women gathering flowers, Built To Bake..., EX, A $28.00

Howard Dustless-Duster, sign, paper, lady in blue stands behind table displaying duster, No Oil To Soil, beveled frame, 32x22½ ", NM, A $1,100.00

Howard Johnson's, cup & saucer, demitasse, EX, D2 .$25.00

Howard Johnson's, bank, plastic, P2 ....$25.00

Howard's Perfection Oil, tin, 1910, pictures a vintage carbine, screw lid, 3x2", EX, D $40.00

Howdy, bottle topper with bottle, cardboard, hands with sandwich on black circle above Howdy, EX, M3.$45.00

Howdy, sign, tin hanger, yellow with Howdy above receding bottles on emblem over black diagonal band, 9x6", VG, A $75.00

Howdy Orange Soda, display, 1930s, die-cut paper, scrolled cutout with hand-held bottle at right of Howdy Orange Soda, 15x42", NM, D $45.00

Howdy Orange Soda, sign, 1920, tin, 2 bottles at left of Don't Say Orange Say Howdy, 9½ x14", NM, D...$90.00

Howdy Orange Soda, sign, 1920s, paper hanger, Don't Say Orange Say above 2 bottles, Howdy below, straight top, pointed bottom, 12x6", EX, D $35.00

Hoyt's German Cologne, sign, mother-of-pearl & reverse-painted glass, fancy graphics, framed, image: 20½ x26", G, A $650.00

Hoyt's German Cologne, sign, paper, classical mother & children at courtyard fountain, lettering above, some tears, vertical rectangle, EX, A $320.00

Hoyt's German Cologne, sign, tin, pictures little girl's face in center of a rosebud, minor flaking & rust, original frame, 31½ x25½ ", G, A $1,100.00

Hoyt's German Cologne, trade card, young girl in night clothes with her dog, G, D $5.00

Hoyt's Selected Sweets, tin, 1920s, 2 children on black & cream checked background, raised lettering on press lid, 5-lb, 9¾x5" dia, EX, A $65.00

HP Hood & Sons Dairy Products, pocket mirror, pictures cow's face encircled by decorative border then lettering, horizontal oval, 2¾", EX, A $180.00

Hub Royal Art Stove, trade card, interior scene with baby crawling toward furnace, Smith & Anthony Stove Co... below, EX, A $12.00

Hubbard Fertilizer Co, pocket pirror, ca 1905, lettered border surrounds busty woman with long flowing hair, Use Hubbard's..., round, EX+, D $330.00

Hubley Guns, display rack, 1960s, metal, Buy Hubley in black & white on yellow with white stripes, Guns on red sunburst, 17x23", G, A $40.00

Hudepohl Beer, sign, self-framed tin, man with corncob pipe & glass of beer beside embossed beer bottle, 19¼ x15¼ ", VG, A $110.00

Hudepohl Beer, tray, tin, with handles, 2 men seated at table playing clarinets, 15¼ x21½ ", G, A $150.00

Hudepohl Brew'g Co's Cincinnati Beer, sign, Vitrolite, barrel flanked by antlered deer, original copper & wood frame, 22½ x18", EX, A $1,000.00

Hudepohl Pure Lager Beer, can, cone-top, Hudepohl in red on white center band, logo above, red background, 12-oz, G, D $30.00

Hudson Authorized Service, sign, porcelain, Hudson Built Cars... over triangle, 42" dia, NM, S2 ....$750.00

Hudson County Consumers Brewing Co, calendar, 1907, pictures factory scene surrounded by hops & wheat, logo upper right, pad missing, framed, image: 17x12", EX, A $900.00

Hudson River Day Line Ferry Boat, sign, cardboard, depicts ferry boat moving between steep shores, Gateway To Happiness, 10½ x19", NM, A $30.00

Hudson's Bay Co's Tea, tin, various colorful graphics on 4 sides, slip lid, 8½ x6x6", VG, M2 .... **$65.00**

Hudson's Soap, display, die-cut cardboard, 2-sided, white baby's head with lettered bib, Make Baby Smile..., 7x4", EX, D **$175.00**

Hugh Campbell's Shag Smoking Tobacco, tin, silhouette of man in profile smoking a pipe, rounded corners, slip lid, 6x4", EX, A **$259.00**

Humble Oil & Refining Co, bank, 1960s, hard vinyl tiger in orange, white & brown accents, 5½ ", EX, A **$28.00**

Humble Rest Rooms, sign, ca 1964, die-cut tin, 2-sided, Top Rated in red on center band of diamond, blue & white ground, 30x30", EX, A **$120.00**

Humboldt Beer, label, pre-1920, pictures eagle flying over stream, Humboldt Brewing Co, 11-oz, G, A **$25.00**

Hummer Cigars, box label, outer, hummingbird at tobacco flower, 4½ x4½ ", M, D **$6.00**

Humphrey's Remedies, display case, wood with tin insert front & back, list of medicines & 77 For Colds..., chipping & fading, 18½ x21x7", A **$175.00**

Hunter Arms Co, envelope, pictures dog with dead game bird, VG, A **$110.00**

Hunter Arms Co, lapel stud, white lettering on red background, some fading, round, VG, A **$35.00**

Hunter Arms Co, postcard, 1910, sepia photo of the factory, used, VG, A **$25.00**

Hunter Baltimore Rye, sign, paper, shows product name lettered above huntsman on horse waving hat, Guaranteed...Pure below, framed, 27x20", EX, A **$40.00**

Hunter's Beer, label, 1933-36, hunter & dog, Superior Brewing Co, U-type permit #788, 12-oz, EX, A **$13.00**

Hunter's Syrup, dispenser, glass bowl with milk glass base, no lid, 9½ x7½ " dia base, EX, A **$65.00**

Huntley & Osborne Crackers, pocket mirror, shaped to look like cracker, 2⅛ " dia, EX, A **$25.00**

Huntoon Paige Coffee, tin, round 1-lb, A **$70.00**

Hunyadi Janos Pills, container, tin, 20 Pills, 25 Cents, slide top, small, EX, D **$8.00**

Hurd's Washing Mixture, sign, paper, woman washing clothes in wash tub & 3 cherubs with bottle, Magical..., fancy graphics, 10½ x13", EX, A **$800.00**

Hurd Shoes, whistle, metal, rectangular shape with advertising, They're Tops above round logo, For Boys & Girls, EX, A **$20.00**

Husemann's Soda, sign, 1920s, embossed tin, black on yellow, Clear & Sparkling, Guaranteed 100% Pure..., 12x19", EX, D **$35.00**

Hushpuppies Shoes, bank, painted hard vinyl, figural basset hound, 7¼ ", EX, D **$25.00**

Husky Hi-Power, gas globe, metal body, blue & white Husky dog above product name, blue & orange border, 15" dia, NM, A **$1,600.00**

Husky Motor Oil, can, 1950s, Husky dog at bottom, product name in blue on white band above, orange ground, pry lid, 1-qt, 5½ ", EX, A **$70.00**

Hussey, Wells & Co Cast Steel, trade card, coated stock, fancy lettered graphics, ...Best Refined Tool Steel..., EX, A **$80.00**

Huxley's Plasma, tin, 1912, floral design on paper label, EX+, D **$12.50**

Huyler's Candy, pocket mirror, pictures young girl, oval, EX, D **$135.00**

Huyler's Cocoa, tin, Huyler's in script above lettered vignettes, screw top, 1/2-lb, 4½ ", EX+, A **$40.00**

Huyler's Vanilla Chocolate, trade card, little girl in rocking chair, If You Only Knew How Nice It Is!, advertising on reverse, EX, A **$16.00**

Hy-Quality Coffee, display, die-cut cardboard hanger, woman seated on swing enjoying a cup of coffee, 38x16", NM, M1 .... **$950.00**

Hydrox Soda, bottle topper, die-cut cardboard, pictures a swimmer above Hydrox 5¢, 7½ x5½ ", NM, A **$3.00**

Hygeia Coffee, blotter, 1920s, coffee can on billboard, A Sign Of Good Taste above, 3½ x6½ ", EX, D **$4.00**

Hyklas Ginger Ale, postcard, photographic fade-away, pictures woman with bottle & glass, English, EX, D. **$75.00**

Hyvis Motor Oil, can, ca 1938, product name in white on black, text below, 1-qt, 5½ ", EX, A **$30.00**

I

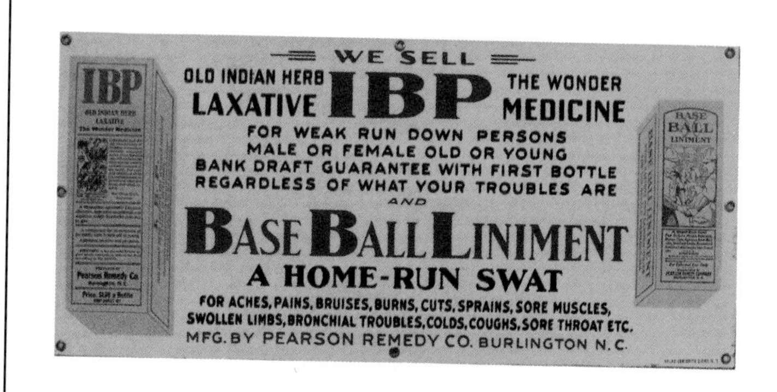

IBP Baseball Liniment, sign, 1910s-20s, porcelain, black & red lettering flanked by product boxes, yellow ground, 12x26", NM, A $1,000.00

Icee Developers Inc, bank, 1970s, molded vinyl, Icee Bear holding a large Icee, 8", M, D **$25.00**

Ide Collars, display, wood with metal frame & glass panel, 2 For 5¢, includes 15 collars, back opens, 48x8x7", EX, A **$190.00**

Ideal Beer, label, 1933-50, Cape Brewing Co, Internal Revenue Tax Paid statement, 12-oz, EX, A **$20.00**

Ideal or Progress Cooking Oil, pocket mirror, maid serves family dinner, lettered border, A Pure Healthful Vegetable Oil..., 2⅛ " dia, EX, A **$425.00**

Ideal or Progress Cooking Oil, pocket mirror, pictures 2 ladies in Victorian kitchen, lettered border, oval, 2¾" long, EX, A **$1,000.00**

IGA, sign, porcelain, eagle on shield, G, D **$85.00**

Iliad Cigars, box label, inner lid, 1922, ancient Greek scene, 6x9", EX, C3 .... **$45.00**

Illinois Springfield Watches, catalog, ca 1915, 30 pages, EX, D **$10.00**

Illinois Watch Co, sign, tin, factory scene with horses & buggies in foreground, Wells & Hope litho, rare, original frame, 32x40", G, A **$400.00**

Imperial Club Skates, trade card, ice skating scene, No Wrenches, Keys, Screws or Nuts To Lose, Can Be Changed To Boots..., EX, A **$22.00**

Imperial Cut Plug Tobacco, humidor, porcelain, CYHP emblem with flags & eagle, 1914 & Imperial Cut Plug on side of container, 7¼", VG, A....................**$22.50**

Imperial Egg Food, sign, paper, colorful image of folks gathering eggs, product name above, Kellogg & Bulkeley, framed, 28x21", NM, D....................**$2,000.00**

Imperial Inc Bus Lines, sign, porcelain flange, 2-sided, Imperial above Coast To Coast Bus Lines crown logo, ...Depot... below, 24x18", EX/G, A **$450.00**

Imperial Roll Films, sign, porcelain, 2-sided, light green with green & white border, product name left of product box, 10x14", EX, M2 ....**$220.00**

Independent Brewing Assoc, pitcher, china with gold leaf trim, image of monk sipping mug of Prima beer, blue background, 12x6¼" dia, VG, A....................**$150.00**

Independent Brewing Co, calendar, 1910, paper, girl in elegant dress & bonnet holding basket of flowers, framed, image: 19½x14½", EX, A **$475.00**

Independent Gasoline, sign, porcelain, 2-sided, Independent Gasoline lettered around Ethyl logo, wavy banded edge, 30" dia, VG/G+, A....................**$205.00**

Independent Lock Co, sign, die-cut tin, 2-sided, key shape, Lock & Key Products.., Fitchburg Mass, Ilco logo in center, 32", G, A....................**$140.00**

Indera Figurfit Swim Suits, pin-back button, black on white, product name at right of girl in swim suit ready to dive, round, EX, A **$36.00**

Index Brand Breakfast Cocoa, tin, yellow panel on cream with encircled portrait of a lady pouring cocoa, advertising above & below, 1-lb, VG+, A..........$110.00

Indian Brand Tobacco, humidor, glass top, rare, EX+, D **$8,500.00**

Indian Gas, sign, die-cut porcelain, 2-sided, red & white dot atop panel reading Indian Gas..., wrought frame, 36x45", EX, A....................**$70.00**

Indian Head Overalls-Pants-Shirts, sign, porcelain, Indian in oval at right of advertising, Made By Morotock Manfg Co..., For Sale Here, horizontal, EX, M1....................**$1,050.00**

Indian Motor Oil, can, 1915-30, Indian head encircled above product & company name, green ground, pour spout & handle, 1-gal, 11", EX, A....................**$600.00**

Indian Motorcycles, pin-back button, Indian Motorcycles lettered diagonally at right of smiling Indian, round, EX, A **$68.00**

Indian Rock Ginger Ale, sign, cardboard, seated girl looking into white bottle above product name lettered in red, 22x14", EX+, M3 ....**$300.00**

Indian Service Car, sign, 1930s, paper, 2-sided, motorcycle with side car in center, service car vignettes in corners, framed, 22x31", NM, A....................**$160.00**

Indianapolis Brewing Co, match safe, embossed logo of winged girl on wheel, overall wear, 2¾x1½", VG, A **$35.00**

Indianapolis Brewing Co, sign, paper, goddess surrounded by cherubs with medals above factory inset, Progress Brand..., framed, 41x31", VG, A........**$1,050.00**

Indianapolis Brewing Co, sign, tin, winged boy presenting wreath at 1904 St Louis Exposition, self-framed, 37½x25½", EX, A **$2,300.00**

Indianapolis Brewing Co, tip tray, pictures labeled bottle, G, D **$32.00**

Ingersoll, stropping set, in original box, M, B1.........**$15.00**

Ingersoll Watch Co, sign, paper, little boy holding up watch, water stain, framed, image: 19x10½", VG, A............**$80.00**

Ingersoll Watches, cabinet, wood, reverse-painted glass front with product lettering in gold, green velvet lining, 9", VG, A **$475.00**

Inside Quality, crate label, Texas citrus, pictures large Black woman, EX, C3 ....**$20.00**

International Harvester Co, catalog, ca 1910, features Deering Corn machines, 24 pages, VG, D...........**$25.00**

International House of Pancakes, server, pottery, hen shape, M, P2....................**$145.00**

International Oil Co, can, 1910-20, company name on world globe, Capitol Hand Separator Oil below, screw lid, ½ gal, 10", G, A $45.00

International Poultry Food, sign, paper, woman feeding hen from box, Makes Hens Lay More Eggs, minor tears/blemishes, wood frame, 27x20", VG, A.....**$210.00**

International Stock Food, display cabinet, wood trapezoid frame with 3 shelves, glass door & side panels, advertising on base, 50x35x6", EX, A **$3,700.00**

International Stock Food, sign, paper, farmer feeding pigs with cows & horses beyond, 3 Feeds For One Cent..., 20½ x28", VG, A **$400.00**

Interwoven Socks for Christmas, sign, cloth, black, green & white lettering on red below Christmas In Old Virginia scene, NC Wyeth, framed, 23x62", EX, A **$155.00**

Invader Motor Oil, can, 1965-present, knight in armor on horse above product name, company name below, yellow ground, 1-qt, 5½ ", NM, A **$30.00**

Invader Motor Oil, sign, 1940s, embossed tin, black, yellow & white with knight on horse & product name above Perfected..., 34x57", VG, A **$245.00**

Invader Motor Oil, storage bin, porcelain with galvanized bottom, advertising & logo on sides, hinged lid, 23x30x20", EX, A $700.00

Invitation Coffee, tin, dark letters on light ground over light letters on dark, slip lid, round, 1-lb, G, A **$15.00**

Iowa Oil Co, sign, porcelain, Iowa Oil Co in bold black lettering on white, 10x72", VG, A **$100.00**

Irish Singer Cigars, box label, inner lid, embossed & gilted picture of Denis O'Sullivan with harp & leprechaun, NM, H1 ....**$12.00**

Iron City Beer, display, cast iron, 3-D bar scene with bartender & customer in top hat, round Iron City logo at right, 10x14", EX, A **$115.00**

Iron City Brewing Co Export Beer, label, pre-1920, Export in script above logo, company name below, EX, A **$16.00**

Iroquois Beer, bottle opener, 1950s, red plastic Indian boy figure, metal opener on top, 4½ x1¼ ", NM, D **$15.00**

Iroquois Brewery, calendar, 1928, profile of young squaw with feathers & beads in her hair, full pad, framed, image: 27½ x13¼", VG, A **$850.00**

Iroquois Refrigeration, sign, polychromed die-cut wood, 2-sided, Indian chief wrapped in red blanket, advertising below, very rare, 72", EX, A.........................**$990.00**

Iso=Vis 'D' Motor Oil, sign, 1950s, embossed porcelain, Top Quality above product name, blue with red & black border, 60x16", NM, A **$150.00**

Ital-Ama Tomato Paste, thermometer, wood, can flanked by World's Finest lettered vertically above text, blue ground, rounded top, 15", VG, A **$25.00**

Iten Biscuit Co Animal Cookies, tin, 1930s, various animals on wheels with clown in center, slip lid & movable tin handle, 2-oz, 2½ x4½ ", VG, A..............**$100.00**

Ithaca Gun Co, catalog, 1900s, pictures a double-barrel shotgun on front, 22 pages, EX, A **$160.00**

Ithaca Guns, pocket catalog, 1902, pictures a double-barrel shotgun surrounded by mallards on front, 8 pages, EX, A **$75.00**

Ithaca Guns, pocket catalog, 1924, pictures 2 guns crossed in center, ...For Field & Trap, 8 pages, EX, A.......**$55.00**

Ithaca Guns, sign, paper, 2 pigeons on a branch, Extinct Passenger Pigeons above, gun & product name below, 24x16", VG, A **$450.00**

ITS Rubber Heels, sign, paper, set of 2 comical interior & exterior images, signed by Frise, framed, 21x19", EX+, M2 ....**$360.00**

Iver Johnson Arms & Cycle Works, postcard, 1907-15, aerial factory view, VG, A......................................**$8.00**

Iver Johnson Bicycle, pin-back button, Boy Scout in script on large center band, round, VG, A **$35.00**

Iver Johnson Firearms, catalog, 1922, pictures a soldier on front, with original mailing envelope, 16 pages, EX, A **$20.00**

Iver Johnson Truss Bridge Bicycle, sign, 1905, self-framed tin, image of bridge & bike surrounded by company name on frame, 26" dia, VG, A..............**$1,350.00**

Ivins Lunch-On-Thins, tin, encircled portrait & lettering on red above product, lettering on lid, hook closure & wire handle, 5½ x5", G-, D.............$45.00

Ivory Soap, sign, cardboard, little girl hanging doll clothes on clothes line, ...For The Toilet, It Floats, framed, 25x17", VG, A **$450.00**

Ivory Soap, sign, die-cut cardboard, creeping baby with bar of soap, matted & framed, image: 12x10½ ", VG, A **$50.00**

Ivory Soap, sign, paperboard litho, product name above girl looking upward, It Floats lettered on frame, 27½ x19½", VG, A **$350.00**

IW Harper's Whiskey, commemorative bottle, 1895, reverse glass label on ovoid flask picturing Grand Army of the Republic medal, 6", G+, A **$150.00**

IW Harper's Whiskey, sign, ca 1910, Vitrolite, cabin scene with bear skin, guns & dog, lettering on horns at top, 24x18", NM, A..**$660.00**

Izaak Walton League of America, sign, embossed tin, list of warnings for campers, hunters & fishermen over Indian, Attention!..., framed, image: 18x12", EX, A **$150.00**

J

J Chr G Hupfel Brg Co, tip tray, pictures brewery, with lettering around rim, Established 1854, minor rust, 5" dia, VG+, A...**$200.00**

J Devar & Sons Whiskey, print, cardboard, library setting with 2 Spaniards & bottles of Highland Whiskey, framed, 22¼x31¼", EX, A **$10.00**

J Hungerford Smith Co, tray, True Fruit Flavors Make Our Fountain..., round, G, D.......................................**$85.00**

J Krauss & Co Washing Machine Mfg, postcard, factory scene, train in foreground, minor creases, P3 ....**$35.00**

J Schriber & Co's Prairie Flower Chewing Tobacco, sign, tin, Indian princess with flowers, braves on horses beyond, framed, image: 20x28", G-, A **$900.00**

J Stevens & Co, letterhead, 1881, pictures a large brown revolver, VG, A...**$60.00**

J Stevens Arms & Tool Co, ad cover, 1905, pictures a rifle, attached sticker reads We Shall Exhibit...Auto Show, red border, edge wear, VG, A...............................**$90.00**

J Stevens Arms & Tool Co, ad cover, 1907, with enclosed letterhead, pictures a gathering of hunters, scarce, VG, A...**$110.00**

J Widman & Co Bohemian Beer, tray, deep-dish, stock image of girl holding bouquet of carnations, lettering on rim, 13" dia, VG, A **$295.00**

J Widman Brewery, match safe, nickel-plated brass, embossed elk, general wear, 2¾x1½", VG, A............................**$215.00**

J&C Green Marshmallows, tin, pictures buildings, rectangular with rounded corners, A **$40.00**

J&J Pattison & Co's Pure Confectionary, sign, paper, factory image with figures in the foreground, Spring Hill, Birmingham below, 23½x20", EX, A..................**$140.00**

J&P Coats Best Six Cord Spool Cotton, sign, embossed self-framed hardboard, gold letters above white spool on black, embellished frame, 30x18", EX, A **$300.00**

J&P Coats Spool Cotton, cabinet, oak, ribbed roll-top opens to reveal racks, 24x31x11", EX, A **$550.00**

J&P Coats Spool Cotton, cabinet, oak, spool shape with composition thread around middle, 4 drawers, 15x22x19½", VG+, A **$600.00**

J&P Coats Spool Cotton, cabinet, oak, 2-drawers with lettered inserts & brass knobs, 8½x21½x17", EX, A...**$500.00**

J&P Coats Spool Cotton, cabinet, revolving 4-sided oak with hinged panels in top, 22¾", VG, A..........**$1,250.00**

J&P Coats Spool Cotton, sign, paper on plaster backing, elegant woman watching man fishing in stream, framed, image: 17½x22", G, A............................**$195.00**

J&P Thread, trade card, ca 1885, Black boy on spool of thread, We Never Fade, 4½x3", EX, P1.................**$20.00**

JA Cigars, sign, porcelain, blue with Smoke in white above JA in gold outlined in white, Cigars in white below, EX, A...**$110.00**

JA Fraser Cattle Dealer, thermometer/barometer, wood, rounded top with advertising, square bottom lettered Veals & Hogs..., 3⅛x1½", EX, A **$70.00**

Jac Jic Soda, sign, tin flange, Drink Jac Jic on round background with red center & white border, 14x18", NM, M3 ....**$180.00**

Jack Daniel's Whiskey, mirror/thermometer, wood frame, 12x22", EX, D **$35.00**

Jack Daniel's Whiskey, rug, 18x27", EX, D **$12.00**

Jack Daniel's Whiskey, statue, white plaster of Paris, 12½", EX, D **$12.00**

Jack Daniel's Whiskey, swizzle stick, 1960s, white hard plastic, full-figure image of Jack Daniels on top of stick, 6½", EX, D **$12.00**

Jack Dempsey's Restaurant, Bar & Grill, matchbook cover, front shows photo of young Dempsey, reverse shows restaurant, 20 strike, front strike, NM, R1....**$8.50**

Jack Frost Sugar Co, doll, Jack Frost, stuffed cloth, blue & white with yellow hair, 17", EX, D.......................**$35.00**

Jack's, crate label, Washington apple, Jack's lettered in white on 4 large playing-card jacks, blue background, 9x11", EX, G1..**$5.00**

Jackie Boy, crate label, 1930s, California apple, red-haired boy in sailor suit, Sebastopol, 10½x9", M, C1......................**$4.00**

Jackie Coogan Kid Candy, pail, tin, yellow with black Jackie Coogan graphic, slip lid & bail, HD Foss & Co, 7-oz, VG, A...**$185.00**

Jackie Coogan Peanut Butter, pail, shows straight forward pose of young Jackie with Peanut Butter lettered above, slip lid & bail, 1-lb, A **$170.00**

Jackie Coogan Salted Nut Meats, tin, Jackie Coogan lettered above boy on elephant at left of Salted Nut Meats, Kelly Co, Cleveland, 11x8" dia, EX, A ..$275.00

Jackson's Best Chewing Tobacco, sign, paper, image of 2 men with plugs & money bag, Though Melancholy..., polka-dot border, 14x11", EX, A **$900.00**

Jackson's Best Chewing Tobacco, trade card, 2 unhappy gentlemen opens to show them healthy & wealthy, EX, A **$30.00**

Jacob Hoffman Brewery, sign, ca 1900, paper, vintage table setting with large bouquet of flowers, cigar & glass of beer, 31x21", EX, D **$110.00**

Jacob Ruppert Beer & Ale, sign, 1940s, tin, navy blue & red lettering on yellow & gray background, ...Famous For Flavor, 11¾x23½", G, A **$75.00**

Jacob Ruppert Knickerbocker Beer, pocket mirror, shows colonial gent standing next to large bottle of beer, lettering below, rectangular, 2¾", VG+, A... **$30.00**

Jacob Schmidt Brewing Co, sign, tin, factory image with busy street scene in foreground, rust/dents/scratches, framed, image: 28x40", G-, A **$600.00**

Jacob Schmidt Brewing Co, sign, tin, 3 hunters toasting to a successful hunt, minor fading/dents/rust spots, framed, image: 21x31", G, A **$300.00**

Jacobson Bros Ginger Ale, sign, cardboard, large bottle on red with Delicious! Try It, Jacobson Bros Lakewood NJ, white border, 24x9", NM, M3 .... **$28.00**

Jacobson Bros Wholesale Liquors, pocket mirror, old lady getting ready to spank child with belt, Are You Wet Or Dry?, oval, 2¾x1¾", EX, A **$260.00**

Jacques Flavoring Extracts, cabinet, reverse-painted glass in wood frame covered with nickel-plated metal, door opens in back, 35", VG+, A **$600.00**

Jacquet & Co Cognac, sign, cardboard, shows horse-drawn wagon loaded with cognac barrels, Champenois litho, Paris, 17x12½", VG, A **$20.00**

Jake Shaefer Havana Cigars, box label, lithographer's proof, early 1900s, portrait with billards scene behind, 10 colors, American Litho Co, EX, A **$300.00**

Jam-Boy Coffee, tin, boy at table enjoying bread & jam in oval on white with product name above & below, screw lid, 1-lb, EX+, A $310.00

Jam-Boy Coffee, tin, Jam-Boy lettered diagonally above seated man enjoying a cup of coffee, screw lid, round, 1-lb, EX, A **$110.00**

James Logan Cigars, pocket mirror, faded image encircled by If You Want To Catch Havana, Smoke James Logan 5¢ Cigar, 2¼" dia, VG+, A **$90.00**

James Parks, crate label, apple, white setter dog in forest, blue border, 10½x9", M, C1 .... **$4.00**

James Pyle's Pearline Cleanser, trade card, 3 girls in elegant dresses & bonnets individually die-cut to fold, full color, 3½x8", EX, D **$12.00**

James V Cardi Italo-American Bread Co, calendar, 1918, features bakery with baker serving customers, full pad, 21½x15", EX, A **$75.00**

Jameson Irish Whiskey, mirror, wood frame, 24x17½", EX, D **$20.00**

Jap Lily Talc, tin, Oriental lady, shaker top, A **$35.00**

Jap Rose Bath Soap, display with 5 boxes of soap, tin, center pictures Japanese children with bar of soap, Bubble Bath..., 14x18", EX, A **$950.00**

Japan Tea, umbrella, floral designs with circular insert of a mastiff dog, 40x60" dia, VG, A **$100.00**

Japanese Deep-Sea Crabmeat, recipe book, 66 recipes, 32 pages, EX, D **$5.00**

Japp's Hair Rejuvenator, sign, ca 1910, tin over cardboard, actual hair samples surrounded by advertising, HD Beach litho, 9¼x13¼", M, A **$130.00**

Jasmine Apricots, can label, pictures fruit & bouquet of flowers, EX, C3 .... **$15.00**

Java & Arabian Mogha Fresh Roasted Coffee, tin, non-pictorial, Montgomery Ward & Co, round screw lid, 8x7", NM, A **$148.00**

Javotte Cigars, box label, inner lid, pictures young woman surrounded by red floral border, 6x9", M, D $8.50

Jay-Bee Motor Oil, can, ca 1915, circular logo with product name above & below, silver on black ground, pour spout & handle, 5", EX, A **$100.00**

Jay-Bee's Cigars, box label, inner lid, pictures blue jay & beehive, 6x9", VG, C3 .... **$18.00**

Jayne's Expectorant & Tonic Vermifuge, sign, paper on paperboard, John Adams in oval, lettering above & below, worn edges/scratches, 28x14", G, A **$140.00**

JC Johnson & Co, sign, paper, caballeros lassoing steers surrounded by vignettes, Harness, Saddles, Leather..., framed, 24x30", G-, A **$2,500.00**

JC Lighthouse Eclipse Halters, sign, dated 1884, paper, horse's head surrounded by Black man, donkey, cow, factories & halters, framed, 20x25, NM, A **$450.00**
JC Penney, catalog, 1963, Spring/Summer, VG+, H2...**$30.00**
JC Penney, catalog, 1965 Christmas, VG, D............**$100.00**
JC Penney, catalog, 1967, VG, D **$25.00**
JC Penney, catalog, 1968, Fall/Winter, VG+, H2........**$25.00**
JC Penney, catalog, 1970, Christmas, VG+, H2..........**$75.00**
JC Penney, catalog, 1975, VG, D **$20.00**
JC Penney, premium book, scarce, D2 ....**$35.00**
JD Plow, pin-back button, plow shape, G, D **$40.00**
Jeep, sign, light-up, glass in tin frame, 2-sided, Jeep in white on blue above Parts-Service in white on red, 19x24", EX, A..**$170.00**
Jeep Willys Motors, mechanical pencil, pictures a red Jeep, EX, D **$20.00**
Jefferson Br'g & Malt'g Co's Lager Beer, sign, tin, jovial Shakespearean-type fellow with glass of beer, self-framed, 23½x17½", VG, A **$350.00**
Jell-O, matchbook covers, Jello Recipe series, man on scale, 20 strike, front strike, set of 9, NM, R1 ....**$2.00**
Jell-O, puppet, Mr Wiggle, soft red vinyl, comes with 2 sample boxes, scarce, 6", EX, A **$359.00**

Jell-O, recipe book, 1915, 'Jell-O & The Kewpies,' includes separate 4-page folder advertising ...Ice Cream Powder, 6x5", VG, A...........................$82.00
Jell-O, recipe book, 1925-26, 'New Jell-O Recipes,' 18 pages, EX, D..**$15.00**
Jell-O, recipe book, 1927, 'Through the Menu with Jell-O,' 20 pages, VG, D **$8.00**
Jell-O, recipe book, 1930, 'Quick Easy Wonder Dishes,' 23 pages, EX, D..**$12.00**
Jell-O, recipe book, 1930, 'The New Jell-O Book of Surprises,' 24 pages, G, D **$4.00**
Jell-O, recipe book, 1933, 'What Mrs Dewey Did with the New Jell-O,' 23 pages, VG, H1 ....**$8.00**
Jell-O, recipe book, 1937, Jack Benny & Mary Livingstone on cover, 23 pages, EX, D..................................**$35.00**
Jell-O, recipe book, 1963, 'Sweet Moments Desserts with Jell-O,' 44 pages, EX, D..**$3.50**
Jena Glass, door push plate, 1930s-40s, porcelain, light bulb above The Famous..., Quality Imports symbol below, 8x3", M, A..**$185.00**

Jenney Aero, pump sign, 1940s, porcelain, red, white & blue, ...Manufacturing Co, Boston Mass on blue border, 9x12", EX, A $210.00
Jergens Oriental Talc, tin, Oriental images on orange can, gold shaker top, VG+, M2 ....**$100.00**
Jergens Talcum Powder, tin, flat oval in gold tones with rose motif arched over oval inset with Jergens lettered diagonally, shaker top, EX, M2 ....**$100.00**
Jerome B Rice & Co Garden Seeds, print, 1895, 'The Flower Market,' 5 children picking flowers, advertising lower left, original frame, 17x23", EX, A **$205.00**
Jerome Flachat Gun Maker's, sign, paper, pictures 2 flintlock rifles & revolvers, matted & framed, 8x10½", EX, A...**$65.00**
Jersey Cream, dispenser, green & red lettering with gold highlights, original pump, 15", VG, A................**$550.00**
Jersey Cream, dispenser, green & red lettering with gold highlights, pump missing/minor discoloration, 11¾", G, A..**$425.00**
Jet-Oil Shoe Polish, display, die-cut cardboard, woman in real cloth dress holding box of shoe polish, 2-piece, 32½x10", VG, A **$175.00**
Jewel Coffee, jigsaw puzzle, man drinks coffee, wife & child hold coat at door, also shows manufacturing process, 10x13", EX, F1 ....**$35.00**
Jewelers Opticians, sign, reverse-painted glass, silver & gold leaf letters & decor, brass bound, 9½x28½", EX+, A..**$425.00**
JG Dill's Best Cut Plug, tin, elegant woman on oval inset at left of product name, slip lid, rounded corners, 4x6", EX, A **$21.00**
JG Dill's Lookout Tobacco, tin, encircled lighthouse, Rough & Ready..., product name above, oval slip lid on shoulder opening, rare, EX, A...........................**$600.00**
JH Friedenwald Wines & Liquors, shot glass, etched letters, Compliments...Baltimore Md, EX, D **$12.00**
JH Johnson Great Western Gun Works, catalog, 1888-89, black lettering on pink cover, engraved illustrations, 64 pages, EX, A **$150.00**
JI Case Threshing Machine Co, sign, embossed tin, pictures steam threshing machine, Side Crank, Traction..., framed, image: 13½x19½", VG, A **$2,750.00**
Jim Beam Whiskey, decanter, Regal China, in presentation case, A...**$20.00**

Jim Dandies Peanuts, tin, children playing baseball with product lettering above, checkered border top & bottom, pry lid, 10-lb, VG, A **$330.00**

Jim Hogg Cigars, sign, paper, pictures James Stephen Hogg, Govenor of Texas, New Govenor Size...Back To 5¢, 9x20", M, D..**$35.00**

Jimmy Murphy Cigars, box label, lithographer's proof, early 1900s, close-up of Mr Murphy smoking cigar, country scene beyond, EX, A...............................**$50.00**

JJ Newberry Co 5, 10 & 25 Cent Store, sign, reverse-painted lettering on crinkled mirror glass, from store in Stroudsburg Pa, framed, 12x48", EX, A..............**$385.00**

JL Taylor & Co Tailors, thermometer, wood, black on white, genie logo at left & above, company name at left & below, rounded top, 22", G, A **$20.00**

JM Childs & Co Agricultural Implements, trade card, lettered graphics, ...Hardware Specialties, 12 To 18 Fayette St, Utica NY, black & white, EX, A **$18.00**

JM Pratt & Co, blotter, 1943, pictures girl removing skirt, multicolored, unused, corner bent/eraser marks, 9x4", D...**$8.00**

JM Pratt & Co, blotter, 1947, pictures girl on motor scooter, multicolored, unused, light stain, 9x4", D..............**$8.00**

Jno C Stocker Brewer, calendar, 1900, girl behind fence surrounded by knotted rope, September sheet, framed, image: 22x16", G, A **$750.00**

Jno C Stocker Brewer, sign, paper, pictures twins with roses & feathered hats, decorative border, framed, image: 22x16", EX, A..**$675.00**

Jno Gund Brewing Co Extra Pale, label, pre-1920, logo upper left, G, A **$25.00**

Jo-An, lug box label, grapes, trumpeting elephant on red seal with white & green 3-D lettering, Stockton Pa, EX, G1..**$2.00**

Joan of Arc Brand Red Kidney Beans, thermometer, painted & stenciled wood, black lettering on white ground, minor paint flakes, 15", G, A..................**$35.00**

Jockey Cigars, box label, outer, jockey & horse jumping stream, 4½x4½", M, C3..**$7.00**

Jockey Club Beer, label, 1933-36, horse race scene, Miami Brewery Inc, U-type permit number, 12-oz, VG, A .**$20.00**

Joe Demarco, crate label, strawberry, bunch of strawberries on blue background, M, C3...........................**$18.00**

Joe Sammy's, crate label, Louisiana yams, Black youngster holding crate of yams, Sunset, 9x9", G1 ....**$4.00**

Johann Hoff's Malt Extract, sign, 1880s, pictures Harrison, Cleveland & Blaine with their wives, large bottle in backround, framed, 40x20", EX, D.....................**$435.00**

John Adams Cigars, label, John Adams arched above portrait flanked by Capitol building & homestead, lettering below, 6x9", EX, D..**$15.00**

John Arnold Brewery, tray, pictures angry bulldog, Lager, Beer & Porter lettered on rim, minor soiling/dents, 13¼x10¼", VG, A **$250.00**

John C Stocker Brewer, calendar, 1903, elegant woman seated in ornate gold chair, February sheet, framed, image: 19x14½", EX, A.......................................**$550.00**

John C Stocker Brewer, sign, oval image of 3 women in rowboat waiting for assistance, appears trimmed, framed, image: 17x22", VG, A **$625.00**

John Clark Jr & Co's Spool Cotton, sign, paper, spools of thread in arched design with medallions in center, Thos Russell..., framed, image: 28x22", G, A..............**$200.00**

John D Jr Hand Soap, tin, John D Jr arched above circle picturing boy, Hand Soap & 3-lb Size Can below, slip lid, 5", VG, A...**$25.00**

John Deere, calendar, 1955, wildlife book, full pad, G, D..**$35.00**

John Deere, catalog, 1948, features various parts, VG, D.**$25.00**

John Deere, lapel pin, 10k with 3 diamonds, pictures deer in profile, EX, D **$65.00**

John Deere, pin-back button, ca 1900, gold bust portrait on white background, blue lettering, EX, D.........**$18.00**

John Deere, pocket ledger, 1940, 70 pages with no writing, EX, D **$8.50**

John Deere, sign, neon, John Deere on green above Authorized Dealer flanked by tractor & deer on yellow, restored, 37x75", EX, D **$2,500.00**

John Deere, thermometer, 150th anniversary, G, D..**$45.00**

John Deere, tractor, die-cast metal with plastic tires, minor scratches, 8" long, VG, D...................................**$125.00**

John Deere, watch fob, brass, G, D **$25.00**

John Deere Farm Implements, sign, porcelain, yellow letters outlined in red on black, running deer logo in center, restored, 24x71", EX, A...........................**$575.00**

John Deere Quality Farm Equipment, sign, 1930-40, tin, product lettering in yellow on black above Clinton Tompkins... in black on yellow, framed, 48x72", EX, A...**$75.00**

John Deere Quality Farm Implements, sign, tin, deer logo on yellow with black lettering, Sold By Gray's Seed..., Sanford-Maine, 12x24", EX, A..................................**$85.00**

John E Bassett Sportsmen's Supplies, trade card, 1909-10, hunt scene flanked by text, game laws of Connecticut on reverse, black & red on buff, EX, A **$44.00**

John Finzer & Bro's Tobacco, clock, wood with raised letters, round glass face, Roman numerals, reverse-painted letters below, 30½", VG+, A $1,600.00

John Gund Brewing Co, sign, paper, oval image of girl with ribbon in her hair above carnations & beer bottles, matted, image: 47x20½", G, A **$350.00**

John Gund Brewing Co, see also Gund's

John Hancock Insurance, calendar, 1893, horse-drawn carriage with building beyond, full calendar, matted & framed, image: 12½x16", VG, A **$45.00**

John Hancock Life Insurance Co, calendar, 1902, company name & year above girl asleep beside large dog, 2 rows of months below, 10½x9½", EX, A **$185.00**

John Hauck Brewing Co, match safe, nickel-plated brass, embossed image of king holding goblet atop world globe, 2¾x1½", G, A **$65.00**

John Kazmaier Brewer, tray, stock image of tavern scene with monks playing cards, ...Altoona Pa on rim, oval, 16¾x13¾", G, A.. **$600.00**

John Kress Brewing Co, calendar, 1899, US fleet leaving for war in shield with eagle atop, framed with metal strips, full pad, 32x20", G, A.............................. **$700.00**

John Krider, Gun Maker, trade card, ca 1845, resting hunters & lettering surrounded by ornate vignettes, black & white, EX, A.. **$575.00**

John Krider Fishing Tackle, booklet, 1878, 'Price List of Fishing Tackle,' no illustrations, 12 pages, light crease, A.. **$28.00**

John Milton Cigars, box label, inner lid, 1908, pictures medieval man, 6x9", M, C3................................... **$35.00**

John Mundell & Co Solar Tip & Pansy Shoes for Children, trade card, little girl standing in front of fireplace, oval logo in lower right, early, scarce, VG, A **$16.00**

John P Squire & Co, jigsaw puzzle, 1899, shows different cuts of meat diagramed on graphic of pig, 7x11", EX, F1....... **$150.00**

John P Squire & Co, see also Squire's

John Preston Cocoa & Chocolate, sign, 1960s, paper, boxes in center, people using product above, factory vignettes below, framed, image: 24x18", G, A... **$800.00**

John Rinchy Wines, Liquor & Cigars, pocket mirror, can-can girl kicking leg before large wine bottle encircled by lettering, foxing, 2¼" dia, G, A........................ **$46.00**

John Roots Bitters, sign, ca 1870, stone litho, angel emerges from fountain above girl aiding sick man under tree, 27½x21½", NM, D......................... **$3,000.00**

John Ruskin Cigar, sign, paperboard, rider reaches from fleeing horse for box of cigars, flanked by Was 8¢ & Now 5¢, framed, 26x19, VG, A **$1,400.00**

John W Henney & Co Motor Vehicles, pocket mirror, pictures touring car, red & black lettering & numbers, rust spots, 3½" dia, D.. **$75.00**

John W Masury & Son House Paints, sign, tin litho, aerial view of train & 2 images of paint cans with company & product lettering, framed, 23x22", VG+, A...... **$1,320.00**

John W Masury & Son House Paints, see also Masury's

John Wieland's Bock Beer, label, 1933-50, ram's head in center, Pacific Brewing & Malting Co, Internal Revenue Tax Paid statement, 11-oz, EX, A **$23.00**

Johnson & Johnson Corn & Bunion Pads, box, 1900-20, wood with various colorful product advertising on large paper labels, some wear, 12½x10½", EX, A **$325.00**

Johnson & Johnson Dental Floss, tin, with contents, miniature, EX, D... **$20.00**

Johnson Gasoline, bridge score card, ca 1920, girl blowing bubbles with pipe as her dog watches, advertising inside, 5¾x4¼", EX, D... **$6.50**

Johnson's Baby Powder, sign, cardboard, baby on globe looking at can of product with moon & stars beyond, For Babies, framed, 22x14½", VG, A.................... **$80.00**

Johnson's Baby Powder, tin, pictures Johnson's baby, 9-oz, VG, D... **$14.50**

Johnson's Baby Powder, tin, 100th anniversary, 5¼x2½", EX, D... **$7.50**

Johnson's Factory Seconds, cigar box, wood, Tunis Johnson Cigar Co, Grand Rapids Mich, 4x12", EX, D.. $12.50

Johnson's Peacemaker Coffee, store bin, tin, cabin form with dog on porch, open door reveals 1915 calendar, hinged roof, 27½x24x18", VG, A......................... **$650.00**

Johnson's Red Cross Kidney Plaster/Belladonna Plaster, box, 1900-20, wood with paper labels, backview of couple at the beach, large hand with lettering, 9½x9", EX, A... **$325.00**

Johnson's Wax, tin, 1920s, colorful image of woman polishing a table, age spotting at bottom/minor lid wear, 2½" dia, VG, D **$18.00**

Johnson Smith Co, catalog, 1950, novelties, toys, etc, 496 pages, VG+, H2 .... **$50.00**

Johnston's Cold Fudge, display, blue-glazed ceramic jar, product name embossed in horizontal oval, flared bottom, no lid, 10x9" dia, EX, A **$75.00**

Johnston's Fluid Beef, trade card, elegant woman cooking, Indispensable In The Kitchen, Geo Brougham..., EX, A **$15.00**

Johnston's Hot Fudge, container, stoneware, electric, silver & black humidor shape, lettered red oval with black band, spoon included, EX, A **$100.00**

Johnston's Hot Fudge, store dispenser, aluminum with heavy pottery insert, Art Deco style graphics in red on silver, 12x8½" dia, EX, P2 .... **$125.00**

Jolly Pops 1¢ Suckers, vendor, painted metal, red with yellow & gold smiling sun on green label, black letters, triangular shape, 20", EX, A................................. **$80.00**

Jolly Roger, crate label, Florida citrus, wickedly smiling pirate with pirate's ship nearby, 9x9", M, C1.......... **$2.00**

Jolly Time Brand Pop Corn Salt, box, cardboard, round with stylized lettering & round logo on 2-color diagonal background, 2-lb, EX, A....................................**$10.00**

Jolly Time Hulless Pop Corn, can, Volumized lettered diagonally over bowl of popped corn with product name above & below, no top, 10-oz, NM, A **$42.00**

Jolly Time Hulless Pop Corn, pail, boy & girl on red bending over white 'bursting' image with Guaranteed To Pop in black, lid & bail, 1-lb, EX, A **$65.00**

Jones & White Artificial Teeth, trade card, ...Dentist's Materials, gives 4 locations below, black on orange, EX, A **$35.00**

Jones Quality Haps, display, painted hard rubber torso wearing 1-piece shirt & short, lettering on base, 24", EX, A **$210.00**

Jordan's Meat, display figure, 1930s, hard rubber pig in delivery hat & overalls carrying sales pad, 11", 6" base, dia, EX, A **$1,025.00**

Jos Divisek School of Music, sign, porcelain, Jos Divisek lettered on diagonal band above School of Music, 24x16", NM, S2 ....**$195.00**

Jos Doelger's Sons Lager Beer, sign, tin with die-cut top, Hofbrau gnome with beer stein surrounded by early hops decor, rare, 28x19½", EX, A **$1,000.00**

Jos Grim's Grand Central Hotel, trade card, vignette of man's growing beer belly from 4 months of drinking beer, black & white, EX, A **$34.00**

Jos Schlitz Brewing Co, tray, deep-dish, factory scene with street scene in foreground, oval inset of Mr Schlitz below, oval, 15x18", G-, A..................................**$75.00**

Jos Stoeckle Brewing Co, sign, self-framed tin, factory scene with 2 portrait insets of the founders in upper right, 25½x38", G-, A..**$185.00**

Jos Suffrin Clothier, match holder, embossed cast iron, Compliments Of... arched above high-top shoe for holding matches, 5½x4", EX, S5........................**$150.00**

Jos Yund & Son Furniture, trade card, product name & lettering in black & white superimposed over furniture vignettes in pink, EX, A **$44.00**

Joseph Hajicek Hutchinson Brewery, tray, interior scene with Grandpa telling a story, lettering on rim, rare, oval, 16½x13¾", EX, A...................................**$2,200.00**

Joseph Spiess Co, clicker, aluminum, pictures Santa, This Came From Toy-Town above, ...Elgin's Best Department Store below, EX, A......................................**$22.00**

Joshua Bixby Quarter & Half Fish Barrels, trade card, black lettering on white, EX, A **$18.00**

Joy Ice Cream Cone, doll, 1989, denim pants & red stockinette blouse with logo, yellow yarn hair with ponytails, 12", N1...**$12.00**

Joy Silver Streak Dual-Valve Rock Drills, watch fob, silver, product name on front, ...Makes Air Do More Work By Joy on back, EX, D **$15.00**

JP Hoeltgen Optometrist, clock, stained wood case with reverse-painted glass door with image of an eye, working, 33", EX, A **$1,350.00**

JP Privley's California Fruit & Pepsin Chewing Gum, cabinet, wood with reverse-painted curved glass front, gold lettering, 18½" long, EX, A **$575.00**

JR Hewitt Saddle Harness & Trunk Maker, sign, paper, pictures early frontier storefront, lettering above & below, minor creasing, framed, image: 14x10", EX...........**$150.00**

Ju'cy Orange, sign, 1947, pictures an orange beside product name above Fresh N' Frosty on wavy band, 8x18", NM, B1 ....**$8.00**

Ju-Vis Beef Tea, sign, porcelain, product name at left of cup of tea labeled A Breakfast Cup 1¢, Sold In Penny Packets, 9x20", VG, A **$145.00**

Judge Best Cigars, box label, inner lid, Judge Best lettered above judge with white hair & beard flanked by book & scroll, 6x9", EX, D.........................$25.00

Juicy Fruit, match holder, tin, oval portrait of the founder, The Man Juicy Fruit Made Famous, light pitting, 4¾", VG, A **$225.00**

Julep, sign, tin, bottle at left, Drink Julep, Six Delicious Flavors, minor scratches/dents, 19x27¼", VG, A **$105.00**

Juliet Perez Cigars, box label, end, sweet little girl in pink dress, M, C1 ....**$3.00**

Jumbo Flour, pocket mirror, 2 kids leaning against barrel, barrel end depicts elephant encircled by lettering, 1¾" dia, EX, A..**$950.00**

June Peas, can label, pictures crystal bowl of peas & red roses, Baltimore Md, M, C1....................................**$2.00**

Junge's Bread, door push plate, 1920s, porcelain, ...For Better Health, blue on yellow, 9½x4", EX, D **$55.00**

Just Suits Cut Plug, tin, round logo flanked by Cut Plug below Just Suits, slip lid, 4x6", EX, A....................**$50.00**

Just Suits Tobacco, sign, porcelain, die-cut pipe with lettering, 6½x16¼", VG, A.......................................**$400.00**

Just the Thing Brand Tobacco, box label, lad handing colonial gent product, lettering arched above, framed, image: 12½x6", M, A **$35.00**

Justice, crate label, 1940s, Florida citrus, statue of Lady Justice, Indian River lettered on moon, Vero Beach, 9x9", M, C3 ....**$4.00**

JWM Field's Champion Whiskey, sign, tin, elegant woman with tray, minor surface pitting, framed, image: 28x19½", EX, A **$10.50**

K

K&B Best Flour, thermometer, wood keyhole shape, K&B logo above, red, yellow & blue on white, flakes/discolored, 10½", G-, A **$15.00**

K&S Bock Brew, label, 1920-28, Kamm & Schellinger Co, L-type permit number, 12-oz, VG, A **$23.00**

K-O, crate label, Washington apple, boxing fist & arm punching out of black background, blue border, 9x11", EX, G1 .... **$10.00**

Kadee Cigarettes, pocket mirror, pictures a Turk on a camel with product name above, A Swell Turkish Smoke, 2⅛" dia, VG+, A **$170.00**

Kaffo Carbonated Coffee Beverage, pocket mirror, rider on galloping horse above product name, Anheuser-Busch Inc, horizontal oval, 2¾" long, VG, A **$30.00**

Kahlua, mirror, wood frame, 19x24", EX, D **$30.00**

Kaier Brewing Co, tray, girl standing cheek-to-cheek with horse, ...Beer, Ale & Porter on rim, oval, 16½x13½", VG, A **$150.00**

Kaier's Beer, sign, cardboard, pictures large Arabian horse, First Prize Winner, Brussels Belgium 1950, 20x16", EX, D **$40.00**

Kaier's Beer, tip tray, stock image of girl with flowers in her hair, Bottled & Pasteurized At Brewery below, 4¼" dia, G, A **$125.00**

Kaier's Beer, tray, pictures a baby surrounded by leaf border, ...Pasteurized At Brewery below, oval, chips/dents, 17x13½", G-, A **$380.00**

Kamm & Schellinger Brewing Co, sign, paper, lion utilizing bottle to climb on top of world globe, ...Challenge The World, framed, image: 32x22", EX, A **$425.00**

Kamm's Fine Beer, sign, cardboard stand-up, Fine Beer Since 1853 above couple in open horse-drawn coach, billowy sky beyond, 18x14", EX, A **$30.00**

Kamo Bird Seed, can label, 1923, mallard duck on water, G, C3 .... **$5.00**

Kanotex, gas globe, 1930s, porcelain with rippled body, product name in red superimposed over star logo, 13" dia, EX, A **$700.00**

Kanotex Oil, display, blimp shape, electrified with propelled fan at bottom, 40" long, VG, A **$600.00**

Kansas City Breweries, pocket mirror, 2 Dutch girls stand before house, Old Fashion Lager lettered on roof, text below, oval, 2¾", EX, A **$100.00**

Kansas Expansion Flour, pocket mirror, product name lettered over large sunflower, The Wichita Flour Mills Co..., 2¼" dia, G-, A **$10.00**

Kansas Expansion Flour, pocket mirror, product name lettered over large sunflower, The Wichita Flour Mills Co..., 2¼" dia, NM, A **$35.00**

Kar B Out Risoline, can, 1930-40, Tune-Up in script above 2 singing birds, red & yellow lettering on black ground, pry lid, 7½", EX, A **$15.00**

Karnak Cigarettes, sign, paperboard, girl in feathered hat & pack of Cork Tip cigarettes, lettering above & below, framed, 22x14", VG+, A **$375.00**

Karo Syrup, doll, 1930s, Karo Princess, painted composition, body is ear of corn covered by green husks, rare, 10½", VG, A **$1,152.00**

Karo Syrup, recipe book, 1933, 'Miracle of the Match,' 32 pages, EX, D **$8.00**

Karo Syrup, recipe book, 1937, '49 Ways to Enjoy Karo,' 30 pages, EX, D **$7.50**

Karpen Guaranteed Furniture, pocket mirror, product name on rectangular label encircled by months of the year, 2¼" dia, VG+, A **$10.00**

Kate Litters Candy Shop, pralines box, early, pictures Mammy, M, D2 .... **$50.00**

Kaweah Maid, label, 1920s, California lemon, Indian girl wearing turquoise beads, Lemon Cove Association, 9x12½", M, C1 .... **$4.00**

Kayo Chocolate Drink, menu board, metal, Kayo boy points to bottle, Tops In Taste...Real Chocolate Flavor above Specials Today, 28x14", EX, D **$125.00**

KC Baking Powder, grocer's want book, pictures the product in maroon & yellow, lined pages inside, 8x4", EX, D **$20.00**

KC Baking Powder, sign, cardboard, pictures Black chef & pancakes, with movable price wheels, A **$30.00**

KC Baking Powder, sign, tin, large KC left of Baking Powder, For Better Living lettered on banner below, lined edge, framed, 12x28", EX, A **$45.00**

Ked's Shoes, catalog, 1925, VG, D **$20.00**

Keebler, cap, cotton with elf embroidered on front, NM, P4 .... **$7.00**

Keebler, cookie jar, ceramic, Keebler elf in window of treehouse form with Keebler emblem, Haeger Pottery Co, EX+, A **$85.00**

Keebler, cookie jar, plastic, head of Ernie the Keebler elf, F&F Mold & Die Works, EX+, D **$95.00**

Keebler, mug, plastic, head of Ernie the Keebler elf, F&F Mold & Die Works, EX+, D **$18.00**

Keeley Brewing Co, tray, ca 1911, colonial men gathered at table in barroom, lettering on rim, rare, minor chips, 13" dia, VG, A $475.00

Keeley Stove Co, pin-back button, ca 1900, red & white with serial number in black, EX, D **$6.00**

Keeley Stove Co, toy skillet, cast iron, Keeley Stove Co... embossed in center, 3½x2⅝" dia, EX, H1 .... **$18.00**

Keen Kutter, ad cover, 1913, colorful logo at left, pictures tools on reverse, EX, A **$40.00**

Keen Kutter, clock, counter-top, red metal case with wrought-iron brackets, red, black & yellow logo on dial, 18" dia, EX, A **$500.00**

Keen Kutter, pin, ax shape, EX, A **$50.00**

Keen Kutter, pin-back button, red & yellow logo on buff, round, EX, A **$40.00**

Keen Kutter, razor, NMIB, A **$16.00**

Keen Kutter, sign, cardboard, scene with man shaving at left of advertising, large razor image & logo at right, 11x21", EX, A **$30.00**

Keen Kutter, sign, cardboard cutout logo in red with yellow & white letters, white border, 13x10", EX+, A **$30.00**

Keen Kutter Safety Razor, sign, ca 1918, paper, various razors & shaving kits with descriptions & prices, logo in center, 14x22", G-, A **$40.00**

Keen Kutter Tools, Cutlery & Mowers, sign, 1950s, paper, Headquarters For..., red, green, yellow & white, 15x43", EX, D **$12.00**

Keene Ice Skates, trade sign, nickel-plated cast iron, shaped as ice skate, 10x37½", VG, A.............. **$7,250.00**

Keene's Ice Cream, tray, wood-grain finish with simulated inlay of Chinese youth, American Art Works litho, 13¼x10½", VG, A **$45.00**

Keens Mustard, box, wood, stenciled advertising on outside, paper label on inside of flip-up lid, 4½x22x12", EX, M2.. **$45.00**

Keens Mustard, sign, cardboard, elderly couple searching for trolley fare, 25x19½", VG, A **$155.00**

Keens Mustard, tin, ornate lithographed panels featuring jester, serving girl, cook dressing roast..., octagonal, 8", EX+, D3 .... **$265.00**

Kego Beer, label, 1933-50, logo above product name, Superior Brewing Co, Internal Revenue Tax Paid statement, 12-oz, VG, A.. **$16.00**

Keil Keys, sign, 1930s, molded metal, 2-sided, red & cream with raised lettering, Keys Made..., minor soiling, 27½x11¾", A... **$150.00**

Keller's Superior Tablets, tin, 1930-40, gold & black lettering on red background, Utica Candy Co..., press lid, overall wear, 5-lb, 7x6" dia, A **$15.00**

Kellogg Co, baseball, 1970s, autographed with Tony's paw print, VG, D **$6.00**

Kellogg Co, blotter, product box next to bowl of flakes with sliced banana, NM, A.................................. **$18.00**

Kellogg Co, book, 'Story Book of Games,' 1931, G, D ... **$35.00**

Kellogg Co, book, 1934, 'Swimming & Diving,' softbound, 3 full-page ads for Kellogg's, 48 pages, minor surface/spine wear, EX, D **$12.00**

Kellogg Co, booklet, 1937, 'The Housewife's Year Book of Health & Homemaking,' 36 pages, EX, D **$10.00**

Kellogg Co, cereal spoon, 1983, stainless steel, Tony the Tiger's image at end of handle, M, A.................. **$21.00**

Kellogg Co, cookie jar, 1968, Tony the Tiger's head in hard plastic, 8x8x7", VG+, A **$92.00**

Kellogg Co, glow-in-the dark character figures, 1980, flexible plastic, commemorating 75th Anniversary, set of 8, 2½", EX, A.. **$48.00**

Kellogg Co, jigsaw puzzle, shows boy on skooter, 1933, G, A.... **$45.00**

Kellogg Co, pamphlet, Mother Goose stories, EX, D **$18.00**

Kellogg Co, pillow doll, 1969, Bingo (from Banana Splits), 14", EX, D **$60.00**

Kellogg Co, plaque, color transfer print on milk glass, side view of little girl holding cereal box, 5", G, A **$80.00**

Kellogg Co, recipe book, 1934, 'The Sunny Side of Life,' 32 pages, G, D... **$10.00**

Kellogg Co, store sign, shows variety pack, EX, D **$200.00**

Kellogg Co, watch set, 1982, features Kelloggs characters, Atlantis, M in EX box, D......................... $65.00

Kellogg's Corn Flakes, cereal box, 1973, ad for Mattel Miss America doll on front & back, full, D........... **$50.00**

Kellogg's Corn Flakes, display, die-cut cardboard, girl in blue & white gingham dress hugging stalk of corn, 45x22", G, A **$200.00**

Kellogg's Corn Flakes, lunch box, plastic, with thermos, NM, D... **$15.00**

Kellogg's Frosted Flakes, bowl & spoon, 1992, pictures Tony the Tiger & USA Olympic logos, NM, P4 ...... **$9.00**

Kellogg's Frosted Flakes, cereal bowl, 1981, plastic, Tony the Tiger, 5" dia, EX, D **$9.00**

Kellogg's Frosted Flakes, cereal box, 1977, with 3-D baseball card offer, full, EX, D.................................... **$35.00**

Kellogg's Frosted Flakes, doll, Tony the Tiger, printed cloth, 14", M, D **$20.00**

Kellogg's Frosted Flakes, postcard, pictures little girl & elephant sharing a box of cereal, I Eat It By The Trunk-Full Too above, small, EX, D............................... **$30.00**

Kellogg's Frosted Flakes, transistor radio, 1980, plastic, Tony the Tiger, 7", M, D **$30.00**

Kellogg's Fruit Loops, doll, 1964, Toucan Sam, 8½", EX, D... **$20.00**

Kellogg's Fruit Loops, push puppet, 1984, Toucan Sam, plastic, 4", M, D **$15.00**

Kellogg's Instant Coffee, jar, 4-oz, EX, D **$8.00**

Kellogg's Kaffee Hag Coffee, tin, 1930, Kellogg's Coffee above & below encircled Kaffee Hag logo, red & black on cream, key-wind lid, 4x5" dia, D **$70.00**

Kellogg's Pop-Tarts, bank, 1980, Milton the Toaster, plastic & paper, 5", M, D **$55.00**

Kellogg's Rice Krispies, bath toy, 1984, Snap! seated in rowboat, vinyl, Talbot Toys, M in EX box, A....... **$35.00**

Kellogg's Rice Krispies, blotter, pictures girl in swing & apple blossoms, lettering on side, multicolored, unused, 5½x3½", D **$6.00**

Kellogg's Rice Krispies, blotter, 1940s, images of Snap!, Crackle! & Pop! minor ink wear on back, 5½x3½", EX, D... **$22.00**

Kellogg's Rice Krispies, coloring book, 1978, '50 Years With Snap!, Crackle! & Pop!' uncolored, 11x8", M, D.......**$25.00**

Kellogg's Rice Krispies, doll, 1984, Snap!, plastic with jointed arms & legs, red hair, in package, 4½", M, D **$15.00**

Kellogg's Rice Krispies, ink blotter, 1930s, Snap!, Crackle!, Pop! playing drums beside cereal bowl, Vernon Grant art, 3½x5¼", EX, A...**$12.00**

Kellogg's Rice Krispies, postcard, 1933, mechanical, swing-out panels with different scenes of Snap! Crackle! & Pop!, 3½x5¼", VG, D **$10.00**

Kellogg's Rice Krispies, push puppet, 1984, Crackle! on red base, plastic, 4", M, D.....................................**$15.00**

Kellogg's Rice Krispies, refrigerator magnet, 1970s, shaped like cereal box, 4½x3", VG+, D.................**$3.00**

Kellogg's Rice Krispies, salt & pepper shakers, pottery, Snap! & Pop!, EX, P2...**$75.00**

Kellogg's Rice Krispies, squeeze toy, 1975, Crackle!, vinyl, 8", EX, D **$20.00**

Kellogg's Rice Krispies, store display box, 1960, Snap!, Crackle! & Pop! on front, N Rockwell illus of boy eating cereal on back, 20x14", EX, D..............................**$95.00**

Kellogg's Sugar Smacks, cereal box, 1970s, with Fairy Tale finger-puppet offer, full, D **$75.00**

Kellogg's Toasted Corn Flakes, pocket mirror, farm girl hugging corn stalks, The Sweetheart Of The Corn, cracked mirror, oval, 2¾x1¾", EX, A..............**$1,250.00**

Kellogg's Toasted Corn Flakes, sign, cardboard, product name in bold letters, Sweetheart Of The Corn in script below, framed, image: 19x24½", VG, A................**$25.00**

Kellogg's Toasted Corn Flakes, sign, tin flange, 2-sided, baby in carriage looking down at box of Kellogg's, Oh! Look Who's Here, EX, A..................................**$2,900.00**

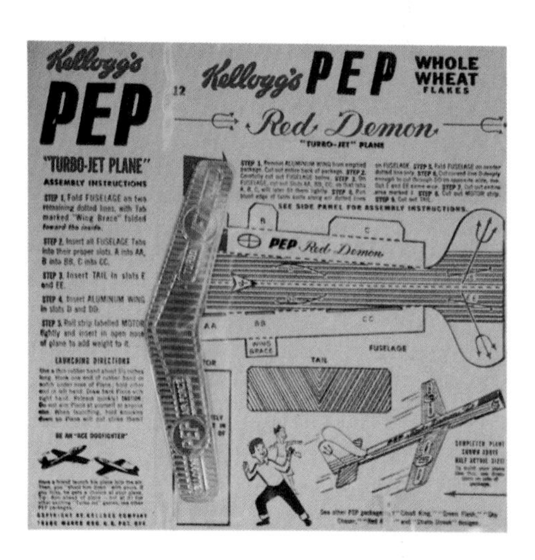

Kellogg's Whole Wheat Flakes, premium, metal wing attached to back of cereal box, Red Demon Turbo-Jet Plane, 1/6 in series, EX, D.........................$50.00

Kellogg Telephone, sign, ca 1902, paper, little girl holding telephone ear piece to puppy's ear, matted & framed, image: 19x12", EX, A..**$300.00**

Kelly Axe & Tool Co, sign, self-framed tin, travelers in Concord coach being being detained by tree, Waiting For A Kelly Axe, allover rust, A...........................**$50.00**

Kelly Nylon Tires, child's cup & saucer, china, features tire graphic on cup, EX, D...................................**$50.00**

Kelly's Aircore Tires, blotter, 1910s, pictures a tire, old car & train, 3½x6", EX, D **$4.00**

Kelly Springfield Tires, sign, 1954, metal, Springfield in script with Kelly above & Tires below, banded rim, oval, 22x36", EX, A..**$80.00**

Kelly Tires, sign, porcelain, Kelly Tires lettered around woman waving from touring car, encircled K on each side, 42" dia, EX, A **$8,500.00**

Kemp's Balsm, thermometer, wood, yellow & black on red, Kemp's Balsm above, For That Cough below, rounded top, touched up, 15", G-, A **$15.00**

Kemp's Nuts, dispenser, metal, glass front, electric, lettered top slants back, nut graphics on lighted cylinder, 21x32x22", EX, A.............................$55.00

Ken-L-Ration, cookie jar, plastic, head of Ken-L-Ration dog in yellow, F&F Mold Die Works, NM, D **$130.00**

Ken-L-Ration, salt & pepper shakers, plastic, black cat & yellow dog, F&F Mold & Die Co, M, D **$22.00**

Ken-L-Ration, sign, die-cut tin, dog's head above Feed Your Dog The Best, Ken-L-Ration, Ken-L-Biskit, Ken-L-Meal, 21x14", M, D...**$65.00**

Ken-L-Ration, sugar bowl & creamer, cat & dog figures, M, D...**$28.00**

Ken-L-Ration, thermometer, painted & stenciled tin, For Best Results! Feed Your Dog..., at left of thermometer, 26½", G+, A **$50.00**

Kendall Motor Oil, banner, 1930s-40s, red, black & white with oil can & Road Proven By Millions above Change Now..., EX+, A...**$100.00**

Kendall Motor Oil, can, 1915-25, pictures the refinery on red background, easy pour spout, scratches/soiling, 5-gal, 14" dia, A **$185.00**

Kendall Motor Oil, sign, painted tin, round 2-finger logo above Kendall lettered vertically, The Dealer Sign Of Quality, 72x12", NM, A **$50.00**

Kendall 2000 Mile Oil, clock, glass, metal frame, hand showing 2 fingers above Kendall The 2000 Mile Oil, 1-12, round, EX, D **$245.00**

Kendall 2000 Mile Oil, sign, die-cut tin, can shape, product name & logo encircled in center, cars on band at bottom, 20x12", M, D **$175.00**

endall 2000 Mile Oil, sign, 1930s, porcelain, 2-sided, 2-finger logo above product name, minor flaking overall, 36" dia, VG, A **$80.00**

ennedy's Chimmie Fadden Biscuit, sign, paper, arrogant Irish Bowery Boy in front of factory, New York Biscuit Co, framed, image: 20x14", VG, A **$900.00**

enneth's Beer, label, 1933-50, Kenneth Brewing Co, Internal Revenue Tax Paid statement, 64-oz, VG, A........**$55.00**

enny's Coffee, pocket mirror, coffee cup with family scene & Kenny's Coffee on cup rim, Always Satisfies on saucer, 2¾" long, EX, A **$180.00**

enny's Hotel Brand Coffee, tin, slip lid with small center wire handle, round, 5-lb, A **$60.00**

ent, cigarette lighter, 1950s, Zippo-type, enamel, 2¼x1½", EX, D **$8.00**

ent Club Beverages, display, cardboard, product name above lady with glass & mock bottle with base where real bottle goes, 33x21", VG, A **$25.00**

entucky Cardinal Apples, label, 1918, pictures cardinal on a branch & 3 large apples, Henry P Barret, 9½x11½", EX, D $45.00

entucky Club Tobacco, thermometer, tin, pipe in ashtray & pocket tin above product name, lettering below, rounded top & bottom, 39", VG, A **$45.00**

entucky Derby, tray, 1974, metal, 100th running, 13x21", EX, D..**$15.00**

entucky Fried Chicken, bank, Colonel Sanders, vinyl, 12½", P2..**$45.00**

entucky Fried Chicken, child's tea set, 1970s, plastic, MIB, P2 ....**$110.00**

entucky Fried Chicken, clock, pictures Colonel Sanders, square, G, D **$365.00**

entucky Fried Chicken, football, rubber, pictures Colonel Sanders, 12", M, D.................................**$15.00**

entucky Fried Chicken, jigsaw puzzle, 1954, shows bucket of chicken, We Fix Sunday Dinner Seven Days A Week..., original wrap, 9x7", M, A...................**$27.00**

Kentucky Fried Chicken, salt & pepper shakers, full figures of Colonel Sanders, M, P2 ....**$95.00**

err Glass, recipe book, 1935, 'Food Fashions of the Hour,' 32 pages, EX, D **$10.00**

Kessler's Whiskey, print, paper litho, 4-man racing scene with product name below, wood frame, 14½x18½", G+, A **$10.00**

Key West Select Cigars, box label, outer, tobacco leaf & key, 4½x4½", VG, C3 ....**$14.00**

Keystone Agricultural Implements, trade card, mechanical, Uncle Sam showing members of all nationalities 4 pieces of farm equipment, wheel spins, EX, A **$80.00**

Keystone Brewery, calendar, 1899, barmaid enticing fellow with beer, Otto Eyring above, February pad, framed, image: 30x15½", VG, A **$900.00**

Keystone Brewery, sign, paper, little girl with oil paints at easel with cat on pillow at her feet, framed, image: 19½x14½", VG, A **$3,475.00**

Keystone Brewery's Bock Beer, sign, paper, Bavarian maid with glass sitting on a barrel, Roehrich & Raab lettered above, framed, image: 27x19", EX, A.....**$1,650.00**

Keystone Ice Cream, sign, porcelain hanger, 2-sided, BW emblem flanked by Ice Cream, Keystone above, white on red, 20x28", EX, A..**$140.00**

Keystone Watch Case Co, watch fob, souvenir of 1893 Columbian Exposition, G, D................................**$40.00**

Kibbe's Peanut Butter, pail, product name & other lettering in oval center, yellow background, slip lid & bail, 1-lb, EX+, A **$110.00**

Kickapoo Indian Remedies, sign, paper, portrait of Chief Red Spear holding war feathers & axe, water spots/edge tears, 23½x17½", G, A **$2,400.00**

Kickapoo Indian Sagwa, display, die-cut cardboard, Indian offering medicinal product, Wonderful Liver, Stomach...Renovator, 69x40", G, A **$3,000.00**

Kickapoo Joy Juice, thermometer, tin, red on yellow, graphics above & below, rounded corners, scratches, 16", G+, A **$35.00**

Kiewel's Beer, label, 1933-36, logo with product name above & below, Kiewel Brewing Co, U-type permit number, 12-oz, G, A..**$5.00**

Kik Cola, door push plate, tin, white with red Kik Cola in shadowed letters, 'Le Cola Des Familles,' horizontal, 3x10", EX, M2 ....**$37.00**

Killdee, crate label, Florida citrus, cute killdeer wading in swamp, M, C1 ....**$3.00**

Kineo Stoves, Ranges & Furnaces, trade card, ice skating scene, Use...Noyes & Nutter Mfg Co, EX, A **$19.00**

King Aerator, sign, tin, The King Aerator in yellow above large yellow barn lettered The King System Of Ventilation..., 19x13", VG, M2.......................................**$125.00**

King Alfred Cigars, box label, inner lid, King Alfred in embossed gold letters above portrait of Saxon King of England, 6x9", EX, D...**$15.00**

King Arthur Flour, blotter, 1930, logo in upper left corner, green & red on white, 6x3½", D **$4.00**

King Arthur Flour, pocket mirror, pictures knight on prancing horse, product name arched above then encircled by belt, 2⅛" dia, EX, A..............................**$300.00**

King Bee Coffee, bin, wood with slanted hinged lid, black stenciled lettering on red, 32x16", EX, A **$468.00**

King Car, poster, 1920s-30s, touring car & lettering in center, ...No Regrets above, decorative border, 36x30", VG, A **$175.00**

King Carlos Cigars, box, King adorned with medal & gold, 5¾x7½x3¼", EX, D **$12.00**

King Carlos Cigars, box label, outer, King adorned with medals & gold, 4½x4½", M, D **$5.00**

King Cole Coffee, tin, pictures Old King Cole being served a pot of coffee, key-wind lid, minor scratches/soiling, 4¼x3" dia, EX, A **$150.00**

King Cole Tea, door push bar, tin, product name in black on yellow, 3x30", VG, M2....................................**$37.00**

King Cole Tea, door push plate, porcelain, white King Cole Tea diagonally above yellow You'll Like The Flavor on black, 11x3", NM, M2..............................**$170.00**

King Cole Tea & Coffee, door push bar, porcelain, King Cole lettered in black at left of red Tea above Coffee on yellow, EX, M2..**$50.00**

King Cotton Cigars, box label, inner lid, pictures 3 balls of cotton, 6x9", M, D **$3.00**

King David, crate label, 1930s, California orange, King with white beard, Yorba Orange Growers Assoc, Placentia, 10x11", M, C1..**$3.00**

King David, crate label, 1930s, California orange, park scene with waterfall & mountain stream, Ivanhoe Mutual Ass'n, 10x11", M, C1 ....**$8.00**

King Fisher Brand Coffee, tin, lettering above & below sunrise logo, slip lid & bail, 5-lb, EX, A...............**$85.00**

King Midas Flour, sign, 1920, paper, girl sitting on lettered fence with baseball scene beyond, matted & framed, 28x21", EX, D3 ....$950.00

King Oscar 5¢ Cigar, sign, paperboard, elegant girl carrying basket of flowers, Wolf & Co litho, matted & framed, 21x15", G, A..**$280.00**

King Pelican Lettuce, crate label, 1920s, crowned green pelican, Clarksburg Cal, 9x6", M, C3.......................**$3.00**

King Powder Co, sign, paper, 'Quick Shot,' pictures a downed mallard, framed, 24x17", VG, A...........**$500.00**

King's Cadets, crate label, 1930s, asparagus, marching soldiers in green coats, M, C3 ....**$2.00**

King's Quick Rising Flour, sign, paper, woman preparing hot cakes on wood cook stove with advertising inset lower left, linen-backed, 26x21", EX, A **$500.00**

King Syrup, ruler, wood, 12", G, D.............................**$4.00**

King Tut, crate label, 1920s, California lemon, Art Nouvea style with glass, sugar bowl & lemons, Santa Barbar 9x12½", M, C1..**$4.0**

Kingan & Co Finest Beef, Lard, Hams & Bacon, pock mirror, Reliable lettered diagonally over sailor at th helm, ham below, oval, 2¾", VG+, A **$60.0**

Kingan's Butterine, sign, paper, Black butler serves ma some butter as he says Mighty Good Butter Sam.. framed, 22¾x17¼", EX, A **$55.0**

Kingfish, crate label, 1930s, asparagus, large fish wear ing a crown leaping out of water, Sacramento Cal, M C1 ....**$1.5**

Kingnut Spread, pin-back button, 1930s, product name i yellow on blue & white background, EX, D **$4.0**

Kings Brewing Co, tip tray, barmaid serving product, le tered rim, oval, 6x4¼", EX, A **$45.0**

Kingsbury Picnic Beer, label, 1933-36, product nam above knight on horse, U-type permit #717, 64-oz, EX A...**$12.0**

Kipling Cut Plug, pocket tin, flat, portrait of the founder a right of Cut Plug, Kipling above, slip lid, EX, A...**$70.0**

Kips Bay Brewing Co, tray, deep-dish, boat laden wit barrels of beer in circular inset flanked by Ales & Porter, 13½" dia, VG+, A **$175.0**

Kirk's Jap Rose Talcum Powder, tin, pictures Orienta lady in circle with lettering above & below, shaker top some wear, A..**$50.0**

Kis-Me-Gum, jar, 8-sided, embossed lid, 10½x4½" square EX, A **$95.0**

Kissel's Garage, sign, 1930s, red tow truck on white in center, white lettering on blue, Delmar 9-2115... 22¼x17", EX, A $75.00

Kist Beverages, bill cap, 1940s, cloth, red & white with advertising on 3 panels, EX, D **$8.00**

Kist Beverages, bottle, 1940s, enameled label, with cap, 7-oz, EX, D...**$12.00**

Kist Beverages, bottle carrier, cardboard, head portraits flank handle, Did You Get Kist Today?, NM, B1....**$3.00**

Kist Beverages, calendar, 1947, lady seated enjoying Kis above full pad, 26x12", EX+, D **$75.00**

Kist Beverages, clock, ca 1931, painted wood case with glass lens, electric, numbers surround advertising, 15½x15½", G, A....................$45.00
Kist Beverages, decal, 1940s, peel & stick, pictures a bottle, Everybody Loves To Get..., 9x12", EX, D.......$16.00
Kist Beverages, decal, 1940s, peel & stick, red die-cut lips with white lettering, 7x15", EX, D....................$14.00
Kist Beverages, menu board, labeled bottle, G, D..$65.00
Kist Beverages, mirror, product logo & Get Kist Here lettered at bottom, 12" dia, EX+, A....................$35.00

Kist Beverages, sign, cardboard, dancing couple beyond girl with bottle & glass, Orange & Other..., Get Kist Here, 24x34", NM, A....................$280.00
Kist Beverages, sign, laminated masonite, sailor girl with bottle at helm, 18x13", NM, A....................$220.00
Kist Beverages, sign, 1940s, die-cut cardboard hanger, 2-sided Kist bottle, 10x3", NM, D....................$20.00
Kist Beverages, sign, 1940s, masonite, stand-up, 2 bottles on tray & Kist logo before girl seated with flower basket, 21x15", NM, D....................$120.00
Kist Beverages, soda jerk's hat, 1950s, paper, red on white, adjustable, EX, D....................$4.00
Kist Beverages, tray, sexy sailor girl next to large bottle on sailboat, plain rim, EX+, A....................$240.00
Kist Beverages, see also Orange Kist
Kittanning Beer, label, 1933-36, Elk Brewing Co, U-type permit number, 12-oz, EX, A....................$21.00
Kleeko Coffee, tin, pictures lettered cup of coffee, The Cup That Pleases, product name above & below, pry lid, EX+, A....................$125.00
Kleenex, display, 1950, 3-D cardboard stand-up, Little Lulu with box of Kleenex, hole in her hand to hold a tissue, 10x7", EX, D....................$20.00
Kleinert's Dress Shields, pocket mirror, I Wear Kleinert's Dress Shields below lady in circular inset with decorative border, 2⅛" dia, NM, A....................$34.00
Klicker Cola, bottle stopper, policeman with large stop sign saying Stop, Drink And Refresh above Klicker on the diagonal, 8x5", NM, A....................$4.00
Kling's Beer, stained glass window, red, blue, green & yellow with ...1911 Beer, Detroit Mich, original frame, 20x28", VG, A....................$575.00
Kling's Bock Beer, label, 1933-50, ram's head in center, Ph Kling Brewing Co, Internal Revenue Tax Paid statement, 12-oz, EX, A....................$16.00
Klondike Cough Nuggets, sign, paper, yellow on red, frontier girl bursts through sign holding product, ...5¢ For Sale Here, framed, 8x12", M, S5....................$585.00
Klosed Krotch Union Suits, pocket mirror, man working with knee on bench at right of advertising, SS Beck, Millersburg Pa below, 2⅛" dia, NM, A....................$43.00
Knapp's Root Beer, trade card, die-cut hand, How To Read The Lines Of The Hand, Compliments of... lettered on wrist, EX, A....................$32.00
Knapsack Matches, dispenser, 8-sided wood frame with lettered glass inserts & metal lid with slot, graphics on inserts, 11x10" dia, EX, A....................$550.00
Knight Cab Co, hat badge, blue & white enamel, pictures 1920s cab, 4x2¼", EX, D....................$185.00
Knouff's Hom-Aid Ice Cream, sign, painted tin, Knouff's in script with Hom-Aid printed on tail above Ice Cream right of sundae, 12x24", EX, A....................$35.00
Knox Gelatine, recipe book, 1915, 'Dainty Desserts for Dainty People,' 42 pages, EX, D....................$14.00
Knox Gelatine, recipe book, 1924, 'Dainty Desserts,' 41 pages, G, D....................$12.00
Knox Gelatine, recipe book, 1929, 'The Health Value of Knox Sparkling Gelatine,' 24 pages, EX, D..........$12.00
Knox Gelatine, recipe book, 1936, 'Desserts, Salads, Candies & Frozen Dishes,' 56 pages, EX, D....................$8.00
Knox Gelatine, recipe book, 1938, 'Knox Quickies,' 24 pages, EX, D....................$10.00
Knox Gelatine, recipe book, 1939, 'Be Fit Not Fat,' 22 pages, VG, D....................$6.00
Knox Gelatine, recipe book, 1952, 'Better Meals with Gel Cookery,' 27 pages, EX, D....................$6.50
Knox Gelatine, sign, cardboard, cute little girl lifting mold to reveal dessert, product box in foreground, 36x18", G-, A....................$275.00
Knox Knit Hosiery, pin-back button, ca 1900, multicolored world globe with green border, yellow lettering, EX, D....................$4.00
Ko Chela, crate label, 1940s, California grapefruit, grapefruit and shell, Coachella Valley, 10x12", M, C3....................$12.00
Kodak, lamp, 1970s, metal with plastic shade, red, amber & black stain glass motif with logo on shade, 17x8" dia, EX, D....................$35.00
Kodak Film, sign, die-cut tin, 2-sided hanger, red & black on yellow, protruding film box right of lettering, unused, 18x14", NM, M2....................$125.00
Kodak Instamatic Cameras, display, plastic, large Instamatic camera with revolving flash cube, 22x21x11", EX+, M2....................$150.00
Kodak Supplies, catalog, 1930, VG, D....................$25.00
Koehler's Lager Beer, label, 1933-50, Erie Brewing Co, Internal Revenue Tax Paid, 12-oz, G, A....................$11.00
Koesters Twin Bread, display, paper-wrapped metal, hanging loaf of bread with twin-girl logos & lettering on all 6 sides, 25" long, VG, A....................$175.00
Kohl's Superfine Steel Cut Coffee, tin, pictures steaming cup of coffee with lettering above & below, slip lid, round, 1-lb, EX, A....................$90.00

Kohler Medicine Co, handbill, 1890, 2-sided, comic scenes, One Night Cure on front, Kohler's Antidote on reverse, edge tear, 7x6", VG **$12.00**

Kohler Mfg Co, handbill, ca 1890, comical images of man before & after using product, One Night Corn Cure, 6x7", VG, H1 ....$14.50

Koko Chocolate, tin, Koko man waves at right of Koko, Hance Brothers & White above, The Best Chocolate, Beats The Dutch, 9½", VG, A **$100.00**

Kooba Cola, sign, tin, right-angled shape in blue with bottom red band, We Serve Kooba A Cola Drink 5¢, 8x10", NM, M3 ....**$40.00**

Kool Cigarettes, clock, glass with metal frame, Willy penguins flank circle lettered Kools Refresh Hour After Hour, round, EX, D...**$280.00**

Kool Cigarettes, display, tin, Willy & open packs of cigarettes, Snow Fresh...America's Most Refreshing Cigarettes, 8x7", VG+, D.................................$25.00

Kool Cigarettes, fan, 1937, die-cut cardboard with wooden handle, Willy the penguin with product, premiums on back, 10x8", VG, D...**$30.00**

Kool Cigarettes, lighter, cast-iron figure of Willy the penguin with hinged head lifting up to expose lighter, rare, EX, A **$382.00**

Kool Cigarettes, match holder, tin, back panel shows Willy the penguin left of Matches with blank price space, 8x7", EX, A **$16.00**

Kool Cigarettes, sign, paper, Switch From Hots To Kools above prancing Willy the penguin, product pack lower right, 15x10", NM, A **$10.00**

Kool-Aid, camping kit, 1960s, red case with small bottle inside, Kool-Aid man's face embossed on front, 9x5", EX, D **$15.00**

Kool-Aid, cups, Strawberry & Goofy Grape, F&F Plastics, 3" dia, NM, D **$20.00**

Kool-Aid, jump rope, Mr Kool-Aid handles, EX, D2..**$25.00**

Kool-Aid, mechanical bank, 1970s, plastic, red Kool-Aid pitcher on yellow base, 7", M, D $25.00

Kool-Aid, ramp walker, 1970s, Choo Choo Cherry, plastic, 3", M, D...**$35.00**

Kool-Aid, snow cone machine, Lanard Toys, NM, D **$10.00**

Koolmotor Bronze Gasoline, banner, cloth, service man tells man in car A Million Motors Built This New Gasoline, gas pump at left, 36x47", VG, A.................**$650.00**

Koppers Coal, pin-back button, 1930s-40s, purple, orange, black & white, EX, D **$4.00**

Koppitz Victory Beer, label, 1933-50, ambulance, Internal Revenue Tax Paid statement, 12-oz, G, A **$12.00**

Korbel Sec California Champagne, sign, self-framed tin, classical lady admiring cluster of grapes on vine left of bottle, 13x19", M, A...**$185.00**

Kostenbader Beer, sign, self-framed tin, girl in bonnet with red ribbon, lettering below, white spotting/minor fading, 19x9", G, A...**$410.00**

Kraft Cheese, recipe book, 1921, 'Cheese & Ways to Serve It,' 32 pages, EX, D **$12.00**

Kraft Kraylets, sign, die-cut tin pig, EX, D **$195.00**

Kraft Macaroni & Cheese, frisbee, white with logo, EX, D **$4.00**

Kraft Macaroni & Cheese, tin, 9x5x2¼", EX, D **$10.00**

(Front)

(Back)

Kraft Macaroni & Cheese, transistor radio, plastic, pictures dinosaurs & dinosaur-shaped macaroni on 1 side, Original on the other, 4x3", M, D $17.50

Kraft Malted Milk, container, aluminum, knob lid, minor dents in lid, otherwise EX, A..............................**$110.00**

Kraft-Phenix Cheese Corp, recipe book, 1933, 48 pages, EX, D...**$10.00**

Kreet Select Beer, label, 1933-50, Crete Brewery, Internal Revenue Tax Paid statement, 12-oz, VG, A..........**$29.00**

Kreuz-Spiel Cigars, box label, inner lid, featuring 5 card players smoking cigars, 6x9", M, C3 ....**$15.00**

Krogers Country Club Coffee, tin, key-wind lid, 1-lb, G, D...**$25.00**

Krokodil Restaurant, postcard, pictures waitress kissing a crocodile, German, NM, P3 ....**$35.00**

Krueger's Beer & Ale, foam scraper, red & white on blue, EX, D...**$15.00**

Kuco Talcum, tin, paper label, EX+, D...................**$150.00**

Kuebler-Stang Brewing Co, mug, hops decorated patriotic shield above company name, 5", EX, D............**$150.00**

Kwickwork Auto Enamel, display, celluloid over metal easel with flipping pages of sample colors of different body styles, 11", VG+, A.....................................**$303.00**

Kyanize Varnishes, pocket mirror, pictures happy & sad man, round, NM, D...**$35.00**

L

L&M Cigarettes, door push plate, Friendly Flavor above open pack, ...Your Taste (underlined) Comes Alive! below, EX+, A **$40.00**

L&M Cigarettes, lighter, metal flip-top with red & white L&M graphics, box shaped as pack of cigarettes, unused, M2 ....**$12.00**

L&M Cigarettes, sign, ca 1960, embossed die-cut tin, yellow & white on red with pack of cigarettes above lettering, 21x18½", EX, A **$25.00**

L&M Cigarettes, thermometer, 1920-40s, red, white & yellow with Reach For... above hand pulling cigarette from package, 13x6", G, A...................................**$35.00**

La Atractiva Cigars, box label, inner lid, 1870, woman holding dove, pastel colors, 6x9", M, C3 ....**$25.00**

La Campana Cigars, box label, outer, gold embossed design, 4½x4½", M, C3..**$2.00**

La Carita Cigars, box label, inner lid, pictures woman holding violets, 6x9", M, D **$5.00**

La Choy, recipe book, 1937, 'Art & Secrets of Chinese Cookery,' 16 pages, EX, D...................................**$5.00**

La Choy Chow Mein Noodles, can label, 1924, pictures Chinese dishes, EX, C3 ....**$12.00**

La Comporita Cigars, box label, inner lid, brunette holding pink rose, M, C1...**$3.00**

La Creole Hair Dressing, pocket mirror, head portraits of 3 ladies, lettered rim, Price Per Bottle $1.00 Retail, 1¾", EX, A...**$240.00**

La Flor de Lincoln Cigars, box label, inner lid, portrait of Abraham Lincoln & signature, 6x9", M, D **$25.00**

La Flora de Leandro Cigars, box label, inner lid, embossed & gilted cameo of Spanish gentleman surrounded by 6 coins & flowers, NM, H1 ....**$6.00**

La Floridan Cigars, box label, outer, 1909, nude woman hidden by daisies, 4½x4½", M, C3 ....**$22.00**

La Gloria de Cuba Cigars, box label, inner lid sample, 1880, lady's head with cigar box & roses before port, OL Schwencke & Co litho, EX, A.........................**$42.00**

La Grata Cigars, box label, inner lid, young woman with fan, 6x9", M, C3..**$10.00**

La Jean Hair Dressing, tin, man on 1 side & woman on the other, Glorified Hair Pomade..., gold, green & black, 3½" dia, EX, D..**$12.00**

La Marica Cigars, box label, inner lid, 1903, elegant woman holding sign, 6x9", M, C3.......................**$14.00**

La Meloda Cigars, box label, outer, woman in purple hat, 4½x4½", M, C3...**$4.00**

La Miretta Cigars, box label, inner lid, plantation scene & sweet-faced brunette, M, C1 ....**$3.00**

La Preferencia Cigar, sign, product name lettered lower left of lady in large hat, 30 Minutes In Havana lettered below, framed, 35x25", EX, A..........................$1,600.00

La Reflection Cigars, pocket mirror, woman resting at water's edge studies reflection, lettering above & below, oval, 2¾", long, VG, A **$140.00**

La Rosa Suprema, box label, outer, somber-faced brunette in lace mantilla, 4½x4½", M, C1 .... **$2.00**

La Sirene Cigars, box labels, inner & outer sample set, 1870s, lady is escorted down stairs, boating beyond, Heppenheimer & Maurer, EX, A **$77.00**

La Valdora Cigars, box label, outer, woman wearing a crown, purple background, 4½x4½", M, D **$10.00**

La Zoos Cigars, box label, inner lid, pictures 5 women in a boat on a lake, 6x9", M, D **$12.50**

Lactart Milk Acid, trade card, pictures milkmaid with cows, G, D **$4.00**

Ladies Home Journal, banner, cloth litho, pictures magazine with little girl on beach, Wild Money...44 Other Features, 10¢, 34x46½", EX, A **$110.00**

Lady Garcia Cigars, box label, outer, pictures a woman & colorful flowers, 4½x4½", M, D **$4.50**

Lady Helen Coffee, container, cardboard with metal pry lid & bottom, EX, D **$55.00**

Lady Luxury Perfume, label, 1910s, pictures lady & swan, 14x12", EX, D **$4.50**

Lady Mary Cigars, label, Lady Mary arched above woman in plumed hat, diagonal corners, 4x4", EX, D **$10.00**

Lafayette Cigars, box label, outer, French military man, 4½x4½", M, C3 .... **$6.00**

Laflin & Rand Infallible Smokeless, pin-back button, Laflin & Rand Infallible Smokeless lettered on flag within wreath, round, VG, A **$18.00**

Laflin & Rand Smokeless Powder, envelope, water hunt scene with hunter aiming rifle, scarce, VG, A **$190.00**

Laflin & Rand Smokeless Powder, sign, 1898, paper, hunter aiming rifle at game birds, framed, 13½x8½", VG, A **$250.00**

Laflin & Rand Smokeless Powder, trade card, 1902, barefoot boy with rifle & dead woodcock, Shot With..., minor soiling, framed, 13x8½", VG, A **$65.00**

Laird's Bloom of Youth, trade card, easel shaped with attached photo of Mary Anderson, Beautifies The Complexion..., EX, A **$32.00**

Lake Erie & Western Railroad, trade card, pictures man waiting for the train, lettering above & below, EX, A **$55.00**

Lake Ridge Brand Bartlett Pears, crate label, 1930s, mountain scene with lake & orchards, 2 large pears in foreground, Kelseyville, 7¼x11", M, C1 .... **$2.00**

Lakeside Grape Juice, tray, deep-dish, From Selected Grapes & Beverage Of Quality flank bottle & grape cluster, 13½" dia, EX, M1 .... **$380.00**

Lakewood Ginger Ale, sign, 1920s, cardboard, bottle flanked by Try It, Delicious above, 24x9", EX, D **$12.50**

Lallemand's Yeast, sign, tin, product image at left with Lallemand's Fresh Yeast For Health, Eat Two Cakes Daily, bordered, 6x9", EX, M2 .... **$28.00**

LaMas Fermosa Cigars, tin, shows little girl, EX+, D **$75.00**

Lamb's Head Beer, stained glass window, reverse-painted lamb's head logo with jewels & floral border, original frame, 21½x64", VG, A **$1,200.00**

Land O' Lakes Butter, bank, wood, G, D **$25.00**

Land O'Lakes Pasteurized Process Cheese, box, wood, red & black lettering, 2½x8", EX, D $8.50

Lander's Satin Candies, pail, children flying kites, playing with squirrel & jumping rope, press lid & bail, dents/scratches, 5¾", A **$50.00**

Lane Bryant, catalog, 1935, Spring/Summer, fashions for stout women, 74 pages, VG+, H2 .... **$40.00**

Lang's Red Cross Cough Drops, tin, lettering above Red Cross lady, slip lid, rectangular, A **$45.00**

Larkin Co, catalog, 1933, Spring/Summer, features general merchandise, 222 pages, VG+, H2 .... **$60.00**

Las Amantes Cigars, box label, outer, 2 lovers in garden, 4½x4½", M, C1 .... **$2.00**

Las Fuentes, crate label, 1920s, California lemon, fountain & orchards, Crocker-Sperry Co, 9x12", M, C3..... **$25.00**

Lash's Bitters, sign, wood with decal transfer on oak panel, woman with horse head, gold leaf letters, soiled, 20x14", VG, A **$350.00**

Lash's Root Beer, dispenser, lettered bulbous milk-glass jar on spigot that clamps on counter, 24", EX, A **$75.00**

Laub's Bread, door push bar, steel, Ask For Laub's Extra Fine Bread stenciled in blue on orange, 30" long, VG, A.. **$20.00**

Lauer Brewing Co, calendar, 1899, paper, girl with tray upheld serving 3 men, full pad, framed, image: 22½x17", EX, A **$900.00**

Lauer Brewing Co, calendar, 1905, factory scene above insert of Porter's Lake Hunting & Fishing Club, framed, image: 27x1/2x19½", G, A **$650.00**

Lauer Brewing Co, sign, paper, Victorian lass holding foaming glass in chariot drawn by charging rams, framed, image: 22x17", EX, A **$1,050.00**

Laurel Flour, cabinet photo, 1880s, baby wearing sign that reads My Mamma Uses Laurel Flour, VG+, D **$45.00**

Laurel Stoves, pocket mirror, pictures Lady Laurel holding loaf of bread, Something Different, Something Better, oval, 2¾", EX, A **$145.00**

Lautz Bro's & Co's Acme Soap, sign, paper, smiling man holding box of soap, minor edge loss/creasing, framed, 17½x21", VG, A **$200.00**

Lava Soap, pocket mirror, features bar of soap coming from box, 2⅛" dia, EX, A **$80.00**

Lava Soap, pocket mirror, features bar of soap coming from box, 2⅛" dia, G, A **$24.00**

Lava Soap, watch fob, celluloid, colorful image of Lava soap & box, EX, D **$26.00**

Lavine Washing Powder, sign, paper, elaborate woman bathing child, inset of factory & child in tub, floral border, framed, image: 12x9", EX, A **$400.00**

Lavine Washing Powder, trade card, 1880s, die-cut cat with product name on collar, 4½", EX, P1 .... **$12.50**

Lavine Washing Powder, trade card, 1880s, palette shape, shows an owl, Hartford Chemical Co, 4½", EX, P1.....**$12.50**

Laxol Castor Oil, tip tray, pictures product, G, D.....**$35.00**

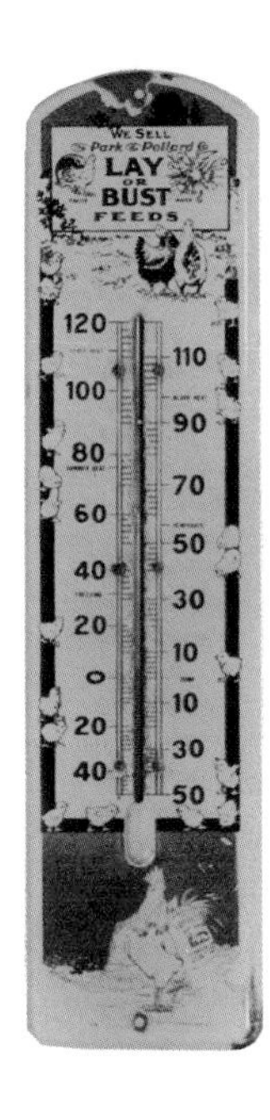

Lay or Bust Feeds, thermometer, porcelain, chickens above, below & around numbered bulb, We Sell... above, arched top, vertical, EX, M1 ....$785.00

Lazell's Unrivalled Perfumes, trade card, colonial couple in a landscape, EX, A...**$10.00**

LC Smith Guns, pocket catalog, game birds on & surrounding log on front cover, well illustrated, 16 pages, VG, A..**$80.00**

LC Smith Long Range Gun, brochure, 1930s, mallards in flight on front, 16 pages, pocket size, EX, A.......................**$45.00**

Le Page's Liquid Glue, counter sign, paperboard, colorful image of lady & oversized bottle of glue, Mends Everything, minor tear, 11x9", VG+, A.........................**$190.00**

Le Roy Little Cigar, sign, tin, Mexican caballero leaning on package of cigars, framed, image: 15x11", EX, A......**$400.00**

Lea & Perrins, recipe book, 1922, 'Seasons Suggestions,' 32 pages, EX, D..**$4.00**

Lea & Perrins, recipe book, 1932, 'Success in Seasoning,' 48 pages, VG, D..**$7.50**

Leary's Bock Beer, label, 1933-50, pictures ram's head, Waterbury Brewing Co, Internal Revenue Tax Paid statement, 12-oz, VG, A..**$26.00**

Lebanon Brewing Co, sign, reverse-painted glass, logo surrounded by hops & wheat, nickel-plated corner brackets, 24x16", EX, A..**$700.00**

Lee Rider Denim, banner, 30x72", N2.....................**$150.00**

Lee Tires, sign, ca 1960, embossed tin, product name in yellow shadowed with black, green ground with yellow border, 72x17", EX, A...**$25.00**

Lee Tires, sign, light-up, reverse-painted glass in metal case, Lee Tires in orange lettering on black, blue border, 8x32", EX, A..**$135.00**

Leech-Lube Motor Oil, can, 1935-45, yellow lettering on navy blue ground, 1-qt, 5½", EX, A **$20.00**

Leggat & Butler's Tobacco, label, elegant woman in circular inset surrounded by floral design, borders trimmed, 9½x12", VG, A...**$200.00**

Leggett's Java Coffee, tin, smaller round lid on red square can, 3-lb, tall, G, A...**$20.00**

Legion Beer, label, 1933-36, Fitger Brewing Co, U-type permit number, 12-oz, EX, A...............................**$15.00**

Lehigh Cement, calendar, 1923, Hendersonville Lumber Co above hunter with bird dog, full pad above The National Cement, 15x9", EX, A.............................**$31.00**

Lehigh Cement, calendar, 1923, Hendersonville Lumber Co above lady with open catalog in outdoor country scene, full pad, 15x9", VG+, A.............................**$20.00**

Leisy Brewing Co, tray, factory image with street scene in foreground, logo on decorative border, oval, 13½x16½", EX+, A...**$3,650.00**

Leitz Beer, tray, deep-dish, eagle logo, Brewers Since 1821... above & below, minor scratches/soiling, 13¼" dia, VG, A..**$125.00**

Lembeck & Betz Eagle Brewery, tray, ca 1911, maiden in red dress holding pink rose, lettering on rim, minor surface scratches, 13x10½", EX, A......................**$450.00**

Lembeck & Betz Eagle Brewing Co, sign, paper, jovial man crofting bottles of beer in Bavarian woodland scene, framed, image: 30x19", G, A................**$1,000.00**

Lemon-Crush, bottle label, 1920s, paper, 2 lemons above Lemon-Crush on diamond, 2⅔x4", NM, D............**$12.00**

Lemon-Julep, sign, tin, bottle left of Drink above Lemon-Julep, In Bottles below, framed, elongated horizontal rectangle, EX, A...**$55.00**

Lemp Beer, display, die-cut tin, Teddy Roosevelt in cavalry uniform with glass beside product stand, 13½x10", EX, A...**$3,750.00**

Lemp Beer, sign, 1930s-40s, die-cut tin, woman holding glass & beer bottle, minor dents, 19½", A.....$1,100.00

Lennox Furnace Co, bank, 1949, ceramic, Lennie Lennox with hand to ear, 7½", NM, D **$150.00**

Leon & Eddie's Restaurant, matchbook covers, ca 1940, panorama set of 10 that makes a picture when books are placed side-by-side, 20 strike, NM, R1............**$41.00**

Leon Levi Jewelers & Opticians, clock, stenciled tin face, black on white metal case, lettering surrounded by numbers, made by Sessions, 14½", VG, A...........**$30.00**

Lerner Newspaper, doll, Newsdog, cloth, EX, D.....**$15.00**

Let 'Em Rip Cigars, box label, outer, 1887, Rip Van Winkle about to take a drink, 4½x4½", EX, C3................**$30.00**

Let-Er-Go Cigars, box label, inner lid, Latin man smoking a cigar, 6x9", M, C3..**$20.00**

Levi's, banner, 1930s, denim, 36x60", M, N2...........**$650.00**

Levi's, doll, cloth, 9", EX, D.......................................**$10.00**

Levi's, statuette, cowboy, 36", M, N2.......................**$900.00**

Levi Strauss Overalls, blotter, 1939, full-color image of the Treasure Island Rodeo, 3½x8", EX, D.....................**$4.00**

Levison Steel Co, blotter, pictures girl with wind blowing her skirt, multicolored, unused, 9x4", D................**$8.00**

Levon, crate label, California melon, large snarly green-eyed lion, green background, 9x11¼", M, C1.........**$3.00**

Lewis Bergdoll Brewing Co, pocket mirror, celluloid, bust-length portrait of girl with long wavey hair, oval, 2¾x1¾", EX, A...**$85.00**

Libby, McNeill & Libby Corned Beef, calendar, 1905, little girl in front of pink flowers, corned beef can beside calendar below, 16½x11", G-, A...........$45.00

Libby, McNeill & Libby Corned Beef, pin-back button, for 1940 anniversary celebration, red, white & blue, EX, D...**$5.00**

Libby, McNeill & Libby Corned Beef, trade card, man & dog traveling through mountains, ...Is Valuable For Explorers & Travelers, EX, A...............................**$26.00**

Libby's Food Products, stickpin, ca 1900, die-cut brass, winged steer head, EX, D....................................**$12.00**

Liberal Life Insurance, pocket mirror, mother holding baby, lettered rim, If The Man On The Other Side..., broken mirror, oval, 2¾", VG, A..........................**$20.00**

Liberty Beer, tray, Princess in circle surrounded by Indian arrow & pipe motif, American Brew Co, Rochester NY, 12" dia, EX, A...**$300.00**

Liberty Flour, sign, cardboard hanger, 2-sided, Liberty arched above & Flour lettered over Statue of Liberty figure, 12" dia, EX, S5..**$75.00**

Liberty Lanterns, sign, ca 1918, die-cut cardboard, 2 sided, bell shape with brown & white lettering large tear, A..$50.0

Liberty Mills Vanity Self-Rising Flour, pocket mirro shows peacock with product name above & below oval, 2¾x1¾", EX, A..**$350.0**

Liberty Root Beer, dispenser, barrel shape with spigo front, decals of foaming mugs & sweaty man, overa wear, 27x16" dia, G, A..**$975.0**

Liberty Tie Cigars, box label, inner lid sample, 1905, patr otic bow tie above bell flanked by eagle emblem Schmidt & Co litho, M, A....................................**$22.0**

Lieberman's Lager Beer, tray, bust-length portrait of gi with long hair in circular inset, Old Style... on rin 13¼x13¼", G, A..**$325.0**

Life Cereal, store display, 1982, cardboard, pictures Mikey 15½x11", EX, D..**$15.0**

Life Cigarettes, door pull plate, tin, Pull lettered above Lif cigarette pack, Filters Best below, rounded corners 9x3", NM, M2..**$18.0**

Life Savers, display, metal, 3-tiered slanted front with large white Life Saver on marquee, allover adver tising, 14x15", EX, A..................................$1,000.0

Life Savers, display, metal, 4 tiers with various flavors of Life Savers across front, 10x30x13½", EX, A....................**$35.00**

Life Savers, display, metal, 5 slanted shelves on base advertising all the flavors, 12x29¾x27", EX, A **$25.00**

Life Savers, display, metal box with end of box & marquee featuring 4 5-Cent flavors, 9x13", EX, A.............**$100.00**

Life Savers, sign, 1920s-30s, porcelain, open pack of Pep-O-Mints on red, After Eating above, Aid Digestion below, 18x8½", NM, A $2,400.00

Life Savers, vendor, ca 1920s, metal, 5 column, revolving, round base, 12½x7½" dia, G, A............................**$75.00**

Lifebuoy Soap, pin-back button, 1920s, red, white & yellow, EX, D **$4.00**

Lifebuoy Soap, sign, die-cut cardboard hanger, 2-sided, old seaman holding round white life preserver with advertising, 16", VG, A.......................................**$500.00**

Lifebuoy Soap, sign, tin, old seaman with head through life preserver in upper right corner with 5¢ advertising on yellow, 6x14, VG, A..**$85.00**

Lifsey's Vim-Herb, thermometer, stenciled metal, blue & red on yellow, product above, lettering at right & below, keyhole shape, 15", G-, A **$20.00**

Lift Cola, sign, tin, Drink in red script above green rays emitting from bottle, It's Good For You in script below, 9x7", NM, M3..**$125.00**

Light House Table Salt, can label, 1923, light shining out to clipper ship, EX, C3...**$15.00**

Lighthouse Cleanser, pin-back button, 1920s, multicolored canister on dark blue background, EX, D ...**$48.00**

Like Diet Drink, see 7-Up

Lilly Brand Pickles, trade card, Victorian picnic scene with pickle jars in lower corners, EX, A.......................**$16.00**

Lilly Corn Starch, trade card, couple with marital difficulties because her cakes are so bad opens to happy couple at table, EX, A **$30.00**

Lilly Pharmaceutical Products, light, 1930s, electric, green & red lettering on green background, Prescription Department..., 11½x30", EX, A......................**$70.00**

Lilly Pharmaceuticals & Biologicals, sign, metal, bordered with bowed top, reads Prescription Department with company name below, 11x30x5", EX, A **$10.00**

Lilly White Bias Fold Tape, display box, metal, slanted 2-tier, gold with black lettering on cream front panel, Extra Fine Quality, 8x15x8", EX, A.......................**$25.00**

Lily Sodas, cracker box, tin, ...Sawyer Biscuit Co, Chicago on red & white striped background, chips/dents, 7x9", VG, D $47.50

Lily White Flour, pocket mirror, 2 young bakers with plate of biscuits, The Flour The Best Cooks Use, worn, horizontal oval, 2¾", VG, A......................................**$110.00**

Lily White Flour, trade card, pictures children playing with kittens, EX, D..**$3.00**

Lime Cola, sign, tin, red on yellow, Drink Lime Cola, Double Size 5¢, 3x20", NM, M3..................................**$40.00**

Lime Kiln Club Tobacco, label, Black men in court session, JJ Bagley & Co, minor overall soiling, 10x13", EX, A..$400.00

Lime Kiln Club Tobacco, sign, 1892, paper, Black men in court session, Calvert Co litho, framed, image: 24x30", EX, A **$800.00**

Lime Squeeze, sign, 1920s, tin, bottle at left of Lime above Drink above Squeeze, 10x28", G+, D **$75.00**

Lime-Away, doll, 1990, white plush kitten, 10", M, N1 ....**$10.00**

Lime-Crush, sign, embossed tin, Drink lettered downward on the diagonal left of Lime- above Crush, 14x19½", G-, A..**$55.00**

Limoneira, crate label, California lemon, white lettering on red background, Santa Paula, 9x12", EX, G1..........**$2.00**

Lincoln, crate label, California orange, orange & blossoms on twig, bright blue background, Lincoln, 10x11", EX, G1..**$15.00**

Lincoln Leonard Co, catalog, 1915, engraved illustrations of tables, couches, chairs, ice boxes, etc, 88 pages, EX, D..**$16.00**

Lincoln Shock Absorber, sign, 1915-25, tin, Lincoln Shock Absorber Snubs The Rub above & left of product image, For All Cars, 24x18", VG, A....................**$180.00**

Lincoln-Zephyr, sign, white Lincoln-Zephyr on blue panel with red horizontal tubing above & below, rounded ends, restored, 14x72", EX, D **$1,600.00**

Link-Belt Speeder, watch fob, brass, pictures shovel & crane, Builders Of The Most Complete Line Of Shovel... on back, EX, D..**$22.50**

Lion Brand Salted Peanuts, tin, diagonal navy & yellow logo on red featuring encircled lion's head in center, pry lid, 10-lb, EX, D3...**$295.00**

Lion Brand Shirts, Collars & Cuffs, display case, wood & glass with reverse-painted sign at top, 66", VG, A...**$750.00**

Lion Brewery, calendar, 1908, lion with front paws on barrel surrounded by factory insets, no pad, framed, image: 16½x13", EX, A.......................................**$220.00**

Lion Brewery Pilsener Beer, sign, reverse-painted glass, lion with front paws on barrel, Pilsener Beer below, framed, oval, M, D3 ....$1,600.00

Lion Coffee, pocket mirror, pictures lion holding product surrounded by lettering, Good Times To Those Who Sell, 2⅛" dia, G+, A...**$225.00**

Lion Coffee, sign, paper, dainty little girl at window surrounded by Easter lilies, minor crease, framed, image: 20x18", G, A **$150.00**

Lion Coffee, sign, paper, lettering above & below girl seated on hearth, Christmas Cards, One In Every Package Of..., 31x22", EX, A **$575.00**

Lion Coffee Co, trade card, 1893, pictures 3 children & cart, Knapp litho, 5¼x7", EX, D $7.50

Lion Gasoline, globe, milk glass with black & orange insets picturing a lion, 17x15", EX+, A...............**$425.00**

Lion Hats, sign, 1950s, cardboard stand-up, pictures a skier, 11x21", G, D **$15.00**

Lion Lager, label, 1933-36, lion's head in center, Lion Brewery Inc, U-type permit number, 12-oz, EX, A..........**$10.00**

Lion Shoe, pocket mirror, gentleman walks dog on leash, The Lion Shoe, It's Up To You, For Sale By..., oval, 2¾", NM, A..**$40.00**

Lipton's Instant Cocoa, sign, ca 1915, tin, woman at table with cocoa pot & mug, 13¼x9", EX, A **$400.00**

Lipton's Instant Cocoa, sign, tin, lady serves herself cocoa & cookies on black ground, box of product lower left, beveled edge, 13x9", EX+, A........$450.00

Lipton's Teas, calendar, 1901, embossed paper, girl with cup of tea surrounded by months, floral ground, framed, image: 12x10", EX, A...............................**$55.00**

Lipton's Teas, sign, paperboard, women of the world in rising steam, Have You Enjoyed Them..., matted & framed, 21x14", VG, A **$450.00**

Lipton Tea, mug, ceramic, red & yellow logo, EX, D . **$4.00**

Lipton Tea, tin, pictures tea pickers & buffalo, 5x4x4", EX, D **$75.00**

Lipton Tea Bags, needle book, no needles, VG, D **$2.50**

Liquidine Automobile Paint, display, composition frame of early auto encloses paint strips, Yarnell Paint Co, with sample paint can, 12", EX, A **$468.00**

Lisco Lager Beer, label, 1933-36, Humboldt Brewing Co, U-type permit number, 11-oz, G, A **$20.00**

Lisk Wash Boilers, tin boiler, paper label with woman & ...Hook On The Sink, Prevents Slipping, wood handles, 16x26", G, A **$75.00**

Lister's Jellies, thermometer, painted wood, red & green on white, product & lettering above, lettering below, arched top, 24", VG, A **$70.00**

Listerine Prophylactic, toothbrush holder, die-cut metal figure of young boy with product name on his shirt, minor scratches, 6", VG, A **$110.00**

Listers Animal Bone Fertilizers, calendar, 1898, Dutch farm scene, full pad, framed, 29x18½", EX, A ...$175.00

Lithia Beer, sign, 1910s, curved porcelain, Lithia in script above diamond logo, black ground, 14x20", EX, D **$395.00**

Lithia Christmas Beer, bottle, long neck, paper label, EX, D **$8.00**

Little African Cigars, box label, outer, alligator chasing a Black baby, 4½x4½", M, D **$25.00**

Little Badger Pop Corn, can, badger on popped corn in oval graphics with product name above, company name below, push top, EX, A **$200.00**

Little Bobbie Cigar, sign, cardboard hanger, ...Awarded Gold Medal, Panama Pacific Internatinal Expo... within hops motif, 10" dia, NM, B1 .... **$10.00**

Little Bobbie Cigar, sign, paper hanger, pictures Scottish boy with box of cigars, scenic background, Always Pleasing...5¢, 11x9", NM, B1 .... **$35.00**

Little Bobbie Cigars, tin, bust portrait above product name & 5¢ on yellow ground, slip lid, 4½x3x3", EX+, A.......... **$48.00**

Little Caesars Pizza, doll, 1990, Pizza-Pizza Man holding slice of pizza, plush, EX, P4 .... **$5.00**

Little Caesars Pizza/Coca-Cola, picnic jug, pictures Pizza Pizza Man & Coke emblems, EX+, P4.................... **$5.00**

Little Debbie Snack Cakes, doll, porcelain, MIB, D. **$40.00**

Little Edmund Cigars, box label, inner lid, 1904, photo of boy on steps smoking a cigar, 6x9", M, C3 .... **$12.00**

Little Ford Cigar, box label, ca 1929, pictures early touring car, R Sonnemann Co, Neenah Wis, black on gray, 4x5½", EX, P1 .... **$12.50**

Little Giant, pump sign, porcelain, globe behind man flexing muscles atop banner reading Little Giant, 10½" dia, EX, A **$160.00**

Little Imps, candy dispenser, devilish face surrounded by lettering, All Who Breathe, 1½" dia, EX, A **$50.00**

Little Warrior Plastic Quick-Bands, tin, product name above blond boy & girl dressed as Indians with colorful bandages at right, Rexall, 4x3x1", EX, D **$12.00**

Liz Cigars, sign, embossed tin, comic strip characters & Palmer Cox Brownies, M Foster & Co Makers..., 9½x13½", VG, A **$3,500.00**

LL Bean, catalog, 1949, features outdoor sporting equipment, 88 pages, EX, D **$24.00**

LL Bean, catalog cover, Fall 1939, hunter aiming rifle with dead bobcat on his back, with original mailing envelope, EX, A.. **$25.00**

Lock Brand Fine Teas, tin, brown, gold & black, Fine Teas above Lock Brand lettered on heart-shaped lock with fancy graphics, 9x7x5", G-, M2............................. **$22.00**

Lodge Spark Plugs, sign, painted tin, 3 horizontal bands with We Fit Lodge Spark Plugs at right of large spark plug image, 12x18", VG, A **$60.00**

Log Cabin Smoking Tobacco, label, Black man sitting in front of cabin, Old Virginia..., borders trimmed, 8x13½", EX, A **$800.00**

Log Cabin Syrup, see Towle's Log Cabin Syrup

London Life Cigarettes, sign, tin, cricket players gathered under awning with product name & 100% Pure Turkish Tobacco..., framed, 38x28", EX, A....................... **$800.00**

London Sherbet Tobacco, pocket tin, upright, product name above ornate logo & graphics, Falk Tobacco Co, EX+, A **$275.00**

Londonderry Lithia Water, sign/blotter holder, tin, product bottle at left of lettering on white shaded background, 4x8", EX+, M2 .... **$45.00**

Lone Star Beer, ashtray, white with gold lettering, triangular, 4½", D **$9.50**

Lone Star Beer, clock, plastic light-up, bottle shape, round clock face flanked by Cold Beer, NM, D **$165.00**

Long Bell Lumber Co, catalog, 1928, features lawn equipment, 36 pages, EX, D **$16.00**

Long Life Motor Oil, can, 1935-45, airplane with cloud in background, product name below, pour spout & handle, 2-gal, 10½", EX, A **$210.00**

Longman & Martinez Prepared Paints, sign, paperboard, colorful vignettes picturing Victorian homes & paint samples, wood frame, 29x28", G+, A................. **$525.00**

Longwood Plantation Syrup, sample tin, M, D....... **$15.00**

Loose-Wiles Co, pin-back button, ca 1900, red, white & blue, EX, D **$8.00**

Lord Baltimore Cigar, sign, 1930s, cardboard, cigar with long ash, Tastes Good below, 7x13", EX, D............**$12.00**

Lord Brown Cigars, box label, inner lid, man in red coat reading a book, 6x9", M, C3..................................**$6.00**

Lord Calvert, pitcher, embossed pottery, brown, Canadian, square, D **$15.00**

Lord Maxwell Ginger Ale, sign, 1940s, embossed tin, To-Days Best Buy above diagonal band with product name, America's Finest below, 13x23", NM, D.....**$75.00**

Lorelei Beer, sign, night scene with bare-chested nymph peering over cliff, Kessler Brewing Co, matted & framed, image: 20x14", G, A $400.00

Lorenz Schmidt's Estate Mt Carbon Brewery, calendar, 1897, paper, girl with dog at her feet, December sheet only, framed, image: 19½x15", G-, A.................**$350.00**

Lorillard's Climax Plug, sign, porcelain, man in white rolling red ball lettered with product name, Push It Along, black ground, 30x30", VG, A..................**$310.00**

Lorillard's Tiger Fine Cut Tobacco, sign, embossed tin, fierce tiger on yellow with lettering above & below, 2 Ounces-5¢, red line border, 10x14", VG, A........**$425.00**

Lorillard Tobacco, display case, wood with incised lettering, etched glass front, 26x39", EX, A................**$495.00**

Lorillard Tobacco, see also P Lorillard

Los Angeles Brewing Co, tip tray, pictures brewery with company name & The Home Of East Side Beer lettered on rim, 5" dia, EX, A..**$250.00**

Los Angeles Brewing Co, tray, factory scene with horse-drawn barrel wagon in foreground, ...Home Of East Side Beer on rim, 13¼" dia, G, A.......................**$550.00**

Lotos Export, pocket mirror, pictures large beer bottle flanked by lettering, Adam Scheidt Brewing Co, some wear, oval, 2¾", VG+, A **$40.00**

Lotta Cola, sign, paper, 16 Ounces on red panel above girl looking up at large tilted bottle, Lotta Cola below, 14x10", NM, M3..**$15.00**

Louis Bergdoll Brewing Co, calendar, 1898, Bavarian couple on royal carpet flanked by men with flagons, full pad, framed, image: 27x20", VG, A **$1,000.00**

Louis Brand Peanut Butter, pail, pictures girl in oval inset with product & company name above & below, 5x5" diameter, G, A **$150.00**

Louis Dobbelmann's Golden Leaf Navy Cut Tobacco, tin, rectangular with rounded corners, EX+, A.....**$70.00**

Louis Obert Brewery, tray, portrait of the founder on oval inset above factory scene, lettering on rim, chips/hairlines, 12" dia, VG, A.....................$450.00

Louisiana Perique Falk Tobacco, pocket tin, upright, black and gold paper-label, slip lid, EX+, A.......................**$125.00**

Louisville Slugger Bats, sign, ca 1953, paper, baseball bat surrounded by portrait vignettes of Mickey Mantle, Yogi Berra, etc, 17x11", EX, A..............................**$96.00**

Love & Beauty Cigars, box label, inner lid sample, 1880s, cherub sitting on nymph's lap, Louis E Neuman & Co litho, EX, A **$99.00**

Love Among the Roses Tobacco, label, bare-breasted woman emerging from floral bouquet, Smoke..., borders trimmed, 8½x13½", VG, A..........................**$400.00**

Love Nest Candy Bar, sign, embossed tin, Love Nest in bold letters above Best Eating Candy Bar In The World, 5¢, 10x28", VG, A **$85.00**

Love Nest Coffee, tin, key-wind lid, unopened, 1-lb, D...**$45.00**

Love Tobacco, trade card, Confederate soldier trades his tobacco for coffee, with Union soldier, Myer's Bros & Co, NM, S5...**$100.00**

Lovell & Covel Co, pail, Jack of Hearts stealing some tarts, slip lid & bail, 3-oz, 3x3" dia, VG, A...............................**$120.00**

Lovell & Covel Co, pail, colorful image of Peter Cottontail stealing pail of candy from cottage, slip lid & bail, 3-oz, 3x3" dia, EX, A **$185.00**

Lovell & Covel Co, pail, Pennsylvania historic landmarks, slip lid & bail, 3-oz, 3x3" dia, VG, A..**$150.00**

Low's Groceries, sign, wood, The Spot To Buy above Low's Groceries in red & silver with black sand paint, framed, 20½x26", VG, A **$130.00**

Lowell Fertilizer Co, calendar, 1914, paper, girl seated in profile with bouquet of roses, full pad, framed, image: 21½x14½", EX, A **$95.00**

Lower's Brewery Co, see V Lower's Gambrinus Brewery Co

Lowney's, spoon, embossed brass, Lowney's lettered on bowl of spoon, 4", EX, M2.................................**$15.00**

Lowney's Chocolates, sign, die-cut cardboard stand-up, 2 ladies & navy man by cannon watch ships & planes, restored, 34x27", EX, M2....................................**$130.00**

Lowney's Chocolates, sign, embossed tin, black on yellow, Bon Voyage With Lowney's Chocolates, single black line border, 12½x16", EX, M2 ....**$52.00**

Lowney's Crest Chocolates, sign, ca 1910s, die-cut tin, Crest Chocolates on green panel before face of smiling boy in Lowney's hat, 12x8", EX+, A..........$750.00

Lowney's Oh Henry!, sign, tin, red & white on red, Eatmore above Lowney's Oh Henry! on fancy panel, It's Cracker-Jack below, 23x35", EX, M2..................**$110.00**

Lubeck Royal Beer, label, 1933-50, Tip-Top Brewing Co, Internal Revenue Tax Paid statement, 12-oz, EX, A.**$30.00**

Lucador Cigars, box label, inner lid, woman & dog in a garden, 6x9", M, C3..**$25.00**

Lucas Battleship White, trade card, for Lucas paint, pictures a battleship, ...Will Stand The Elements On Land & Sea, EX, A **$15.00**

Lucas Lamps & Bells, sign, 1900-10, self-framed tin, woman seated on box along roadside, lion logo lower left, rare, 24x18", EX, A **$3,200.00**

Lucas Paints, sign, 1904, litho, shows giant man 'painting' the town, Use Lucas Best Value lettered in sky, 36x24", EX, D...**$750.00**

Lucas Paints & Varnishes, jigsaw puzzle, giant painter kneels among homes while holding house in left hand & can & brush in right, 7x6", EX, F1....................**$85.00**

Lucky Bill Cigars, box label, outer, pictures a young boy wearing knickers, 4½x4½", M, D.............................**$2.50**

Lucky Curve Plug Cut Tobacco, tin, baseball player flanked by product name, red, yellow & white, slip lid, fading/chips/scratches, 4x7", G, A **$225.00**

Lucky Hit Tobacco, bucket label, long-haired girl with quiver of arrows & blackbird, 13x7", EX, D........................**$35.00**

Lucky Lager Beer, ashtray, white with gold & red lettering, 5¾x5¾", D...**$9.50**

Lucky Star Ginger Ale, sign, tin, features large bottle, vertical, EX, A **$10.00**

Lucky Strike Brand Apples, crate label, 1920s, hunter aiming at buck near a lake, Stolich & Diklich, Watsonville Cal, 10½x9", M, C1 ....**$3.00**

Lucky Strike Cigarettes, sign, cardboard, man & woman floating in the air, Flat Fifties, 50 Cigarettes 27¢, 42½x26", VG, A **$350.00**

Lucky Strike Cigarettes, sign, cardboard, pictures package of cigarettes, Have You Tried... in script above, framed, image: 18x13½", EX, A..**$90.00**

Lucky Strike Cigarettes, sign, 1900-20, self-framed die-cut metal, lion & Nature In The Row... above product name in red square, 39x28", VG, A...........................**$3,200.00**

Lucky Strike Cigarettes, sign, 1910-20, tin, 2-sided, black lettering on red with green border, 2 birds & white roses on back, 24" dia, VG, A **$400.00**

Lucky Strike Cigarettes, sign, 1936, cardboard stand-up, Christmas scene on carton above Give A Christmas Carton... & open pack, 30x20", M, D3...$375.00

Lucky Strike Cigarettes, tip card, encircled portrait of Dorothy Marshall, Cream Of The Crop, Give Me Lucky Strike..., 5½x4", EX, D..........................$65.00

Lucky Strike Tobacco, clock, wood case with black lettering on red round center surrounded by black Roman numerals on white, 15" dia, EX, A **$450.00**

Lucky Strike Tobacco, clock, wood case with molded composition front panels, RA Patterson Top Co... on tin face, working, 28", G, A **$200.00**

Lucky Strike Tobacco, tin, product & company name encircled in center, Genuine Roll Cut lettered above & below, 1-lb, 6x4", EX+, A **$242.00**

Luden's 5¢ Cough Drops, sign, embossed die-cut tin, scrolled emblem with Luden's above box & Menthol Candy 5¢, ...Quick Relief, 7x10", VG, A..........$950.00

Luis Martinez Cigars, box label, outer, pictures woman offering cigars to children, 4½x4½", M, D **$7.00**

Lundborg's Rhenish Cologne, trade card, die-cut bottle, EX, A **$15.00**

Lurido Cigars, box label, inner lid sample, 1909, girl's head with long flowing hair in sunburst, Geo Schlegel litho, VG, A...**$26.00**

Luter's Pure Lard, tin, pictures Mammy on both sides, red & yellow, slip lid & bail, EX, D **$40.00**

Lutz & Schramm Co Baked Beans, pocket mirror, pictures can of product, 2⅛" dia, EX, A..................**$160.00**

Luxum Beer, label, 1933-36, Modesto Brewery Inc, U-type permit number, 11-oz, EX, A...............................**$20.00**

Luxury Bread, ruler, wood, Eat Luxury Bread, 12", EX, D.**$5.00**

Luxury Bread, trolley sign, 1929, cardboard, Ask For...Famous For It's Flavor, red, white & blue, 11x21", EX, D...**$18.00**

Luxury Cigarettes, sign, paperboard, girl sitting sideways facing front holding product, lettering above & below, framed, 25x17", EX, A..**$325.00**

Luzerne County Brewing Co, tray, view of Battlefield of Gettysburg, lettering above & below, decorative rim, oval, 13¾x16¾", EX, A.......................................**$500.00**

Luzianne Coffee, needle holder, can shape, with 4 packages of needles, 4½x2¾", EX, D..........................**$42.00**

Luzianne Coffee, tin, product name lettered above graphic featuring West Bend Percolator Only $5.95, Coffee & Chicory below, 1-lb, VG, A **$20.00**

Luzianne Coffee, tin, product name lettered above Mammy pouring coffee, Coffee & Chicory lettered below, pry lid, VG, A...**$36.00**

Lyall & Buchannan Tobacco, sign, paper, 1 of 4, fire-fighting scene, minor water stain & soiling, matted & framed, 20x26" with mat, VG, A **$100.00**

Lydia E Pinkham's Vegetable Compound, compact, ca 1910, hinged lid with portrait & facsimile signature, Yours For Health, reverse has ad text, 2⅛"dia, EX, A **$50.00**

Lydia E Pinkham's Vegetable Compound, tape measure, 1910, celluloid, shows image of Lydia, Yours For Health, Vegetable Compound..., Bastion Bros, EX, H1 ....**$40.00**

Lydia E Pinkham's Vegetable Compound, tatting shuttle, 1910, celluloid, front has portrait, reverse has signature & inscription, 3" long, VG+, A..............................**$16.00**

Lykens Brewing Co, calendar, 1912, mother & child with dog walking across creek on a board, full pad, framed, image: 23x16½", EX, A..**$300.00**

Lykens Brewing Co, calendar, 1913, paper, baby walking to mom & dad on table, full pad, matted & framed, image: 16x18", EX, A...**$115.00**

Lykens Brewing Co, tray, stock image of girl hugging horse, Home Of Cream Top Lager Beer on rim, oval, 16¾x13¾", EX, A **$250.00**

Lyon's Pola Maid Ice Cream, display, composition & cast iron, ice cream cone with pointed bottom, embossed lettering in red and black, VG, A **$600.00**

Lyon's Tea, sign, embossed tin, Always The Best above & below product name, 10x17", EX+, M2.......................**$60.00**

M

M Hemingway & Sons, cabinet, walnut, early cash-register shape with curved-glass front, 4 shelves, bottom drawer, 18x21x16", EX, A..................$1,600.00

M Hohner Harmonicas, display, 3-tier folding wood box, inner lid litho showing people playing harmonicas, how-to book included, EX, A...............................**$50.00**

M&M's, package lid/Christmas ornament, 1980s, plastic, plain or peanut M&M wearing Santa hat, 2½", M, D...........**$2.50**

M&P Chili Con Carne, can label, pictures bowl of chili & Spaniard with guitar, M, C3 ....**$15.00**

M&S Beverages, sign, embossed bottle, orange, yellow & black, 2 corners bent/small paint chips on edges, 36x17", EX, D **$65.00**

Ma's Root Beer, bottle, amber glass, yellow & red painted label, NM, M3 ....**$8.00**

Ma's Root Beer, can, steel, EX, D **$4.00**

Ma's Root Beer, sign, tin, bottle cap on yellow left of It's Always A Pleasure To Serve You on white, 14x18", NM, M3 ....**$120.00**

Ma's Root Beer, sign, tin, yellow with Drink in script above Ma's portrait left of Ma's in black, bottle at right, 12x28", NM, M3 ....**$135.00**

Mac Nicol's Saloon, Vienna Art plate, tin, bare-chested girl surrounded by ornate floral border, overall wear, 10" dia, G, A **$245.00**

MacArthur-Zollars Motor Co, pin-back button, company name & address lettered around early touring car & Mac Z in fancy lettering, round, EX, A **$37.00**

Macaulay 10 Cent Cigar, sign, product name arched above signature portrait flanked by castle & buildings, High Grade 10¢ Cigar below, 24" dia, VG+, A...**$240.00**

Maccoboy Snuff, jar, ceramic, Fine Maccoboy lettered in oval, knob lid, EX+, A....................**$55.00**

Mack Trucks, display, die-cut porcelainized metal bulldog wearing large collar, 28x35", EX+, A **$950.00**

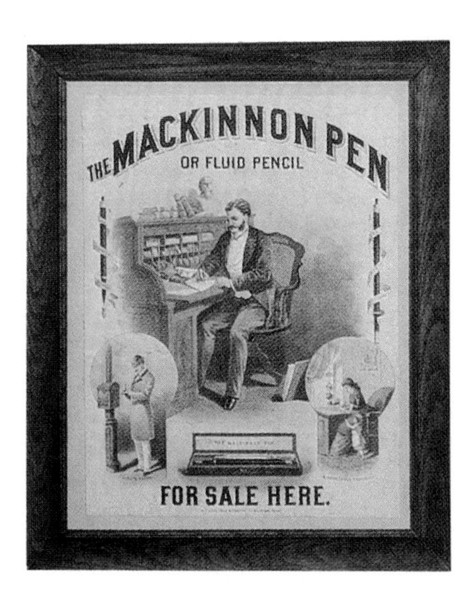

Mackinnon Pen, sign, paper, gentleman at roll-top desk writing a letter, ...Fluid Pencil For Sale Here, framed, 18½x14½", VG, A $1,250.00

MacLaren's Peanut Butter, container, tin, cup shape with handle, shows boy & girl on 1 side, advertising emblem on reverse, no lid, 3", EX, M2 ....**$160.00**

MacLaren's Peanut Butter, cup, tin, pictures boy & girl with bike, press lid, side handle, EX, A....................**$130.00**

MacLaren's Peanut Butter, pail, tin, cream with MacLaren's... lettered in white on red shield with gold outline, pry lid & bail, 13-oz, G, A....................**$90.00**

Madie Cigars, box label, inner lid, Madie arched above girl in scarf flanked by roses, America & Quality First below, 6x9", EX, D **$10.00**

Maestro Cigars, sign, die-cut cardboard, gentleman in formal attire enjoying cigar above Maestro in diagonal script, 14½x17", EX, A....................**$20.00**

Magic Chef Gas Ranges, salt & pepper shakers, 1950s, plastic, full figures of Magic Chef on round bases, 5", M, D **$35.00**

Magic Gasoline, sign, painted tin, Use above Magic surrounded by red lightning bolts & Gasoline lettered on gas globe, 24x18", VG, A....................**$350.00**

Magic Yeast, store dispenser, product name vertically in bold letters with owl encircled at top, minor wear, 27x3", G, A **$225.00**

Magnificos Cigars, sign, tin, oval image of seated man in tuxedo enjoying a cigar, Manufactured By T Lee, only 1 known, 24x18", EX, M2 ....**$4,000.00**

Magnolene Motor Oil for Fords, sign, porcelain flange, 2-sided, Magnolene above Motor Oils For Fords, Reduces Vibration, For Sale Here, 16x22", VG+, A....................**$450.00**

Magnolia Brand Condensed Milk, box, wood, fancy black lettering & graphics imprinted on ends, bottom cracked/wear to wood, 7x19x13", VG, A **$25.00**

Magnolia Gasoline, globe, metal body, glass lens, magnolia graphic with product name above & below, 16" dia, VG, A....................$1,500.00

Magnolia Gasoline, sign, porcelain, 2-sided, white Magnolia Gasoline around white encircled Motor Oil, 3 magnolia graphics, 42" dia, G, A....................**$240.00**

Magnolia Petroleum Co, sign, porcelain, 2-sided, company name around Magnolia Gasoline Sold Here, magnolia graphic above, 29" dia, VG+, A **$275.00**

Magnus Beck Brewing Co, tip tray, eagle surmounting barrel & shield, lettering on rim, minor soiling/wear, 4¼" dia, VG, A....................**$120.00**

Mahlon Haines Shoe Wizard, pocket mirror, photo portrait of man in bow tie encircled by white line, lettering around, foxing, 2¼" dia, G, A....................**$11.00**

Maid's Sure Cure, trade card, pictures Palmer Cox Brownies moving a pumpkin, EX, A **$12.00**

Mail Pouch Quality Tobacco, display, full-color image of the 1915 Pacific Exposition, American Litho Co, 36x45", EX, A....................**$1,000.00**

Mail Pouch Tobacco, sign, tin, black with Chew lettered in white, Mail Pouch in yellow, 2x18", EX, A....................**$165.00**

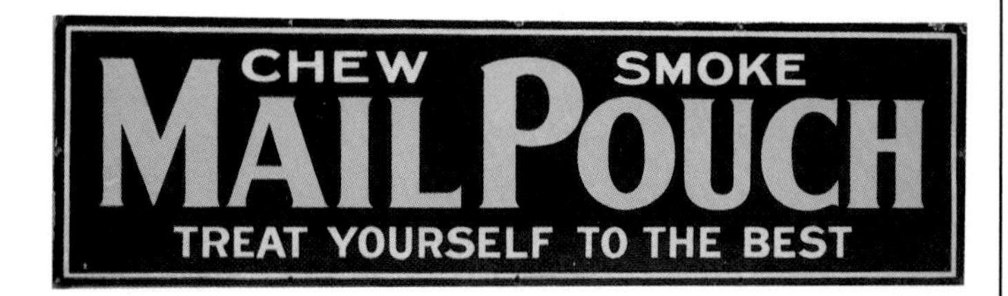

Mail Pouch Tobacco, sign, tin, white and yellow lettering on black ground, Chew & Smoke...Treat Yourself To The Best, 12x40", EX, D3 ....$285.00

Mail Pouch Tobacco, thermometer, porcelain, Treat Yourself To The Best, Chew... above & below, blue, white & yellow, 72x18", G, A **$325.00**

Mail Pouch Tobacco, thermometer, porcelain, Treat Yourself To The Best, Chew... above & below, blue, white & yellow, 38x8", VG, A...**$90.00**

Mail Pouch Tobacco, trade card, pictures baby in diaper, G, D **$20.00**

Maillot, crate label, Spanish citrus, bicycle racer & oranges, M, C3..**$45.00**

Malibu, crate label, 1920s, California orange, Indian looking out from peak, Mupu Citrus Assn, Santa Paula, 10x11¾", M, C3..**$18.00**

Malkins Best Black Pepper, tin, red, white & blue, product name on bull's-eye above Pure Black Pepper & company name, EX+, M2..**$8.00**

Mallard Sportload Shotgun Shells, box, mallard in flight above product name, blue on red, 12-gauge, VG, A..**$20.00**

Malt Breakfast Food, sign, paper, little girl feeds cereal to birds, See! Little Birds, I Eat What's Good..., Malted Cereals Co, 24x22", G, A.......................................**$25.00**

Malt Kneipp, sign, 1940s, open bag of Malt Kneipp on blue ground, Indispensable Comme Le Plain!, framed, 49½x33", VG, A...............................$150.00

Malt Marrow, label, pre-1920, McAvoy Brewing Co, G, A **$29.00**

Malted Grape-Nuts, dispenser, tin reservoir with flip-top glass lid, metal base, 15¼", G, A.........................**$110.00**

Maltex Breakfast Cereal, blotter, green & black on white, sunrise scene with boy fishing, unused, 6x2¾", D.**$4.00**

Maltex Breakfast Cereal, pin-back button, 1930s, red, white & blue, wear at bottom edge, D **$4.00**

Maltop Toddy Powdered Drink, tin, copyright 1925, key-wind lid, 4¼x3½" dia, VG, A **$10.00**

Mammy Beverage Co, soda bottle, 1910-20, glass with embossed Mammy, 14", EX, D **$395.00**

Mammy's Favorite Brand Coffee, pail, Mammy with tray of steaming coffee, CD Kenny Co, slip lid & bail, straight-sided, 4-lb, EX+, A **$500.00**

Mandeville & King Co Flower Seeds, box, wood with dove-tailed corners, has compartments, inner paper label with floral scene, hinged lid, 12" long, G+, A **$60.00**

Mangels & Schmidt's Bread, pin-back button, ca 1900, red, blue & black logo on gold, EX, D **$5.00**

Manhattan Cigars, box label, outer, bald eagle on US crest, 4½x4½", M, C3..**$35.00**

Manhattan Cocktail Tobacco, pocket tin, flat, I Crow... under red rooster, You Smoke We Drink under red cocktail glass, 1x4½x3¼", G, H1 ....**$22.00**

Manhattan Coffee, tin, product name over mountain peak, 70 Cups In Every Pound & tilted cup of coffee at top, key-wind lid, 1-lb, EX+, A **$30.00**

Manhattan Delight Sugar Cones, canister, tin, rolled waffle cone graphic in center of product lettering, slip lid, 15¼x12" dia, EX, A **$90.00**

Manila Blunts Cigars, label, 1930s, lettering & 2 For 5¢/10 for 25¢ over scene with oxen-drawn cart full of tobacco, 6x9", EX, D **$5.00**

Manley's Best Jumbo Pop Corn, tin, product name & elephant on shield over popping corn background, 10-lb, EX, A **$50.00**

Manor House Coffee, tin, paper label pictures landscape with horse & rider, lettering above slip lid, 1-lb, EX, A.......**$30.00**

Mansfield's Pepsin Gum, display case, glass with decaled image of woman holding pack of gum, ...Blood Orange, Peppermint, 11½x6½", VG, A **$1,800.00**

Manufacture D'Acier Poli, display, 12 corkscrews attached to cardboard, overall soiling, 10x13", G, A **$150.00**

Many Miles Transmission Oil, can, 1915-25, yellow letters on black with early red race car in center, red ground, screw lid & handle, 1-gal, EX, A......$190.00

Mapacuba Cigar, tin, embossed scene of Cuba, Blunt lettered in upper corners, slip lid, square, EX+, A...**$70.00**

Mapacuba Tobacco, box, square, NM, H3 ....**$55.00**

Marathon Motor Oils, sign, tin, marathon runner & touring car at left of product name above Best In The Long Run, framed, 14x42", EX, A.............................**$1,100.00**

Marathon Products, sign, 1930s, porcelain, 2-sided, product name lettered on green around runner on black, gold edge, 30" dia, G, A **$355.00**

Marathon Products, sign, 1930s, porcelain, 2-sided, product name lettered on green around runner on black, gold edge, 48" dia, EX, D3 ....$1,200.00

Marathon Tires, sign, self-framed tin, 2 couples in open car driving downhill, 22¾x16¾", G-, A..............**$100.00**

Marbles Outing Equipment, pocket catalog, 1938, pictures an elk with mallards flying overhead, orange & black, 32 pages, EX, A...**$35.00**

Marcel Curler, sign, 1920s, cardboard, pictures flapper girl with hair gadget, 11x14", EX, D **$16.00**

Marie Antoinette Havana Cigars, pin holder, Havana Cigars on center band with lettering above & below, ...Geo P Lies & Co..., black & green, EX, A..........................**$20.00**

Marietta Paints, sign, porcelain, 2-sided emblem reading Marietta Paints, 21x21", EX, D1..........................**$135.00**

Mariposa, crate label, apple, colorful butterfly & flowers, 9x10½", M, C3..**$35.00**

Marlboro, poker dice in original leather pouch, MIB, D2...**$35.00**

Marlboro, matchbook cover, ...20 for 20¢, 20 strike, front strike, NM, R1 ....**$7.50**

Marlboro, sign, embossed metal, full-color image of cowboy riding horse & pack of cigarettes, minor scratches, 24x18", VG+, P4 ....**$20.00**

Marlin Firearms Co, billhead, 1890s, engraved shotgun, VG, A **$95.00**

Marlin Firearms Co, catalog, 1911, pictures 3 rifles on cover, well illustrated, 122 pages, EX, A **$130.00**

Marlin Firearms Co, catalog, 1926, pictures man cleaning rifle while boy & dog watch, retail price list included, 24 pages, EX, A **$45.00**

Marlin Firearms Co, pocket catalog, 1922, nonpictorial cover, features repeating rifles & shotguns, 20 pages, VG, A **$22.00**

Marlin Firearms Co, sign, 1905, paper, hunter behind large rock, A Gun For The Man Who Knows... below, signed Goodwin, framed, 23x13", VG, A............**$850.00**

Marlin Guns, letterhead & envelope, 1916, envelope shows youth holding shotgun, letterhead shows factory scene, EX, S5 ....**$125.00**

Marlin Repeating Rifles & Shotguns, sign, 1908, paper, pictures downed mallards, logo & lettering below, signed Muss, framed, 24x15", VG, A..................**$850.00**

Marquette Club Ginger Ale, sign, cardboard stand-up, smiling man with real glass eyes holding bottle, Mixes Best For Your Guests, 11", NM, B1 ....**$45.00**

Marquette Club Ginger Ale, sign, die-cut cardboard, bug-eyed man in hat holding out large bottle, Mixes Best For Your Guests, EX, A...**$20.00**

Marshall & Wendell Piano Co, sign, die-cut cardboard, man in top hat holding sign reading The Peerless...Piano, The Artists' Choice, 5x3", EX, D.....................................**$30.00**

Marshall Field & Co, catalog, 1976 Christmas, features gifts for children, 44 pages, VG, D...............................**$20.00**

Marshall Field & Co Frango Mint Chip Cookies, cookie jar, ceramic, shaped as dark green cookie bag with white lettering & graphics, NM, D **$55.00**

Marshall Fields, pin-back button, 2 children peeking at Santa, Meet Me At Marshall Fields above & below, rare, round, EX, A...**$109.00**

Marshall-Wells Hardware, catalog, 1950s, 4,140 pages, VG+, H2..**$100.00**

Martell Cognac, tray, 1950s, metal, pictures the Cognac Man, minor paint wear, 14" dia, EX, D **$30.00**

Martha Washington Coffee, tin, pictures Martha Washington, 1-lb, NM, D **$45.00**

Martin L Bradford & Co Fishing Tackle, trade card, 1860s, ...Fishing Rods, Reels, Lines, Artificial Flies..., red on white, rare, EX, A **$140.00**

Martin Xtra Special Ethyl, gas globe, ca 1935, Martin logo on blue & white striped background above Xtra Special... in red, 13½" dia, EX, A..........$275.00

Martin-Alexander Lumber Co, letterhead & cover, July 18, 1901, engraved image of woman among pine cones & branches, VG, D **$18.00**

Martine's Patent Kerosene Burner, sign, paper, features 2 families with & without product, CA Evans litho with watermark, framed, image: 14¾x12", G, A.........**$200.00**
Marvel Health Belt, display, waist mannequin on wood pedestal diplaying the Marvel Health Belt, Chas Quenzer Inc, belt ripped, 27", G, A.............................**$35.00**
Marvel Kidney Beans, can label, beans in dish & fresh beans on ivory background, Danville Ill, G1.......................**$2.00**
Marvels Cigarettes, thermometer, tin, pictures a bird & open pack of cigarettes at top, The Cigarette Of Quality below, 12x4", EX+, A...**$125.00**
Marven's Biscuits, door push bar, tin, white logos flank white Marven's Biscuits above Favourites Since 1905 on red, minor edge rust, M2.....................................**$32.00**
Marvin Smith Co, catalog, 1907, engravings with descriptions & prices, 97 pages, EX, D...........................**$18.00**
Marvine for Headache & Neuralgia, sign, tin, ivory lettering on green with ivory outlined border, Take...At Your Druggist, 10x14", EX, A...**$22.50**
Maryland Casualty Co, sign, tin, company name above round logo flanked by types of insurance, Home Office Baltimore, framed, 12x23½", EX, A.......................**$45.00**
Maryland Club Mixture Tobacco, pocket tin, pictures Maryland Club Building in center circle, orange, blue & white, curled lid, 4x3½x1", VG, A......................**$350.00**
Mascot Cereal, pin-back button, Rin-Tin-Tin, The Lightning Warrior lettered around his image,¾", NM, A......**$16.00**
Mascot Crushed Cut Tobacco, pocket mirror, small dog encircled by product name, 2⅛" dia, EX, A..........**$70.00**
Mason & Rich Pianos, letter opener, girl in harp-shaped inset above product lettering, squared bottom, blunt-pointed top, 6x1½", EX, M2.................................**$90.00**
Mason's Challenge Blacking, display box, wood, 3 Doz, No 4 above circle logo on front label, large circle logo on inner lid label, 5x12x8", EX, A......................**$140.00**
Mason's Root Beer, bottle topper, die-cut cardboard, figure in boat with Enjoy Mason's Old Fashioned Root Beer over sail, 9x5", NM, A....................................**$5.00**
Mason's Root Beer, can, steel, EX, D.........................**$4.50**
Mason's Root Beer, menu board, tin, white & black on yellow, Mason's lettered on black M left of Root Beer above, 27x19", NM, M3..**$80.00**
Massata Talcum Powder, tin, pictures full-length standing pose of Oriental lady, shaker top, EX, A.............**$25.00**
Massey-Harris Sales Service, sign, 1940s, porcelain, hand holding plow blade flanked by Farming Equipment lettered in blue & green, 18x59", EX, A.................**$330.00**
Master Cigar, cutter, cast iron, key-wind cutter with insert picture from tobacco label in flat marqee, 3½x6x4¼", G, A......**$150.00**
Master Trucks Inc, inkwell, cast iron, early truck with driver on beveled base, embossed lettering on sides of truck bed, 8x7x3", VG, A...................................**$210.00**
Masterpiece Pimientos, can label, 1929, pictures 2 red peppers, EX, C3...**$3.00**
Masury's, see also John W Masury & Son
Masury's Pure Colors, sign, tin, man mixing colors while merchant points to cans of paint, Sentenne & Green litho, framed, image: 18x24", G, A.....................**$400.00**
Matador Granulated Mixture, tin, matador & bull with product name arched above, slip lid, 4x4", EX, A...**$35.00**
Mathie Beer, pocket mirror, Mathie lettered in script diagonally across top of beer bottle, For Purity & Quality, oval, 2¾", EX, A..**$85.00**
Mathie Brewing Co, calendar, 1907, die-cut cardboard, cherub & flowered beauty in gondola, full pad, framed, 15½x14½", EX, A...**$1,300.00**
Mathie Brewing Co, Vienna Art plate, 1905, tin, elegant girl wearing a turban surrounded by ornate border, 10" dia, EX, A...**$50.00**
Mathie Red Ribbon Beer, pocket mirror, Mathie diagonally lettered over neck of beer bottle surrounded by other lettering, oval, 2¾", VG, A..........................**$45.00**
Mauchchunk Beer, sign, neon, metal cased, corrosion/transformer missing from interior, 14x26x7", G-, A.......**$825.00**
Maumee Coal, sign, embossed tin, Indian's head in left profile with lettered headband & feathers, Maumee Coal below, 16x15", VG, A................................**$225.00**
Mavis, sign, tin flange, labeled bottle, Drink...Real Chocolate Flavor, blue, brown & yellow, 9½x12½", NM, B1..**$120.00**
Max Factor, sample display, has different shades of lip stick, lip gloss & nail polish, 27x12½", EX, A.......**$20.00**
Maxim Motor Co, presentation pen & pencil set, wood base with cast-iron emblem, gold graphics & lettering, 20 Yrs..., 6x11x10", EX, A....................................**$25.00**
Maxwell House Coffee, pocket mirror, shows square coffee can with Best On Earth & Sealed Cans Only lettered above & below, oval, 2¾", EX, A.......................**$300.00**
Maxwell House Coffee, tin, pictures waiter serving man on side, Canadian, key-wind lid, 1-lb, EX, A..........**$5.00**
Maxwell House Coffee, tin, 1920-30, cup with last drop at left of product lettering, Vita-Fresh Vacuum Packed above, 4-lb, EX, A..**$110.00**
Maxwell House Coffee, tin, 1992, 6½x4¼x2¾", EX, D...**$10.00**
May's Glycerine Menthol Lozenges, tin, lid shows fancy period lettering & decor, May Drug Co, flat rectangle with rounded corners, ¾x4x2", VG, D.................**$20.00**
Mayer Shoes, sign, ca 1905, cardboard, pictures high-heeled shoe in circular inset, red, yellow & black, 6x36", EX, D...**$35.00**
Mayo's Cut Plug Tobacco, banner, canvas, colorful rooster standing on tobacco plugs, Light & Dark, framed, image: 29½x18", EX, A...**$85.00**
Mayo's Cut Plug Tobacco, lunch box, tin, dark blue with gold lettering & graphics, flat lid with wire handle, 5x8x4", NM, A..**$48.00**
Mayo's Plug, sign, porcelain, product name above rooster standing on tobacco crate, Smoking Cock O' The Walk below, 13x7", VG A...**$375.00**
Mayo's Tobacco, clock, Baird Regulator, wooden figure-8 with embossed lettering around Roman numerals & below, 31x19x4", EX, A.....................................**$900.00**
Mayo's Tobacco, roly poly, Mammy smoking corncob pipe, minor age wear, 7x6" dia, VG, A..............**$413.00**
Mayo's Tobacco, roly poly, Satisfied Customer, age wear/scratch on right side of face, 7x6" dia, VG, A.**$800.00**
Mayo's Tobacco, roly poly, Singing Waiter, some wear, scarce, 7x6" dia, VG..**$300.00**
Mayo's Tobacco, roly poly, tin litho of Mammy with hands folded & tobacco pack in front pocket, minor dents, 7x6" dia, VG+, A...**$450.00**

Mayo-Skinner Automatic Wind Shield Cleaner, display, die-cut cardboard, Drive Safely In... above back view of man driving in rain, 28x32", EX, A $800.00

Maytag, sign, 1920s, metal flange, heart shape with The Maytag above early washing machine, The Way To Her Heart, 18x17", EX, A $8,000.00

Maytag Multi-Motor Oil, can, 1-gal, EX, D........................$45.00

Mazola, recipe book, 1915, 24 pages, EX, D..............$14.00

McArthur, Wirth & Co Butcher's & Packer's Tools & Machinery, catalog, 1900, features wooden butcher's block on cover, Syracuse NY, appears EX, A.......$10.00

McCalls Paysandu Ox Tongues, trade card, diecut of couple having an elegant dinner, Order...In Tins, shades of brown, EX, A $40.00

McCormick, calendar, 1911, paper, hunters & dead game, full pad, framed, image: 20x13", EX+, A $175.00

McCormick, sign, paper, 'Back from the War' & 'Gold Producers in the Klondike,' framed, pair, 36x24", EX+, M1 ....$1,200.00

McCormick & Co Bee Brand Teas, Spices & Extracts, pocket mirror, features products in center with building below, lettering around, oval, 2¾", VG, A................................$270.00

McCormick Harvester, print, ca 1888, paper, 'Battle Of Atlanta,' insets of machinery in upper corners, matted & framed, 30x40½", NM, D3 ....$1,450.00

McCormick-Deering, catalog, ca 1925, features seeding equipment, VG, D $25.00

McCormick-Deering Farm Machines, sign, embossed tin, company name lettered in yellow on black above dealer name in black on yellow, 10x28", EX, A...$75.00

McCormick-Deering Farm Machines, walking stick, EX, D2...$35.00

McCormick-Deering Service, sign, porcelain, 2-sided, Service lettered over radiator, McCormick-Deering arched above, oval, 24x32", G, A $300.00

McDonald's, bank, 1980s, plastic Ronald McDonald seated on white round base, 7½", M, D $25.00

McDonald's, character glass, 1977, McDonaldland Action Series, shows Big Mac on roller skates & kids on skooter, 6⅛", M, D $10.00

McDonald's, Christmas ornament, 1990, elf swinging from arch, wrap-around lights, MIB, D...........................$12.00

McDonald's, clock, electric, plastic, hamburgers as numbers, Ronald McDonald below, 28x12x5", EX, A $125.00

McDonald's, coloring board, 1981, pictures Ronald McDonald & the gang, 9x9¾", M, D $3.00

McDonald's, doll, Hamburglar, stuffed cloth, 17", EX, D $25.00

McDonald's, road map, 1964, premium, Washington DC Capital Beltway with locations of restaurants, black, red & white, 22x17", NM, D $18.00

McDonald's, telephone, 1985, plastic Ronald McDonald on white base, 10", M, D..$90.00

McDonald's, wristwatch, 1970s, numbers surround seated Ronald McDonald, black bands, not working, moderate wear, 1¼" dia, A $50.00

McDougall-Butler Paints, sign, early 1900s, tin flange, logo superimposed over a buffalo on orange background, minor yellowing/chips, 14x18", A .$280.00

McGarvey Coffee, tin, key-wind lid, 1-lb, EX, D...........$20.00

McGovern Beer, sign, paper, kicking mule & bottle, small water mark, glass frame, 12x9", VG, D.................$30.00

McGovern's Irish Ale, label, 1933-50, Internal Revenue Tax Paid statement, 12-oz, EX, A $10.00

McGregor Socks, display, hollow rubber, 3-D sock with smiling face atop base reading McGregor Happy Foot, 17x12", EX+, M2 ....$50.00

McHenry Draft Beer, label, 1933-36, logo above product name, McHenry Brewing Co, U-type permit number, 32-oz, VG, A $14.00

McKee High Grade Refrigerators, postcard, mother & daughter beside open refrigerator, Don't You Want Something Good? lettered below, EX, D $30.00

McKesson's Aspirin, thermometer, ca 1945, porcelain, brown & cream, Best For Pain... above product, some flaking, 27x7", A **$250.00**

McKessons Pharmaceutical Products, jigsaw puzzle, 1933, pictures druggists, Quality For Over 100 Years, 14x11", EX, D **$30.00**

McLaughlin's Coffee, trade card, 1892, little girl & boy drawing pictures, 5x7", VG, D **$4.00**

McLaughlin's Fresh Kept Coffee, tin, 1-lb, 4", VG, D.**$38.00**

McLeod-Hatje Liquor Merchants, tray, pictures 3 puppies chewing on playing cards, decorative leaf border, oval, 13½x16½", NM, D **$400.00**

Mead Cycle Co, catalog, 1918, features Ranger bicycles & supplies, 64 pages, VG+, H2 .... **$80.00**

Meadow Gold Brooms, display, metal, yellow advertising panel centered on black wire frame that holds 6 brooms, 24x17¾", EX, A **$175.00**

Meadow Gold Ice Cream, sign, die-cut masonite, Meadow Gold Ice Cream emblem above Please Pay When Served, vertical, EX, M1 .... $125.00

Meadow Gold Ice Cream, sign, porcelain, Smooth-Freeze in diagonal script above Meadow Gold Ice Cream, 28x20", EX, A **$135.00**

Meadows Insurance Agency, thermometer/mirror, stenciled paperboard under glass in metal frame, lettering above & below, 36", G+, A **$25.00**

Meadville Pure Rye, sign, early 1900s, oval image of woman with roses, product name in blue above, original frame, 28x23½", VG, A **$160.00**

Meadville Whiskey, sign, early 1900s, die-cut tin, labeled bottle, C Shonk litho, rare, minor scratches/wrinkles, 11½", A **$1,400.00**

Mecca Cigarettes, sign, 1912, paper, girl in hat with hands on hips giving knowing look, lettering below & on black frame, 20x11", VG+, D3 .... **$395.00**

Medaglia D'Oro Coffee, tray, pictures woman enjoying cup of coffee in circle inset over volcanic landscape, lettered rim, 10½x13½", G-, A **$10.00**

Medalist Cigar-ettes, tin, flat, with contents, product name above & below gold medal, slip lid, VG, A.......... **$12.00**

Medalist Cigars, box label, inner lid, 1903, California coat-of-arms & 2 gold medals, 6x9", M, C3 .... **$14.00**

Medicated Merit Powder, tin, painted loving cup logo, silver, blue & gray, slip lid, 2-oz, EX, D **$10.00**

Meek & Beach Co, sign attachment, girl left of ad text giving advantages of well-placed signs by the same company, 3½x8¼, VG, A **$230.00**

Melachrino Cigarettes, sign, self-framed tin, display of cigarette packages, The Cigarette Of All Nations, 15½x19½", VG, A **$150.00**

Mellin's Baby Formula, postcard, split-image of children with sleds, left side in color, right side ready for kids to color, NM, P3 .... **$40.00**

Mellin's Food, sign, cardboard stand-up, baby seated in chair, Mellin's Foods & Our Baby lettered below, 24", EX, A $280.00

Mellin's Food, trade card, 1892, pictures a smiling child, Good Morning Mamma!, 3x4", EX, P1 .... **$10.00**

Mellor & Rittenhouse Licorice Lozenges, container, early 1900s, tin with glass insert, floral graphics with lettering, hinged lid shows wear, 7", A **$20.00**

Melorol Ice Cream, pin-back button, 1930s, red & white, several thin scratches, D **$12.00**

Melox Dog Foods, sign, porcelain, white & black dog on red ball with product name, The Foods That Nourish lettered below, 26x18", EX, A **$750.00**

Melrose Gasoline, pump sign, 1940s, porcelain, white with blue M shadowed in black, white & yellow lettering, minor scratches, 12" dia, A **$85.00**

Melrose Marshmallows, tin, lettering flanked by roses, slip lid, round, EX, A **$70.00**

Memory, crate label, 1920s, California orange, silhouette of girl in frame beside pink rose in vase, Porterville, 10x11", M, C1 .... **$8.00**

Mennan Quinsana, tin, prescription label reads CN Williams Pharmacy, Elizabethtown NY, 5/24/55, shaker top, 5", EX+, P4 .... **$10.00**

Mennen Baby Powder, tin, ...New Baby Powder above baby's face emerging from rose petals, EX, A **$15.00**

Mennen Baby Powder, tin, tall round shape with blue & white vertical-striped paper label, VG+, M2......... **$24.00**

Mennen's Flesh Tint Talcum, pocket mirror, pictures a talcum tin, Not A Rouge above, A Pink Talcum Exquisitely Perfumed below, oval, 2¾", EX, A **$72.00**

Menter & Rosenbloom Co, pocket mirror, shows pretty little girl with company name arched above & address below, minor wear, 1¾" dia, VG+, A **$130.00**

Menthilles Pastilles de Menthe, sign, cardboard, gentleman & 3 women holding breath mints, circular logo & lettering below, 13x9½", VG, A **$55.00**

Mentholatum, sign, die-cut cardboard, nurse by large tube holding paper reading Many Uses One Cost, remedies below, 43x31", NM, A $190.00

Mentholatum, tin, ca 1915, colorful image of little girl in nurse's uniform holding container of Mentholatum, 1½" dia, VG, D **$14.50**

Merchant's Gargling Oil, sign, paper, 3 horses drinking from trough, A Liniment For Man & Beast below, framed, image: 14x21½", EX, A **$650.00**

Merchants Awning Co, paperweight, glass, red, white & black, company name arched above Carpaulins & Tents To Hire..., oval, 3x4", VG, M2 ....**$20.00**

Merchants Queen Cigars, box label, inner lid, portrait of a woman with fields beyond, 6x9", M, D **$4.00**

Mercury, sign, neon, Mercury in red neon on blue panel, die-cut wing atop, restored, 14x72", EX, D ...**$1,600.00**

Mercury Outboard, sign, pictures outboard motor, Sales & Service, G, D **$149.00**

Meriam & Morgan Paraffine Co, trade card, factory flanked by logo, ...Boston, Mass above & below, EX, A **$34.00**

Merit Motor Oil, can, 1940s-50s, Merit on blue ribbon in center, red ground, pry lid, 1-qt, 5½", EX, A **$20.00**

Merit Separator, tip tray, rectangular with flat scalloped edge, pictures separator with advertising around, EX, S5 ....**$115.00**

Merita Bread, bread end label, shows the Lone Ranger on Trigger with Merita lettered above, Hi-Yo-Silver below, red border, EX, S1 ....**$25.00**

Merita Bread, sign, 1954, tin, Lone Ranger on Trigger above large loaf of bread, It's Rich, Buy Merita Bread, 36x24", G+, A **$525.00**

Merita Bread, sign, 1954, tin, Lone Ranger on Trigger above large loaf of bread, It's Rich, Buy Merita Bread, 36x24", NM, M1 ....$1,650.00

Merkel's Tooth Powder, tin, ca 1917, red, black & gold, twist top, 4½x2", EX, D **$12.00**

Merrick's Spool Cotton, spool cabinet, cylindrical oak with gold lettering on curved glass, revolving interior, 23x18" dia, EX, A **$450.00**

Merrick's Thread, trade card, patriotic image of little girl playing a drum beside baby holding flag, lettering above, EX, A **$19.00**

Merrick's Thread, trade card, Statue of Liberty & view of Manhattan, Liberty Enlightening The World..., circular logo lower right, EX, A **$21.00**

Merrimack Brand Feeds, sign, craft paper, red & black Indian logo, lettering above & below, ...Farmer's Exchange, framed, image: 23x13", EX, A **$40.00**

Merrimack Motor Oil, can, 1930-40, red, black & white with product name above Indian's head, screw lid & handle, 10-qt, 10¾", VG, A **$15.00**

Merry Christmas & Happy New Year Peanut Butter, pail, tin, emerald green with gold lettering on cream emblem with gold leaves, Compliments Of Jos N Essel, 1-lb, EX, A **$300.00**

Messett's Musical Entertainers, sign, paper, Black man holding torn umbrella, red lettering above, 1920s, center crease, framed, 39x11", EX, A **$475.00**

Meteor Lemons, crate label, 1930s, meteor streaking through evening sky with lemons in foreground, San Fernando Ca, 9x12½", M, C1 ....**$2.00**

Metropolitan Life Insurance Co, booklet, 1928, 'Health Heroes,' features story of Florence Nightingale with portrait on cover, 24 pages, G, D **$3.00**

Metropolitan Life Insurance Co, pin-back button, company name in blue center with building, Health & Happiness... on yellow rim, ⅞" dia, EX, H1 ....**$6.00**

Metropolitan Life Insurance Co, recipe book, 1927, 64 pages, EX, D **$12.00**

Metropolitan Life Insurance Co, recipe book, 1934, 'The Family Food Supply,' 23 pages, EX, D **$5.00**

Metropolitan Life Insurance Co, recipe book, 1940, 64 pages, EX, D **$4.00**

Metropolitan Life Insurance Co, trade card, 2 kittens trying to get goldfish in bowl, EX, A....................... **$18.00**

MGM Records, thermometer, stenciled tin, black on yellow, cat character holding up sign, rounded corners, 39", G+, A **$120.00**

MH&M Shoes, sign, embossed die-cut tin, black lettering on yellow arm & hand with pointing finger, 6½x28", EX, A **$220.00**

MI Furbish Fly Lines, trade card, trout trademark flanked by Silk, Linen, Lisle & Cotton..., Waterproof... below, black & white, EX, A.. **$26.00**

Mi-Boy Tomatoes, can label, smiling boy, M, C3............... **$2.00**

Mica Axle Grease, tin, 1900s, wagon wheel flanked by Trade Mark, ...Standard Oil Co above & below, white & blue, 1-lb, 4" dia, EX, A **$20.00**

Michelin, air compressor, 1920-30, Michelin man sitting on cast-metal housing, plate reads R Toussaint..., rare, 11", EX, A **$950.00**

Michelin, ashtray, 1940s, molded white plastic Michelin man mounted on black plastic ashtray, 5", EX, A **$35.00**

Michelin, display, 1920-40s, plaster Michelin man with Michelin Tires lettered on front, rare, base chipping, 32x16", G, A **$1,100.00**

Michelin, jacket patch, Michelin man, blue & white with gold trim, 3x3", EX, D **$3.50**

Michelin, playing cards, reproduction of early Montaut racing scene, sealed, MIB, D **$15.00**

Michelin, sign, 1920-30s, embossed tin, 2-sided, Michelin man on bicycle, Michelin on orange band across top, rare, 30x30", EX+, A...................................... **$1,600.00**

Michelin, sign, 1950s, porcelain, Michelin man & tire below product name, yellow with blue border, V-shaped bottom, 32x24", EX, A.......................... **$160.00**

Michelin, stained-glass window, Michelin above running & waving Michelin man with black tire on blue background, 31x34", NM, A **$900.00**

Michelin Tires & Tubes, sign, 1920s, porcelain, yellow product name left of Michelin man relaxing in large tire on dark blue, 18x60", NM, D3....$2,650.00

Michelin X, clock, white plastic 6-sided frame, white numbers & running Michelin man on blue ground, Michelin X below, 14x16", EX, A.................................... **$135.00**

Michigan Stove Co, pocket mirror, advertising Garland Stoves & Ranges, Largest Makers Of Stoves In The World, oval, 2¾", NM, A **$27.00**

Micro-Lube, display stand, wire shelves with metal panel featuring Air Force jet, 34x20", EX, A.................. **$75.00**

Middlesex Mutual Fire Insurance Co, calendar, 1895, colorful image of house & church in country setting, full pad, matted & framed, image: 12x8", VG, A **$75.00**

Midland Power Brake Equipment, sign, embossed metal flange, Authorized Distributor... in black above Midland... in yellow on green, oval, 20x26", EX, A... **$250.00**

Midori Melon Liqueur, mirror, wood frame, 17x17", EX, D... **$15.00**

Milady Coffee, tin, 1920-40, paper label, rose in vase at left of Thrift-T-Vac... logo, Milady above & Coffee over vase, 1-lb, EX, A.. **$195.00**

Milkmaid Brand Milk, sign, porcelain, milkmaid at left of ad text, Largest Sale In The World, some nicks on frame, 48x32", A **$325.00**

Milky Way, tin, 1991, hearts & cupids, 6¼x4", EX, D.. **$7.50**

Millbrook Bread, pencil clip, 1930s, red, white & blue, EX, D... **$18.00**

Miller Beer, inflatable shamrock leaf, green with Miller logos, 36x36", EX+, P4 .... **$8.00**

Miller High Life Beer, display, metallic-gold plastic figure of the Miller girl on base with logo, 2", EX, A **$90.00**

Miller High Life Beer, matchbook cover, features product name with bottles on ice on reverse, 20 strike, front strike, NM, R1 .... **$5.00**

Miller High Life Beer, sign, die-cut tin stand-up, cowgirl with large bottle of beer, Champagne Of Bottled Beer, 72x36", G, A **$400.00**

Miller High Life Beer, sign, glass, girl on crescent moon at left of product name, The Champagne Of Bottled Beer below, EX, M1 .... **$85.00**

Miller High Life Beer, sign, neon, logo in script, in original packing crate, 23x29½x13", G, A **$225.00**

Miller High Life Beer, tip tray, pictures mansion, carriage & figures, G, D **$20.00**

Miller High Life Beer, tray, deep-dish, Miller in diagonal script above girl seated in crescent moon flanked by High & Life, 14" dia, EX, A **$75.00**

Miller Line Typewriter Ribbon, tin, square, EX, D... **$5.00**

Miller Lite, Ertl bank, 1950, Chevy Truck, M, D **$25.00**

Miller's Soap, pin-back button, ca 1900, blue & white, EX, D... **$5.00**

Miller Tires, ashtray, embossed rubber tire shape with glass insert, Miller Deluxe, Long Safe Mileage..., 8 holders, 7" dia, EX, H1 .... **$42.00**

Miller Tires, sign, gear & outdoor scene, S2 .... **$125.00**

Miller Tires, sign, porcelain, white Miller Tires in stylized lettering above Geared-To-The-Road, yellow border on blue, 22x73", EX, A **$110.00**

Miller Tires, watch fob, brass, pictures tire with arm through it, product name on back, EX, D **$45.00**

Miller-Piehl Co, catalog, ca 1930, features farm buildings, 64 pages, EX, D **$16.00**

Million Dollar Grape, sign, tin, Refreshing in script on vertical solid & striped ground above circle with product name, EX, A.. **$65.00**

Milton Bradley, catalog, 1971, 60 pages, VG+, H2... **$40.00**

Milwaukee Binders & Mowers, match holder, tin, product name above logo flanked by Always Reliable, red white & blue, minor pitting, 5", G, A **$15.00**

Milwaukee Harvester Co, sign, paper, pictures horse-drawn thresher above hay rakes, Milwaukee Leads..., edge tears/paper loss, 36x24", G, A **$550.00**

Milwaukee Harvesting Machines, match holder, embossed die-cut tin, farmer with basket holder, match strike under basket, 6x4", EX, A **$125.00**

Milwaukee Harvesting Machines, match holder, tin, pictures a cowboy behind crate with logo flanked by Always Reliable, 5½", G+, A **$120.00**

Minck Brewing Co, tray, stock image of pretty girl with roses in her hair, advertising on reverse, 17¼x12¼", EX, A **$185.00**

Miners & Puddlers Long Cut Tobacco, pail, pictures miners at work, B Leidersdorf Co, slip lid & bail, 6½x5½" dia, EX, A **$165.00**

Minneapolis Brewing Co, mug, ceramic, hops decorated logo in center of barrel-shaped mug, 4", EX, D...**$135.00**

Mint Julep Products, pin-back button, 1950s, maroon lettering on pale green background, EX, D **$3.00**

Minute Man Service, sign, porcelain, 2-sided, Minute Man in script above running service man, 30" dia, EX, A $1,600.00

Miracle, crate label, 1928, California orange, genie with tray of oranges, orchard & mountains beyond, Placentia, 10x11", M, C1 ....**$4.00**

Miramar, crate label, 1930s, California lemon, coastal scene, Crocker-Sperry Co, Montecito, 9x12", M, C3 ....**$16.00**

Mirror Candies, pocket mirror, Like Lovely Psyche, Good & Pure, 1¼" dia, EX, A..**$250.00**

Misco Orange Soda, sign, 1930s, die-cut cardboard, orange with bottle of soda in center, 4x12" dia, EX, D....**$12.00**

Miss Daisy Cigars, box label, inner lid sample, 1880s, patchwork design with Miss Daisy, silhouetted couple, Witsch & Schmidt litho, EX, A **$60.00**

Miss Gibson Cigars, box label, outer, woman in feathered hat, 4½x4½", M, C3..**$6.00**

Miss Princine Baking Powder, cup, tin, red with Miss Princine pictured in center, white product name above & below, with lid, VG+, A **$25.00**

Mission, crate label, 1930s, California lemon, pictures Santa Barbara mission & large lemon, 5½x12½", M, C1 ..**$3.00**

Mission Beverages, sign, cardboard, 2-sided, Open in orange above Mission Beverages on blue with tilted bottle & oranges, 10x14", NM, M3 ....**$20.00**

Mission Grapefruit Juice, dispenser, green conical glass bowl set on round cast base with metal top & insert, 12½x6½" dia, VG **$90.00**

Mission Malt Tonic, label, pre-1920, shield shape, Los Angeles Brewing Co, 12-oz, EX, A.......................**$30.00**

Mission of California, display, die-cut cardboard, life-size figure of lady in black & red dress serving Mission drinks, 60", EX, M2...**$275.00**

Mission Orange, bottle, 1946, clear with black & white label, 7-oz, EX, D **$8.50**

Mission Orange, dispenser, embossed barrel-shaped glass container on black glass base, with spigot, lid missing/rim chips, 13", VG, A **$60.00**

Mission Orange, fan, cardboard with wooden handle, yellow, orange & blue with oranges, Keep Cool With..., EX, M3 ....**$35.00**

Mission Orange, sign, embossed tin, yellow with Drink Mission Orange on green beside tilted bottle, Naturally Good, 11x28", EX, M3..**$85.00**

Mission Orange, sign, tin flange, Mission Orange Ice Cold on black & orange bottle cap, round, NM, M3 ..**$155.00**

Mission Orange, sign, 1940s, die-cut carboard hanger, 2-sided, product name on 1 of 2 oranges with leaves & blossoms, 6", NM, D..**$20.00**

Mission Orange, sign, 1950s, die-cut cardboard, cartoon image of bottles squeezing an orange, 11½x8", EX, D...........**$28.00**

Mission Orange, thermometer, tin, large bottle on white, 17x5", NM, M3 ....**$75.00**

Mission Orange Juice, dispenser, peach conical glass bowl set on round cast base with metal top & insert, 12½x6½" dia, VG,A **$50.00**

Misty Joe, crate label, California vegetable, Black dining-car steward, We Serve The Best, Salinas, G1 ....**$5.00**

Mitchell's Premium Beer, bottle, long neck, foil label, G, D...**$12.00**

Mity-Nice Bread, pin-back button, 1920s, yellow & blue, ad text on paper back, EX, D **$22.00**

MJB Coffee, tin, MJB above Coffee in script, 3-lb, EX, A..**$40.00**

MM Corsets, trade card, 1880s, corset shape with protruding angel on front, sold by GT Haley, Gardiner Me, 6x3½", EX, P1 ....**$15.00**

Mo-Ka Coffee, tray, Drink... 2 Cents Lb, G, D.....**$395.00**

Mo-Ka Coffee, tray, lady with horse, round, G, D...**$325.00**

Mobil, bank, 1970s, dark red plastic pig wearing white sailor's hat with Mobil lettered on top, 6½x3½" dia, EX, A **$25.00**

Mobil, emblem, die-cut porcelain, red Mobil horse with white highlights, 36", EX, A...............................**$450.00**

Mobil, emblem, 1920s-40s, die-cut porcelain, red Mobil horse with white highlights, rare, 72", EX+, A.............**$1,000.00**

Mobil, hat with bill & correct buttons, brown with cream patch bordered in blue with blue lettering & red horse, EX+, A...**$175.00**

Mobil, weathervane, die-cut metal, Mobil horse atop rod with NSEW letters, 24", NM, A **$2,700.00**

Mobil Handy Oil, can, red Mobil horse logo, plastic spout, 4-oz, EX, D **$10.00**

Mobil Marine White, pump sign, porcelain, white with black & red Mobil above black Marine above White outlined in black, rectangular, EX+, A **$150.00**

Mobil Tires, sign, embossed tin, cream with blue Mobil above red Mobil horse, blue Tires below, blue border, 48x24", VG, A **$235.00**

Mobil Upperlube, sign, light-up flasher, glass front, hand holds can left of text, Socony-Vacuum logo on tin frame, 9x16", EX, A **$325.00**

Mobilgas, banner, cloth, It's Here! above Mobil horse image at left of Flying Horse Power, New Mobilgas below, 32x57", G+, A **$200.00**

Mobilgas, display, die-cut cardboard, shaped like medal with ribbon, Mobil horse above America's Largest Selling Gasoline, VG, A **$90.00**

Mobilgas, lens, red Mobil horse with white & blue highlights above blue Mobilgas on white, fading to paint, 16½" dia, G, A **$120.00**

Mobilgas, sign, 1953, die-cut porcelain shield, Mobil horse above ...Special in black & red, black border, 12x12", EX, A $180.00

Mobilgas, toy tanker truck, tin, red & white cab with red tanker, Ford on doors, Mobilgas & Mobil horse on tanker, 3x9", EX, A **$175.00**

Mobiloil, banner, cloth, features tilted Mobiloil can with Mobil horse, Socony-Vacuum Oil Company Inc, Made In USA, 39x29", G, A **$90.00**

Mobiloil, calendar, 1933, Follow The Magnolia Trail around inset of boat on water & product emblems, July/Aug/Sept, 23x14", G, A **$75.00**

Mobiloil, can, 1935-45, Mobil horse & product name on white, text on red ground below, pry lid, 5½", 1-qt, EX, A **$10.00**

Mobiloil, chart, 1950, paper, A Guide To Correct Lubrications above can, Lubrication Recommendations below, 13 pages, 26x16", A **$75.00**

Mobiloil, sidewalk sign, porcelain, iron frame, blue Mobiloil above Mobil horse & wing-shaped symbol, no base, 19x36", EX, A **$125.00**

Mobiloil, sign, cardboard, early airplane flying over truck & car, ...World's Quality Oil, 28x20", G-, A **$225.00**

Mobiloil, sign, 1930-40s, porcelain, red Gargoyle highlighted with black in center, Drain & Refill..., 30x36" EX, A **$325.00**

Mobiloil AF, display stand, metal with 8 uniquely shaped quart bottles of Gargoyle oil, sides marked Mobiloil AF 10x18x11", G, A **$413.00**

Mobiloil Arctic, display rack, 1935-45, metal with 8 diamond-shaped glass bottles, white lettering on red, each bottle 1-qt, M, A **$1,000.00**

Mobiloil Artic, sign, porcelain, 2-sided, red & black on white, Make The Chart... & Gargoyle logo above product name, 9" dia, VG+, A **$350.00**

Mobiloil B, can, 1935-41, red Gargoyle above product name & (Extra Heavy), text below, screw lid & handle, 5-gal, 14½", VG, A $70.00

Mobiloil BB, pump sign, 1935-45, porcelain, black & red Gargoyle above product name, Vacuum Oil Co Ltd below, 9x11", VG, A **$140.00**

Mobiloil Certified Service, sign, porcelain, 2-tone circular border surrounds Gargoyle logo above Mobiloil & Certified Service, 20x20", VG+, A **$375.00**

Mobiloil Marine, sidewalk sign, porcelain, cast-iron base, Mobil horse above product name, white background, 31" dia, EX, A **$650.00**

Modax, tip tray, die-cut litho featuring Indian chief, Drink Modax lettered on headdress, Made From Indian Herbs, 5", EX, A **$800.00**

Model Smoking Tobacco, sign, metal, cartoon image of mustached man holding pipe at left of Yes I Said 10¢..., 11x34", VG, A **$95.00**

Model Smoking Tobacco, sign, metal, cartoon image of mustached man smoking pipe at right of For Pipe Or Cigarette..., 11x34", EX, A **$140.00**

Model Smoking Tobacco, sign, self-framed tin, caricature of an Indian smoking pipe & displaying product, Did You Say 10¢?, 16x6½", NM, B1 .... **$85.00**

Modoc Brand Pears, crate label, 1940s, Indian chief with outstretched arms, black background, Medford Oregon, 7¼x11", M, C1 .... **$3.00**

Moerlein Lager Beer, label, 1933-50, Derby Brewing Co, Internal Revenue Tax Paid, 12-oz, VG, A **$13.00**

Moerlein's Beer, sign, tin, alluring girl with serving tray, The World's Triumphant Master Brew, rare, framed, image: 28x20", EX, A **$1,600.00**

Moerlein's Beer, sign, 1911, reverse-painted glass, woman being handed glass of beer in open touring car, framed, 32½x24½", EX, A..............$2,500.00

Moet & Chandon Champagne, banner, canvas, gold lettering on white background, 68x27", EX, D...........**$6.50**

Mogul Egyptian Cigarettes, box, cardboard, product name above bearded man in turban, 3x2¼", EX, A............**$5.00**

Mogul Egyptian Cigarettes, sign, paper, Egyptian woman with gold coin necklace, minor paper loss/chips/soiling, framed, image: 25x17½", G-, A **$90.00**

Mogul Egyptian Cigarettes, sign, self-framed tin, Mogul smoking cigarette, decorative border 24x20", G-, A.**$75.00**

Mohawk Carpet, doll, Tomy, cloth, 16", EX, D.........**$20.00**

Mohawk Gasoline, sign, porcelain, Mohawk Gasoline lettered on band around Indian head in profile, was neon, 47½" dia, EX+, A **$2,500.00**

Mohawk Tires, sign, metal, yellow Mohawk above Tires on green with yellow lined border, 17x59", G, A **$75.00**

Mohican Coffee, tin, circular inset with Indian chief in profile, Mohican above & Coffee below on black band, screw lid, 1-lb, VG, A $105.00

Mokaine Liqueur, sign, embossed self-framed tin, Mokaine lettered diagonally above image of man seated at table, 13¾x9¾", G, A...**$25.00**

Molson's Stock, Export Ales & Cream Porter, match striker, tin, white Molson's arched above product name on blue, white & blue border, 9x4", EX, M2...........**$52.00**

Momonick Silk Co, cabinet, wood with mirrored front, drawer at bottom, 4 shelves inside, lettering above & below mirror, 40x22x16", EX, A.........................**$325.00**

Mona Motor Oil, can, 1915-25, airplane, boat, car, tractor & refinery on blue, black & cream lettering, screw lid, 1-gal, 11", EX, A **$600.00**

Mona Motor Oil, sign, self-framed tin, product name on elongated diamond in center, Tune In K-O-I-L, Listen To... below, 11x35", G, A **$160.00**

Monadnock Coffee, tin, scenic landscape in round logo on yellow with white lines, product lettering above & below, screw lid, 1-lb, NM, A.............................**$115.00**

Monadnock Peanut Butter, pail, oval landscape with product name above & below, slip lid & bail, 1-lb, EX, A...**$250.00**

Monarch Axle Grease, pail, 1935-45, pictures an eagle, red with black seal & red lettering, slip lid, 5¼x5" dia, VG, A **$25.00**

Monarch Cigars, box label, 2 lithographer's proofs, wildlife scene flanked by Havana Filled & Hand Made, 1 of 11 colors/1 brown, EX, A..............................**$91.00**

Monarch Cocoa, tin, lion logo on 4 sides, light blue, black & gold, 1-lb, VG, A **$15.00**

Monarch Coffee, container, 1930s, cardboard, lion logo in center, Reid, Murdoch & Co, Chicago, 3-lb, D $125.00

Monarch Coffee, sample tin, EX, D **$35.00**

Monarch Orange Pekoe Tea, tin, pictures glass of iced tea with lemon, Monarch in blue & lion logo above, slip lid, 6x3", EX, D **$22.50**

Monarch Peanut Butter, pail, black with round Teenie Weenie lion logo on white shield, sealed lid & bail, 10-oz, EX, A..**$175.00**

Monarch Popcorn, pail, blue with white Monarch shield featuring lion with shooting popcorn, slip lid & bail, 14-oz, EX, A **$170.00**

Monarch Sweet Pickles, cabinet/dispenser, metal with 4 removable ceramic containers with glass lids, lion logo & lettering, 43" long, VG, A **$750.00**

Monarch Tea, tin, pictures lion & tea plantation, 4½x2½x2½", EX, D **$55.00**

Monarch Typewriter Co, pocket mirror, typewriter encircled by Every Word Written On The Monarch Is Visible & other lettering, 2⅛" dia, EX, A **$60.00**

Monarch Typewriters, postcard, 1911, photographic image of woman typing, Tired At Three O'clock, No Sir! I Use The Monarch, EX, D **$45.00**

Monark Skeet Shells, box with contents, hunter encircled above product name, 12-gauge, EX, A **$45.00**

Monet & Goyon Macon, sign, 1926, man on motorcycle on shaded ground, Motocyclettes 2 Et 4... above, signed OK Gerard, framed, 48x33", VG, A.........$85.00

Monogram Brand High Grade Coffee, tin, paper label, pry lid, EX, A **$30.00**

Monogram Grease & Oils, sign, porcelain flange, 2-sided, Monogram lettered on diagonal band, Grease above left, Oils below right, 15x24", EX+, A **$375.00**

Monongahela Valley Rye, sign, reverse-painted glass, ...Imperial Cabinet Bourbon, Olena & Craig, Sole Agts, NY, framed, image: 12x24", VG, A **$175.00**

Montag Pipe & Pipeless Furnaces, sign, porcelain flange, red & white, minor edge chips, 10x18", G+, A **$95.00**

Montague Chocolates, pocket mirror, head portrait of pretty young lady in profile with a rose in her long flowing hair, oval, 2¾", EX, A **$80.00**

Monterey Beer, label, 1933-36, Salinas Brewing & Ice Co, U-type permit label, 11-oz, EX, A **$33.00**

Montgomery Ward, catalog, 1916, VG, D **$85.00**

Montgomery Ward, catalog, 1932, Christmas, G, D. **$75.00**

Montgomery Ward, catalog, 1932, Spring/Summer, VG+, H2 .... **$60.00**

Montgomery Ward, catalog, 1950, Christmas, EX, D... **$75.00**

Montgomery Ward, catalog, 1956, Christmas, VG+, H2.. **$75.00**

Montgomery Ward, catalog, 1969, Christmas, features GI Joe, Matt Mason, Barbie & more, EX, D **$35.00**

Montgomery Ward, catalog, 1970, VG, D **$25.00**

Montgomery Ward, catalog, 1971, Fall/Winter, VG+, H2 .... **$20.00**

Montgomery Ward & Co Fresh Roasted Coffee, container, cardboard & metal, blue with cream lettering & design, vertical rectangle, 5-lb, EX, A **$85.00**

Montgomery Ward Fishing & Hunting, catalog, 1950, VG+, H2 .... **$25.00**

Montgomery Ward Pure Food Groceries, catalog, 1917, May/June, 92 pages, VG+, H2 .... **$40.00**

Moore's House Colors, sign, porcelain flange, 2-sided, We Sell above large paint can, 20x16", VG+, A........ **$170.00**

Moore's Ice Cream, sign, tin, Curb Service above soldier left of Moore's Guarded Quality, Ice Cream below, framed, 34x26", EX, A **$25.00**

Moore's Ice Cream, sign, 1950s, paper, pictures waitress with ice cream scoop, Hand Packed To Take Out..., 9x20", EX, D **$15.00**

Moose Beer, sign, wood, Better Than Ever above Moose in diagonal script, The Pride Of The Monogahela Valley below, 7x15", EX, A **$85.00**

MoPar Parts, sign, painted metal flange, 2-sided, oval with Plymouth-Dodge-Desoto-Chrysler... around MoPar Parts, 17x24", G+, A **$185.00**

Morell Tilson & Sons, pocket mirror, close-up of cupid shooting arrow, You Will Find It At..., rectangular, rounded corners, 2¾", EX, A **$400.00**

Morgan's Sapolio, sign, die-cut litho shows Black child's face emerging from center of watermelon, lettering on rind, 11¾" long, EX, A **$25.00**

Morjon Brand Apples, crate label, 1930s, little boy blowing horn surrounded by shrubs & 2 large apples, San Francisco Cal, 10½x9", M, C1 .... **$2.00**

Morning Glow Coffee, tin, product name lettered about sailing ship silhouetted over sunburst, key-wind lid, 1-lb, EX, A **$35.00**

Morning Star Salmon, can label, pictures ships on open sea & salmon, M, C3 .... **$8.00**

Morrell's Pride Meats, fan, 1920s, die-cut heart, Morrell's Pride in script above grocer boy, 9x8", EX, D...... **$25.00**

Morris Foods, pin-back button, 1920s, yellow, black, red & white, EX, D **$4.00**

Morris Supreme Peanut Butter, pail, tin, horizontal lettered oval over beach scene with children, bail handle, no lid, 12-oz, EX, A **$200.00**

Morrison Plows, sign, self-framed tin, factory scene with buggies in the foreground, None Better, Few As Good..., 13½x19½", G, A **$55.00**

Morses Duchess Brand, tin, ca 1922, pictures same elegant lady on all 4 sides, black background, screw lid, 5-lb, 10", EX, A **$40.00**

Morton's Iodized Salt, blotter, 1930s, ice skating scene, Children Are Becoming More Healthy..., grocery store imprint, 3¼x6¼", VG, A **$21.00**

Morton's Iodized Salt, needle book, 1970, blue, white & yellow cardboard with red foil needle inserts inside, some needles missing, 4x3", VG, A...................... **$23.00**

Morton's Iodized Salt, paperweight/mirror, pictures container with product name arched above, blue, white, green & gold, 3½", VG+, A **$38.00**
Morton's Iodized Salt, pin-back button, yellow dots encircle the Morton girl above product name & When It Rains..., 1¾" dia, VG, A **$34.00**
Morton Salt, dispenser, tin, hangs on wall, EX, D2 .... **$100.00**
Morton Salt, mugs, 1968, pictures Morton Salt girl, set of 4, MIB, D **$25.00**
Morton Salt, pencil clip, 1930s, blue & white, EX, D .. **$8.00**
Morton Salt, pocket mirror, 1940s, celluloid, Morton Salt girl, with umbrella, When It Rains-It Pours, 3x2", EX, A **$51.00**
Morton Salt, tin, 1985, 5x4" dia, EX, D **$5.00**
Mosco, sign, cardboard stand-up, girl in undergarmets using product, Corns & Callouses Removed By..., 9", NM, B1 .... **$8.00**
Moses Cough Drops, tin, fancy graphics with circular inset of upright can on lid, orange & black, slip lid, minor flaking, 4x6", G, A **$280.00**
Moss Rose Apricots, can label, early stone litho of 2 apricots on background of roses, EX, G1 .... **$8.00**
Moth-Ene, display, die-cut cardboard, moth looking down on 3 tins of Moth-Ene, ...Kills Moths Their Eggs & Larvae.., 8x13", NM, A **$48.00**
Mother Goose Shoes, display, counter-top, 3-D hard rubber goose with vinyl clothes, case missing, 12½", EX, A.. **$95.00**
Mother Penn Motor Oil, can, head portrait of an elderly woman encircled above product name, 1-qt, NM, A.. **$20.00**
Mother's Bread, spoon, building in bowl, G, D **$20.00**

Mother's Oats, sign, 1920s-40s, 'Mother's Boy,' pictures boy in leopard skin, logo in bottom corner, framed, 27x19½", EX, A $95.00

Mother's Worm Syrup, match holder, tin, mother giving kids a dose, fancy top & bottom, yellow & green holder, 7x2", EX+, A **$575.00**
Motley's Roller Flour, pocket mirror, pictures hanging sack of flour, Highest Quality Bread Flour lettered on rim, oval, 2¾", EX, A **$90.00**
Motocyclettes 2 Et 4 Temps, sign, ca 1930, lettering above & below silhouette of motorcyclist on white, orange & yellow design, 46x26", EX, D3 .... **$1,250.00**
Motorlube Oil, can, 1900-20, early touring car with demons dancing about, cream & black, pour spout & handle, rare, 1-gal, 6", VG, A **$550.00**
Mount Carmel Beer, tip tray, pretty girl with roses, lettering on rim, spotting/soiling, 4" dia, VG, A **$200.00**
Mount Gay Eclipse Barbados Rum, counter display, composition board, metal anchor, holds 1 bottle, EX, D **$15.00**
Mount Kineo Beverages, sign, pictures large bottle, Dexter Bottle Co, red, white & blue, 19x9", EX, D **$40.00**

Mount Penn Stoves, Heaters & Ranges, toy skillet, cast iron, exterior embossed Mount Penn Stoves, Heaters & Ranges, Reading Pa, 2½" dia, EX, H1 .... $24.00

Mount Pleasant Brewing Co, sign, paper, woman holding fan surrounded by flowers, creasing/overall soiling, framed, 17½x14½", G+, A **$225.00**
Mountain Dew, bottle, 1965, green with red & white label, 10-oz, EX, D **$8.50**
Mountain Dew, sign, 1966, tin, pictures a hillbilly, 35", G, D **$245.00**
Mountain Dew Whiskey, sign, embossed celluloid, image of woman in robe picking grapes & ink-stamped logo, wood frame, 9x5½", EX, A **$275.00**
Mountaineer Coffee, tin, paper label, key-wind lid, 1-lb, G, D **$15.00**
Movie Star Health Bread, pin-back button, 1930s, blue & white, 2½", EX, D **$15.00**
Moxie, ashtray, brass, G, D **$35.00**
Moxie, bottle cap, 1950s, metal with cork lining, pictures the Moxie man, NM, D **$8.00**
Moxie, display, die-cut cardboard, Moxie lady in sailor-type hat pointing finger, Drink Moxie panel below, 17", EX, A **$175.00**
Moxie, display, 3-D wood & composition, bottle shape early label, I Am Full..., 35x11½" dia, VG, A **$950.00**
Moxie, drinking glass, bell shape with etched Drink Moxie, EX+, A **$49.00**
Moxie, drinking glass, embossed with Moxie flag logo, flared rim, fluted bottom, NM, A **$50.00**
Moxie, drinking glass, embossed with Moxie flag logo, fluted bottom, M, A **$55.00**

Moxie, fan, ca 1910, celluloid with die-cut slogan on each segment, 6" long, VG, A **$75.00**

Moxie, fan, copyright 1916, 2-sided cardboard, pictures Murie Ostriche, man & woman in canoe on back, 8x6", VG+, A **$49.00**

Moxie, fan, copyright 1922, 2-sided cardboard, pointing Moxie man on front, boy on horseback on reverse, 8x7", EX, A..**$157.00**

Moxie, fan, girl wearing necklace, G, D **$75.00**

Moxie, fan, 1920s, cardboard, Moxie lettered at right of lady in hat tipping full glass, 9x8", NM, D...........**$60.00**

Moxie, magazine ad, 1923, 'Boston Traveler,' 3 babies in box & 2 others inset above man at desk, EX, S3 ....**$36.00**

Moxie, match holder, die-cut tin, Moxie bottle atop box, Learn To Drink Moxie, Very Healthful, soiling/chips, 7x3", VG, A..**$275.00**

Moxie, mug, embossed glass, chip in bottom, 5x3" dia, G, A..**$20.00**

Moxie, mug, hourglass shape with handle, embossed Moxie on 1 side, NM, A..**$61.00**

Moxie, sheet music, Moxie Fox Trot Song lettered on geometric design above man on white horse & open car, framed, EX, A **$25.00**

Moxie, sheet music, pictures famous Rolls Royce Moxiemobile, Frank Archer on back, EX+, D **$65.00**

Moxie, sign, cardboard, die-cut, 2-sided, features pointing Moxie man, 16x16", NM, D **$295.00**

Moxie, sign, cardboard, pointing Moxie man on gold metallic ground, black frame, 21x21", VG+, A....................**$220.00**

Moxie, sign, cardboard, pre-1900, Moxie in gold on black ground, framed, rare, 5x7", E+, A.......................**$1,012.00**

Moxie, sign, cardboard, red & black on white, serrated emblems surround Thousands Of People Have Discovered..., 20x26", VG+, S5....................................**$165.00**

Moxie, sign, cardboard die-cut, cream lettering on round red, blue & black background, Drink..., Quinches..., 37x30", VG, A..**$20.00**

Moxie, sign, cardboard die-cut, hand holding straight-sided bottle, EX, M3..**$45.00**

Moxie, sign, cardboard die-cut, 1930s, baseball kid with vintage Moxie bottle, He's Got Moxie, 5¢ above, 13x8", EX, D..**$180.00**

Moxie, sign, porcelain, 1956, hand with straight-sided bottle at right of Drink Moxie logo, blue border, 34x44", M, D3 ....$375.00

Moxie, sign, tin, decorative oval with Drink above Moxie, Distinctively Different below, 20x28", VG, A **$235.00**

Moxie, sign, tin, elves displaying case of Moxie, Learn To Drink...Very Healthful, Send A Case Home, 14x20", EX, M1 ....**$550.00**

Moxie, sign, tin, embossed, Drink Moxie, Distinctively Different lettered in oval, Donaldson Art Sign Co, 7¼x33", M, A **$225.00**

Moxie, sign, tin, embossed, Drink Moxie on red background with yellow trim, minor scratches, 19x27", EX, A..**$325.00**

Moxie, sign, tin, embossed, elf pointing to large case of Moxie, Send A Case Home, Learn To Drink..., 14x20", G+, A..**$300.00**

Moxie, sign, tin, embossed, hanger, Moxie lettered in gold on green ground, wavy border, 3x5", EX+, A **$341.00**

Moxie, sign, tin, embossed, lady pouring a glass, Of Course You'll Have Some...It's So Healthful..., restored, scarce, A..**$2,950.00**

Moxie, sign, tin, embossed & stenciled, Drink...A Two Minute Vacation in white & yellow on red, scalloped rim, 32" dia, G, A **$125.00**

Moxie, sign, tin, girl on horse in touring car, sign in background, ...Distinctively Different, framed, image: 13x24", G, A **$350.00**

Moxie, sign, tin, self-framed, crowd running up stairs to Moxie bottle at the Hall of Fame, Eclipses..., 54x19", EX, A **$450.00**

Moxie, sign, tin, self-framed, 1933, car with white horse at Moxie billboard, Candy, Soda, Cigars on banner, 30x54", EX, A................................$4,000.00

Moxie, sign, tin on wood, die-cut, pointing Moxie man atop panel with braided border reading Drink Moxie, G, A **$1,300.00**

Moxie, soda jerk's hat, 1950s, red & blue on white linen-textured paper, Drink Moxie, minor scuffs on 1 side, VG, D **$22.00**

Moxie, thermometer, tin, bottle & circular logo above ...Good At Any Temperature, Moxie boy below, 25½x9½", VG, A **$300.00**

Moxie, thermometer, tin, bottle & circular logo above ...Good At Any Temperature, Moxie boy below, 25½x9½", NM, A..**$550.00**

Moxie, thermometer, 1910s-20s, die-cut tin, Moxie man & girl holding out glass flank bulb, Drink Moxie below, 9½x12", VG, A **$1,500.00**

Moxie, tip tray, ca 1907, Moxie girl's head (face forward) with glass, Moxie & I Like It lettered above & below, 6" dia, A..**$230.00**

Moxie, tip tray, Moxie girl leaning on chair enjoying product, 5¢, Delicious, Feeds The Nerves, touched up, 6" dia, EX, A..**$700.00**

Moxie, tip tray, Moxie lettered over floral background, 6" dia, NM, S5 ....**$185.00**

Moxie, tip tray, Moxie lettered over floral background, 6" dia, VG, A **$55.00**

Moxie, tip tray, Moxie Makes You Eat, Sleep, & Feel Better lettered on label in center of tray, 6" dia, A **$40.00**

Moxie, tip tray, 1900-10, Moxie girl tipping glass on floral background, I Just Love Moxie, Don't You?, 6" dia, EX, A...**$400.00**

Moxie, toy car, tin, early blue open car with rider on white horse, 6½", EX, A $2,700.00

Moxie, toy car, tin, early red open car with rider on black horse, one side is slightly faded, 6½", EX, A $3,400.00

Moxie, vegetable dish, pictures Moxie man, rare, oval, 9½" long, EX, D **$125.00**

Mr Bubble, bank, 1970s, pink plastic Mr Bubble with blue lettering, 9½", M, D **$75.00**

Mr Clean, figure of Mr Clean, 1961, vinyl, 8", M, D....**$100.00**

Mr Cola, sign, bottle cap shape, G, D **$225.00**

Mr Good Malt Syrup, can label, 1930, smiling bald man, EX, C3 ....**$8.00**

Mr Goodbar, arm floats, child's, M, D.......................**$10.00**

Mr Thomas 5¢ Cigar, tip tray, black tomcat in center flanked by None & Better, product name on rim, slight dent, 4¼" dia, EX, A..**$500.00**

Mrs Dinsmores Cough Drops, tin, Mrs Dinsmore's on banner above early portrait, Cough Drops below, slip lid, round corners, 8¾x5x5", EX, D **$260.00**

Mrs Fields Cookies, cookie jar, ceramic, white with red, Mrs Fields script logo, Made With Love & Other Natural Ingredients, M, D...**$25.00**

Mrs Lane's Coffee, tin, Mrs Lane's in script above small head portrait, Coffee lettered below, key-wind lid, 1-lb, EX+, A **$54.00**

Mrs Leland's Old Fashioned Candies, tin, 1962, pictures old-time kitchen, plastic lid, 3x5" dia, EX, D........**$10.00**

MS Hovey & Co, trade card, Manufacturers Of Best Quality Cable-Laid Linen Twines...167 River Street, Troy NY, EX, A **$17.00**

Mt Hamilton Grapes, can label, grapes & observatory on ornate green & red background, G1.......................**$8.00**

Mt Pleasant Peanut Butter, pail, tin, yellow with outlined lettering over black mountain graphic, slip lid & bail, 1-lb, NM, A **$190.00**

Mt Whitney Beer, label, 1933-36, Fresno Brewing Co, pictures snow-capped mountains, U-type permit number, 11-oz, G, A...**$6.00**

Muehlebach Brewing Co, pocket mirror, The Beer That Builds You Up arched above large beer bottle, company name below, oval, 2¾", EX, A **$70.00**

Mug Old Fashioned Root Beer, sign, copyright 1950, die-cut, foaming mug of root beer, ...By Belfast Since 1877, NM, D1 ....$185.00

Muhammad Ali Shoe Polish, tin, pictures Muhammad Ali, round, M, D **$20.00**

Muhlenberg Brewing Co, calendar, 1899, paper, girl presenting seasons greetings, Lager Beer & Porter, April pad, framed, image: 19x15", EX, A **$900.00**

Muhlenberg Brewing Co, calendar top, 1900, paper, girl with baton in decorative oval, framed, image: 22½x17", EX, A **$2,000.00**

Mulford's Toilet Talcum, tin, pictures Victorian lady on oval with lettering above & below, shaker top, EX, A **$85.00**

Mulsified Cocoanut Oil Shampoo, sign, cardboard, girl with long wavey hair in negligee surrounded by flowers, overall soiling, 34x22", VG, A **$120.00**

Munsing Wear, pin-back button, 1930s, white lettering on pale green, EX, D **$5.00**

Munsing Wear, sign, die-cut tin, kids on teeter-totter, ...Suit You on round pivot base, 22x21", EX, A **$4,050.00**

Munsing Wear Union Suits, sign, die-cut tin, pictures 6 kids in their Union suits, Perfect Fitting..., fading/scratches/chips, 16½x24", VG, A....... **$1,700.00**

Munsingwear, doll, 1970, vinyl penguin, 7", EX, D **$18.00**

Munsingwear, sign, 1914, canvas, 2 girls modeling long johns for Grandma, signed Myles, original frame, 27½x35½", EX, A **$900.00**

Munsingwear Union Suits, trolley sign, 1920s, cardboard, pictures man & 2 children in Union Suits, ...Cover You With Satisfaction, 11x21", NM, D $150.00

Munyon's Homoeopathic Home Remedies, display cabinet, wood with tin insert on all sides, oval portrait of Dr Munyon on slant front, 14½x14x12", G, A **$200.00**

Murad Bey Cigars, box label, outer, Arab on horse holding his pistol up, 4½x4½", M, D **$7.00**

Murad Turkish Cigarettes, box, tin, Egyptian queen lounging on altar with sun rising over Egyptian desert beyond, hinged lid, 2x6x3", EX+, A **$60.00**

Murad Turkish Cigarettes, sign, paper, charging Turk on horseback with saber raised, cigarette pack in background, framed, image: 26x17", VG, A **$350.00**

Murad Turkish Cigarettes, sign, paper, Turkish man viewed from behind in left profile, lettering above, product below, framed, 26½x10", G+, A **$200.00**

Murad Turkish Cigarettes, sign, paperboard, Turkish girl holds tray with pack of cigarettes above head on green ground, framed, 39x27", G, A **$350.00**

Murine, calendar sign, 1937, lady uses Murine on sign above calendar showing February 6/7, green woodgrain border, 17x9", VG, A **$1,300.00**

Murphys Oil Soap, sample tin, round, VG, D **$11.00**

Murrells Snow Cap Lard, pail, 4-lb, EX, D **$16.50**

Musky Soft Drinks, sign, die-cut cardboard in shape of fish with 2 cutouts for hands to keep fish stories in check, Whopper Stopper, EX+, A **$250.00**

Mustang, crate label, 1930s, California orange, cowboy on bucking horse, Los Angeles, 10x11¾", M, C3 .... **$12.00**

Mutton Tallow with Camphor, tin, 1920s, pictures a sheep flanked by lettering, full, 2x3", EX, D **$14.00**

Mutual Gasoline, globe, plastic with glass insert, a running rabbit, red, white & blue, 17x15", EX+, A **$100.00**

Mutual Life Insurance Co of New York, sign, cardboard, company name & product name surrounded by ornate floral border, framed, G, A **$75.00**

My Girl Cigars, box label, inner lid sample, 1890s, encircled girl flanked by ship & crown, vignettes below, OL Schwencke & Co, M, A **$72.00**

My Wife's Salad Dressing, bottle, 1920s, embossed glass, EX, D2 .... **$20.00**

Myers Pumps, calendar, 1919, paper, portrait insets & factory view above variety of products, full pad, framed, image: 48x17", VG, A **$150.00**

N

N-Be-Co Syrup, can label, 1914, Black boy eating bread, M, C3 .... **$85.00**

Nabisco, cookie jar, 1974, pottery, tan barrel-shaped jar with red trim, white Nabisco embossed across front, McCoy 78, EX+, D **$85.00**

Nabisco, see also National Biscuit Co

Nabisco Pretzels, doll, Mr Salty, stuffed cloth, 11", EX, D **$10.00**

Nabisco Uneeda Bakers, store jar, embossed glass, ball shape with slanted top, 10" dia, EX, A **$45.00**

Nabob Pure Brand Paprika, tin, green, red & white, Nabob arched above Brand Pure Paprika, vertical rectangle, NM, M2 .... **$12.00**

Nadco, lug box label, California grape, Spanish senorita dancing on blue background, white lettering, Visalia, G1 .... **$3.00**

Nadruco Royal Rose Talcum Powder, tin, tall flat oval with large rose over vertical floral motif, shaker top, EX+, M2 .... **$105.00**

Nanga Saki Cigars, box label, inner lid sample, 1870s, Japanese figure seated in garden flanked by banner, Heppenheimer & Maurer, EX, A **$25.00**

Narragansett Ale, tray, The Famous Old Narragansett Ale lettered in gold with black on red, gold & black hops motif on rim, 13" dia, EX, A **$80.00**

Narragansett Banquet Ale, label, pre-Prohibition, 12-oz, EX, A **$23.00**

Narragansett Beer, sign, paper roll-down, woman in plumed hat sitting at table with beer stein, matted & framed, 23x17", VG, A **$150.00**

Narragansett Cranberries, can label, Indian shooting bow & arrow, Lynn Ma, EX, G1 .... **$10.00**

Narragansett Dark Ale, label, 1933-36, U-type permit number, 12-oz, EX, A **$15.00**

Narragansett Export Beer, label, 1933-50, Internal Revenue Tax Paid statement, 12-oz, EX, A **$15.00**

Narragansett Half Stock Dark Ale, label, pre-Prohibition, 12-oz, EX, A **$40.00**

Narragansett Lager, sign, gold-painted cutout letters on screen with rope trim, Narragansett in diagonal script, framed, 48x69", VG+, A **$303.00**

Nash, booklet, 1950, sepia tones, 4 pages, NM, D **$6.00**

Nash, pin-back button, There's None As New As Nash lettered in red on white, round, EX, A **$21.00**

Nash Auto, playing cards, double deck, pictures automobiles, in original box, G, D **$49.00**

Nash Mustard, bank, glass Donald Duck figure with yellow & green tin lid, 4½x2⅜", EX, D **$95.00**

Nash's Clay Crispettes, pin-back button, ca 1900, red & white logo on green background, EX, D **$4.00**

Nash's Monroe Crispettes, pin-back button, ca 1900, yellow & white logo pennant on blue ground, EX, D **$4.00**

Nation's Choice Whiskey, flask, red, white & blue paper label pictures Parker-Davis, very rare, EX, D **$425.00**

National Batteries, sign, embossed tin, flying eagle superimposed over bold National, Batteries lettered below, lined border, 12x20", VG, A **$150.00**

National Beer, tip tray, deep-dish, cowboy on horse bursting through paper, The Best In The West, flat gold rim, 4½" dia, VG, A **$200.00**

National Beer, tray, cowboy on horse bursting through paper, National Brewing Co lettered on rim, oval, 16x13", G, A $700.00

National Beer, tray, man pouring himself a glass of beer, A Good Judge, National Brewing Co, rust spots/scratches/chips, 13" dia, G-, A **$75.00**

National Biscuit Co, clock, wood case, logo on round face, boy in yellow slicker & company name on lower glass panel, limited edition, EX, A **$400.00**

National Biscuit Co, display rack, oak, 3 shelves with cross-bar brace, stenciled gold & black lettering above & below, 55½", VG, A **$575.00**

National Biscuit Co, display rack, oak, 3 shelves, National Biscuit Company lettered in black, 38x25½", M, A **$400.00**

National Biscuit Co, sign, oak, 2-sided, long & narrow with National Biscuit Company in shadowed lettering, EX, A **$400.00**

National Biscuit Co, see also Uneeda

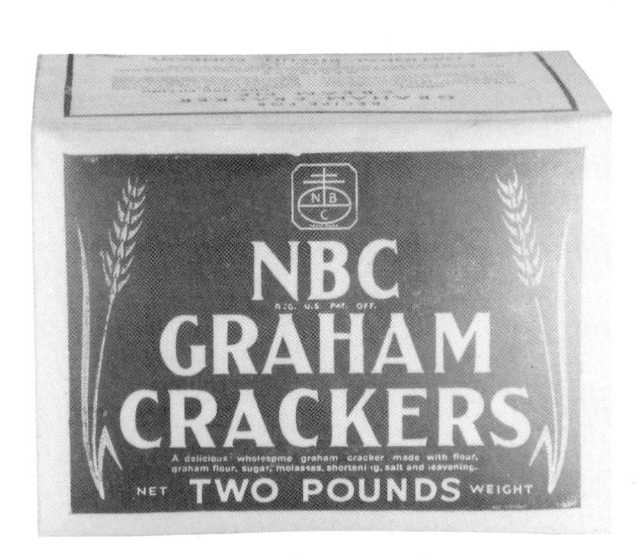

National Biscuit Co Graham Crackers, box, red & white, ...Two Pounds, 5⅛x8", EX, D $35.00

National Biscuit Co Uneeda Biscuit, letter opener, tin, handle is boy in yellow slicker, 8" long, VG, A **$62.50**

National Biscuit Co Uneeda Biscuits, cereal bowl, pictures boy in yellow rain slicker inside & out, marked Warwick China, 5" dia, M, D $50.00

National Brewery Co, tray, pictures factory & bottle of product with National in script, decorative rim, some wear, 10x14", VG, A **$120.00**

National Brewery Co White Seal, sign, hanging, crystalloid with cardboard backing, elegant woman with bottle & glass in ornate border, 14x10", EX, A **$800.00**

National Brewing Co, tip tray, bearded fellow with gun & dog, ...Steelton Pa on rim, minor rim chips/lightly soiled, 4¼" dia, VG, A..**$130.00**

National Brewing Co, tip tray, portly fellow & Black jockey discussing horse race, minor chips/soiling, 4¼" dia, EX, A..**$400.00**

National Brewing Co, tip tray, portly fellow & devilish looking child playing golf, ...Steelton Pa on rim, minor soiling, 4¼" dia, VG, A..**$260.00**

National Cigar Stand Co, light, mica with fringed bottom, patriotic lettering on front panel, Black & White 5¢ Cigar on side, rare, VG, A **$2,650.00**

National Cigar Stand Co, tip tray, classical lady with crown of daisies in hair surrounded by various product labels on rim, 6" dia, VG+, A............$25.00

National Cream Separator, stick pin, flag shape in red, white & blue stripes with advertising featuring separators on 2 oval insets, EX, A **$26.00**

National Dairy Malted Milk, container, aluminum, knob lid, minor paint loss/slight denting on lid, A **$160.00**

National Fire Insurance Co, ledger marker, flag & Columbia with shield & eagle, Kellogg & Bulkeley, minor flaking/overall soiling, 12½x3", G, A **$25.00**

National Food Co, trade card, pictures bunnies & flowers, slight corner bend, D **$4.00**

National Hay Tedder, sign, red, white & blue shield with horizontal oval of hay tedder, lettering above, 21x17", EX, A **$25.00**

National Life & Accident Insurance Co, calendar, 1935, colorful image of barnyard animals playing instruments, shows 12 months, framed, 13½x10½", G, A.........**$25.00**

National Lightning Protection Co, sign, cardboard, black lettering on green background, ...St Louis Mo, Minneapolis Minn..., 9x23", EX, D..............................**$25.00**

National Premium Brewing Co, globe, milk glass with reverse-painted glass inserts picturing lion logo, 17x15" dia, NM, A...**$850.00**

National Protective Legion, calendar, 1908, child holding sword & white flag with logo, full pad, framed, minor edge wear, 26½x21", A **$35.00**

National Wax Thread Sewing Machine, sign, 1868-70, sewing machine & Best In The World in center, product name above & below, 21x23", NM, D..........**$375.00**

Natural Chilean Soda, sign, 1940s, tin flange, 2-sided, Black man's face in corner, ...Yassuh! Uncle Natchel, 15x21½", EX, A................................$175.00

Nature's Remedy, sign, happy man surrounded by bags & stacks of money above box of product, lettered band above & below, 41x26", EX, A **$45.00**

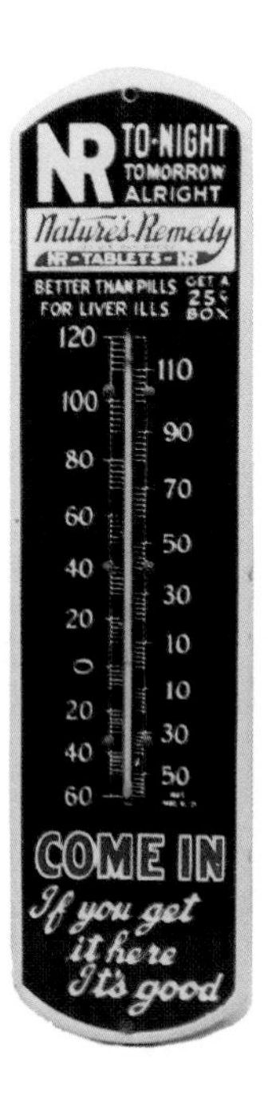

Nature's Remedy, thermometer, porcelain, red & white on blue, white border, advertising above & below, rounded ends, 26", NM, D3 ....$375.00

Nature's Remedy Tablets, pocket mirror, product name lettered across nose of face viewed close-up, lettered border, 2 cracks, 2⅛" dia, VG, A..........................**$40.00**

Navy Brand Firecrackers, package, 1928, pictures a sailor, 3x2½", EX, D **$10.00**

Nazareth Cement Co, blotter, pictures bag of cement, red, white & blue, unused, 6x3½", D **$2.50**

BC Bread, bread end label, promotional, Walt Disney character Chip from Chip & Dale fame, Trade 'Em With Your Friends, EX, S1 .... **$6.00**

BC Bread, bread end label, cartoon character Kayo Mullins, copyrighted News Syndicate Co Inc, EX, S1 .... **$7.00**

BC Bread, bread end label, shows Donald Duck in high stride, Donald Duck In Canada lettered below, red background, EX, S1 .... **$3.00**

eathery Credit Jewelry, clock, wood with lettering on bottom glass panel, working, 39", G, A **$150.00**

ebo Cigarettes, sign, paperboard, girl stands with hand up to jeweled ear, product shown in heart-shaped inset, framed, 27x19", G-, A $200.00

ebraska Girl Cigars, box label, inner lid, 1902, woman on horse with dog chasing them, 6x9", EX, D ... **$18.00**

ebraska Seed Co, display rack, wood case with 7 slanted shelves, company name & address lettered above, 45x29", EX, A $400.00

ebraska Seed Co, pin-back button, children teeter-tottering on tipped-over barrel with garden's bounty, Seeds That Grow!..., round, EX, A **$240.00**

ecco Wafers, display rack, tin, revolves on round base, advertising on top & inner panel, 19", G, A **$230.00**

Nectar Cigars, box label, inner lid, woman holding wine glass, 6x9", M, C3 .... **$22.00**

Neeco Coffee Soda, lapel pin, metal, round with I Drink above smiling boy in sombrero lettered Necco, Coffee Soda below, bendable tab, EX, A......................... **$20.00**

Nehi, bingo card, wood, Par-T-Pak, 8x5", EX, A **$14.00**

Nehi, blotter, Drink Nehi, Bottled Energy!, VG, A **$11.00**

Nehi, bottle, 1967, clear with red & white label, 10-oz, EX, D **$6.00**

Nehi, bottle carrier, cardboard, Take Home A Carton..., NM, B1 .... **$5.00**

Nehi, calendar, 1927, girl on edge of life boat with bottle, large bottle lower left, full pad, 24x14", EX, A **$110.00**

Nehi, cooler, metal, legs with rollers & open shelf, 2 sides with Nehi in beveled letters & bottle before woman's leg, VG, A **$485.00**

Nehi, sign, painted tin, bottle on oval right of Nehi in beveled letters, Drink upper left, checked border, 18x45", EX, A **$75.00**

Nehi, sign, tin, Drink Nehi Beverages & tilted bottle on white with green border, 18x54", VG+, M3 .... **$95.00**

Nehi, sign, 1920s, embossed tin, blue & red on yellow, We Serve Nehi, Ice Cold, 3½x19½", NM, D **$60.00**

Nehi, sign, 1920s, embossed tin, Nehi lettered above bottle, 8x5½", NM, D **$90.00**

Nehi, sign, 1920s, scalloped reverse-painted glass in easel-back frame, Drink Nehi Ice Cold in silver, EX, D **$795.00**

Nehi, sign, 1920s, tin, bottle on oval at right of Drink Nehi Ice Cold, 12x29½", G+, D **$50.00**

Nehi, tray, bather caught up in ocean wave & bottle, labeled rim top & bottom, vertical rectangle, VG+, A $160.00

Nehi Bottling Co, seltzer bottle, green glass, with spigot, EX+, A **$100.00**

Nehi Orange, decal, tilted bottle over sunburst rays, ...And Other Nehi Flavors, 12x7", NM, A **$22.00**

Neiman Marcus, purse mirror, gold letters slightly fading, D **$15.00**

Nesbitt's, sign, cardboard, seated lady in white formal holding bottle, blue dot reading ...A Soft Drink..., 19x26", EX, M3 .... **$80.00**

Nesbitt's, sign, cardboard, 2 little girls having Nesbitt's party with dolls at table, round logo lower right, 25x36", NM, A $350.00

Nesbitt's, sign, embossed tin, Nesbitt's in script above large bottle, 26x7", NM, S2..**$125.00**

Nesbitt's, sign, tin, Drink Nesbitt's California Orange beside tilted bottle & 5¢ In Bottles, 11x27", NM, B1 .....**$125.00**

Nesbitt's, thermometer, embossed tin, 2 angels drinking from straws from the same large bottle, All This Goodness..., 27", VG, A...**$90.00**

Nesbitt's, thermometer, tin, Don't Say Orange Say Nesbitt's above professor leaning on bottle, 22¾", G+, A...**$40.00**

Nesbitt's, thermometer, tin, Drink Nesbitt's California Orange above, slanted bottle below, rounded top & bottom, 27", VG+, A...**$80.00**

Nesbitt's, thermometer, tin, Nesbitt's Made From Real Oranges above, slanted bottle below, striped background, 27", VG, A...**$55.00**

Nesbitt's Hot Chocolate, warming plate, electric, back panel shows Dutch scene with turning & lettered windmill blades, 16¼x9", EX, A.................................**$150.00**

Nestea, dispenser, upright glass barrel lettered Iced Nestea on stoneware base with company label, metal top, 16½", EX+, A...**$35.00**

Nestle Quik, bank, Bunny Money, M, D2 ....**$15.00**

Nestle Quik, booklet, 'Magic Tricks,' 1978, premium, NM, P4 ....**$5.00**

Nestle Quik, mug, hard plastic bear shape, P2..........**$18.00**

Nestle Quik, mug, 1980s, plastic, Quik bunny with ear handles, 4½", M, D **$10.00**

Nestle Quik, pitcher, brown plastic with original paper label, Free When You Buy One 2 Lb Can (Any Flavor)..., 9¾", M, D **$14.00**

Nestle Quik, tin, pictures a house on front, green background, 8x6¼x2½", EX, D.......................................**$5.00**

Nestle's Baby Meal, postcard, chromolitho, pictures naked baby getting out of a horse-drawn buggy, German, EX, D..**$35.00**

Nestle's Hazelnut Chocolate, dispenser, embossed tin & glass case, blue & gold paper labels on front, ball feet, 10" long, VG, A **$70.00**

Nestle's Milk Food, trade card, Little Miss Muffet & large can of product, nursery rhyme above, EX, A.................**$15.00**

Nestle's Original Toll House Cookies, cookie jar, heav American pottery with gold trim, chocolate chip cooki on reverse, M, P2 ....**$110.0**

Nestle's Semi-Sweet Chocolate, recipe book, 1957, 6 pages, EX, D **$8.5**

Nestle's Swiss Milk Chocolate, store case, etched glass, 3 tiered, back door missing, 15½x12x11", EX, A...**$175.0**

Netcraft Fishing Tackle, catalog, 1958, 154 pages, VG+ H2..**$20.0**

Nettleton Shoes, postcard, fade-away style, picture woman giving her husband a pair of shoes for Christ mas, The Right Gift..., EX, D **$30.0**

Neversink Distillery, sign, reverse-painted glass, brewer buildings & busy street scene, Samuel Bugh... below framed, image: 20x28", G-, A **$200.0**

New & True Coffee, pocket mirror, pictures large can o coffee, 2¾x1¾", EX, A..**$65.0**

New Brunswick Fire Insurance, blotter, ca 1920, unused 4x9", EX, P1 ....**$7.0**

New Brunswick Tires, trade card, bicycling scene with gir riding on handle bars holding banner, ...Are Up To Date, sepia browns, EX, A...................................**$36.0**

New Burch Plows, sign, wood, bold white lettering wit Trade Mark B at left, ...Made At Crestline, Ohio, blu ground, 17x72", G-, A **$100.0**

New Castle Fire-Works Manufacturing Co, poster, 3 nymph in allegorical scene, lettering above, New Inventions Fo 1913, gilt frame, 19½x14½", G+, A..............................**$160.00**

New Deal, crate label, Washington apple, stud poker hand showing 4 top cards of a royal flush, Wenatchee, 9x11", G1 ...**$5.00**

New Empire Cooking Stove, sign, paper, iron stove flanked by For Coal Or Wood..., product name above matted & framed, image: 28x20", EX, A **$900.00**

New England Brewing Co, tray, stock image of elk in grass by mountainous lake, oval, 13¾x16½", G-, A **$75.00**

New England Fertilizer Co, calendar, 1914, paper, gir seated in window sill with flowers in background, ful pad, framed, image: 23x15", VG+, A.....................**$75.00**

New England Telephone & Telegraph Co, sign, porcelain company name on band around lettered bell, Local & Long Distance Telephone, 11x11", VG, A **$80.00**

New Haven Dairy Ice Cream, sign, porcelain, Quart & Pint Bricks, red & white, chips, 27x21", D **$65.00**

New Home Sewing Machine, sign, comical scene of lady sewing man's pants with him in them on yellow background, framed, 44½x30½", EX, A **$700.00**

New Home Sewing Machine Co, trade card, 1881, pictures family in western scene, New Home In The Far West lettered in upper right, EX, A **$19.00**

New Idea Farm Equipment Co, jigsaw puzzle, shows farm scene with machinery, 7½x16½", F1 ....**$35.00**

New King Snuff, pocket mirror, ca 1920, pouch of snuff pictured above product name, rectangular with rounded corners, EX, A **$90.00**

New Lebanon Brewing Co, sign, paper, girl in elegant evening attire with glass of beer flanked by lettering, framed, image: 27x19½", EX, A..........................**$625.00**

New Method Self Starting Pocket Lighter, display box, die-cut cardboard, man in cap lighting cigar with a New Method lighter, 1 boxed lighter, EX, A **$15.00**

New Process Gas Range, match holder, gold, red & silver label on black-painted metal, ...Saves Time & Gas, 3¼", EX, A **$120.00**

New Process Starch, trade card, double image of Chinese man having problems ironing & Victorian woman doing perfect job, EX, A **$24.00**

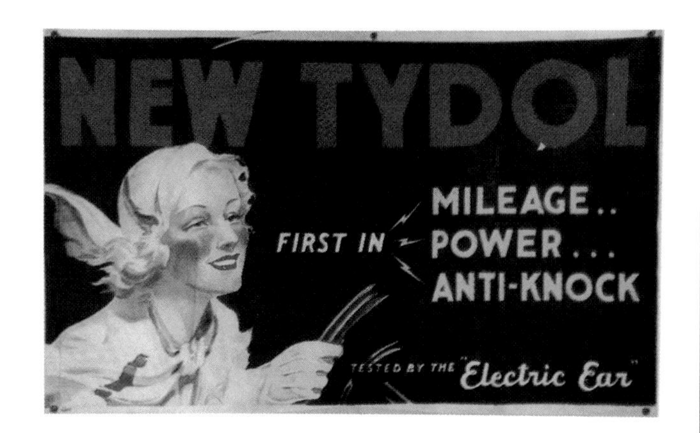

New Tydol, banner, cloth, woman left of lettering, First In Mileage, Power, Anti-Knock..., 36x59", EX, A $225.00

New York Life Insurance Co, poster, paper, man & boy on bicycle with flag dated 1897, minor creasing & fading, framed, 21x15", G, A **$150.00**

New York Times Newspaper, clock, composition, figure-8 shape, Have You Read The Times This Morning embossed on pendulum panel, 31x18½", G, A.. **$500.00**

New Yorker Beverages, sign, embossed tin, shows product name with illustrated couple in formal attire & tilted bottle, 33x56", EX, A **$210.00**

New Yorker Cigars, box label, outer, pictures a pilgrim, 4½x4½", M, C3 .... **$3.00**

New-Way Engines, pocket mirror, engine in center with The New-Way Air Cooled arched above, Lansing Michigan USA below, 2¼" dia, NM, A **$80.00**

Newark Shoe Mfg Co, keychain tag, early 1900s, silvered brass, engraved shoe on 1 side, company name on the other, EX, D **$8.00**

Newberry Shoe, match holder, die-cut tin, Wear The Newberry Shoe in gold on black, nail hole top center, 4¼", G+, A **$75.00**

Newburgh Brand Keystone Overalls & Pants, sign, porcelain flange, Keystone Union Made Overalls & Pants emblem at left of company name, minor chips, EX, A **$266.00**

Newport Cigarettes, ashtray, white china, pictures 3 packages of cigarettes, 4¾" dia, D **$12.00**

Newport Cigarettes, cap, 1980s, embroidered name & insignia, MIB, P4 .... **$7.00**

Newsboy Cut Plug Tobacco, trade card, 'Where Is Mother,' pictures group of puppies, VG, D **$7.50**

Newsboy Cut Plug Tobacco, trade card, copyright 1892, 'Waiting for the Fishing Party,' shows man seated beside tackle box, VG, A **$18.00**

Newsboy Cut Plug Tobacco, trade card, 1892, 'The Peacemaker,' painting of 2 women & a man, directions for other paintings on back, 6x3", EX, P1 .... **$10.00**

Niagara Fire Insurance Co, sign, paper, small image of Niagara Falls, ...Cash, Capitol, New York, $1,000,000, framed, 16x21½", VG, A **$250.00**

Niagara Shoes, sign, ca 1910, embossed tin over cardboard, oval image of Niagara Falls above product name & lettering, 19x9", EX, D **$400.00**

Niagra Searchlight, counter display, paper litho, 8x9", A **$20.00**

Nichol Kola, counter display, pressed paper, 11x18", A..... **$5.00**

Nichol Kola, door push plate, 1936, embossed tin, pictures a bottle, Drink America's Taste Sensation above & below, 24x8", EX, D **$55.00**

Nichol Kola, pin-back button, 1930s, red & white, EX, D.. **$8.00**

Nichol Kola, sign, ca 1936, embossed tin, stiff-legged waiter serving 5¢ bottle, America's Taste Sensation, 35¾x12", EX, A **$135.00**

Nichol Kola, sign, die-cut cardboard, bathing beauty seated with hand on hip holding bottle, Drink... below, EX, A $160.00

Nichol Kola, sign, embossed tin, bottle cap with white Nichol on red above red Kola on white, black background, 14½x14", EX, A **$10.00**

Nichol Kola, sign, embossed tin, lettered bottle cap form on square background, 14x14½", NM, A **$40.00**

Nichol Kola, sign, 1930s, tin, bottle cap flanked by soldier & bottle, 12x30", EX, D **$50.00**

Nichol Kola, sign, 1936, embossed tin, America's Taste Sensation above 5¢ Bottle, Twice As Good lettered below, 35½x12", EX, A **$70.00**

Nicolene Motor Oil, sign, porcelain, red & white on green, 36x24", EX, D **$600.00**

Niehoff Automotive Products, sign, light-up, metal rim, glass face, company name on center band, Authorized above & Distributor below, 11" dia, G+, A **$30.00**

Night Rider, crate label, peach, cowboy on galloping horse, 7x8", M, C3 .... **$12.00**

Nikolai Vodka, salt & pepper shakers, Russian figures, M, P2 .... **$175.00**

Nikolai Vodka, statuette, 1970s, plaster, dancing Russian figure, 12", M, D **$75.00**

Nine Star Lager, label, 1933-36, 9 surrounded by stars, Muessel Brewing Co, U-type permit number, 1-gal, EX, A **$33.00**

Nittany Ale, label, 1933-50, Philipsburg Brewing Co, Internal Revenue Tax Paid statement, 12-oz, EX, A **$36.00**

NL Co Lozenges, tin, glass front, allover floral decor with product name at top, black, gold & silver, slip lid, 8x6", EX, A **$250.00**

Noble 5¢ Cigar, counter display, tin with glass top & slide drawer, 4 men smoking cigars, Everybody's Smoking It, 15x12x18", VG, A **$400.00**

Nolan's Fine Shoes, trade card/calendar, 1880, shows revolutionary era couple on front, calendar on back, 2½x3¾", EX, P1 .... **$6.00**

None Such Mince Meat, Pumpkin & Squash, clock, pumpkin-shaped cardboard in tin pie pan, advertising surrounded by numbers on pumpkin graphics, 9½" dia, VG, A $400.00

Noon Day Stove Polish, sign, paper, women doing household chores with baby & dog looking in stove, Most Brilliant..., 21½x17", EX, A **$4,000.00**

Nor'Way Anti-Freeze, thermometer, metal, Norway man peering from behind thermometer, Be Safe All Year, rounded corners, 26", G-, A **$25.00**

Nor-Mont Pears, can label, pictures polar bear & pear, Lynn Ma, EX, G1 .... **$8.00**

Nor-Mont Sweet Peas, can label, 1929, polar bear on glacier, EX, C3 .... **$25.00**

Norka Ginger Ale, sign, 1930s, tin, pictures tilted bottle, ...Tastes Better, 12x24", EX, D **$40.00**

Norris Locomotive Works, broadside, image of the plant surrounded by lettering, engine vignettes in bottom corners, framed, 16½x13¼", VG, A **$300.00**

Norse Coffee, pail, tin, red & black, Norse Coffee above & below graphic on scrolled emblem, slip lid & bail, 9x7" dia, VG+, M2 .... **$60.00**

North Country, crate label, Washington apple, photo image of 3 apples, 3-D white logo, Stadelman Fruit Co, 9x11", EX, G1 .... **$3.00**

North Pole Smoking Tobacco, lunch pail, man at pole with bear looking on, red, white & blue, bail handle, 6x6x4", VG, A **$300.00**

North Star Tobacco, pocket tin, flat, scarce, EX, D ... **$500.00**

North Western Pale Export Beer, label, pre-1920, logo above North Western in script, G, A **$40.00**

North-Western Cigars, box label, inner lid, embossed gold leaves, 6x9", M, C3 .... **$2.00**

Northampton Brewing Co Lager Beer, tip tray, hand holding 3 bottles, lettering on rim, minor background creasing/rim chips, 4¼" dia, VG, A **$85.00**

Northern Bath Tissue, doll, 1986, plush/vinyl, premium, M, D **$42.00**

Northland Ice Cream, sign, die-cut porcelain, large ice cream cone with tree logo on ice cream & product lettering on cone, 85x36", VG+, A **$325.00**

Northrup, King & Co's Clover & Alfalfa Seed, thermometer, porcelain, black lettering on yellow background, 27", EX, A **$80.00**

Northwestern National Life Insurance Co, paperweight, glass, pictures building, G, D **$22.00**

Norton's Fine Candies, trade card, 1890s, pictures 3 cats mixing candy, 237 Kearney St, 3x5", EX, P1 .... **$10.00**

Nosler Bullets, display board, pictures various game at left of 56 bullets, framed, 13x19", VG, A **$120.00**

Nu Icy, sign, self-framed embossed tin, bottle at left on 3-color background, Drink...Flavors You Can't Forget, 36x60", NM, A $350.00

Nuding Brewing Co, sign, paper, men in tavern sampling brew, ...Allentown, Pa above, framed, image: 14x22", VG, A **$950.00**

Nugget Casino, vase, pottery figure of Nugget Sam, 7½", M, P2 .... **$95.00**

NuGrape, calendar, 1957, complete, EX, D **$25.00**

NuGrape, display, die-cut cardboard stand-up, yellow product label above sandwich by large bottle, 13x10", NM, M3 .... **$80.00**

NuGrape, match holder, embossed tin, G, D **$79.00**

NuGrape, menu board, tin, NuGrape & tilted bottle above chalkboard, vertical rectangle with rounded corners, VG, M2 .... **$30.00**

NuGrape, sign, embossed tin, bottle at left of lettering, ...Not Grape Juice, A Flavor You Can't Forget, 11¾x23¾", G-, A **$55.00**

NuGrape, sign, 1930s-40s, embossed tin, Drink... upper left of tilted bottle, A Flavor You Can't Forget, 12x16", EX+, A **$160.00**

NuGrape, sign, 1950s, tin, Drink upper left of underlined NuGrape, Contains Pure Grape... below, rounded corners, 19x27", EX, M2 .... **$42.00**

NuGrape, syrup dispenser, glass bowl with milk glass base, no lid, 11½x8" dia, VG, A **$45.00**

NuGrape, thermometer, 1940s, embossed tin, bottle shape, purple & red with gray highlights, 16", M, A..................**$135.00**

NuGrape, tray, Drink NuGrape lettered above mother & child by outdoor fountain, plain rim, horizontal rectangle, NM, A $250.00

NuGrape, tray, hand with bottle surrounded by burst of light rays in oval inset, lettering on rim, 13x10", VG+, M2..**$52.00**

NuGrape, tray, woman standing in moonlight holding bottle, EX+, A..**$120.00**

NuGrape, tray, woman standing in moonlight holding bottle, American Art Works, 13¼x10½", NM, A.......**$160.00**

NuGrape, tray, woman standing in moonlight holding bottle, American Artworks, overvarnished/some rim wear, 13¼x10½", VG, A **$55.00**

NuGrape/Pepsi-Cola/Orange-Crush, bowl, 3 different logos in 3 different colors with bold green line around rim, Wellsville China, 6¼" dia, NM, A.................**$110.00**

NuGrape/Pepsi-Cola/Orange-Crush, plate, 3 different logos in 3 different colors with bold green line around rim, Wellsville China, 7" dia, NM, A...................**$120.00**

Numrich Arms, display, die-cut revolver, 2-sided, opens to show gun fired, VG, A..**$15.00**

Nutmeg State Beer, label, 1933-50, Eastern Brewing Corp, Internal Revenue Tax Paid, 12-oz, VG, A....................**$16.00**

Nyal's Family Remedies, sign, embossed tin, yellow with Nyal's Family Remedies Good For You in red above AJ Farmer in black, 10x20", EX, A.............................**$15.00**

O

O'Keefe Beer, mug, glazed ceramic with logo, twist handle, 8", P4..**$15.00**

O'Sullivans Heels, blotter, lower half of man putting on shoe with heel visible, unused, 6x3", D **$2.50**

O-So-Good Coffee, tin, pictures steaming cup of coffee with product name above & below, red, white & blue, scratches, 10", G, A **$130.00**

Oak Motor Oil, sign, porcelain, 2-sided, Oak (woodlook letters) & Motor Oil over tree graphic, text flanks trunk, 17x26", EX/VG, A **$750.00**

Oak Motor Suit, pocket mirror, product name above man standing before car wheel & fender, The Suit That Suits..., oval, 2¾", VG, A **$70.00**

Oakland Pontiac, sign, porcelain, 2-sided, Oakland Service Pontiac, 24x36", EX+, S2.....................................**$550.00**

Obermeyer & Liebmann Bottled Beer, cart, wood box with metal handle & painted wheels, product name lettered on sides, 43x16", scarce, EX, A..............**$1,500.00**

Obermeyer & Liebmann Erlanger Brau, label, dated 1903, pictures bird at left, G, A **$11.00**

OCB Cigarette Paper, box, full, 3¼x10x2", A...................**$50.00**

Occident Flour, display, tin panel with 7 convex display windows showing the different stages of flour production, 14" long, G+, A..**$250.00**

Occident Flour, sign, tin, sack of flour pictured at right of product name, Slate Hill Feed & Coal Co lettered above, framed, EX, A...**$450.00**

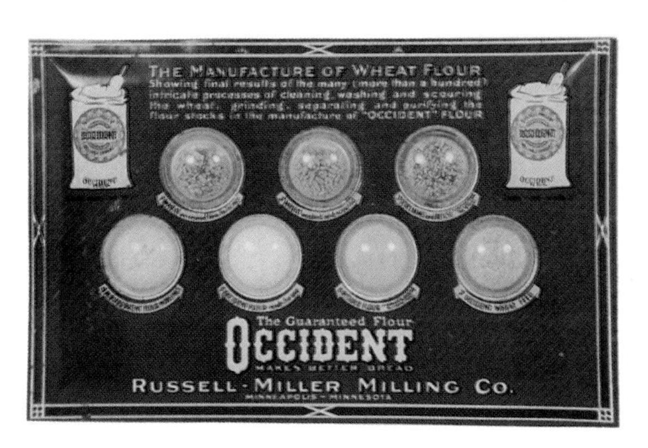

Occident Flour, sign, 1920-40, tin, shows wheat samples ground into flour, flour bags & text above, minor dent/paint chips, 9x14", A.................$325.00

Occident Flour, thermometer, wood, brown & green logo on tan above, Occident Flour Makes Better Bread, rounded, 15", EX, A **$95.00**

Occident Flour, thermometer, 1920-40, embossed tin, Good Baking... in cream letters above flour sack, red background, 16x4", VG, A **$40.00**

Oceanic Cut Plug Tobacco, bag, cloth, stamped logo of encircled sailing ship with Oceanic above & Cut Plug below, 2-oz, NM, A **$9.00**

Oceanic Tobacco, package label, EX, D....................**$10.00**

Ocklawaha Cigars, box labels, inner & outer sample set, 1870s, riverboat steams down tropical river, Heppenheimer & Maurer litho, EX, A.............................**$385.00**

Oconto Brewing Co, tip tray, pictures pretty girl in profile, Compliments of The Oconto Brewing Co, 4" diameter, NM, A **90.00**

Oconto Holiday Beer, label, 1933-50, Internal Revenue Tax Paid statement, 12-oz, EX, A **$10.00**

Oh Boy Gum, sign, tin, fairy whispers in boy's ear, his hand fanning 4 flavors of gum, 1¢ It's Pure! on black, 15½x7¼", EX+, A...**$105.00**

Oh Henry Candy, sign, paper, sliced candy bar in open wrapper flanked by Anytime You're Hungry, Oh Henry! & 10¢, 24x54", EX, A **$65.00**

Oh-Cee, crate label, California lemon, large O around smaller C, Orange Grove Ca, 9x12", G1.................**$3.00**

Ohio Oil Co Marathon, sign, 1952-62, painted tin, marathon runner & Best In The Long Run encircled at left, red background, 24x36", EX, A...................**$100.00**

Oilzum Automatic Transmission Fluid, can, fiberboard, product name on blue band at bottom of inverted orange triangle with Oilzum Man on white, 1-qt, EX, D3...**$25.00**

Oilzum Motor Oil, clock, glass front, product name arched above Oilzum man on wedge shape, Choice Of Champions below, 15" dia, NM, A **$950.00**

Oilzum Motor Oil, clock, plastic, product name arched above Oilzum man on wedge shape, Choice Of Champions below, 16x16", NM, A...............................**$160.00**

Oilzum Motor Oil, sign, tin, 2-sided, proprietor's business listed above America's Finest Oil, can at right of Oilzum below, 36x60", EX, A $1,700.00

Oilzum Motor Oils & Lubricants, can, 1935-45, pictures Oilzum man with product name & lettering in his cap, orange background, 5-qt, 9½", NM.....................**$160.00**

Oilzum Motor Oils & Lubricants, sign, porcelain, the Oilzum man with lettered hat above America's Finest Oil, paint chips, vertical, VG, M1.......................**$550.00**

OJA Bath Salt, package with contents, pictures woman in bathtub, EX, D **$6.50**

OK Pilsener Beer, label, 1933-50, Garden City Brewing Co, Internal Revenue Tax Paid, 12-oz, G, A.................**$5.00**

OK Quality Used Cars & Trucks, clock, plastic, white encirlced OKs indicate 12-3-6-9 on simulated wood background, white letters below, 15x13", EX, A..**$20.00**

Old Abe Cigars, box label, end, portrait of President Lincoln, 2½x5", M, D..**$2.00**

Old Acme Coffee, tin, 1-lb, 4", G...............................**$20.00**

Old Anchor Cream Ale, label, 1933-50, Brackenridge Brewing Co, Internal Revenue Tax Paid statement, 12-oz, G, A, A **$9.00**

Old Aquaintance Cigars, box label, inner lid sample, 1880s, 2 waterscapes with lettered label, wood frame border, Witsch & Schmidt litho, EX, A.................**$39.00**

Old Battle Creek Beer, label, 1933-36, Food City Brewing Co, U-type permit number, 12-oz, EX, A.............**$10.00**

Old Blackhawk Beer, label, pre-Prohibition, pictures an Indian Chief, Independent Brewing & Malting Co, VG, A.....**$60.00**

Old Bohemian Lager Beer, label, 1933-36, star logo above Old Bohemian on diagonal center band, U-type permit number, 12-oz, VG, A **$16.00**

Old Bohemian Pilsener, label, 1933-36, Roosevelt Brewing Co, U-type permit number, 1/2-gal, EX, A.....**$38.00**

Old Bond Cigars, tin, portrait of George Washington flanked by As Good As A Bond, 5¢ above, Now 2 For 5¢ below, slip lid, 6x4", EX, A..............................**$60.00**

Old Boston Brewery Stock Ales, sign, paper, oval factory scene with brew master toasting at right, early, rare, matted & framed, image: 18x22", G-, A.............**$300.00**

Old Bushmill Irish Whiskey, mirror, wood frame, 16x17", EX, D..**$15.00**

Old Chum Tobacco, tin, 2 jolly gents sharing pipe in 2 different scenes, slip lid, round, VG, M2 ....**$75.00**

Old Colony Beverages, sign, tin, product name in red on yellow in white colonial-style frame on blue, Ask For Your Favorite..., 19x27", EX, M3 ....**$75.00**

Old Colony Beverages, sign, tin, white Old Colony on red wavy banner on blue ground, Beverages in black below, horizontal rectangle, NM, M3.................**$125.00**

Old Coon Sour Mash, sign, self-framed tin, night scene with hunters taking a break, Theobald & Son Co, 22¼x28¼", EX, A...**$650.00**

Old Drum Whiskey, key chain charm, 1930s-40s, plastic, white lettering on red, You Can't Beat It on reverse, EX, D...**$3.00**

Old Duck Handmade Sourmash Whiskey, sign, reverse-painted glass, 2 maidens feeding swans, lettering below, gold-trimmed wood frame, 19¾x16⅝", EX, A........**$125.00**

Old Dutch Beer, pin-back button, 'Old Dutch' arched over old couple enjoying brew, The Good Beer, Krantz Brewing Co, round, EX, A **$28.00**

Old Dutch Cleanser, sign, porcelain, We Sell above product can, Large Sifter Can 10¢ lettered below, 20x14", EX+, M1 ....$575.00

Old Dutch Cleanser, swivel stick pin, Old Dutch Cleanser can shape, good color, EX, A...............................**$27.00**

Old Elm Cream Ale, label, 1933-50, Burton Products Inc, Internal Revenue Tax Paid, 12-oz, EX, A.................**$48.00**

Old Export Beer, thermometer, colorful bottle, Cumberland Brewing Co, small dings, 15x6", VG, D....................$42.00

Old Faithful Beer, label, 1933-36, logo above product name on diagonal center band, Gallatin Brewing Co, U-type permit number, 12-oz, EX, A $26.00

Old Glory Cigars, tin, eagle in flight flanked by lettering, product name above & below, red background, square, EX, A $71.00

Old Gold Cigarettes, box, cardboard, red & black lettering on yellow with red border, P Lorillard Co, minor wear, 4½x6", D....................................$12.00

Old Gold Cigarettes, display, die-cut cardboard, elegant lady with pair of dogs at left of advertising, Earl Christy artwork, 36x48", EX, A.....................$375.00

Old Gold Cigarettes, sign, cardboard stand-up, photo image of Fred Waring & His Pennsylvanians, Listen Every Wednesday..., 18x24", EX, A.......................$50.00

Old Gold Cigarettes, sign, cardboard stand-up, David Ross speaking on CBS radio, 18x24", VG+, A $20.00

Old Gold Cigarettes, sign, painted metal, yellow with Old Gold in large letters above Cigarettes, Not A Cough In A Carload, 12x36", G, A.......................................$40.00

Old Gold Cigarettes, sign, paperboard, product name in bold letters above girl leaning on rock, framed, 20x15", VG+, A $325.00

Old Grand Dad Whiskey, bust figure, painted composition, ...Bottled In Bond on base, crazing/age cracks, 11½", G, A..$20.00

Old Grand Dad Whiskey, mirror, wood frame, 22½x18", EX, D...$25.00

Old Harvest Whiskey, sign, self-framed tin, interior scene of Black family with boy reaching for whiskey bottle, 16x22¼", G, A $1,475.00

Old Heidelberger Beer, label, 1933-36, St Cloud Brewing Co, U-type permit number, 12-oz, VG, A $12.00

Old Holland Blend Tea, tin, octagon shape with pictorial graphics on 4 sides, slip lid, 8x7x5", G-, M2 ....$18.00

Old Honesty Cigars, box label, inner lid sample, 1880s, blacksmith with mallet & anvil, OL Schwencke & Co litho, EX, A $84.00

Old Inn Lager, label, 1928-33, Adam Scheidt Brewing Co, L-type permit number 125, 12-oz, EX, A $41.00

Old Ivory Salt, blotter, early 1900s, pictures container & circus elephant, 8¼x4", VG, D................................$6.50

Old Judge Cigarettes, sign, die-cut cardboard, Black man in monocle & tan hat with cigarette in mouth, 6½x4", EX, D..$125.00

Old Judge Cigarettes, sign, die-cut cardboard, sailor in blue with cigarette in mouth, 6½x4", EX, D $85.00

Old Judge Coffee, tin, 1950-60, owl in round inset flanked by Vacumm Packed, product name above & below, red, yellow & white, 1-lb, EX, A $95.00

Old Judge Irradiated Coffee, tin, owl logo with product name & other lettering, 2-lb, EX+, A $55.00

Old Judson Whiskey, match holder, tin, rectangular back with round corners, girl offers dad a glass, mom helps with coat, 5x3½", EX, A.............$150.00

Old King Cole Beer, label, 1933-50, A-One Brewing Co, Internal Revenue Tax Paid, 11-oz, VG, A...........................$15.00

Old Lincoln Whiskey Co, watch fob, silver, pictures an owl, Look For The Owl, Sign Of Quality... on back, EX, D...$45.00

Old Log Cabin Bourbon Whiskey, container, log cabin in diamond-shaped inset above product name & lettering, complete with contents, 8½x4", G, A $200.00

Old Manhattan Beer, label, 1933-50, Food City Brewing Co, Internal Revenue Tax Paid, 12-oz, EX, A **$11.00**

Old Master Coffee, tin, 1925-35, bearded man in oval inset on 2-toned background, Old Master Coffee below, 3-lb, EX, A **$155.00**

Old Master Coffee, tin, 1930-40, paper label, bearded man in oval flanked by flowering vines, Old Master... above & below, 1-lb, EX, A **$130.00**

Old Mill Cigarettes, sign, paperboard, girl in front of mill holding cigarettes, diagonal lettering on fence rail, framed, 19x14", EX, A $600.00

Old Mill Malt Syrup, can label, 1929, pictures a large windmill, EX, C3 ....**$12.00**

Old Milwaukee Beer, cap, corduroy with embroidered front, EX+, P4 ....**$5.00**

Old Mission Malt, label, 1920-28, eagle logo, Los Angeles Brewing Co, 11-oz, EX, A **$30.00**

Old Mixon Cigars, box label, inner lid, pictures a peach & 2 burning cigars, 6x9", M, C3 ....**$8.00**

Old Monterey Bock Beer, label, 1933-50, Monterey Brewing Co, Internal Revenue Tax Paid statement, 11-oz, EX, A **$22.00**

Old Mr Boston Fine Liquors, clock, embossed tin key-wind, bottle shape, man in top hat on cap, round clock in center of bottle, 22x11", VG, A **$375.00**

Old North State Smoking Tobacco, cigarette papers, Old North State lettered above tobacco leaf, Brown & Williamson Tobacco Corp below, NM, A **$20.00**

Old North State Smoking Tobacco, sign, embossed tin, 2 gents in hats looking up at large product pack, Always Fresh, Mild & Mellow, 27½x19½", G+, A **$1,650.00**

Old Orchard, crate label, 1920s, California pear, 2 little girls in orchard with lots of gilt decor, Santa Clara, 7¼x11", M, C1 ....**$2.00**

Old Overholt Rye, clock, light-up, It's Always Time For Old Overholt... at left of round clock face, 9x14x4½", G, A **$65.00**

Old Overholt Whiskey, sign, tin, 2 hunters & an Irish setter in field sharing bottle of whiskey, minor chips & soiling, framed, 28x36", EX, A **$850.00**

Old Ozark Beer, label, 1933-50, Appleton Brewery Co, Inte nal Revenue Tax Paid, 1-qt, EX, A **$23.0**

Old Plantation Coffee, bag, Black man moving large sack coffee with steamboat beyond, EX, D **$10.0**

Old Q Cigars, box label, outer, 1908, bust portrait of elderly man, 4½x4½", M, C3 ....**$5.0**

Old Reading Beer, sign, colorful litho of a tavern scen 23x31", VG+, A **$10.0**

Old Reliable Coffee, pocket mirror, dock worker restir on coffee crate, product name arched above, min scratches, 2⅛" dia, VG+, A **$60.0**

Old Reliable Coffee, sign, embossed tin, Old Reliable Co fee lettered in white on black, thin white outlined bo der, 2½x20", EX, A **$45.0**

Old Reliable Coffee, sign, tin, Always Good upper left gent in Russian-type hat above product name & pac age, vertical, EX, M1 ....**$625.0**

Old Reliable Coffee, tin, 1937, key-wind, 1-lb, EX, D **$35.0**

Old Reliable Peg Top, door plate, 1920s-30s, porcelain, crea & brown with black border, 12¼x4", EX, A **$220.0**

Old Reliable Typewriter Ribbon, tin, pictures a beaver, E D **$20.0**

Old Schenley Whiskey, sign, tin, hunter wearing coonsk hat with rifle, I've Struck The Trail, overall wea framed, image: 28x19½", G, A **$300.0**

Old South Ale, label, 1933-36, waiter carrying tray, Southeaste Brewing Co, U-type permit number, 12-oz, EX, A......**$13.0**

Old Spring Whiskey, bottle, clear glass with red letterin 10", EX, A **$20.0**

Old Squire Pipe Tobacco, pocket tin, orange with whit Old Squire lettered above circular portrait of same, 1(& Pipe Tobacco below, EX, A **$107.0**

Old Statesman Tobacco, tin, square corners, VG, D..**$385.0**

Old Topper Snappy Ale, can, cone-top, 12-oz, EX, D ...**$24.0**

Old Town Canoes & Boats, catalog, 1939, colorful canc & boating scene on cover, 38 pages, EX, A **$80.0**

Old Town Canoes & Boats, catalog, 1949, colorful canc & boating scene on cover, 45 pages, EX, A **$50.0**

Old Valley Whiskey, sign, self-framed tin, 3 men surveyin bottle of whiskey, ...Special Quality, Cook & Ber heimer Co, 20x16", G, A **$100.0**

Old Virginia Cheroots, sign, We Smoke Old Virginia Ch roots, Do You? above Uncle Sam smoking a ciga signed FN Blue, framed, 23x15", A **$1,500.0**

Old 99 Ale, label, 1933-36, pictures 2 barrels, Brownsvil Brewing Co, U-type permit label, 12-oz, VG, A...**$20.0**

Oldbru Bock Beer, label, 1933-50, ram's head in cente Detroit Brewing Co, Internal Revenue Tax Paid stat ment, 12-oz, VG, A **$15.0**

Old Virginia Ale, label, 1933-50, Old Virginia in scri above Ale, Internal Revenue Tax Paid statement, 12-o EX, A **$10.0**

Oldsmobile, pitcher, etched glass, Olds Motor Works Lansing Mich, 8", rare, M, S5 ....**$250.0**

Oldsmobile, showroom catalog, 1951, hard-bound, Rock Engine Cars lettered lower right, Earth logo above le 10x13¾", VG, A **$60.0**

Oldsmobile Service Guild, sign, 1940s-50s, cardboar smiling service man, It's Good To Know..., logo & te below, rectangular, framed, G, A **$250.0**

Oliver & Robinson Cigars, paper label, clay-coated, Victorian lady with fan & cherubs in rectangular inset, fancy graphics, 13x10½", G, A....................................**$200.00**

Oliver Chilled Plow Works, pocket mirror, Mr Oliver's name arched above his portrait, company name below, oval, 2¾x1¾", EX, A..**$150.00**

Oliver Chilled Plow Works, pocket mirror, Mr Oliver's name arched above his portrait, company name below, foxing, oval, 2¾x1¾", G, A.................................**$48.00**

Oliver Chilled Plows, phamplet, ca 1880, 2 full pages of testimonials, some stain, G, D................................**$5.00**

Oliver Implements, sign, die-cut tin flange, Plow Makers For The World across world globe surrounded by company name, 18x18", EX, A................................**$160.00**

Oliver Standard Visible Writer, pocket mirror, pictures smiling girl standing behind typewriter, oval, 2¾", EX, A..**$50.00**

Oliver Typewriter, pin-back button, ca 1900, pictures typewriter in black & white with red border, white lettering, EX, D..**$12.00**

Olixir Supreme Cylinder Top Oil, sign, painted metal, 2-sided, lightning bolts flank lettered oval, 10¢... upper left, 20¢...upper right, 9x16", G, A........................**$25.00**

Olson Rug Co, catalog, 1942, 38 pages, VG+, H2.....**$35.00**

Olt's Cream Ale & Superba Beer, pocket mirror, pretty fairy holds up glass of ale on blue background with red & white lettering, 2⅛" dia, EX, A.$1,300.00

Olt's Game Callers, pocket catalog, 1932, nonpictorial cover, price list laid in, well illustrated, 8 pages, EX, A......**$40.00**

Olympia Beer, calender, 1901, 6 individually matted cards picturing women surrounded by flowers, framed, image: 10x13", EX+, A.......................................**$500.00**

Olympia Beer, tray, pictures lady on bottle, Capitol Brewing Co, paint chips on rim, 13", VG, D................**$20.00**

Omaha School Supplies, catalog, 1936, 202 pages, VG+, H2..**$40.00**

Omar Cigarettes, sign, profile of girl with eyes closed & head bowed in circular inset with lettering above & below, framed, 28x22", G, A...............................**$80.00**

Omar Cigars, box label, inner lid, Arab & camel scene, 6x9", M, D...**$5.00**

Omar Pearls, pocket mirror, head portrait of gypsy lady wearing 3 strands of pearls, product name below, rectangular, 2¾", EX, A...**$30.00**

Omar Turkish Blend Cigarettes, sign, paperboard, 2 fashionably dressed men conversing, The Joy Of Life, 20 For 15¢, wood frame, 21½x15", VG, A..............**$100.00**

Oneida Animal Traps, catalog, No T137, 1938, swimming beaver on cover, well illustrated, dealers price sheet included, 30 pages, EX, A....................................**$40.00**

Oneida Animal Traps, foldout, 1936, 3-panel with illustrated price sheet, EX, A......................................**$16.50**

Oneida National Bank, doll, Indian boy, printed cloth, 14", EX, D..**$8.00**

Ontario Brand Peanut Butter, pail, blue ocean view on white, product name above & below, geometric band top & bottom, 1-lb, EX, A....................$160.00

Ontario Brand Peanut Butter, pail, metallic gold with black lettered horizontal oval logo, slip lid & bail, 1-lb, EX, D3...**$75.00**

Opaline Motor Oil, can, 1916-18, race car with Sinclair Sinco Oils on grill, beige background, pour spout & handle, 1-gal, 11", EX, A................................**$1,100.00**

Opaline Motor Oil, sign, porcelain, red & green on white, 2-tone border, Now While You Wait Drain & Refill With New Opaline, 24x36", VG, A.......................**$50.00**

Opalite Silver Polish, pin-back button, ca 1900, blue, white & gold, stain at bottom, D..........................**$5.00**

Opera Soda, sign, tin, Opera in script above bottle, C'est Si Bon! in script below, Canadian, vertical with rounded corners, EX, A...**$85.00**

Opia Cigar, tip tray, pictures lady framed by crescent moon with flowers & stars, product name on rim, 4⅜" dia, VG+, A...**$250.00**

Orange Blossom Tobacco, label, bare-chested girl peeking through orange-covered vines, JJ Bagley & Co Detroit, 10x13½", EX, A...................................**$500.00**

Orange Candy Kitchen, calendar, 1911, die-cut cardboard, little boy playing violin while kittens play, matted & framed, 19x15", EX, A.......................................**$100.00**

Orange Flower Cologne, trade card, 1890, pictures flowers, Flint's Pharmacy, Oakland Ca, 2¾x3½", VG, P1.........**$6.00**

Orange Kist, fan hanger, Kist character with bottle saying Take It From Me, We Serve..., 8¼x6⅛", EX, A **$14.00**

Orange Kist, sign, cardboard, Drink Orange Kist above shadowed bottle & oranges, 14x10½", EX, A **$45.00**

Orange Kist, sign, cardboard hanger, diamond shape, orange & blue, Kiss Away Your Thirst...Ice Cold In Bottles, 7x10", NM, B1 ....**$6.00**

Orange Rainier Dry, label, 1920-28, lettering over orange slice, 12-oz, VG, A..**$15.00**

Orange Special Soda, bottle topper, oranges & blossoms surround white emblem reading Delicious Orange Special Soda, 7x8", NM, A..**$3.00**

Orange Squeeze, sign, die-cut cardboard, advertising card & oranges by bathing beauty posed with knees up holding bottle, EX, M1 ....**$165.00**

Orange Squeeze, sign, tin, Orange upper left of bottle, Squeeze & With The True Fruit Flavor lower right on yellow, 12x28", NM, M3....................................**$135.00**

Orange-Crush, bottle opener, 1920s, chrome-plated, pictures Crushy & bottle of Crush Dry, pocket-size, unused, M, D **$15.00**

Orange-Crush, calendar, 1925, girl on beach with parasol, October page, framed, vertical, VG, M1 ....$600.00

Orange-Crush, calendar, 1946, shows girl with panda bear, Drink Orange-Crush on diamond logo, full pad, 31x16", NM, D **$155.00**

Orange-Crush, calendar top, 1920s, flapper girl posed above oranges surrounding oval featuring bottle at left of text, NM, A..**$302.00**

Orange-Crush, calendar top, 1932, beauty queen on Orange-Crush pedestal, framed, EX, A **$125.00**

Orange-Crush, clock, metal frame, glass lens, 12-3-6-9 & dots surround bottle cap, round, EX, D **$260.00**

Orange-Crush, clock, reverse-painted glass, lines flank clock above Drink..., rare, 16" dia, NM, S2 ....**$2,000.00**

Orange-Crush, clock, reverse-painted glass, 36x19", N2.**$165.00**

Orange-Crush, decal, 1967, peel & stick, Enjoy A Fresh New Taste!, 10x10", EX, D **$6.00**

Orange-Crush, decal with envelope, 1950, features Lil' Abner & gang, Ah Pronounces Th' Offishul Drink Of Dogpatch..., 4x7", NM, A **$8.00**

Orange-Crush, decals for store window, set of 3 with paper dividers & instructions, 24x12", M, D **$150.00**

Orange-Crush, display, die-cut cardboard stand-up, ...It's My Brand! Orange-Crush... on posted sign above cowboy with bottle, EX, A **$110.00**

Orange-Crush, door push plate, porcelain, green with Come Again & Thank You in diagonal script above & below orange dot, 9x4", NM, M2 ....**$280.00**

Orange-Crush, door push plate, 1920s, tin, Come In! Drink Orange-Crush above tilted bottle with straw, 12x3½", NM, M1..$300.00

Orange-Crush, mechanical pencil, Mexican, NM, A .**$20.00**

Orange-Crush, mirror, Orange-Crush Carbonated Beverage at bottom, Crushy figure at top, 11x9", NM, A ...**$100.00**

Orange-Crush, sign, cardboard, New! above bottle left of Glorious Golden... & Served Here with Crushy figure on white, 14x11", NM, M3 ....**$75.00**

Orange-Crush, sign, celluloid, Enjoy (underlined & on the diagonal) above Orange-Crush on center band, 9" dia, EX, A **$85.00**

Orange-Crush, sign, flange, 1940s, 2-sided, Drink Orange-Crush at left of bottle in snow, 14x22", NM, D...**$195.00**

Orange-Crush, sign, paper, pictures musical group above Hootenanny Party Special, 10¢ Off & 6-pack, 24x18", NM, M3...**$12.00**

Orange-Crush, sign, paper, 1940s, pictures hand holding 6-pack of Orange-Crush, Serve These Favorites At Home..., 14x22", EX, D **$16.00**

Orange-Crush, sign, plastic, embossed, Enjoy Orange-Crush Ice Cold left of bottle on blue ground, 'icy' bottom edge, 9x11", EX, A **$30.00**

Orange-Crush, sign, plastic, light-up, 1960s, metal case, bottle cap & orange slices recede to It's Goodness Begins..., 12x20", EX, M2 ....**$80.00**

Orange-Crush, sign, tin, embossed, Feel Fresh! above Drink...Carbonated Beverage & Crushy figure, diagonal with round corners, EX, A **$95.00**

Orange-Crush, sign, tin, embossed, 1930s, Drink Orange-Crush above tilted bottle over branch of oranges & blossoms, 36x18", EX, A $375.00

Orange-Crush, sign, tin, embossed, 6-pack at left of Take Home A Handipack..., Carbonated Beverages, 6 Bottles for..., 12x28", NM, A...**$453.00**

Orange-Crush, sign, tin, yellow, black & white on orange diamond, ...Only One...Carbonated Beverage, Crushy figure, 18x18", NM, M3 ....**$145.00**

Orange-Crush, soda jerk's hat, paper, orange & blue on white, Drink Orange-Crush right of Crushy figure, NM, M2...**$6.00**

Orange-Crush, syrup dispenser, brown glass, original carrying case, damage to case, 13x7" dia, EX+, A **$130.00**

Orange-Crush, thermometer, die-cut tin, large bottle form with Orange Crush lettered above thermometer, 28x7", EX, A..**$110.00**

Orange-Crush, thermometer, tin, white with Get The Happy Habit above ribbed bottle right of bulb, rounded ends, chipped, 19x6", M2 ....**$80.00**

Orange-Crush, thermometer, 1950s, tin, blue & orange, bottle cap above numbered bulb, rounded corners, 16x6", EX+, D **$60.00**

Orange-Crush, toy truck, windup, logoed decals on side of open cargo bed, London Toy, Canadian, gear missing/axle loose, VG, M2 ....**$60.00**

Orange-Crush, tray, Crushy figure in triangle over orange motif, lettered rim, vertical rectangle, VG+, A....**$180.00**

Orange-Crush, tray, oranges in geometric circles around Crushy figure in center circle, vertical rectangle, VG+, A **$190.00**

Orange-Crush, tray, 1931, scarce, scratches/wear, D**$85.00**

Orange-Crush/Pepsi-Cola/NuGrape, bowl, 3 different logos in 3 different colors with bold green line around rim, Wellsville china, 4¾", NM, A.......................**$100.00**

Orange-Crush/Pepsi-Cola/NuGrape, plate, 3 different logos in 3 different colors with bold green line around rim, Wellsville china, 7", NM, A **$120.00**

Orange-Julep, tray, bathing beauty holding glass & parasol, product name on rim, 13¼x10½", EX+, A...**$130.00**

Orange-Julep, tray, seated sunbather holding parasol & glass, Drink... on rim, rectangular, EX+, A **$130.00**

Orbit, crate label, 1930s, California orange, orange-shaped meteor in starry sky, Exeter Citrus Assoc, 10x11", M, C1 ....**$3.00**

Orchard Park Coffee, tin, flat, key-wind, 1-lb, EX, D......**$12.00**

Orcherade, sign, cardboard, Orcherade lettered above lady in floral hat holding up product bottle, 3-tone border, vertical, EX, M1 ....**$325.00**

Orcherade, sign, cardboard, Orcherade lettered above 2 ladies with 1 pouring from bottle into glass held by other, vertical, EX, M1 ....$425.00

Orchid, crate label, Florida citrus, 2 cattleya orchids & grapefruit half in chilled silver bowl, green background, 9x9", M, C1..**$2.00**

Orchid Pork & Beans, can label, 1924, bowl of beans & pink orchids, M, C3..**$10.00**

Oregon Apples, crate label, blue, yellow & red, 9x10½", EX, C3 ....**$5.00**

Oregon Orchards, crate label, 1940s, Oregon pear, comical duck with umbrella, Medford, 8x11", G1........**$15.00**

Oreo Cookies, Christmas ball, pictures Oreo cookie dressed as Santa, MIB, D2 ....**$20.00**

Oreo Cookies, doll, copyright 1983, vinyl with movable head & arms holding an Oreo cookie, pink dress & Oreo hat, 4½", VG, A **$56.00**

Oreo Cookies, tin, 1986, pictures woman talking on phone, 8x6x2½", EX, D...**$10.00**

Oreo Cookies, tin, 1991, red or green, pictures Santa & girl on lid, 2½x6¼", EX, D...**$5.00**

Oriental 'Show You' Products, jigsaw puzzle, pictures different products in Japanese garden setting, 10x13", EX, F1 ....**$75.00**

Oriental Brewery, calendar, 1898, boating scene with logo & lettering above, minor creases, framed, image: 27½x19½", EX, A...**$1,100.00**

Oriental Rose Talcum Powder, tin, Oriental lady standing at left of advertising, shaker top, oval, A.............**$25.00**

Original Kalamazoo Spring-Tooth Harrows & Cultivators, sign, paper, colorful image of horse-drawn harrow with inserts of equipment, framed, image: 22x28", NM, A..**$2,450.00**

Orkideer, crate label, Florida citrus, 2 men in dugout full of oranges with deer watching, 9x9", M, C1 ....**$2.00**

Orkin Exterminating Co, bank, 1960s, papier-mache, Otto the Orkin Man on green base, 8", EX, D ...**$400.00**

Orletta Cigars, box label, outer, elegant woman surrounded by medallions, 4½x4½", VG, D **$5.00**

Orphan Boy Tobacco, sign, 1930s, paper, pictures a mule & full-color cloth tobacco pack on yellow background, 15x12", EX, D **$44.00**

Oscar Mayer, bank, plastic Weinermobile, USA Olympic logo, 9¾" long, NM, D **$10.00**

Oscar Mayer, money clip, brass with raised image of the Weinermobile, 2¼" long, EX, A...........................**$15.00**

Oscar Mayer, ring, flexible plastic, yellow band with Little Oscar's head in red, EX, A...................................**$13.00**

Oscar Mayer, Weinermobile, 1950s, plastic with wrap around windows, Little Oscar rises & falls when pushed or pulled, 10" long, VG, A $173.00

Oscar Mayer, Weinermobile, 1991, plastic with wrap around windows, no figure, 10" long, EX, A........**$28.00**

Oscar Mayer, whistle, 1950s, red plastic shaped as weiner with red on yellow band, 2" long, EX, A.............**$13.00**

Oscar's Beverages, sign, 1950s, tin, goofy waiter & tilted bottle, red, white, green & black, 12x32", EX, D...**$60.00**

Osceola Cigars, box labels, inner & outer sample set, 1880s, portrait of Indian, spears & shield behind, Geo S Harris litho, VG/EX, A **$141.00**

OshKosh B'Gosh Overalls, sign, 1930s-40s, porcelain, pictures Uncle Sam in overalls, Union Made... in white on red, some flaking, 10x30", A **$600.00**

Oswego Candy Works, tin, 1920s-40s, red with gold highlights, black letters, ...Wholesale Candy..., press lid & bail, 8x6" dia, G, A **$35.00**

Otard Cognac, ashtray, pottery, white with blue lettering, Chateau De Cognac in blue on white, made in France, triangular, 6", D....................................**$15.00**

Otello Cigars, box label, inner lid, scene from Shakespeare play, 6x9", M, C3 ....**$18.00**

Otis A Smith Specialties in Hardware & Fire Arms, letterhead, 1883, large revolver in ochre, VG, A......**$18.00**

Otto F Ernst Saddles, sign, embossed tin, black lettering on yellow, ...Sheridan, Wyoming, Write For Catalog, 9x20", VG, A **$60.00**

Otto Huber Brewery, tray, Bavarian family around table with little boy taking sip of beer, A Chip Off The Old Block, oval, 16½x14", VG, A **$600.00**

Our Hero Java & Mocha Blend, canister, round with various images of military officers with Our Hero arched above each, slip lid, 5-lb, G, A.............................**$65.00**

Our Pick, crate label, 1930s, California pears, rooster & basket of fruit, Loomis Fruit Growers Assn, 7½x11", M, C3.............**$5.00**

Our Pride Cigars, box label, inner lid sample, 1880s, bust portrait of lady with head turned right, OL Schwencke & Co litho, EX, A..**$36.00**

Our Seal Peaches, can label, 1924, little girl next to basket of fruit, EX, C3..**$30.00**

Our Style Pilsener Beer, label, 1933-50, Garden City Brewing Co, Internal Revenue Tax Paid statement, 12-oz, EX, A..**$23.00**

Oval Brand Jumbo Blanched Salted Peanuts, tin, brown with brown & yellow horizontal oval peanut logo outlined in gold, Peanut Specialty Co, pry lid, 10-lb, NM, D3.......**$275.00**

Oven-Kist Biscuits, toy truck, very early van-type with advertising on side panels, worn/scratched, 4x7½", G, M2.....**$300.00**

Overland, sign, porcelain, 2-sided, Service & Genuine Parts arched above & below Overland in script, oval, 30x40", EX+, S2 ....**$695.00**

Ovum Thorley's Poultry & Game Spice, sign, porcelain, For Producing Eggs arched above lettered egg logo on red background, overall wear, 32x23", G, A **$15.00**

Owl Cigar, sign, die-cut paperboard, 2-sided, owl in a tree flanked by Now 5¢, Sackett & Wilhelms litho, 11½", EX, A **$180.00**

Owl's Theatrical Cold Cream, tin, 2 owls flank fancy emblem with product lettering, The Owl Drug Store, screw lid, 4¼x3" dia, EX+, D **$30.00**

Owl Throat Pastilles, tin, 1920-30, product & company name bordered by continuing S shapes, brown, red, orange & gold, 2¾x3⅝", NM, A............................**$40.00**

Ox-Heart Chocolate & Cocoa, sign, embossed tin, round Ox-Heart logo at left of product lettering on black, red border, 4½x20", EX, A.................$125.00

Oxford Chocolates, pocket mirror, scholarly lady with product name below, oval, 2", EX, A...................**$50.00**

Oxford Chocolates, pocket mirror, scholarly lady with product name below, oval, 2", G, A **$30.00**

Oxnard, crate label, 1930s, California lemon, man tilling soil with team of oxen, 9x12½", M, C1 ....**$2.00**

Oxygenated Bitters, broadside, paper, black lettering on white, ...Sure Remedy For Dyspepsia, Asthma..., matted, image: 23x17½", VG, A.......................................**$100.00**

Oyster Stews, store lantern, tin with lettering on white painted glass inserts, 18x9½", G, A....................**$350.00**

Ozama Coffee, trade card, 1880s, child with picnic basket fending off a bee, 3¼x5", EX, P1 ....**$14.00**

P

P Barbey & Son Brewers, calendar, 1903, die-cut cardboard, pretty girl on oval with lilac border, full pad, framed, image: 21x16", EX, A..............................**$425.00**

P Barbey & Son Brewers, calendar, 1907, cardboard, oval image of girl in fur-trimmed jacked flanked by logo, May pad, framed, 24x19½", G, A **$975.00**

P Barbey & Son Brewers, sign, die-cut cardboard & paper, oval portrait of girl with dragonfly, framed, image: 24x19½", VG, A **$725.00**

P Barbey & Son Brewers, sign, paper, oval image of girl in fancy dress & feathered bonnet surrounded by flowers, framed, 22½x17", EX, A **$1,050.00**

P Lorillard & Co, cabinet, wood with 2 etched glass doors, decorative railing around top, marked 1760 & 1883, rare, 48x35", EX, A **$3,300.00**

P Lorillard & Co, cigarette papers, 2 ladies in horizontal oval with company name lettered above, other lettering below, yellow, NM, A **$6.00**

P Lorillard & Co, see also Lorillard's

P Lorillard Century Tobacco & Snuffs, label, attached to cardboard lid, bare-chested Indian Princess being presented tobacco leaves, 10½x8¾", VG, A............ **$325.00**

P&O Canton Plows, sign, wood, large letters with small horse-drawn plow at left, yellow & black, overall fading/color loss, 10"x10', A.................................. **$100.00**

P&P Cigars, box label, inner lid, woman in forest, 6x9", EX, C3 .... **$28.00**

Pabst Blue Ribbon Beer, bottle opener, 1930s, die-cut steel, full-color bottle, 4x1", EX, D **$20.00**

Pabst Blue Ribbon Beer, display/light, metal, figural boxer beside beer bottle with At Popular Prices on sign above, 20x9½x7", G-, A **$130.00**

Pabst Blue Ribbon Beer, glass, 8-oz, D...................... **$4.00**

Pabst Blue Ribbon Beer, light, stein shape, clear glass with logo, 18", EX+, P4 .... **$15.00**

Pabst Blue Ribbon Beer, sign, die-cut tin, pictures Black porter & conductor in train window, EX, D2 .... **$125.00**

Pabst Blue Ribbon Beer, sign, embossed tin, Rip Van Winkle & bottle with mountains beyond, Brew That Brings Back Memories, 12x17½", G+, A........................ **$160.00**

Pabst Blue Ribbon Beer, sign, paper, beer bottles with plate of raw oysters, original frame with brass tag, 21¾x25½", G-, A... **$45.00**

Pabst Blue Ribbon Beer, sign, paper, team of horses pulling wagon load with Wilbur's Tonic, Pabst Famous Blue Ribbon..., framed, 17x34", VG, A................. **$45.00**

Pabst Blue Ribbon Beer, sign, 1940s, tin & cardboard, Pabst above lettered blue ribbon behind tilted 15¢ bottle & In Bottles, 9x13", NM, A **$75.00**

Pabst Blue Ribbon Beer, sign, 1940s, tin & cardboard, Pabst above lettered blue ribbon behind tilted bottle (no price), In Bottles, 9x13", EX, A...................... **$55.00**

Pabst Blue Ribbon Beer, tray, elderly man pouring glass of beer, 13x11", EX, D **$85.00**

Pabst Blue Ribbon Beer, tray, embossed plastic, blue, 13¼" dia, D **$8.00**

Pabst Blue Ribbon Beer, tray, factory scene & large circular logo, Perfected Brewing In America..., decorative rim, 12x17¼", G, A **$90.00**

Pabst Blue Ribbon Beer, tray, sunburst logo surrounded by hops, overall fading/wear, 12" dia, G-, A **$25.00**

Pabst Blue Ribbon Beer, tray, 2 gnomes carrying oversized flagons & signs, decorative rim, oval, overall chips/dents, 15¼x18½", G-, A **$85.00**

Pabst Brewing Co, employee badge, silvered brass, back removes for insertion of identification, EX, D **$8.00**

Pabst Brewing Co, postcard, 1935, aerial view of the factory, EX, D **$2.50**

Pabst Brewing Co, sign, paper, oval image of girl with glass held high, circular logo at bottom, framed, image: 26½x19", G, A... **$400.00**

Pabst Brewing Co, sign, paper, panoramic view of factory with company name flanked by 2 gold emblems below, framed, 40x52", EX, A $1,000.00

Pabst Brewing Co Bohemian Beer, label, pre-1920, company name above leaf logo flanked by Bohemian Beer, EX, A **$20.00**

Pabst Extract, calendar, 1903, paper, babies from all nations holding calendar sheets, stork at bottom, framed, image: 28x11", VG, A **$375.00**

Pabst Extract, sign, ca 1904, tin, hand bursting through paper holding bottles forming barbell, gold raised rim, oval, 9x13", EX+, A $646.00

Pabst Milwaukee, sign, ca 1890, reverse-painted glass, letter B on leaf in center, original ornate frame, 28" dia, VG, D **$495.00**

Pacific Beer, tray, 1912, Mt Tacoma, NM, D **$70.00**

Pacific Butchers' Supply Co, pocket mirror, company name arched above bull's head with butchering tools below, minor wear, 2⅛" dia, VG+, A................**$450.00**

Pacific Mutual Life Insurance Co, pocket mirror, mother listens as child says prayers, Should The Man On The Other Side Die Tonight..., 2¼" dia, EX, A............**$70.00**

Pacific Shoes, pocket mirror, Pacific on the diagonal at left of high-top shoe, Friedman-Shelby Shoe Co logo below, 2¼" dia, VG+, A **$55.00**

Packard, instruction book, 1910, black & white illustrations with orange & black lettering throughout, 56 pages, G, A...**$55.00**

Packard, pin-back button, Packards arched above a Packard car, scarce, round, EX, A........................**$35.00**

Packard, sign, neon, white Packard lettered vertically on blue panel, red neon tube at right, restored, vertical, 9½ ft, EX, D **$1,800.00**

Packard, sign, Packards from 1899-1948 shown in swirling line, Golden Anniversary Packards lettered below, 29x23", NM, D **$150.00**

Packard Automatic Windshield Washer, display, cardboard trifold, pictures lady at wheel of car with windshield wipers working, EX, A..............................**$45.00**

Packard Automotive Cable, display, painted tin, yellow on dark blue, measurement scale in yellow on left side, advertising above, 36x10", VG+, A.......................**$35.00**

Packard Service, manager's coat, early 1900s, denim, Packard in black, 1 original button, scarce, soiled & faded, size 38, VG, A **$90.00**

Packer's Healing Tar Soap, tin, 1890-1910, colorful painted label, contains original unopened bottle of soap with label, 3¼x2½x1", EX, D......................**$16.00**

Page Baby Talc, tin, product name above mother playing with baby, pyramid shape, 5x3", EX, D.............................**$30.00**

Page Corylopsis Talc Powder, tin, pictures Oriental lady, oval can that graduates to a smaller top, EX, A...**$30.00**

Page Woven Fence Co, trade card, mother & children watching buffalo fight through fence, Don't Be Afraid Darling, This Is..., EX, A.......................................**$22.00**

Pal Ade, sign, embossed self-framed tin, Your Pals Drink... in heart shape beside bottle, lettering below, 16x16", EX, A...**$80.00**

Pal Razors, display, wood case with die-cut paper figure pointing to Pal Shaving Headquarters, various razors, 22½", VG, A...**$65.00**

Pala Brave, crate label, 1930s, California orange, Indian chief in full headdress, Bradford Bros Inc, Placentia, 10x11", M, C1..**$3.00**

Palacine Oil Co, can, early 1900s, red with product name lettered over red barrel on cream label, screw lid, 1/2-gal, 6", EX, A **$145.00**

Pall Mall Cigarettes, sign, early 1900s, reverse-painted glass, gold lettering on red background, ornate frame, 28½x36½", EX, A...**$1,000.00**

Palm Cigars, sign, embossed tin, product & 3 For 5¢ flank product name, That Different Smoke!, company name below, 6x19", EX, A **$15.00**

Palmer's Lotion & Talc for Men, tin, embossed, EX, D **$38.00**

Palmer's Perfumes, trade card, die-cut vase of flowers, Solon Palmer NY, Estb 1847 lettered on foot of vase, EX, A **$15.00**

Palmolive Soap, pin-back button, 1930s, red, white & blue, EX, D **$6.00**

Palmolive Talcum Powder, tin, embossed Palmolive on band across palm tree, Talcum Powder lettered above, pyramid shape, 5x2½x1¾", EX, D........................**$35.00**

Palo Alto, lug box label, tall redwood tree & white lettering on red background, EX, G1..................................**$4.00**

Pamco Tobacco, tin, embossed, lettering within scroll designs above & below Pamco, slip lid, oval, 4¼x4¼", EX, A **$70.00**

Pan-Am Gasoline & Motor Oils, jigsaw puzzle, 1933, gas station scene at water's edge with children pumping gas into auto & boat, 10x13½", EX, F1 ....$45.00

Pan-Am Gasoline & Motor Oils, sign, 1935-45, porcelain, Pan-Am on band over sunburst in center, Gasoline above, Motor Oils below, 42" dia, NM, A...........**$250.00**

Pan-Am Quality Gasoline, sign, porcelain, Pan-Am torch emblem above Quality Gasoline, 17x13", EX+, D1...**$140.00**

Panama Typewriter Ribbon, tin, bronze, EX, D **$8.00**

Papec Feed & Forage Equipment, sign, 1940s, Papec in large yellow letters, For Farming Systems, Dairy-Live-stock-Poultry, 12x24", EX, A **$25.00**

Papillon Cure, sign, paper, lady sparsely dressed with Black man holding runner around her feet, framed, image: 28½x21½", G-, A **$165.00**

Par-O-Vis Motor Oil, can, 1960s, Par-O-Vis in blue on yellow sunburst, blue ground, 1-qt, 5½", EX, A..................**$10.00**

Para Pride Motor Oil, can, outline of plane above Para Pride lettered diagonally above band with 2 speeding cars, Canfield Oil Co, 1-qt, EX, A..........................**$40.00**

Parade, crate label, 1930s, California lemon, drum major leading parade of drummers, Saticoy, 9x12½", M, C1 ......**$2.00**

Paradise Crackers, pin-back button, 1930s, red, white & blue, slightly darkened, EX, D...............................**$4.00**

Paradise Tomatoes, can label, embossed bird of paradise, Lynn Ma, EX, G1 ....**$8.00**

Paragon Mixture, pocket tin, upright, Cut Plug in oval with product name above & below, scarce, oval, VG, A..**$165.00**

Paratroop Boot Polish, tin, shows scene with paratroopers, black & white, NM, B1 .... **$6.50**

Pard Dog Food, clock, numbers around dog in doghouse with bobbing head ticking off seconds, electric, 15½x15½", VG+, A **$275.00**

Paris Garters, display case, dark wood, stenciled gold, white & blue logo on marquee, with 4 boxed garters, 14", VG+, A **$65.00**

Paris Garters, display case, wood with stenciled black & gold lettering, slanted glass front, back panels fold down, 3-tier, 16", G, A **$30.00**

Paris Manufacturing Co, catalog, features furniture from the Paris Maine furniture company, includes price list, 28 pages, EX, A **$70.00**

Park & Pollard Co's Lay or Bust Feeds, thermometer, 1920s?, porcelain, chicken graphics, arched top, rounded corners at bottom, 27x7", VG, A **$525.00**

Park & Tilford Chocolates--Bon Bons, display box, 8 compartments with glass covers, shield logos flank company & product name on sides, 15x15", VG, A **$35.00**

Park Elite Beer, label, 1933-50, Park Brewing Co, Internal Revenue Tax Paid statement, 32-oz, VG, A **$5.00**

Park-Davis Products, sign, glass, black, orange & gold, This Pharmacy Is Your Fortress Of Health, ...Your Safeguards, framed, 13x25", EX+, M2 .... **$60.00**

Park-Knit School Stocking, thermometer, paper face, degrees arched above lady holding stockings, product name below, 9¼" dia, G+, A **$40.00**

Parke's Newport Coffee, tin, factory view in horizontal oval with product name above & below, pry lid, 1-lb, EX, A **$140.00**

Parker Brothers High Grade Double Guns, mail-in gun tag, minor fading/light crease, A **$45.00**

Parker Guns, catalog, 1929, pictures mallards in flight, well illustrated, 32 pages, minor edge staining on some pages, A **$90.00**

Parker Guns, pocket catalog, 1927, hunter & dog resting, red & black, well illustrated, 16 pages, EX, A **$110.00**

Parker Pencil Service, vendor, 5¢, ca 1930, white metal, Everywhere Folks Write, 10x9x5", VG, A **$50.00**

Parker Pens, lamp, black metal shade with reticulated lettering on wood base, missing shade trim piece, 18¼" long, G, A **$130.00**

Parker's Cutaneous Charm for Skin, trade card, vignettes showing various uses, blue, brown & white, EX, A **$26.00**

Parker-Gordon's Class Cigars, tin, product lettering above In Workmanship & Quality, slip lid, rectangular, EX+, A **$39.00**

Parkview Coffee, tin, steaming cup of coffee flanked by little girls, product name above & below, key-wind lid, 1-lb, VG+, A **$80.00**

Parmenter & Polsey Fertilizer Co, calendar, 1908, paper, bust-portrait of elegant girl in oval surrounded by fancy border, full pad, 21x13½", VG+, A **$375.00**

Parole Cigars, box label, inner lid sample, 1879, side view of jockey on horse, New York Label Co, EX, A **$175.00**

Parrot Peanut Butter, pail, green with red Parrot lettered above red & green parrot, white Peanut Butter below, bail handle, very rare, VG, A **$605.00**

Parry Buggy Manufacturing Co, pocket mirror, factory image, G, D **$150.00**

Parsley Brand Salmon, tip tray, center graphics with lettering around rim, 4" dia, EX, A **$40.00**

Partner Cigars, label, Partner lettered in fancy horizontal oval above side-by-side portraits of 2 men in vertical ovals, 4x4", EX, 4 .... **$12.00**

Pass Book Cigars, box label, outer, railroad ticket, train & ship, 4½x4½", M, C3 .... **$28.00**

Patent Paint Co Sun-Proof Paints, stickpin, ca 1900, embossed brass, trademark image of smiling sun, inscriptions on reverse, EX, D **$8.00**

Patterson Mfg Co, pocket mirror, shows lady reclining on the Patterson Hammock Couch, rectangular with rounded corners, 2¾" long, EX, A **$375.00**

Patterson Perserving Co, sign, paper, products displayed in lower corners of picnic scene, framed, 16¾x21¾", EX, A **$375.00**

Patton Brewing Co, watch fob, celluloid on metal, G, D **$40.00**

Patton's Sun-Proof Paints, display, tin, shaped as paint can, colorful graphics on yellow, rear door opens for storage, bail handle, VG, A **$550.00**

Pau Cola, jigsaw puzzle, ca 1890, shows boy dispensing drink to mother & child, 6x8", EX, F1 .... **$60.00**

Paul Jones Tobacco, pocket tin, red, upright, rare, EX, D **$2,500.00**

Paul Jones Whiskey, drinking glasses, 1960s, clear with gold & red logo, set of 4, 5x3" dia, NM, D **$28.00**

Paul Jones Whiskey, sign, die-cut tin, 'Temptation of St Anthony,' kneeling child between Mammy & gent, curled corners, 14x20", VG, A $1,600.00

Paul Jones Whiskey, sign, tin, various dead game hanging on cabin wall, original frame, 58x44", G, A **$300.00**

Paula, crate label, 1930s, California lemon, senorita with fan & Red Ball logo on green, Santa Paula, 9x12", M, C3 .... **$18.00**

Pavonia Beer, sign, die-cut paper, woman in period costume with foot on barrel, framed, image: 24x12", G, A **$45.00**

Pay Car, sign, porcelain, Safety First logo above Chew Pay Car, red, white & blue, edge chips, 6x3", G, A **$55.00**

PC Lewis Mfg Co's Reclining Rocking Chair, trade card, pictures 2 chairs, The Celebrated Rip Van Winkle..., attached coupon for World's Fair offer, EX, A **$16.00**

PCW Cough Drops, sample tin, red, slip lid, square with rounded corners, A **$25.00**

Peachy Double Cut Tobacco, pocket tin, upright, peach on stem pictured on yellow ground with product name above & below, 4x2½", EX, A **$75.00**

Peachy Double Cut Tobacco, pocket tin, upright, peach on stem pictured on yellow ground with product name above & below, 4x2½", NM, A $150.00

Peachy Ribbon Cut Chewing Tobacco, box, cardboard, peach on yellow with white side panels, product lettering above and below, holds 1 doz packs, 9x5x5", NM, A **$12.50**

Peacock Brand China Tea, tin, green & gold with product name above colorful image of peacock, pry lid, Oriental lettering, 1-lb, VG, A **$5.00**

Peacock Condoms, tin, full-color peacock, M, D **$35.00**

Peacock Lima Beans, can label, blue peacock & ornate design, EX, C3 .....**$5.00**

Peak Coffee, tin, product name lettered on mountain peaks, screw lid, 1-lb, VG+, A **$40.00**

Peak of the Market Quality Vegetables, sign, porcelain, product name lettered over mountain peak above group of vegetables, 32x20", VG, M2 .....**$700.00**

Pearl Waist, sign, photographic print of young girl standing at right of Q logo in upper left, framed, 39½x28½", G+, A **$210.00**

Pears Soap, sign, paper, 3 young girls making flower arrangements by marble fountain, signed WS Coleman, framed, 27x18½", VG, A **$75.00**

Pedro Cut Plug Smoking Tobacco, pail, tin, yellow with round king-of-spades logo, red & black lettering, red trim, wire handle, 4x8x5", VG, A **$105.00**

Peerless Dyes, cabinet, wood with paper front, roll top, veiled Bedouin girl with camel train below, early, 32x19x11", G, A **$600.00**

Peerless Hardwater Soap, container, glass ball shape, metal lid missing, 10", G, A **$40.00**

Peerless Hardwater Soap, container, glass ball shape with metal lid, 10", EX, A **$120.00**

Peerless Ice Cream, clock, plastic light-up, product name in script over painter's palette, It's Time For...It's Good, 16" dia, EX, A **$135.00**

Peerless Leather Top Dressing, tin, 1910-25, touring car in gold rectangular inset, product name above & below, press lid, 2-pt, 5", EX, A **$20.00**

Peerless Maid Confections, tin, 1930s-40s, candies & lady with parasol on yellow, candy cane design in corners, screw lid, 5-lb, 10", EX, A $40.00

Peerless Motor Oil, can, 1935-45, blue eagle flanked by Highest Quality, product name above & below, minor fading, 1/2-gal, 6½", VG, A **$110.00**

Peerless Rubber Manufacturing Co, sign, paperboard, Uncle Sam reads Naval Review before rainbow graphics, framed, 28x20, EX+, A $2,600.00

Peg Top Cigars, door push plate, porcelain, brown on off-white, The Old Reliable above vertical cigar, 5¢, brown border, 4x13", NM, M2 .....**$130.00**

Peg Top Cigars, sign, porcelain, brown & white cigar on yellow ground, The Old Reliable, 5¢ above & below, scratches, 14x28", G, A **$60.00**

Penafiel Aqua de Mineral Water, tray, product name lettered on cap, Mexican, minor paint flakes, D......**$12.00**

Penguin Motor Oil, can, 1935-45, red, white & blue with penguin in center, product name above, heavy wear, 1-qt, 5½", A..**$120.00**

Peninsular Stoves, pocket mirror, company name & products lettered above aerial view of factory, horizontal oval, 2¾", EX, A..**$60.00**

Penn Beer, calendar, 1912, paper, girl in green & black outfit & hat, Consumers Brewing Co, full pad, framed, image: 31x16", EX, A..**$400.00**

Penn Esther Kitchen Range, sign, wax paper under glass with chain border, Victorian lady in kitchen at her Penn Esther stove, 8½x7", EX, A........$175.00

Penn Glenn Motor Oil, can, 1935-45, yellow propeller with PQ logo, red & blue product name in center, 1-qt, 5½", EX, A...**$110.00**

Penn Mutual Life Insurance, watch fob, embossed metal, portrait of William Penn, with name on banner, EX, A...**$65.00**

Penn Power Motor Oil, can, 1915-25, green & cream with man holding shield & club, Nourse Oil Co..., screw lid & handle, 1/2-gal, 6", G, A................................**$350.00**

Penn-Drake Motor Oils, sign, tin, 2-sided, 100% Pure... logo above Penn-Drake diagonally over early homestead, Motor Oils below, 28x21", G, A **$140.00**

Penn-Guin Motor Oil, sign, tin, penguin in top hat, Change To Fortified Triple-Film above 100% Pennsylvania... on shield, 36x60", NM, A...........................**$91.00**

Penn-Royal Oil, can, 1930s, 100% Pure logo in center, product name above & below, green & black background, pry lid, 1-qt, 5½", EX, A.........................**$30.00**

Pennant Cigars, sign, reverse-painted glass, baseball inset lettered National League, silver foiled letters, VG, A..**$330.00**

Pennant Draught Beer, label, 1933-50, logo above product name, Illinois Brewing Co, Internal Revenue Tax Paid statement, EX, A..**$12.00**

Pennsylect Coreco Motor Oils, sign, porcelain, product name lettered on the shape of Pennsylvania, Good & Tough lettered above, 20x30", NM, D **$550.00**

Pennsylvania Game Commission, sign, tin, Hunting Is Unlawful, minor rust in top corner, VG, D..........**$40.00**

Pennsylvania Motor Oil, can, 1935-45, Heart O' Pennsylvania lettered over red heart on silver & blue, red, blue & silver lettering, 6", EX, A................................**$100.00**

Pennsylvania Patrician, ashtray, tire shape, clear insert, D..**$14.00**

Pennsylvania Rubber Co, sign, paper, girl in profile wearing flowered straw hat, matted & framed, image: 21½x20", EX+, A..**$600.00**

Pennsylvania Tires, sign, painted metal, black with yellow Tires lettered above & below vertical Pennsylvania, yellow border, 60x15", G, A.....................................**$70.00**

Penny Post Cut Plug, lunch pail, tin, Penny Post in script above logo & ornate graphics, wire handle, brass hinged lid, EX+, A...**$225.00**

Pennzoil, can, 1915-45, Pennzoil superimposed on bell, text below, yellow backgound, easy pour spout, 5-gal, 14" dia, VG, A..**$200.00**

Pennzoil, can, 1935-40, Main Liner airplane & Pennzoil lettered over red bell, Be Oil Wise & owls below, 1-qt, 5½", EX, A...**$30.00**

Pennzoil, can, 1935-45, oval logo top center on red, yellow & black background, pry lid, 1-lb, 5", EX, A.**$15.00**

Pennzoil, mechanical pencil with perpetual calendar, green, yellow, red & black, EX, D **$20.00**

Pennzoil, pump sign, porcelain, yellow Pennzoil oval over sun rays on black ground, 100%...Safe Lubrication, 15x13", EX+, A..**$325.00**

Pennzoil, sign, ca 1971, tin, red arrow on white background, Drive To Hold in bold white letters, oval logo above, EX, A...**$35.00**

Pennzoil, sign, porcelain, black & red on yellow, Pennzoil lettered diagonally across red bell, 100% Pure..., oval, 14x31", EX, D3........................$125.00

Pennzoil, sign, porcelain, red arrow & Expert Lubrication on white background, 9x30", EX, N2................**$145.00**

Pennzoil, sign, 1955, tin, Spanish, Pennzoil superimposed over red bell, Calidad..., yellow with black border, horizontal, EX, A...**$145.00**

Pennzoil Outboard Motor Oil, sign, painted die-cut metal, 2-sided, product name above Pennzoil over bell, Safe Lubrication below, 12x17", NM, A **$120.00**

Penoka, crate label, Canada apple, red apple with crown above early vista of orchards, 9x11", EX, G1..........**$3.00**

Penrod Tomatoes, can label, pictures 3 children in costumes with their dog, M, C1..................................**$2.00**

People's Store, pocket mirror, smiling girl in bonnet, Clothing On Credit lettered above, company name below, oval, 2¾", VG+, A....................................**$90.00**

Peoples Pure Ice Co, pocket mirror, lady's image in block of ice with company name arched above, Whelling W Va below, oval, 2¾", G, A.................................**$108.00**

Pep Boys Super Motor Oil, can, 1915-25, blue, red & yellow with lettering over large diagonal center band, pour spout & handle, 1-gal, EX, A..................**$1,000.00**

Pepsi-Cola, ad, 1937, full-page from Baltimore Sunday Sun, tilted 5¢ bottle, Pepsi=Cola...A Nickel Drink, 22x16", NM, A..**$90.00**

Pepsi-Cola, apron, 1930s, pictures tilted bottle with Pepsi & Pete above Pepsi=Cola lettered across double pocket, VG, A..**$275.00**

Pepsi-Cola, apron, 1950s, canvas, vendor's waist apron in red & blue on white with Pepsi-Cola lettered across front, 22", NM, D..**$42.00**

Pepsi-Cola, ashtray, glass, bottle cap logo above Lafayette Beverages, NH..., oval, NM, A...........................**$110.00**

Pepsi-Cola, award, square walnut plaque with metal bottle cap bordered by embossed brass plates with Per Capita Award & 1953, EX+, A...**$45.00**

Pepsi-Cola, award, 1930s-40s, gold bottle on pyramid base, enameled or heavily painted inlay, EX+, A........**$320.00**

Pepsi-Cola, bag rack, 1930s, metal, 2-sided, features Pepsi & Pete on Bigger-Better Pepsi=Cola wavy band, 19x24", VG+, A...................................$475.00

Pepsi-Cola, bag rack, 1930s-40s, metal, Pepsi=Cola bottle cap flanked by Take Home 6 Bottles Today & Bigger Better, 17x38", EX, A..**$300.00**

Pepsi-Cola, bank, composition, cooler shape with Pepsi-Cola Ice Cold Sold Here, 3¾x3", G, A.................**$55.00**

Pepsi-Cola, bank, 1940s, gull-wing cooler with Pepsi=Cola logo, NM, A...**$240.00**

Pepsi-Cola, bank, 1945, plastic, upright 5¢ vending machine, embossed Drink Ice Cold with oval Pepsi=Cola logo, Marx, 7x3", EX+, A.................**$110.00**

Pepsi-Cola, baseball cards, 1989, set of 12 Mark McGuire cards distributed 1 per 12-can carton, M, D.........**$35.00**

Pepsi-Cola, blotter, 1905, Drink 5¢ Pepsi=Cola with Delicious! Delightful! above, At Founts Also In Bottles below, rare, EX+, A...**$425.00**

Pepsi-Cola, blotter, 1905, For Brain Fag & Body Drag Drink above printed Pepsi-Cola 5¢, At All Soda Fountains... below, VG+, A.......................................**$300.00**

Pepsi-Cola, blotter, 1930, Pepsi & Pete The Pepsi-Cola Cops lettered on panel at left of Pepsi & Pete with tilted 5¢ bottle, EX, A...**$90.00**

Pepsi-Cola, blotter, 1945, Pepsi=Cola cap at right of girl serving 2 bottles of Pepsi with Tempty...Tasty flanking head, NM, A...**$95.00**

Pepsi-Cola, booklet, 1938, large bottle on stage with cityscape background commemorating 38th anniversary, EX+, A...**$90.00**

Pepsi-Cola, bottle, amber glass with original blue on white paper label, Milton, Mass Distibuting Co, VG, A..**$45.00**

Pepsi-Cola, bottle, painted label, Pepsi-Cola, full, 8-oz, NM, A..**$6.00**

Pepsi-Cola, bottle, painted label, Pepsi-Cola, 12-oz, NM, A...**$6.00**

Pepsi-Cola, bottle, painted label, Pepsi=Cola, full, 8-oz, NM, A..**$10.00**

Pepsi-Cola, bottle, paper label, Pepsi=Cola, 12-oz, EX, A..**$20.00**

Pepsi-Cola, bottle, 1905, embossed glass, Escombia Bottling Co, Pensacola Fla, rare, NM, A...............**$1,000.00**

Pepsi-Cola, bottle, 1907-12, embossed amber glass, Birmingham Ala, NM, A..**$55.00**

Pepsi-Cola, bottle, 1915-25, embossed clear glass, Pepsi-Cola Bottling Works, LM Squires Proprietor, Burlington NC, 7-oz, NM, A...**$80.00**

Pepsi-Cola, bottle, 1950s, glass, swirl design with oval Sparkling Pepsi-Cola labels, 1-qt, EX, A............**$130.00**

Pepsi-Cola, bottle, 1954, clear with red & white label, 10-oz, EX, D..**$10.00**

Pepsi-Cola, bottle, 1974, clear with red & white label, 16-oz, EX, D...**$8.50**

Pepsi-Cola, bottle carrier, 1930s, natural wood, blue & red graphics, wood handle with cutout, 11x8", NM, D.....**$80.00**

Pepsi-Cola, bottle carrier, 1940s, pictures a bottle cap, Family Case, 59¢, 10x16", EX, D **$65.00**

Pepsi-Cola, bottle carrier, 1945, cardboard, 6 Big 12-oz Bottles, bottle cap flanked by Bigger & Better at bottom, unused, B1...**$30.00**

Pepsi-Cola, bottle opener, embossed metal, Pepsi-Cola in red, made by Starr Co, 3x2½", VG, D..................**$15.00**

Pepsi-Cola, bottle opener, 1930s, tin, bottle shape, 4", EX+, D...**$35.00**

Pepsi-Cola, bottle opener, 1950s, heavy silverplated metal, embossed bottle cap in center, The Drink Of Friendship on back, EX, A...**$50.00**

Pepsi-Cola, bottle topper, 1930s, foil, 5¢ bordered by Nickel Drink Worth A Dime on round panel atop Pepsi=Cola logo, EX+, A...................................**$185.00**

Pepsi-Cola, cake carrier, metal, red, white & blue with Pepsi logo, 9x11" dia, EX+, D **$50.00**

Pepsi-Cola, calendar, 1909, lady in plumed hat lifts glass, Drink 5¢ Pepsi=Cola... above, August page below, framed, 19x10", EX, A.....................................**$1,400.00**

Pepsi-Cola, calendar, 1911, girl in thoughtful pose displaying glass, Drink 5¢ Pepsi=Cola... below, March pad, framed, EX+, A $1,600.00

Pepsi-Cola, calendar, 1913, girl in large hat with glass looks over shoulder, Drink Pepsi-Cola printed above July pad, framed, G-, A.......................................**$150.00**

Pepsi-Cola, calendar, 1921, bare-shouldered lady with head tilted up looking forward, by Rolf Armstong, full pad, framed, EX+, A **$2,100.00**

Pepsi-Cola, calendar, 1941, cardboard, smiling party girl holding Pepsi bottle, full paper pad flanked by rectangular logos, NM, A $220.00

Pepsi-Cola, calendar, 1942, snowy farm scene, Dec 1941 cover sheet with oval Pepsi logo flanking numbers, metal strip at top, EX, A **$100.00**

Pepsi-Cola, calendar, 1942, starts with April featuring distant farm with rolling hills, oval logo, VG, A **$45.00**

Pepsi-Cola, calendar, 1945, features famous artists, oval Pepsi=Cola logo, complete, EX+, A **$55.00**

Pepsi-Cola, calendar, 1946, complete, 23x15", NM, A.......**$80.00**

Pepsi-Cola, calendar, 1947, Pepsi-Cola Presents Paintings..., complete, metal strip at top, VG+, A **$60.00**

Pepsi-Cola, calendar, 1948, complete, 23x15", NM, A...**$60.00**

Pepsi-Cola, calendar, 1950, January & December months upper left & lower right of ice skater seated with bottle, complete, EX+, A **$210.00**

Pepsi-Cola, calendar, 1950, 6 pages featuring 2 months & girls in different poses, artist signed, metal strip at top, 22x13", EX, A..**$210.00**

Pepsi-Cola, calendar, 1954, self-framed cardboard stand-up, tear-off pad with sign on backing, May sheet, EX+, A...**$45.00**

Pepsi-Cola, calendar top, 1954, celluloid, features lady with hand on hip, Refresh Without Filling & bottle cap, oval, 12x8", EX, A...**$60.00**

Pepsi-Cola, can, 1940s, cone-top, 12-oz, EX, A.......**$200.00**

Pepsi-Cola, can, 1940s, cone-top, 12-oz, NM, A......**$260.00**

Pepsi-Cola, cash register marquee, 1940s, tin, 2-sided, 1 side with Today's Special, Please Count Your... on reverse, EX, A..**$325.00**

Pepsi-Cola, character glass, Harvey Cartoons collector series, Casper the Ghost, blue lettering, 6¼", M, D............**$10.00**

Pepsi-Cola, character glass, Harvey Cartoons collector series, Hot Stuff, black lettering, 6¼", M, D..........**$10.00**

Pepsi-Cola, character glass, Leonardo collector series, Sweet Polly, black lettering with white Pepsi logo, 6¼", M, D **$30.00**

Pepsi-Cola, character glass, Leonardo collector series, Underdog, black lettering with white Pepsi logo, 6¼", M, D **$15.00**

Pepsi-Cola, character glass, Visual Creations collector series, pictures an owl, I Only Have Eyes For You, 6¼", M, D **$50.00**

Pepsi-Cola, character glass, Ward Productions collector series, Bullwinkle, white lettering & logo, 6¼", M, D **$20.00**

Pepsi-Cola, character glass, Ward Productions collector series, Mr Peabody, black lettering, 6¼", M, D.....**$10.00**

Pepsi-Cola, character glass, 1966, Super Heroes collectors series, Batman, 6¼", M, D....................................**$20.00**

Pepsi-Cola, character glass, 1973, Warner Bros collector series, Bugs Bunny, black lettering, Federal Glass Co, 5⅛", M, D...**$20.00**

Pepsi-Cola, character glass, 1973, Warner Bros collector series, Daffy Duck, black lettering, Federal Glass Co, 5⅛", M, D...**$20.00**

Pepsi-Cola, character glass, 1973, Warner Bros collector series, Elmer Fudd, white lettering, Federal Glass Co, 6¼", M, D...**$10.00**

Pepsi-Cola, character glass, 1976, Super Heroes series, Robin the Boy Wonder, M, D...............................**$12.00**

Pepsi-Cola, character glass, 1976, Warner Bros action series, Road Runner & Wile E Coyote, M, D **$10.00**

Pepsi-Cola, character glass, 1976, Warner Bros action series, Yosemite Sam & Bugs Bunny, M, D..........**$20.00**

Pepsi-Cola, character glass, 1977, Hanna-Barbera collector series, Flintstones, M, D..**$20.00**

Pepsi-Cola, character glass, 1977, Hanna-Barbera collector series, Josie & the Pussycats, M, D.......................**$20.00**

Pepsi-Cola, character glass, 1977, Hanna-Barbera collector series, Scooby Doo, M, D **$30.00**

Pepsi-Cola, character glass, 1977, Happy Birthday Mickey series, Mickey presenting roses to Daisy, M, D....**$50.00**

Pepsi-Cola, character glass, 1977, Jungle Book series, Baloo bear, M, D **$50.00**

Pepsi-Cola, character glass, 1977, Jungle Book series, King Looie gorilla, M, D **$70.00**

Pepsi-Cola, character glass, 1978, Happy Birthday Mickey series, Donald playing violin while Huey, Louie & Dewey plug ears, M, D **$15.00**

Pepsi-Cola, character glass, 1978, Happy Birthday Mickey series, Uncle Scrooge about to pick up money with spiked cane, M, D **$15.00**

Pepsi-Cola, character glass, 1979, Looney Tunes series, Bugs Bunny with suitcase full of carrots & Elmer with shotgun, M, D **$10.00**

Pepsi-Cola, checkers game, 1970s, wood, features Pepsi cans & Mountain Dew cans on checkerboard, 14x14", NMIB, A **$100.00**

Pepsi-Cola, clock, paper face with Plexiglas lens, metal frame, Sessions Clock Co, 14½x14½", G, A....**$25.00**

Pepsi-Cola, clock, 1920s, animated windup with burgundy case, ballerina turns in bottom on the hour, made in Germany, EX, A $525.00

Pepsi-Cola, clock, 1920s, animated windup with white case, ballerina turns in bottom on the hour, cracks in side of case, VG, A....**$325.00**

Pepsi-Cola, clock, 1930s, round, reverse-painted face, neon tube around numbers, Drink Pepsi=Cola, Bigger & Better, rare, G, A **$1,600.00**

Pepsi-Cola, clock, 1930s, rectangular Pepsi=Cola logo, Drink above, neon around numbers, 18x18", VG+, A ...**$800.00**

Pepsi-Cola, clock, 1940, wood frame, Time For Cloverdale Beverages above Pepsi=Cola, electric, cord is cut, 15x15", VG, A **$525.00**

Pepsi-Cola, clock, 1940s, light-up, 1-12 numbered around Pepsi-Cola logo, 15" dia, EX+, D....**$300.00**

Pepsi-Cola, clock, 1940s, masonite, plastic lens, embossed Drink Pepsi=Cola Now! cap, numbers around, not working, 14x14", VG, A **$230.00**

Pepsi-Cola, clock, 1940s, metal, painted numbers & Drink Pepsi=Cola Now! bottle cap embossed on lens, 13x13", EX, D3....**$650.00**

Pepsi-Cola, clock, 1941, glass front with metal frame Pepsi=Cola bottle cap surrounded by numbers, neon square, EX, A....**$775.00**

Pepsi-Cola, clock, 1950s, metal rim, glass lens, round electric light-up with large bottle cap on yellow, 30" dia EX, A....**$350.00**

Pepsi-Cola, clock, 1950s, tin face & frame, glass lens slanted bottle cap logo, bordered by numbers, 16x16" EX, A....**$250.00**

Pepsi-Cola, clock, 1951, plastic, Drink Pepsi-Cola Ice-Cold bordered by smaller symbols, light-up not working, 12' dia, VG, A....**$280.00**

Pepsi-Cola, clock, 1960s, metal frame, plastic lens, Pepsi logo at 12 with numbers 3, 6 & 9, 18x14", EX+, D **$65.00**

Pepsi-Cola, coaster, 1940s, cork, Pepsi=Cola logo in red, white & blue, 4" dia, NM, D **$22.00**

Pepsi-Cola, cone cup holder, 1943, Bakelite, oval Pepsi=Cola decals, original paper cup with Pepsi-Cola bottle caps, 5", EX+, A....**$150.00**

Pepsi-Cola, cooler, picnic, 1940s, metal, gray with red logo, 12x18x9", EX, D....**$100.00**

Pepsi-Cola, cooler, picnic, 1950s, white Drink Pepsi-Cola on medium blue, metal handle, opener upper right, small, VG+, A **$135.00**

Pepsi-Cola, coupon, 1910, for free glass of Pepsi, graphics on both sides, The Pepsin Drink Containing Fruit Juices &..., EX+, A....**$290.00**

Pepsi-Cola, decal, 1960, pictures a bottle cap on yellow ground, Have A Pepsi below, 12x12", EX, D....**$25.00**

Pepsi-Cola, display, die-cut cardboard stand-up, Santa holds bottle by head with gifts at feet, bottle cap logo, 19x10", NM, A....**$105.00**

Pepsi-Cola, display, die-cut cardboard stand-up, Santa with bottle & trees at feet, Merry Christmas bottle-cap logo, 19x10", NM, A....**$105.00**

Pepsi-Cola, display, die-cut cardboard stand-up, 1920s-30s, plain Pepsi=Cola logo on wavy band with floral motif, 22x40", G, A **$175.00**

Pepsi-Cola, display, die-cut cardboard stand-up, 1930s, bottle with Pepsi=Cola logo on 5¢ Five Cents 5¢ base, 16", EX+, A **$450.00**

Pepsi-Cola, display, die-cut cardboard stand-up, 1930s, girl under umbrella with Pepsi & Pete writing in sand, 40x30", NM, A **$3,300.00**

Pepsi-Cola, display, die-cut cardboard stand-up, 1930s, Pepsi & Pete flank 6-pack with Bigger & Better Pepsi=Cola, 14x20", EX, A....**$1,050.00**

Pepsi-Cola, display, die-cut cardboard stand-up, 1930s, 6 bottles & scrolled Bigger & Better banner, Drink 5¢..., 15x19", NM, A....**$650.00**

Pepsi-Cola, display, die-cut cardboard stand-up, 1930s-40s, running Pepsi cop holding sign saying ...Pepsi-Cola 5¢, 8", EX, A **$350.00**

Pepsi-Cola, display, die-cut cardboard stand-up, 1940s, life-size Black waitress with metal 6-pack stands by large bottle, VG, A **$1,400.00**

Pepsi-Cola, display, die-cut cardboard stand-up, 1940s, Now At Our Fountain above Pepsi=Cola on wavy band, Big...5¢, 11x6", EX, A **$150.00**

Pepsi-Cola, display, die-cut cardboard stand-up, 1950s, Santa with bottle against snow, ...Greetings bottle cap, 20", EX, A..**$60.00**

Pepsi-Cola, display, die-cut cardboard stand-up, 1950s, Santa with bottle & standing with gifts at feet, bottle cap logo, 54", NM, A..**$210.00**

Pepsi-Cola, display, die-cut cardboard stand-up, 1960s-70s, high-stepping Santa with bottle & pipe, Norman Rockwell, EX+, A..**$60.00**

Pepsi-Cola, display, die-cut cardboard stand-up, 3-D, 1950s, girl in shorts with bottles on ice & array of food, 20x16", VG+, A..**$45.00**

Pepsi-Cola, display rack, 1930s, metal, 2-sided, 2 die-cut bottles at each end of 2-tier rack with slogan panels, 47x27", EX+, A **$1,700.00**

Pepsi-Cola, display rack, 1930s-40s, metal, 2-case rack designed for stacking or counter-top use, unusual, EX, A..$100.00

Pepsi-Cola, doll, plush elf with yellow felt hat, green shirt & red pants, logo on black plastic belt, 20", NM, D....**$35.00**

Pepsi-Cola, door handle, 1940s, slender upright handle with square advertising mounting plates top & bottom, Bigger & Better, NM, A.....................................**$170.00**

Pepsi-Cola, door plate, 1940, red, white & blue, Come In For... above Pepsi=Cola 5¢ banner, Buy It By... below, 10", NM, A **$475.00**

Pepsi-Cola, door push bar, porcelain, modern Pepsi-Cola logos flank black Prenez Un Pepsi on yellow, French Canadian, 3x30", EX, M2.......................................**$80.00**

Pepsi-Cola, door push bar, steel, Say Pepsi, Please at left of bottle cap, scratches/rust, 33" long, G, A.........**$25.00**

Pepsi-Cola, door push bar, steel plate over wire bar with diamond design, Pepsi on bottle cap flanked by Say..., 30" long, G+, A..**$45.00**

Pepsi-Cola, door push bar, steel plate over wire bar with diamond design, Say..., Please at left of bottle cap, 30" long, VG, A..**$65.00**

Pepsi-Cola, door push plate, 1950s, tin, yellow, Enjoy A Pepsi on white center, bottle caps top & bottom, round ends, 4x13", EX, A..**$150.00**

Pepsi-Cola, door push plate, 1950s, tin, yellow, Pepsi=Cola bottle caps top & bottom, blue Pick A Pepsi in center, 14x4", EX+, A **$175.00**

Pepsi-Cola, fan, 1905, paper, ratan handle, Pepsi=Cola lettered above boy sipping from glass, EX, A..$1,350.00

Pepsi-Cola, fan, 1912, cardboard, girl sips from straw in bottle with Drink Pepsi=Cola printed below, missing wood handle, VG, A..**$800.00**

Pepsi-Cola, fan, 1940, cardboard, Pepsi=Cola on white line with 5¢ & bottle graphic, Pepsi & Pete on reverse, wood handle, NM, A..**$95.00**

Pepsi-Cola, fan, 1940s, paper with wood handle, 2-sided, Pepsi logo on front, comic scene on back, minor soiling, EX, A $45.00

Pepsi-Cola, fountain pen, 1930s, plastic, blue & red on white, Pepsi logos & blue stripes around barrel of pen, 5", NM, D..**$110.00**

Pepsi-Cola, game, 1941, promotional spinner game featuring 'Vest Pocket Baseball,' VG+, A **$300.00**

Pepsi-Cola, hat, soda jerk, 1930s-40s, oilcloth, Drink Pepsi=Cola 5¢, Worth A Dime, VG, A **$80.00**

Pepsi-Cola, hat, soda jerk, 1970s, paper, red, white & blue, Have A Pepsi Day!, adjustable, EX, D....................**$4.00**

Pepsi-Cola, ID token, 1930s, gray metal badge shape with raised image of an eagle & 2 bottles, Delicious..., 1½x1¼", EX, D....................**$28.00**

Pepsi-Cola, kaleidoscope, 1970s, can shape, EX, D..**$25.00**

Pepsi-Cola, lighter, 1930s-40s, straight-sided bottle shape with oval Pepsi=Cola logo, 2", NMIB, A..............**$80.00**

Pepsi-Cola, lighter, 1950s, applied bottle-cap logo to 1 side, Zippo brand, EX, A....................**$40.00**

Pepsi-Cola, lighter, 1950s, gold harp shape with bottle cap logo on 1 side, Crownharp brand, EX, A..........**$110.00**

Pepsi-Cola, lighter, 1950s, painted metal, musical, slanted bottle cap on 1 side, Drink Pepsi-Cola in script on other, 3x2", EX, A....................**$130.00**

Pepsi-Cola, lighter, 1950s, yellow metal, Drink lettered on flip-top, slanted bottle cap on body, 3½", EX, A..............**$70.00**

Pepsi-Cola, matchbook cover, full-length ad with 5¢ tilted bottle on striped background, Bigger & Better, 20 strike, EX, R1....................**$1.25**

Pepsi-Cola, mechanical pencil, white with 3 blue stripes flanking red Pepsi-Cola in script, EX+, A............**$30.00**

Pepsi-Cola, menu board, tin, black Have A Pepsi left of bottle cap on yellow above chalkboard, round corners, 30x20", EX+, M3....................**$75.00**

Pepsi-Cola, menu board, tin, Pepsi-Cola on wavy band above chalkboard, red & black rope-like border, 30x19½", G, A....................**$100.00**

Pepsi-Cola, menu board, 1940, wood, Pepsi=Cola on wavy band above slots for menu items, Goes Great With A Sandwich!, 24x12", EX, A....................**$475.00**

Pepsi-Cola, menu board, 1940s, embossed tin, Pepsi=Cola bottle cap above chalkboard, beveled-look edge, 27x18½", EX+, A....................$325.00

Pepsi-Cola, menu board, 1950s, Have A Pepsi in script at left of slanted Pepsi-Cola bottle cap on striped background, 30x19", EX, A....................**$90.00**

Pepsi-Cola, menu board, 1950s, tin, Special Today lettered at top, bottle cap & Hits The Spot lettered below, 30x19½", G, A....................**$100.00**

Pepsi-Cola, menu holder, 1950s, free-standing table-top, EX, D....................**$50.00**

Pepsi-Cola, miniature 6-pack, 1950s, vertical white & blue striped carton & 6 bottles, bottle-cap logo & printed Pepsi-Cola, EX, A....................**$60.00**

Pepsi-Cola, miniskirt, 1960s, Feeling Free, A............**$25.00**

Pepsi-Cola, mirror, elongated vertical with Pepsi=Cola on white wavy band, flaking/stains, G+, A....................**$203.00**

Pepsi-Cola, music box, 1982, stuffed Pepsi & Pete, plays original Pepsi jingle, in original package, NM, A..........**$70.00**

Pepsi-Cola, napkin, embroidered cloth, simply says Pepsi-Cola, light stains, EX, A....................**$65.00**

Pepsi-Cola, napkin dispenser, 1940s, 2-tone with Drink in script above napkin opening, Pepsi=Cola bottle cap on sides, EX, A....................**$550.00**

Pepsi-Cola, note pad, ca 1915, postal rates with weights & measures noted on inside cover, 5½x2¾", EX, A.**$45.00**

Pepsi-Cola, note pad, 1920-21, girl on front, couple on back, calendar on inside back cover, NM, A........**$75.00**

Pepsi-Cola, painting, ca 1938, pastel, Pepsi-Cola headquarters, believed to be original artwork for ads, matted, 25x34", EX, A....................**$160.00**

Pepsi-Cola, paperweight, etched glass, bottle-cap shape with vertical Pepsi-Cola oval logo, NM, A...........**$55.00**

Pepsi-Cola, pin, metal & enamel, safety award commemorating 12 years, Pepsi=Cola in center, ½", M, A....................**$30.00**

Pepsi-Cola, pin, 1942, metal, Pepsi=Cola embossed on bar attached to ball lettered Scholastic Softball Champions, 1x1¼", NM, A....................**$65.00**

Pepsi-Cola, plate, 1983, china, pictures 1909 girl in plumed hat lifting glass, decorative border, 1 of 1000, Lenox, MIB, A....................**$90.00**

Pepsi-Cola, pocket mirror, Victorian Pepsi girl lifting glass before tavern scene, 5¢, oval, 2¾x1¾", VG+, A....................$2,700.00

Pepsi-Cola, radio, Bakelite bottle on round base, repainted label/crack on base, works well, M2................**$440.00**

Pepsi-Cola, radio, 1950s, blue plastic floor cooler with bottle-cap knob on side, Ice Cold & oval Pepsi=Cola logo on front, EX, A....................**$160.00**

Pepsi-Cola, radio, 1950s, upright vending machine, Pepsi-Cola lettered at top, leather case, 7", NM, A..........**$230.00**

Pepsi-Cola, radio, 1964, upright vending machine, Pepsi lettered over bottle cap on top panel, Please below, 7", NMIB, A $200.00

Pepsi-Cola, radio, 1967, rectangular floor cooler with Pepsi logo on all sides, electric, NM, A $275.00

Pepsi-Cola, radio, 1970s, bottle form with oval Pepsi-Cola label, 8½", NM, A $35.00

Pepsi-Cola, radio, 1970s, can form, 5", NMIB, A $35.00

Pepsi-Cola, recipe holder, 1940s, die-cut cardboard bottle with pocket for recipe booklet, 10", EX, A $400.00

Pepsi-Cola, salesman's sample, 1930s-40s, cooler, medium blue with red white & blue Pepsi=Cola oval on front, scarce, VG+, A......$3,200.00

Pepsi-Cola, salt & pepper shakers, 1940s, decaled bottles, Souvenir Of Cleveland Ohio, NMIB, A $190.00

Pepsi-Cola, salt & pepper shakers, 1970s, glass & metal, swirl type, screw-on caps, 4", NM, D......$40.00

Pepsi-Cola, seltzer bottle, amber glass, Pepsi-Cola Bottling Co, Jacksonville Fla, EX+, A $900.00

Pepsi-Cola, seltzer bottle, clear glass, Pepsi-Cola Bottling Co, Jacksonville Fla, Delicious-Healthful logo, few chips, VG, A $600.00

Pepsi-Cola, shade, 1970s, stained glass, with Pepsi=Cola logo, NM, A $150.00

Pepsi-Cola, shot glass, 1989, Happy New Year, EX, D $3.50

Pepsi-Cola, sign, aluminum, 1930s, 12-oz bottle & 5¢ below The Swing Is Open To Pepsi=Cola, Bigger & Better, 26x20", VG+, A......$350.00

Pepsi-Cola, sign, cardboard, self-framed, 1930s, bare-backed girl with bottle & straw looks over her shoulder, 34x25", EX, A......$1,000.00

Pepsi-Cola, sign, cardboard, self-framed, 1930s, pretty girl with wind-blown hair holds bottle with straws, by Ebert, 31x24", EX, A......$725.00

Pepsi-Cola, sign, cardboard, self-framed, 1930s-40s, girl in red, white & blue with bottle against blue background, 31x24", VG+, A......$575.00

Pepsi-Cola, sign, cardboard, self-framed, 1930s-40s, girl on beach with cooler, Pepsi's Best...Take No Less, 29x41", EX, A......$255.00

Pepsi-Cola, sign, cardboard, trolley, 1940s, Where Fun Begins & bottle cap left of family with bottles, framed, 12x30", VG+, A......$350.00

Pepsi-Cola, sign, cardboard, trolley, 1950s, girl & magazine with slanted bottle-cap logo, The Light Refreshment, 11x28", EX, A......$220.00

Pepsi-Cola, sign, cardboard, trolley, 1950s, party couple with bottles of Pepsi, Wonderful With Snacks, More Bounce..., 11x28", G, A......$60.00

Pepsi-Cola, sign, cardboard, trolley, 1963, Come Alive! You're In The Pepsi Generation! below 4 skiers & bottle, 11x28", EX+, D $35.00

Pepsi-Cola, sign, cardboard, 1905, girl with hand on hip lifts glass high, Drink Pepsi=Cola... above, rare, framed, 27x21", G, A $400.00

Pepsi-Cola, sign, cardboard, 1907, girl in profile lifts glass, Drink Pepsi=Cola above, may be only 1 known, 24x16", EX+, A $8,500.00

Pepsi-Cola, sign, cardboard, 1909, girl in plumed hat lifts glass, Delicious-Healthful above, rare, framed, 24½x19½", G, A......$600.00

Pepsi-Cola, sign, cardboard, 1910-15, girl in floppy hat with head tilted sips from straw in straight-sided bottle, 24x18", G, A $500.00

Pepsi-Cola, sign, cardboard, 1910-15, girl in hat at table holding glass, straight-sided bottle on table, rare, 30x20", VG, A......$1,050.00

Pepsi-Cola, sign, cardboard, 1919, bare-shouldered girl with head tilted back, Rolf Armstrong, original wood frame, 31x25", EX, A......$2,600.00

Pepsi-Cola, sign, cardboard, 1930s, girl with bottle & straw holds onto fruit tree branch, matted & framed, 25x19", VG+, A $325.00

Pepsi-Cola, sign, cardboard, 1930s, posed beach girl with tray displaying bottle & glass, 26x18", G, A $375.00

Pepsi-Cola, sign, cardboard, 1933, bottle & 2 glasses at left of 10¢, Pepsi=Cola above, Two Large Glasses..., 10x16", EX, A $450.00

Pepsi-Cola, sign, cardboard, 1936, features Clean! 5¢ bottle, Bigger & Better, A Nickel Drink Worth A Dime, 16x8", EX+, A $180.00

Pepsi-Cola, sign, cardboard, 1940s, couple on bank after swimming with several bottles on tray, Hits The Spot logo, 26x18", G, A......$150.00

Pepsi-Cola, sign, cardboard, 1940s, girl holds glass, Pepsi=Cola bottle cap on left shoulder, Pepsi's Best..., 24x36", NM, A **$275.00**

Pepsi-Cola, sign, cardboard, 1940s, girl in bonnet holds bottle with straw, oval Pepsi=Cola logo, self-frame missing, 23x18", EX, A **$325.00**

Pepsi-Cola, sign, cardboard, 1940s, girl in rose-covered circle with Pepsi=Cola bottle cap, Pepsi's Best..., 24x36", EX, A **$425.00**

Pepsi-Cola, sign, cardboard, 1940s, girl kneeling in garden enjoys 5¢ bottle, oval Pepsi=Cola logo upper left, 35x28", VG+, A $600.00

Pepsi-Cola, sign, cardboard, 1950s, Be Sociable, Have A Pepsi & bottle cap upper right of 2 couples, horse & dog, 26x38", EX, M3 .... **$145.00**

Pepsi-Cola, sign, cardboard, 1950s, girl in knit cap with bottle, Pepsi-Cola bottle cap lower right, Any Weather's..., 24x36", EX, A **$160.00**

Pepsi-Cola, sign, cardboard, 1950s, party table with bottles of Pepsi on ice, The Light Refreshment, framed border, 20x18", G, A **$85.00**

Pepsi-Cola, sign, cardboard, 3-D, 1950s, tennis girl in striped shorts kneels in profile, Refreshes Without Filling, 22x16", VG+, A **$100.00**

Pepsi-Cola, sign, cardboard cutout, embossed, 1967, foil laminated chick pops out of egg, Taste That Beats..., 12x16", EX, A **$80.00**

Pepsi-Cola, sign, cardboard cutout, 1917, girl stands on case of Pepsi to open giant straight-sided 5¢ bottle, 34x20", VG, A **$4,700.00**

Pepsi-Cola, sign, cardboard hanger, die-cut, framed ocean scene, bottle cap upper left & bottle emerging from water, 19x31", EX, A **$780.00**

Pepsi-Cola, sign, cardboard hanger, die-cut, 1940s, bottle hangs from oval reading Drink Iced Pepsi=Cola, unused, 16x6", M2 .... **$225.00**

Pepsi-Cola, sign, cardboard hanger, 1940s, girl holding glass, Sing Out For Pepsi, Pepsi=Cola on wheat border, 20" dia, VG+, A **$400.00**

Pepsi-Cola, sign, celluloid, 1936, Pepsi=Cola above bottle flanked by In Bottles & 5¢, 13x5", NM, D **$650.00**

Pepsi-Cola, sign, celluloid, 1940, Ice Cold above Pepsi=Cola on white band, Sold Here below, 9" dia, VG+, A **$260.00**

Pepsi-Cola, sign, celluloid, 1950, bottle cap with Drink Pepsi=Cola Now!, 9" dia, G+, A **$250.00**

Pepsi-Cola, sign, celluloid, 1950s-60s, photo image of Black lady talking on telephone, Refresh Without Filling, 12x8", EX, A **$30.00**

Pepsi-Cola, sign, celluloid, 1951, bottle cap with Drink Pepsi-Cola, 9" dia, EX, A **$90.00**

Pepsi-Cola, sign, celluloid, 1952, bottle cap with Pepsi-Cola & More Bounce To The Ounce on tag with ribbon, 9" dia, VG, A **$100.00**

Pepsi-Cola, sign, celluloid, 1958, Say Pepsi-Please & bottle cap on white square left of bottle, 9x11", NM, D **$60.00**

Pepsi-Cola, sign, flange, oval Drink Pepsi-Cola Here logo on yellow rectangle, rounded corners, EX, M2..$250.00

Pepsi-Cola, sign, flange, features Pepsi=Cola lettered in center, Ice Cold & Sold Here above & below, 10x14½", VG, A **$250.00**

Pepsi-Cola, sign, flange, 1939, round Pepsi=Cola logo with Ice Cold above & Sold Here below, 16" dia, EX+, D **$400.00**

Pepsi-Cola, sign, flange, 1940s, 2-sided, red, white & blue, Ice Cold Pepsi=Cola..., 10x15", EX+, A **$375.00**

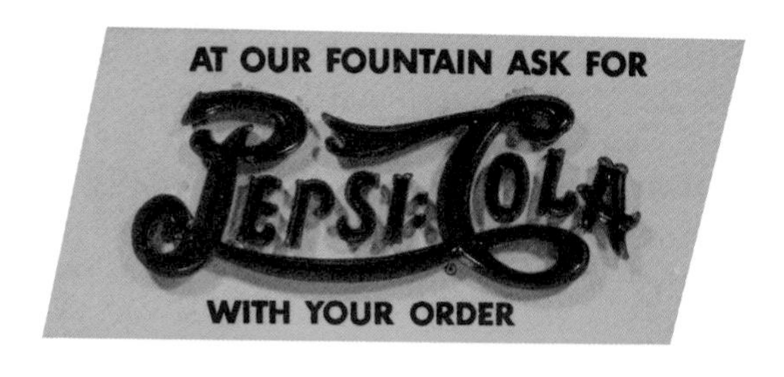

Pepsi-Cola, sign, masonite, 1940s, hot pink plastic molded over Pepsi=Cola for neon look, At Our Fountain Ask For..., EX+, A $325.00

Pepsi-Cola, sign, metal, Ice Cold lettered above & Sold Here lettered below early Pepsi-Cola lettering, 9" dia, MIB, A **$315.00**

Pepsi-Cola, sign, paper, The Light Refreshment Buy Pepsi & bottle cap on yellow above By The Carton & price dot, 19x11", NM, M3 .... **$22.00**

Pepsi-Cola, sign, paper, 1940s, bottle cap logo, Listen To Counter Spy, Pepsi's Radio Thriller!, 8x19", VG+, D..**$25.00**

Pepsi-Cola, sign, paper, 1940s, bottle cap lower left, ...Counter Spy in receding letters, Pepsi's Radio Thriller, 8x19", NM, D **$40.00**

Pepsi-Cola, sign, paper, 5¢ above Pepsi & Pete measuring a large bottle of Pepsi, I Make Sure You Get A Big..., 40"x7 ft, EX, A **$950.00**

Pepsi-Cola, sign, porcelain, Enjoy A Pepsi on white ray pointing to bottle cap on yellow, Canadian, 12x30", EX, M2 ....**$120.00**

Pepsi-Cola, sign, porcelain, 1940s, More Bounce To The Ounce! above bottle appearing to burst through sign, 48x18", NM, A **$1,250.00**

Pepsi-Cola, sign, tin, die-cut, 1936, bottle with arrow pointing to 6-sided Pepsi=Cola label, Refreshing/Healthful, 30", VG, A..**$250.00**

Pepsi-Cola, sign, tin, die-cut, 1942, bottle, oval Pepsi=Cola neck label, 5¢ above 6-sided label, Sparkling/Satisfying, 30", NM, A..................$750.00

Pepsi-Cola, sign, tin, die-cut, 1945, bottle, oval Pepsi=Cola neck label, Sparkling & 12-oz lettered on larger label, 30", EX, A..**$550.00**

Pepsi-Cola, sign, tin, die-cut, 1950s, bottle cap with Pepsi-Cola logo, 18" dia, NM, A..................................**$230.00**

Pepsi-Cola, sign, tin, embossed, Drink (underlined) Pepsi=Cola 5¢ above Refreshing & Healthful on white, 11½x23", NM, A..**$525.00**

Pepsi-Cola, sign, tin, embossed, Drink...5¢, Refreshing & Healthful in red & blue lettering on cream, framed, 22¾x11¼", NM, A...**$275.00**

Pepsi-Cola, sign, tin, embossed, early logo, Here's Health below, green, red & yellow, framed, image: 19½x27½", G-, A **$300.00**

Pepsi-Cola, sign, tin, embossed, early logo flanked by 5¢, red, white & blue, good sheen, 10x30", VG, A..**$350.00**

Pepsi-Cola, sign, tin, embossed, Pepsi over bottle cap on white field left of Say Pepsi Please on yellow, 11x31", M, D3 ....**$285.00**

Pepsi-Cola, sign, tin, embossed, 1905-15, Drink in upper left corner, Pepsi=Cola in center, Here's Health lower right, 13x39", EX, A..**$1,000.00**

Pepsi-Cola, sign, tin, embossed, 1910, straight-sided bottle at left of printed Drink Delicious Pepsi-Cola, Very Refreshing, VG, A **$2,100.00**

Pepsi-Cola, sign, tin, embossed, 1910-15, Drink on tail of C in Pepsi-Cola, Delicious & Refreshing on connected tail, 4x10", NM, A **$325.00**

Pepsi-Cola, sign, tin, embossed, 1930s, Drink Pepsi=Cola 5¢ above Refreshing & Healthful, 6x17", VG, A.**$130.00**

Pepsi-Cola, sign, tin, embossed, 1931, Drink Pepsi=Cola above hourglass bottle, Here's Health in script below, 39x13", EX+, A **$1,500.00**

Pepsi-Cola, sign, tin, embossed, 1940, Drink above 5¢ Pepsi=Cola 5¢ on white band, America's Biggest Nickel's Worth, 10x30", NM, A..........................**$525.00**

Pepsi-Cola, sign, tin, embossed, 1940s, red, yellow & blue, Drink Pepsi=Cola, 12 Ounces 5¢, Peps You Up..., 18x28", VG, A..**$170.00**

Pepsi-Cola, sign, tin, embossed, 1950s, Drink Pepsi-Cola on bottle cap with ribbon, 27x31", EX+, A.........**$160.00**

Pepsi-Cola, sign, tin, embossed, 1950s, Drink...Delicious Delightful, green ground bordered in red, 3½x9⅞", M, A...**$180.00**

Pepsi-Cola, sign, tin, Pepsi=Cola left of 5¢ dot on yellow above Bigger & Better, red border, round top corners, 10x20", NM, M3 ....**$145.00**

Pepsi-Cola, sign, tin, Pepsi=Cola on wavy band above Ice Cold 5¢, Bigger-Better, 23x20", VG+, A.............**$285.00**

Pepsi-Cola, sign, tin, self-framed, embossed, 5¢ dot lower right of Pepsi=Cola on white wavy band, Drink above, 36x59", VG, A...**$120.00**

Pepsi-Cola, sign, tin, Take Home A Carton Of Pepsi=Cola, Refreshing & Healthful lettered at left of 6-pack, 12½x23", VG, A **$395.00**

Pepsi-Cola, sign, tin, white & green on green, Drink Pepsi=Cola, Delicious..., red & wood-grain border, 9x20", VG, M3 ....**$250.00**

Pepsi-Cola, sign, tin, 1908, lady with roses lifting glass, plain 5¢ logo below, gold raised rolled rim, 11x9", NM, A...$4,500.00

Pepsi-Cola, sign, tin, 1910-15, Drink Delicious-Delightful lettered on Pepsi=Cola logo, red, white & green, 13½x27½", VG, A **$550.00**

Pepsi-Cola, sign, tin, 1930s, Take Home A Carton Of Pepsi=Cola, Refreshing & Healthful left of Bigger & Better carton, 12x23", NM, A **$575.00**

Pepsi-Cola, sign, tin, 1930s-40s, Pepsi bottle flanked by 12 Ounces 5¢, red & silver lettering, cream background, 12x5½", EX, A..**$600.00**

Pepsi-Cola, sign, tin, 1930s-40s, Pepsi=Cola on wavy band over tilted 5¢ bottle, Bigger-Better below, blue ground, 50x16", VG+, A...**$350.00**

Pepsi-Cola, sign, tin, 1962, on yellow ground, black Say Pepsi Please lettered at left of Pepsi-Cola bottle cap, 32x68", M, D3...**$475.00**

Pepsi-Cola, sign from drink rack, Pepsi-Cola in bold letters over bottle cap on cream with gold border, brackets, 11x22", EX+, M2 ....**$56.00**

Pepsi-Cola, sign from stainless-steel dispenser, nickel-plated & painted brass, oval Pepsi=Cola logo with 5¢ in circle, VG, A **$140.00**

Pepsi-Cola, spoon holder, 1930s-40s, stoneware, cylinder shape with oval Enjoy Pepsi=Cola logo, round lid, crazing, 6", VG, A **$525.00**

Pepsi-Cola, straw box with straws, 1930s, 5¢ bottle with 2 straws over Pepsi=Cola wavy band, Now For 5¢..., top missing, VG+, A **$140.00**

Pepsi-Cola, straw box with straws, 1950s, see-through band around middle of striped box, slanted bottle cap above, 11", EX, A **$110.00**

Pepsi-Cola, straw holder, glass with chrome top & holder, 11½", EX, D **$25.00**

Pepsi-Cola, straw holder, 1909, tin, 4-sided holder with girl in plumed hat lifting glass, Drink 5¢ Pepsi=Cola above, 6x3x3", VG, A $7,500.00

Pepsi-Cola, straw holder, 1930s, stainless steel, 2-tone with tall back & Pepsi=Cola logo on short front, beveled base, 4x4", VG, A **$180.00**

Pepsi-Cola, straw holder, 1930s-40s, stoneware, tall cylinder shape, oval Enjoy Pepsi=Cola, VG+, A..................**$325.00**

Pepsi-Cola, string holder, 1940s, metal, 2-sided, Join The Swing To above Pepsi=Cola on wavy band, Bigger & Better 5¢, 16x12", EX, A.....................................**$475.00**

Pepsi-Cola, syrup bottle, 1910, Drink Delicious Pepsi-Cola on applied label with gold leaf, metal cap, EX+, A...$1,450.00

Pepsi-Cola, syrup dispenser, hard plastic & metal, multiplex, single spigot, 3", G, A **$35.00**

Pepsi-Cola, syrup dispenser, 1900-05, decorated china, stylized flowering tree motif with embossed lettering, VG+, A $6,500.00

Pepsi-Cola, syrup dispenser, 1915-25, white on green oval Pepsi=Cola logo on ribbed milk-glass base with flared glass vessel, VG, A...**$1,500.00**

Pepsi-Cola, syrup dispenser, 1950s, stainless steel, embossed lettering shaped like outboard motor, tab knob missing, EX, A...**$400.00**

Pepsi-Cola, syrup dispenser tab knob, musical type with ends being bottle cap form with plain Pepsi=Cola logo, EX, A **$250.00**

Pepsi-Cola, syrup jug, 1910-15, clear glass, round with small loop handle at neck, embossed round logo, 1-gal, NM, A...**$500.00**

Pepsi-Cola, thermometer, 1930s, reverse-painted glass in metal frame, Deco look with Bigger & Better slogan, rare, EX, A **$1,000.00**

Pepsi-Cola, thermometer, 1940, tin, arched top & bottom, Buy Pepsi=Cola, Big Big Bottle above ...Hits The Spot, 27", EX, A **$290.00**

Pepsi-Cola, thermometer, 1941, arched top & bottom, thermometer bulb is girl's straw in bottle, Pepsi=Cola below, 27", EX+, A $600.00

Pepsi-Cola, thermometer, 1941, tin, girl drinking from straw in bottle, Pepsi=Cola on wavy band below, 27", VG, A **$250.00**

Pepsi-Cola, thermometer, 1951, dial, metal frame, glass lens, Drink Pepsi-Cola Ice Cold bordered by numbers, 12" dia, NM, A $275.00

Pepsi-Cola, thermometer, 1951, tin, bottle cap above bulb, Any Weather Is Pepsi Weather on card with ribbon below, 27", G, A **$50.00**

Pepsi-Cola, thermometer, 1954, tin, embossed bottle cap above bulb, The Light Refreshment below, rounded corners, 27", EX, A **$150.00**

Pepsi-Cola, thermometer, 1956, tin, Have A Pepsi on white V-shaped field tapering to slanted bottle cap, 27", EX+, A **$150.00**

Pepsi-Cola, thermometer, 1957, tin, Have A Pepsi on white field tapering down to bottle cap on yellow, round corners, 27", NM, D **$110.00**

Pepsi-Cola, thermometer, 1967, tin, Say Pepsi Please on yellow above, stylized Pepsi cap logo below, squared corners, 28", NM, A **$70.00**

Pepsi-Cola, thermometer, 1973, tin, stylized Pepsi-cap logo top & bottom, squared corners, 28", NM, A **$35.00**

Pepsi-Cola, tip tray, 1906, blue & white, The Pepsin Drink above Drink 5¢ Pepsi=Cola, Refreshing-Invigorating below, 6" dia, VG, A **$1,000.00**

Pepsi-Cola, tip tray, 1906, blue & white, The Pepsin Drink above Drink 5¢ Pepsi=Cola, Refreshing-Invigorating below, 6" dia, EX+, A $2,700.00

Pepsi-Cola, tip tray, 1906, red & gold Drink Refreshing Invigorating Pepsi=Cola on black, plain gold rim, horizontal oval, EX+, A $1,150.00

Pepsi-Cola, tip tray, 1908, girl in thoughtful pose with logo below, Delicious, Healthful on rim, crazing, oval, 6 x 4", G+, A **$550.00**

Pepsi-Cola, tip tray, 1908, girl with roses lifting glass, 5¢ Pepsi=Cola below, oval, 6x4", NM, A **$2,500.00**

Pepsi-Cola, tip tray, 1909, girl in plumed hat lifting glass, Drink 5¢ Pepsi=Cola, Delicious-Healthful below, oval, 6x4", VG, A **$800.00**

Pepsi-Cola, tip tray, 1910, girl in thoughtful pose displays glass, Drink 5¢ Pepsi=Cola, oval, 6x4", EX+, A...$950.00

Pepsi-Cola, tip tray, 1950s, black with floral decoration, advertising on back, rectangular, 5x7", G+, A......**$30.00**

Pepsi-Cola, toothpick holder, 1940s, plastic, oval Drink Ice Cold Pepsi=Cola logo on center marquee flanked by round holders, EX, A **$325.00**

Pepsi-Cola, toy hot dog stand, 1945, wood & metal pull-type with bear, striped umbrella with Pepsi=Cola, Cass Toys, EX, A..**$525.00**

Pepsi-Cola, toy hot dog wagon, 1940s, plastic with detachable man & umbrella, bottle logo on sides, by Ideal, NMIB, A..**$925.00**

Pepsi-Cola, toy ice cream shop, in box marked My Merry Ice Cream Shop, bottle-cap logo on sides, 6x7", unused, VG, M2..**$21.00**

Pepsi-Cola, toy syrup dispenser, 1950s, plastic, white soda fountain-type with slanted bottle cap & Pepsi-Cola in print, NMIB, A **$100.00**

Pepsi-Cola, toy truck, metal, yellow with trim, open cargo bed holding 2 cardboard 6-pack cartons, Canadian, 8x18", EX+, M2 ....$500.00

Pepsi-Cola, toy truck, 1930s-40s, wood, Buddy L long-nose van with Railway Express & Pepsi=Cola decals, 16" long, VG, A **$1,450.00**

Pepsi-Cola, toy truck, 1950s, tin, van with bottle & round Pepsi-Cola logo on top, 1950s script logo on sides, friction, 4", EX+, A...**$210.00**

Pepsi-Cola, toy truck, 1950s-60, plastic, white with Pepsi=Cola bottle cap on doors, open cargo bed holds cases of Pepsi, NMIB, A......................................**$550.00**

Pepsi-Cola, toy truck, 1954, metal, 2-tone cab & divided open cargo bed, bottle cap logo on each end, 6", NM, A..**$500.00**

Pepsi-Cola, toy truck, 1958, tin, Ny-Lint with various logos in cargo bed, enclosed top & back, open sides, 16", VG+, A **$100.00**

Pepsi-Cola, toy truck, 1960s, plastic & tin, red with Fresh Drink bottle & round 1950s logo on enclosed cargo bed, 4", NM, A **$80.00**

Pepsi-Cola, tray, 1908, girl with roses lifting glass, plain 5¢ Pepsi=Cola logo below, some restoration, oval, 14x11", EX+, A...**$2,600.00**

Pepsi-Cola, tray, 1909, girl in plumed hat lifts glass, Drink 5¢ Pepsi=Cola Delicious-Healthful below, oval, 14x11", NM, A...**$1,500.00**

Pepsi-Cola, tray, 1910, girl in thoughtful pose with glass, Drink 5¢ Pepsi=Cola, Delicious... on rim, oval, 14x11", EX+, A......................................$950.00

Pepsi-Cola, tray, 1930s, red, white & blue with 3 singers under tree bordered by Pepsi=Cola Hits The Spot..., 11x14", G+, A **$50.00**

Pepsi-Cola, tray, 1939, tilted bottle over US map, Bigger & Better, Coast To Coast & Pepsi=Cola lettered on rim, 11x14", EX, A $380.00

Pepsi-Cola, tray, 1940, bouquet of stylized flowers with musical Pepsi logo at bottom on black with connected dots, 11x14", NM, A **$50.00**

Pepsi-Cola, tray, 1940, Pepsi=Cola on white wavy band, Enjoy above, Hits The Spot & musical notes below, 11x14", EX, A **$90.00**

Pepsi-Cola, tray, 1940s, deep-dish, large Pepsi=Cola bottle cap with lettering inside rim, 13" dia, EX, A **$265.00**

Pepsi-Cola, tray, 1950s, deep-dish, slanted Pepsi-Cola bottle cap bordered on 4 sides with printed Pepsi, 13x13", EX, A **$80.00**

Pepsi-Cola, tray, 1950s, Everess in snow-capped letters above Sparkling Water over mountains, It's Good For You below, 14x11", VG, A **$70.00**

Pepsi-Cola, tray, 1955, deep-dish, Coney Island scene, plain rim, 12" dia, NM, A **$45.00**

Pepsi-Cola, tray, 1970s, deep-dish, shows 3 bottles in ice, lettering on inside rim, 13" dia, EX, D **$20.00**

Pepsi-Cola, tray, 1987, celebrating 50 years, scenes of various buildings, New Haven Missouri, oval, 11½x14½", NM, D **$25.00**

Pepsi-Cola, vending machine, blue with white & red, dome top, 10¢ & bottle cap above, Drink...Ice Cold cap below, 52x24, VG, A **$850.00**

Pepsi-Cola, watch fob, enameled Delicious, Healthful logo in center, plain on back, VG, A **$200.00**

Pepsi-Cola, watch fob, 1900-05, embossed with eagles & 2 bottles, #U6705 on back, EX, A **$55.00**

Pepsi-Cola, watch fob, 1900-05, pewter, John Smith & Pocahontas, Invigorates & early logo on back, EX, A **$85.00**

Pepsi-Cola/NuGrape/Orange-Crush, bowl, ceramic, 3 different logos in 3 different colors with bold green line around rim, Wellsville, 4¾" dia, NM, A **$100.00**

Pepsi-Cola/NuGrape/Orange-Crush, plate, ceramic, 3 different logos in 3 different colors with green line around rim, Wellsville, 7" dia, NM, A **$110.00**

Pepsol, tray, 1920s-30s, Drink Sparkling Pepsol in oval, Healthful & Refreshing below, lettered border, rectangular, G-, A **$40.00**

Pepto-Bismol, bank, 1970s, 24 Hour Bug, molded vinyl, 7", M, D $35.00

Pepto-Bismol, sign, cardboard, Upset Stomach on green banner arched above man in striped pajamas holding bottle, EX, M3 .... **$65.00**

Pepto-Bismol, sign, die-cut cardboard, large bottle of product, 27¼x8⅛", EX, A **$45.00**

Perfect Pipe Tobacco, pocket tin, upright, paper label, NM, H3 .... **$20.00**

Perfection Cigarettes, sign, copyright 1909, paperboard, product name above & below portrait of woman in red, framed, minor tear, 26x20", EX, A $400.00

Perfection Cigarettes, sign, paperboard, lady in plumed hat facing right, product highlighted in circle, lettering below, framed, 29x20", G-, A **$140.00**

Perfection Cigarettes, sign, printer's proof, paperboard, Perfection arched above girl in wide-brimmed hat, wood frame, 16x11", EX, A **$230.00**

Perfection Distilled Water, sign, porcelain, 15x26", NM, D1 .... **$90.00**

Perfection Dyes, sign, cardboard, For Silk, Woolen, Cotton & Feathers lettered in oval center, framed, image: 13½x9½", EX, A **$50.00**

Perfection Kerosene, sign, painted tin, 2-sided, product name above genie's oil lamp, Made By The Standard Oil Company below, 14x18", EX, A **$110.00**

Perfection Oil Stoves, catalog, 1937, VG, D **$20.00**

Perfection Spectacles & Eye Glasses, display case with 10 pairs of glasses, embossed tin & glass with reverse gold letters, door opens in rear, 10", G, A **$300.00**

Perfectos Cigars, box labels, inner & outer lid samples, 1910s-? 3 baseball players before wood structure, Conover litho, EX/M, A **$315.00**

Perma-Lift Corsets, display, plaster figure, Deco stylized image of woman wearing product, ...No Bones About It..., 19x25x5½", VG, A **$60.00**

Permit Cigar, sign, cardboard, woman lighting match, A Good Cigar lettered below, framed, image: 28x21½", G, A **$200.00**

Perry Davis' Pain Killer, sign, tin, large bottle in center of workers gathering raw products, Pain Killer lettered above, 18x54", G, A **$1,600.00**

Perry's Beverages, door push plate, light radiating behind tilted bottle, Perry's Beverages above, NM, A........................**$70.00**

Perry's Beverages, sign, tin, Perry's on banner, light rays emitting from bottle, Quality Beverages, It's Triple Filtered, 14x20", NM, M3...**$55.00**

Persiana Cigars, box label, 1880s, inner lid sample, lounging Persian lady, Witsch & Schmidt, EX, A...........**$80.00**

Pet Evaporated Milk, sign, paper, 2 cans of product in front of various fruits, dated 1927, Better Flavor..., 10x21", EX, A..**$25.00**

Pet Nonfat Dry Milk, recipe book, 1954, 30 pages, EX, D..**$4.00**

Pete Hagens 100 Proof Rye Liquor, sample bottle, metal screw-on cap, 5", EX, P4.......................................**$10.00**

Peter Hand's Bock Beer, label, 1933-36, ram's head in center, Peter Hand Brewery Co, U-type permit number, 12-oz, EX, A..**$22.00**

Peter Pan, crate label, Washington apple, Peter Pan sitting in apple tree above slanted logo, 9x11", EX, G1....**$5.00**

Peter Pan Ice Cream, sign, self-framed embossed tin, Demand Peter Pan above seated Peter Pan & Ice Cream, Take Home A Pint, 30x21", EX, A..........**$155.00**

Peter Pan Peanut Butter, coloring book, unused, D2..**$15.00**

Peter Pan Peanut Butter, recipe book, 1963, 26 pages, EX, D..**$3.50**

Peter Pan Peanut Butter, tin, product & company names lettered on emblem flanked by images of Peter Pan, press lid, 6-oz, 2¾", EX, A....................................**$55.00**

Peter Pan Peanut Butter, tin, product & company names lettered on emblem flanked by images of Peter Pan, press lid, 25-lb, 10x10½" dia, VG+, A.................**$150.00**

Peter Paul's Charcoal Gum, full package, G2..........**$28.00**

Peter Rabbit Baby Powder, tin, flat-sided, baby with parasol & friends riding on swimming turtle, rabbits watching, red shaker top, 4", EX, A.......$100.00

Peter Rabbit Peanut Butter, pail, various scenes of Peter Rabbit & friends on blue, The Newton Tea & Spice Co at bottom, pry lid & bail, 1-lb, G, A....................**$145.00**

Peter Schuyler Cigar, sign, porcelain, Get Back Of A lettered on back of man's head with cigar above product name, lined border, 12x36", EX, A.......................**$35.00**

Peters Ammunition, display, die-cut cardboard, pictures hunter behind display of cartridges, Here's The Place To Get..., 42x25", VG, A.....................................**$300.00**

Peters Ammunition, sign, paper, father watching son shoot, product name above, metal strips top & bottom, signed Moskowitz, 20x14", VG, A.......................**$700.00**

Peters Ammunition, trade card, for Victor shotgun shells, pictures box & shell, A Smokeless Shell At A Lower Price..., VG, A...**$50.00**

Peters Cartridge Co, calendar, 1904, sepia image of a moose in winter scene, December pad, metal strips top & bottom, VG, A...**$650.00**

Peters Cartridge Co, calendar top, 1898, 'His Last Leap,' pictures leaping buck, minor wrinkles, square, framed, A...**$180.00**

Peters Cartridge Co, trade card, colorful image of dog beside hunter shooting gun, Water Proofed Prize Paper Shot Shells below, rare, EX, A............................**$330.00**

Peters Cartridges, pin-back button, pictures large cartridge, Experts Use..., red ground, round, VG, A **$25.00**

Peters League Paper Shot Shells, box, product name above & below running rabbit, pictures a wounded mallard on back, 10-gauge, G, A **$270.00**

Peters No 12 Target, pin-back button, red P on yellow background, round, VG, A **$50.00**

Peters Referee Shells, pin-back button, pictures a cartridge over large P, round, VG, A **$50.00**

Peters Shells, pin-back button, pictures a mallard flying through center of large P, round, VG, A **$45.00**

Peters Shells, pin-back button, red & gold shell, Shoot Peters Shells above & below, round, VG, A........................**$30.00**

Peters Shells, stickpin, brass, oval shape with large P surrounded by Shoot Peter's Shells, ½", NM, A.........**$60.00**

Peters Shells & Cartridges, pin-back button, duck hunter standing beside large P lettered Peters Shells & Cartridges, ⅞" dia, NM, A...**$65.00**

Peters Shells & Cartridges, pin-back button, man shooting at target in center of large P, round, VG, A.....................**$40.00**

Peters Shells & Cartridges, pin-back button, red P on light blue, product name lettered on gold border, round, VG, A...**$25.00**

Peters Shells & Cartridges, sign, die-cut paperboard, hunter shooting at birds in flight through large P, Sold Here & Everywhere, 11x8½", G-, A.......................**$20.00**

Peters Shoes, calendar, 1924, features lady with fan, Deco border, September-December pad on courtesy panel below, 18½x8", EX, A **$60.00**

Peters Shoes, clock, nickel-plated case, product name in black & white script on face, 15x15", VG, A............**$60.00**

Peters Shoes, pocket mirror, Peters Classic Shoes on skirt hem above high-top shoes, 2¼" dia, EX, A..............**$60.00**

Peters Shoes, sign, reverse-painted glass in illuminated hanging metal case, product name in orange script on gold, 7x26", G, A...**$90.00**

Peters Shoes, store display, die-cut tin, diamond logo in center, holds 1 pair of shoes, overall soiling/fading, 8½", G-, A **$25.00**

Pettijohn's Breakfast Food, sign, paper, bear family in winter scene feeds Little Red Riding Hood, framed, 13x10½", NM, A..**$225.00**

Pettijohn's Rolled Wheat, canister, cardboard, shows bear looking over cliff, EX, A **$225.00**

Pflueger Fishing Tackle, catalog, No 156, 1936, well illustrated, 128 pages, EX, A..**$35.00**

PH Davis Custom Tailors, playing cards, complete, M, D...**$4.00**

PH Zang Brewing Co, sign, paper, sleeping monk surrounded by others, matted & framed, image: 15x20", NM, A..**$450.00**

Phaneuf's Corner Clothiers, mirror, reverse-painted mother-of-pearl & gold foil lettering on black above mirror, wood frame, 17½x11½", G, A..................**$50.00**

Phenix, sign, die-cut tin, ...For Your Thirst Or Tired Nerves, Very Healthful, 5¢, Sparkling Delicious, 26x19½", G, A..**$200.00**

Phil Nase Sporting Goods, blotter, 1923, pictures young boy stuffing pillow in his pants, multicolored, unused, 6x3½", D **$15.00**

Philco Lazy-X Radio, jigsaw puzzle, lady seated in chair with dog at her feet listening to radio, 10x13", EX, F1...$35.00

Philgas, salt & pepper shakers, plastic, green gas pumps with black script logo, EX, D **$30.00**

Philip Morris Cigarettes, pin-back button, bellboy shouting Vote For Philip Morris, round, EX, A.......................**$44.00**

Philip Morris Cigarettes, ruler, 1940s, thin plastic with colorful image of bellboy, 6" scale above, 2x6¼", NM, D...**$22.00**

Philip Morris Cigarettes, sign, cardboard, image of bellboy above reminder from hotel management about safety of smoking, 6x6", NM, D............................**$18.00**

Philip Morris Cigarettes, sign, cardboard, image of Lucy & Desi beside open pack, 41x29", EX, A......................**$324.00**

Philip Morris Cigarettes, sign, cardboard stand-up, boy holds carton & pack on base reading Call For Philip Morris, 14x5", EX, A **$55.00**

Philip Morris Cigarettes, sign, die-cut cardboard, heads of Lucy & Desi in Santa's hat above cigarette carton over brick chimney, 36x24", VG, A............................**$200.00**

Philip Morris Cigarettes, sign, tin, bellboy above 2 packs of cigarettes, Call For..., black background, minor scratches, 46x16", VG, A...................................**$275.00**

Philip Morris Cigarettes, sign, tin, bellboy carrying oversized pack of cigarettes, Buy 'em Here!, Call For...King-Size Or Regular, 14x12", NM, B1..........................**$75.00**

Phillies Cigar, sign, embossed tin, pictures a cigar, yellow, red & black, EX, D **$48.00**

Phillips Petroleum Co, paperweight/mirror, 1930-55, silver letters on black rim band, Silver Anniversary arched above 66 logo, 4" dia, EX, A **$120.00**

Phillips 66, ashtray, glass, shield logo & Tank Wagon Service, bright orange & black, 4¼x4¼", EX, D **$15.00**

Phillips 66, bank, 1940s-50s, embossed glass, Phill Up With Phillips 66, See What You Can Save, minor scratches, 5x5", A **$75.00**

Phillips 66, booklet, 1952, 'How To Watch Football,' with scedules, 48 pages, EX, D.....................................**$10.00**

Phillips 66, gas globe, 1930s-40s, orange & black shield logo with black border on white, 13½" dia, EX, A...$130.00

Phillips 66, key chain/pen knife, shield logo, orange, black & cream, EX, D **$25.00**

Phillips 66, salt & pepper shakers, plastic gas pumps, orange & cream with black & orange decals, 1 marked Ethyl, 2¾x1x1", EX, A **$45.00**

Phillips 66, sign, embossed porcelain, orange & black shield logo above slanted 66, 48x48", EX, A....................**$160.00**

Phillips 66, sign, porcelain, 2-sided, white with Phillips 66 above & below Ethyl logo, 30" dia, VG/G, A...........**$350.00**

Phillips 66 Flite Fuel, airplane, punch-out cardboard, 8x10½", NM, B1 ....**$5.00**

Phillips 66 Outboard Motor Oil, can, 1930s-40s, boat scene with logo above, Outboard Motor Oil in black below, screw lid, 1-qt, 7½", EX, A........................**$35.00**

Phinney-Walker Clock for Automobiles, sign, cardboard stand-up, product name above large clock, On Time, Models For Every Type Of Car, 20x15", VG, A ..**$325.00**

Phoenix Brewery, match safe, nickel-plated brass, embossed Phoenix trademark on both sides, 2¾x1½", G, A..**$65.00**

Physicians Motor Club of Philadelphia, sign, porcelain, blue on white with red Maltese cross in center, 9x6", EX, D **$125.00**

Picant Cigars, box label, outer, lettering above saloon girl with butterfly wings sitting on smiling crescent moon, 4x4", EX, D **$15.00**

Piccadilly Needles, package, ca 1925, airplane motif, complete, 3x5", EX, P1 ....**$20.00**

Pickaninny Brand Peanut Butter, pail, tin, yellow with red, yellow & silver Pickaninny logo in horizontal oval, slip lid & bail, 1-lb, VG, A **$325.00**

Pickwick Ale, sign, self-framed tin, 3 men at table toasting mugs of ale, minor chips/dents/scratches, 28½x22¼", VG, A **$425.00**

Picobac Sliced Plug, pocket tin, flat, hand holds leaves above diagonal band reading Picobac Sliced Plug, 15¢ lower right, 2x3", EX+, M2 ....**$14.00**

Picobac Tobacco, pocket tin, upright, hand holds leaves above diagonal band lettered Picobac, The Pick Of Tobacco, 10¢, Very Mild, VG, M2 ....**$14.00**

Piedmont Cigarettes, folding chair, wood, dark blue back with Piedmont lettered diagonally in white, ...The Virginia Cigarette, EX, A **$175.00**

Piedmont Cigarettes, sign, cardboard, Piedmont above portrait of lady in plumed hat & fur collar, product lower right, 28x22", EX+, M1 ....**$625.00**

Piedmont Cigarettes, sign, 1920s-30s, curved porcelain, Piedmont above open pack, The Virginia Cigarettes below, vertical, NM, A $360.00

Piedmont Special Bock Beer, label, 1933-50, Southern Breweries, Internal Revenue Tax Paid statement, 12-oz, EX, A **$16.00**

Piel Bros Beer, bar caddy, full-color figures of Bert & Harry, 2 yellow plastic inserts, minor paint wear, 8½x8x3⅜", P2 ....**$90.00**

Piel Bros Beer, clock, electric, metal with glass front, pictures Bert & Harry, 13x13", EX, P2 ....**$125.00**

Piel Bros Beer, salt & pepper shakers, 1950s, ceramic, full figures of Bert & Harry Piel, 3" & 4", M, D **$75.00**

Piel Bros Brewery, sign, oilette, cowboys in open touring car getting directions from Indians on horseback, framed, image: 18x26", EX+, A **$550.00**

Piel Bros Lager Beer, sign, porcelain shield, 2-sided, white on blue, Real German..., 25x24", EX, A **$3,475.00**

Pierce Cycle Co, sign, paper, couple on veranda with bicycles in the foreground, Also Makers Of Arrow Cycles, 52x36", G, A **$700.00**

Pierce Pennant Motor Oil, radiator cover with slot for crank, 1920s, 2-sided, pictures a pennant, 12x20", EX, D...**$50.00**

Piff's Beverages, sign, tin, pictures bottle, G, D......**$135.00**

Pig Tail Cigars, box label, outer, Pig Tail in script above fat pig in rectangular field with fancy border, diagonal corners, 4x4", EX, D **$5.00**

Pig-Skin Tobacco, pocket tin, nugget shape with product name & other lettering, rare, VG, A **$220.00**

Piggy Pears, crate label, 1940s, lady pig carrying basket of pears, Medford Ore, 7½x11", M, C3 ....**$4.00**

Pildoras Catarticas De Ayer, sign, paper, winged angel distributing product, ...Medicinas Purgantes, minor soiling, 13½x10½", EX, A **$200.00**

Pillsbury, bank, 1987, Poppin' Fresh, ceramic, 7½", MIB, D $25.00

Pillsbury, clock radio, 1986, plastic with attached Poppin' Fresh, Quartz, radio not working, 9½x4½x4½", VG, A **$60.00**

Pillsbury, doll, Cupcake Bear, plush, 13", EX, D.......**$35.00**

Pillsbury, doll, Poppin' Fresh, soft vinyl with jointed head, 7", EX, D **$8.00**

Pillsbury, doll, 1970s, Poppin' Fresh, stuffed cotton, 14½", VG, H1 ....**$9.00**

Pillsbury, doll, 1972, Poppie Fresh, vinyl with jointed head, 6", EX, D **$15.00**

Pillsbury, finger puppet, Poppie Fresh, vinyl, 3½", EX, D **$15.00**

Pillsbury, playhouse, 1974, tall-peaked vinyl house containing Bun Bun, Popper, Poppie & Poppin' Fresh, 14x11x3", VG, A **$232.00**

Pillsbury, recipe book, 1927, '100 Delicious Foods From 4 Basic Recipes,' EX, D **$6.00**

Pillsbury, recipe book, 1948, 'Baking Is Fun,' by Ann Pillsbury, 64 pages, EX, D **$8.00**

Pillsbury, recipe book, 1951, '100 Prize-Winning Recipes,' 2nd Grand National, EX, D **$15.00**

Pillsbury, recipe book, 1955, '100 Grand National Recipes,' 6th edition, 96 pages, EX, D **$10.00**

Pillsbury, recipe book, 1965, '100 New Bake Off Recipes,' 16th edition, 95 pages, EX, D **$5.50**

Pillsbury, recipe book, 1980s, 'Incredible Crescents,' 96 pages, EX, D **$2.50**

Pillsbury, salt & pepper shakers, 1970s, both Poppin' Fresh, white glazed ceramic with blue accents, 3½", VG, D $22.00

Pillsbury, telephone, 1980s, plastic, Poppin' Fresh with arms extended to hold receiver, 14", M, D **$90.00**

Pillsbury, utensil holder, 1983, Poppin' Fresh, ceramic, 8", EX, D **$16.00**

Pillsbury's Best Flour, blotter, Pillsbury man carrying flour sack, green & white, 6x3", G, D **$3.00**

Pillsbury-Washburn Flour Mills Co Limited, sign, paper, eagle atop barrel with Pillsbury's Best logo, inset of factory scene below, framed, 30x24", G, A **$750.00**

Pilot Beer, label, 1933-50, Louis Ziegler Brewing Co, Internal Revenue Tax Paid statement, 12-oz, EX, A **$18.00**

Pilot 10 Cent Plug Chewing Tobacco, tin, pictures early airplane, EX, D **$130.00**

Pilsener Bread, pin-back button, 1930s, brown & white, pinpoint nicks, EX, D **$5.00**

Piney Woods Belle, crate label, Florida citrus, grove of trees & fruit, 9x9", M, C3 .... **$6.50**

Pingree Shoe, pocket mirror, bust-length portrait of elegant girl in profile, The Girl Of The Pingree Shoe below, oval, EX, A **$80.00**

Pinkussohns Potpourri Smoking Tobacco, pocket tin, upright, nonpictorial paper label, slip lid, 3½", EX+, A **$50.00**

Pinkussohns Tobacco, pocket tin, upright, paper label, EX+, H3 .... **$50.00**

Pinzon All Havana Cigar, pin cushion, celluloid, man in uniform with lettering above & below, ...M Perez Co Key West, EX, A **$61.00**

Pioneer Coffee Co, spice set in wooden rack, cans: 5½", rack: 13½" long, EX, D **$75.00**

Pioneer-American Lager Beer, label, 1933-36, Lange Products, U-type permit number, 12-oz, EX, A **$31.00**

Piper Heidsieck Chewing Tobacco, sign, embossed paper, product name diagonally, with tobacco packs above & below, wood frame, 12½x15", EX, A **$190.00**

Piper Heidsieck Chewing Tobacco, watch fob, silver, US seal on front, piper with bagpipe & lettering on back, EX, D **$32.50**

Piper Heidsieck Plug Tobacco, sign, paper, half-length pose of elegant lady, lettering above, matted & framed, 28x18", EX, A **$330.00**

Pippens Cigars, product box, cardboard, Pippens boldly lettered on red apple resting on 2 smoking cigars, Five Cigars above, 5x3", VG, A **$25.00**

Pippins 5¢ Cigar, sign, embossed tin, Pippins Cigar 5¢ arched over orange, 10x19½", G-, A **$15.00**

Pippins 5¢ Cigar, tip tray, red apple form with product name lettered boldly in center, 5x3½", NM, A ..$325.00

Pittsburg Automatic Gas Water Heater, pocket mirror, product flanked by Quick Hot Water & Turn The Faucet, lettering above & below, oval, 2¾", NM, A **$105.00**

Pittsburg Butchers & Packers, pocket mirror, draped nude resting on bank at water's edge, Your Next Order lettered below, oval, 2¾", G, A **$182.00**

Pittsburgh Paints, sign, porcelain, embossed product name with letters in various colors on white, 2 sections: 23x58"/23x68", EX, D3 .... **$375.00**

Pittsburgh Proof Products, sample, celluloid, Sun-Glo Finish logo shines over company name above 8 sample colors, 19x5", EX, A **$25.00**

Pittsburgh Brewing Co, sign, cardboard, From Pittsburgh Brewing Company in white stair-step letters left of company seal, 22x41", EX, A **$55.00**

Pizza Hut, bank, 1969, plastic, Pizza Hut Pete, 7½", EX, D2 .... **$50.00**

Planet, crate label, California orange, orange floating in deep blue space, green lettering, 10x11", G1 ... **$20.00**

Planters, ashtray, bisque Mr Peanut standing beside peanut shell, Mr Peanut stamped on base, 4½x3", EX, A .. **$120.00**

Planters, belt buckle, child's, tan plastic, pictures Mr Peanut & guns, 2x4", EX, D **$45.00**

Planters, Bic lighter, Mr Peanut, M & unused, P2 ..... **$12.00**

Planters, blinker, electrified, Mr Peanut, right eye blinks, rare, 24x6", EX, A **$4,500.00**

Planters, bookmark, 1920s-30s, die-cut cardboard Mr Peanut, speckled orange, black & white, 8x3", EX, D **$14.00**

Planters, coloring book, Around The World With Mr Peanut above Mr Peanut standing before world map, Book No 3, 7x10", EX, M2 ..... **$14.00**

Planters, commemorative coin, limited edition, silver with embossed Mr Peanut flanked by 1916-1991, 2¼" dia, M, A **$55.00**

Planters, costume, fiberglass figure of Mr Peanut, Planters Mr Peanut lettered on hat, chips to body, 50x20" dia, G, A **$475.00**

Planters, counter display, tin, die-cut Mr Peanut on both sides of flanged front, 4½x7½x7½", G, A **$1,500.00**

Planters, display, ca 1948-52, Mr Peanut figure made of plastic resins & fiberglass, repainted & repaired, 8ft 10" tall, VG, A **$9,600.00**

Planters, display, 1930s, wood-jointed Mr Peanut in gray top hat with cane in both hands, 8½", EX+, M2 ..... **$450.00**

Planters, doll, Mr Peanut, cloth, EX, D **$15.00**

Planters, lapel pin, die-cut tin litho of Mr Peanut, 1½", NM, A **$18.00**

Planters, mechanical pencil, 1960s, metal & plastic, 3-D image of Mr Peanut on top, blue, yellow & gold, 5½", EX, D **$22.00**

Planters, optical illusion card, features Mr Peanut in dark circle, Spooky Picture, directions & advertising below, 5x3", EX, A **$8.00**

Planters, paint book, 1960s, features presidents from Washington through Eisenhower with insert of Kennedy, 32 pages, 11x8", NM, D **$22.00**

Planters, paperweight, metal, Mr Peanut standing on base with embossed lettering, Compliments Planters Nut..., 7x3", EX, A **$575.00**

Planters, peanut bag, paper, lettering over diamond graphics with Mr Peanut lower left, The Peanut Store, 80-oz, NM, A **$15.00**

Planters, peanut bag, paper, Mr Peanut at right of tall flag with Pennant promoting Salted Peanuts, 6x3", NM, A **$7.00**

Planters, peanut bag, paper, Mr Peanut promoting Planters Hot Roasted Fresh Peanuts, The Peanut Store, 24x7½", NM, A **$17.00**

Planters, peanut bag, paper, Planters in script above Mr Peanut waving flag lettered Pennant, The Nickel Lunch, 6x3", NM, A **$6.00**

Planters, pin, from 1939 World's Fair, on original card reading Wear A Lucky Mr Peanut, 2", NM, A **$61.00**

Planters, plate, 1970s, Mr Peanut, pewter type, 1 of 3,000, 6" dia, P2 ..... **$35.00**

Planters, pocket knife, Nov 2, 1976, flat gold peanut with raised letters, Taylor Cutlery, 2⅞" closed, NM, D **$27.00**

Planters, pop gun, paper, Mr Peanut in oval grip, Bang! For Planters Peanuts, rare, 5x8¾", VG, A **$200.00**

Planters, ramp walker, 1984, Mr Peanut, plastic, 3", M, D. **$30.00**

Planters, sack, 1950s-60s, black & red on brown burlap with image of Mr Peanut, 2-lb, 14x8", NM, D **$30.00**

Planters, salt & pepper shakers, ceramic Mr Peanut figures with diamond glass eye, S&P on hats, minor color loss, 4½", G, A **$55.00**

Planters, salt & pepper shakers, red plastic Mr Peanut figures, 3", NM, D $8.00

Planters, scale, Mr Peanut figural on platform scale, rare 45", EX, A **$16,250.00**

Planters, sign, painted tin, Mr Peanut at left of Planters The Name For Quality, blue & yellow awning borders top, 13x24", VG, A **$20.00**

Planters, snack dish & 4 cups, metal with Mr Peanut in center, gold designs on bottom & sides, dish: 6", cups: 3", EX+, P4 ..... **$45.00**

Planters, spoon, silverplated, Mr Peanut on handle, Caltan, 5" long, NM, D $24.00

Planters, store display, 1960s, clear amber plastic head with blue hat, used for selling peanuts, 12x10" dia, EX, D **$40.00**

Planters, store jar, glass, barrel shape, embossed images of Mr Peanut, peanut finial, 12x8½" dia, EX, A **$225.00**

Planters, store jar, glass, commemorating 75th Anniversary, embossed Mr Peanut & lettering, 8¼", EX, D **$12.50**

Planters, store jar, glass, embossed image of running Mr Peanut, peanut finial, 12x8" dia, VG, A **$250.00**

Planters, store jar, glass, embossed peanuts on 4 corners, peanut finial on lid, minor chips on lid, 13x8" dia, EX, A **$150.00**

Planters, store jar, glass, embossed Planters on 4 sides, with lid, 7x7", EX, A **$105.00**

Planters, store jar, glass, round fish-bowl shape with 2 flat sides, Planters embossed on base, top missing, 11x9½x7", EX, A **$20.00**

Planters, store jar, glass, slanted front, yellow lettering, light pitting on metal lid, 10x8x5", VG, A **$25.00**

Planters, store jar, glass, 6-sided, embossed with 5¢ Pennant logo flanked by Mr Peanut, not original lid, 12", EX, A **$50.00**

Planters, store jar, glass with painted-on lettering, pictures Mr Peanut & lettering on tin lid, 10", EX, A **$75.00**

Planters, straw, 1960s, white plastic with 3-D Mr Peanut mouthpiece, yellow or green, 8", NM, D **$10.00**

Planters, tote bag, 1979, vinyl, full-color image of Mr Peanut, 9x10", M, P2 ..... **$35.00**

Planters, toy car, plastic, Mr Peanut driving peanut car, 2½x5", EX, A **$500.00**

Planters Cocktail Peanuts, punchboard, product name & 5¢ above cans flanking listed numbers on white field, punchboard below, unused, NM, A **$61.00**

Planters Mixed Nuts, tin 1944, images of Mr Peanut on sides & top, 3x2½", VG, D **$28.00**

Planters Notola Peanut Oil, tin, images with Mr Peanut on all sides, screw lid & wire handle, with original box, 5-gal, 14x9¼", G, A **$60.00**

Planters Peanut Butter, pail, multiple images of Mr Peanut playing instruments & flying in the air, press lid & bail, 1-lb, 4x3½" dia, G, A **$600.00**

Planters Peanut Butter, tin, round with Homogenized Planters... lettered over peanut background with Mr Peanut image, key-wind lid, EX, M2 .... **$35.00**

Planters Pennant Brand Salted Peanuts, tin, lettering above & below logo, pry lid, dents/scratches, 5-lb, G, A **$60.00**

Planters Pennant Brand Salted Peanuts, tin, lettering above & below logo, pry lid, 5-lb, EX+, A **$230.00**

Platero, crate label, Spanish citrus, charging bull on colorful background, EX, C3 .... **$10.00**

Platolene 500, pump sign, porcelain, white & black on red, Platolene on ribbon below 500 over checkered flag, 12" dia, NM, A $650.00

Player's Navy Cut Cigarettes, tin, sailor's portrait in round lettered life preserver over coastal scene, Navy Cut... in script on sides, 2x3", EX, A...... $17.50

Player's Navy Cut Tobacco, sign, tin, features sailor against yellow background, Player's Please in script below, 29x19½", VG, A **$130.00**

Plen Tee Color, crate label, apple, smiling Indian girl & red apple, 10½x9", M, C1 .... **$2.00**

Plenty Copy Typewriter Ribbon, tin, pictures cornucopia, EX, D **$30.00**

Plezola, pocket mirror, Drink above Plezola, The New Drink on tail, horizontal oval, EX+, A **$68.00**

Plow Boy Chewing & Smoking Tobacco, tin, with contents, farmer resting in field with product name above & below on paper label, slip lid, NM, A **$125.00**

Plum Sun Cured Tobacco, pocket mirror, pictures plum branch with Plum in large letters, smaller lettering above & below, 2⅛" dia, EX, A **$240.00**

Plymouth, booklet, 1953, black, blue & white, 8 pages, NM, D **$6.00**

Plymouth, matchbook, 1940, EX, D **$5.00**

Plymouth, pin-back button, Latest, Greatest Plymouth lettered on flag in center, Four Years Better... above, round, EX, A **$24.00**

Plymouth Belvedere Sport Coupe, postcard, 1955, glossy, 5½x3½", NM, D **$6.00**

Plymouth Brewing & Malting Co, tray, girl talking on stick telephone, Two Cases Of...Please, fading to image/rim chips, 13" dia, G, A **$150.00**

Plymouth Cordage Co, catalog, 1938, features nautical rope, 32 pages, VG, D **$15.00**

Plymouth Rock Cigars, box label, inner lid sample, 1870s, portrait of early steamship, Heppenheimer & Maurer litho, EX, A **$113.00**

Plymouth Rock Gelatine, recipe book, 1910, 'Dainties & Household Helps,' EX, D $18.00

POC Extra Dry Beer, sign, cardboard, Set 'Em Up Again! upper right of 2 men bowling, product name with glass & bottle below, 20x15", EX, A **$45.00**

Poinsetta, crate label, 1930s, California orange, red poinsetta on black ground, Filmore Citrus Assoc, 10x11", M, C1 .... **$5.00**

Point Bock Beer, bottle, long neck, paper label, Stevens Point Brewery, VG, D **$10.00**

Point Ellis, can label, Washington salmon, seashore scene with fishermen & lighthouse, gilt decoration, McGowan, M, C1 .... **$5.00**

Pointer Beer, label, 1933-36, product name above pointer dog, Pointer Brewing Co, U-type permit number, 12-oz, G, A **$38.00**

Pola-Kiss, lug box label, California grape, Pola-Kiss formed in ice, blue on red, Lodi, G1 .... **$2.00**

Polar Bear Tobacco, humidor, tin with slant front, product flanked by Always Fresh on front, bear on both sides, lift lid, 14x18", G, A **$375.00**

Polarine, display, hot air balloon with hanging fan, stenciled lettering over red & yellow surface, 28x16" dia, G, A **$700.00**

Polarine Motor Oil, can, 1915-25, red & blue logo on cream, text below, silver ground, screw lid & handle, 1/2-gal, 7", EX, A **$95.00**

Polarine Motor Oil, can in original Standard Oil Co wooden crate, can pictures open touring car, crate: 14½x11x10½", VG, A **$500.00**

Polarine Oil & Greases, sign, porcelain, 2-sided, Polarine arched above Oil & Greases For Motors, Standard Oil Co Of NY below, 22x12", VG/G-, A **$210.00**

Poll-Parrot Shoes, bank, cardboard can with metal ends, Poll-Parrot advertising, 2¼", EX, A **$40.00**

Poll-Parrot Shoes, bank, plastic shoe, G, D **$20.00**

Poll-Parrot Shoes, coloring book, Howdy Doody, 1950s, M, D **$45.00**

Poll-Parrot Shoes, decal, ca 1940, pictures large parrot, Poll-Parrot Shoes For Boys & Girls, VG, D **$10.00**

Poll-Parrot Shoes, display, 1950s, painted plaster, colorful parrot perched on branch, product name on base, 15", M, D $200.00

Poll-Parrot Shoes, pin-back button, parrot at left of I Wear Poll-Parrot Shoes, ⅞" dia, NM, A **$8.00**

Poll-Parrot Shoes, sign, die-cut porcelainized tin parrot outlined with neon tubing, Poll-Parrot lettered in red on white, 38x22", EX, A **$1,150.00**

Poll-Parrot Shoes, whistle, 1930s, heavy cardboard with metal mouthpiece, orange & black with logo & other graphics, 12x1" dia, EX, D **$30.00**

Polly Gas, pump, 1950s, Kelly green sides with yellow front, Polly Parrot decal on front, repro globe lights up, restored, 81", A **$1,300.00**

Polly Stamps, sign, painted metal, 2-sided, Parrot on perch saying 'Ask For' above Polly Stamps, Premiums-Trade-Cash, 28x20", M, D1 .... **$95.00**

Polo Beer, tray, deep-dish, polo player in circular inset above product name, scratches/minor discoloration, 12" dia, G, A **$65.00**

Polo Club Beverages, sign, embossed tin, polo stick & lettering in white on green, background light pitting, 3x20", G, A **$150.00**

Pomeroy's Finger-Pad Truss, trade card, ...For The Relief & Cure Of Hernia..., violet on white, VG, A **$30.00**

Ponciana Chewing Gum, pocket mirror, pack of gum with WJ White above, Chewing Gums below, America's Favorite, horizontal oval, 2¾", EX, A **$100.00**

Pond's Extract, trade card, pictures young girl on horseback with German shepherd running along side, 3¼x4", EX, P1 .... **$12.00**

Ponds Dream Flowers Talcum Powder, tin, 6 1/2-oz, VG, D **$9.50**

Pontiac, booklet, 1964, 16 pages, NM, D **$6.00**

Pontiac, calendar, 1949, red embossed logo above full pad, dealer logo below, 32x20", EX+, D3 .... **$185.00**

Pontiac, pin-back button, 1930s, multicolored, EX, D ... **$12.00**

Pontiac, weathervane, ca 1952, painted die-cut tin, red Pontiac Indian in center, rare, EX, A **$650.00**

Pontiac, windshield scraper, 1957, EX, D **$5.00**

Pontiac Authorized Service, sign, 1950s, porcelain, blue Pontiac Indian surrounded by bold white lettering, minor scratches, 42" dia, EX, A $300.00

Pony Brand Marshmallows & Candy, tin, features 2 circus ponies, slip lid, round, A **$60.00**

Pony Brand Sugar Butter, pail, slant-sided, pictures 2 ponies, green, blue & silver, Canadian, press lid, 13-oz, EX, A **$600.00**

Pony Post Cigars, box label, inner lid, shows Pony Express rider, 6x9", M, C3 .... **$18.00**

Pop Kola, sign, 1940s, cardboard, pictures lady with Pop Kola, 13½x10½", EX, D **$15.00**

Pope Motorcycle, token, 1877-1913, embossed metal, 1" dia, NM, M2 .... **$48.00**

Pope's Rifle Air Pistol, trade card, pictures mosquitoes biting boy on front, pistol & testimonials on reverse, black & white, EX, A **$40.00**

Popeye Pop Corn, can, cardboard with metal ends, Popeye lettered diagonally at right of his image, Pop Corn below, 1-lb 4-oz, EX, A **$48.00**

Popper's Ace Tobacco, dispenser, tin box with slanted glass top, 10¢ flank Popper's Ace on top panel, biplane & text on sides, 9x6x7", EX, A.........$600.00

Popsicle, sign, embossed tin, yellow Popsicle lettered on diagonal black band over red, black border, 10x28", VG, A..$210.00

Popsicle, sign, paper, pictures boy with thumbs up & a Popsicle, Dee-Licious...Frozen On A Stick in center, 7½x18", EX, A **$25.00**

Porter House Cigars, box label, inner lid sample, 1880s, couple outside inn with round inset of hearth at left, Witsch & Schmidt litho, EX, A **$31.00**

Portland Brewing Co, Vienna Art Plate, elegant girl surrounded by ornate floral border, advertising on reverse, 10" dia, VG, A **$65.00**

Portland Lawn Sprinkler Co, trade card, pictures the product, Little Giant Traveling Lawn Sprinkler, Price $15.00..., EX, A **$34.00**

Portuondo Cigars, thermometer, wood, black & red lettering on faded white background, Genuine Portuondo Cigars lettered above, 21", G-, A **$10.00**

Possum Cigars, tin, opossum surrounded by lettering on red background, slip lid, round, EX+, A............. **$180.00**

Possum Yams, label, pictures big opossum holding a yam, M, C1 .... **$2.00**

Post Bran Cereal, doll, Cali Quail, 1986, cloth, colorful logo on back, 6", M, N1 .... **$10.00**

Post Sugar Crisp, bowl, yellow plastic with embossed Indians, premium, M, P2.. **$35.00**

Post Toasties, ad, paper, hand pouring milk on bowl of cereal, cereal box & several peaches at left, matted & framed, 12x15", EX, A **$110.00**

Post Toasties, car mug, ceramic, EX+, P4 .... **$8.00**

Post Toasties, cereal box, red top panel with yellow Post Toasties, yellow bottom panel with 4-star graphics, 8½", EX, A **$40.00**

Post Toasties, display, die-cut cardboard, 2 kids in swing below single boxes with letters atop, letters: 75"/kids: 29x18", EX+, A..........................$18,500.00

Post Toasties, string holder, tin, pictures box of cereal, turns as string is dispensed, 4½x11½" dia, G, A............. **$725.00**

Post Wheat Puffs, doll, Sugar Bear, stuffed cloth, premium, MIB, D2.. **$30.00**

Poster Cigars, box labels, inner & outer sample set, 1870s, boy hangs poster on fence, Post No Bills, Heppenheimer & Maurer, EX/M, A **$86.00**

Postmaster Smokers, tin, pictures an elderly postmaster flanked by 2 For 5¢, orange background, slip lid, round, EX+, A.. **$44.00**

Postum, string holder, tin, Drink Postum, There's A Reason in center with Health arched above & First below, 11½" dia, VG, A **$55.00**

Postum Cereal Co, recipe book, '101 Prize Winning Recipes,' gray cover, 32 pages, G, D **$4.00**

Pow-Wow Cigars, box label, lithographer's proof, early 1900s, Indian flankedby warrior's shields, 10 colors, American Litho, VG, A **$165.00**

Power-Lube Motor Oil, sign, 1930s, porcelain, 2-sided, tiger & lettering above Smooth As... & 100% Pure logo, 19x28", EX, A... **$750.00**

Power-Lube Motor Oil, sign, 1930s, porcelain, 2-sided, tiger & lettering above Smooth As... & 100% Pure logo, 19x28", G, D **$500.00**

Prager Malt Extract, can label, 1929, Germans in field picking grapes, VG, C3 .... **$15.00**

Prairie Farmer Protective Union, sign, heavy metal, 12x8", EX, D $40.00

Prairie Flower Tobacco, pocket tin, flat, rare, EX+, D ..$895.00

Prairie Garden, crate label, Florida citrus, tropical orchard scene, 9x9", M, C3 ....$6.00

Prall's Root Beer, dispenser, frosted glass with stenciled lettering, sheet metal base with 4 glass balls on claw feet, 19½", G, A $210.00

Pratt's Veterinary Remedies, cabinet, wood with embossed tin front, horse head in circular inset above list of products, 33x17x7½", EX, A..................$1,400.00

Preferencia Cigar, sign, 1920s, pictures elegant lady in red, 30 Minutes in Havana, product name etched in wood frame, 35½x25", EX, A $3,500.00

Preferred Stock Cigars, box label, inner lid sample, 1880s, gracious lady seated among flowers fanning herself, OL Schwencke & Co litho, EX, A $36.00

Premier Apple Butter, can label, embossed image of apple butter on slice of bread, white background, EX, G1 ....$6.00

Premium Cigars, box label, outer, patriotic American woman & cigars, 4½x4½", M, C3 ....$14.00

Premo Cameras & Supplies, catalog, 1915, 48 pages, VG+, H2 ....$50.00

Presto Pressure Cooker, recipe book, 1947, 127 pages, EX, D $7.50

Presto Pressure Cooker, recipe book, 1966, 64 pages, EX, D $6.00

Presto Stove Polish, tin, ornate graphics surround lettering, Kills Rust, Polishes Steel...JJ Baden & Co, red & black, 3½" dia, EX, D............................$10.00

Presto-o-lite Batteries, door push plate, porcelain, red & white divided background, lettering above & below hand & battery image, 12x4", EX, A $121.00

Preston & Merrill's Infallible Yeast Powder, trade card, 2 little girls in bonnets with their dog, Unrivalled For Strength, Purity & Reliability..., EX, A $20.00

Prestone Anti-Freeze, thermometer, porcelain, white & blue on gray, blue & red, You're Safe & You Know It, chipped, 36", G, A..$30.00

Prestone Anti-Freeze, thermometer, porcelain, white on silver, blue & red, Eveready logo above product name, Does Not Boil Away, 36", G+, A $30.00

Prestone Anti-Freeze, thermometer, 1950s, porcelain gray, blue, red & white, ...With Exclusive Magnetic Film... above & below, 36", VG+, A.....................$75.00

Pride of Durham Tobacco, sign, paper, queen presenting product to king & the Conquistadors, framed, image 15½x22", VG, A $200.00

Pride of Reidsville Pipe Tobacco, sign, The Man Who Smokes... above man with pipe in mouth & holding product package, framed, 19½x13½", EX, A.........$210.00

Pride of the River, crate label, 1920s, California pears view of riverboat with large pears in foreground Locke, 7½x11", M, C3...$12.50

Prima Rosa Cigars, box label, inner lid, Cuban lady leaning on tobacco bales, 6x9", EX, C3 ....$10.00

Primley's California Fruit Chewing Gum, box, mountain scene with lake at bottom, 20 Bars, minor fading, 8x4¼x1", VG+, A $175.00

Primley's California Fruit Chewing Gum, sign, cardboard, bear holding pack of gum beside beehive, Better Than Honey, matted & framed, image: 22x13½", VG, A..$3,200.00

Primley's Chewing Gum, display case, wood frame with curved glass front, 10x18½x12", EX, A $350.00

Primley's Pepsin Sticks Chewing Gum, clock, wood, wall regulator, appears EX, A.............................$875.00

Primley's Sticks, sign, embossed tin, Always Fresh upper right of lady taking gum from man's pocket, restored, rare, 19½x14", EX, A $1,300.00

Primo Beer, label, Hawaii Brewing Co, 11-oz, EX, A $60.00

Primo Bock Beer, label, 1933-36, ram's head in center, Hawaii Brewing Co Ltd, U-type permit number, 1-pt, EX, A $51.00

Primo Salvator Beer, label, 1933-36, Hawaii Brewing Co Ltd, U-type permit number, 11-oz, EX, A $41.00

Primrose Ice Cream, sign, die-cut cardboard hanger, lady in swing enjoys dish of ice cream, Primrose above, framed, 39", VG+, A........................$1,500.00

Prince Albert Tobacco, display box, Prince Albert above oval portrait, Crimp Cut Long Burning Pipe & Cigarette Tobacco below, 10x8", EX, A $30.00

Prince Albert Tobacco, humidor, glass with tin lid & paper labels, Humi-Seal, VG, H1 ....**$18.00**

Prince Albert Tobacco, match safe, canister shape with embossed lettering on lid & side, 2½x1¼", VG, A...**$30.00**

Prince Albert Tobacco, sign, early 1900s, tin, pictures man's face smoking pipe & tobacco box, black with gold rim, edge wear, 24" dia, A $380.00

Prince Albert Tobacco, sign, embossed tin, No Other Tobacco Can Be Like..., red & black on yellow, minor rust/nail holes, 12x23½", D..................................**$80.00**

Prince Albert Tobacco, sign, paper, ...National Joy Smoke upper right of Chief Joseph, Nez Perce, light background, framed, 31x24½", NM, A....................**$2,200.00**

Prince Albert Tobacco, sign, tin, Chief Joseph, Nez Perce above product & National Joy Smoke, framed, image: 25½x19½", VG, A **$950.00**

Prince Douglas Cigars, box label, inner lid, man in armor with flags & swords, 6x9", M, D...........................**$14.00**

Prince Hamlet Cigars, tin, 1950s, embossed image of Prince Hamlet with castle scene beyond, slip lid, round, EX+, A...**$134.00**

Prince Maurice Cigars, box label, outer, pictures man in royal attire, 4½x4½", M, D **$5.00**

Princess Prize Cigars, saloon box, mahogany, with shoulder strap, interior label of princess lounging with hookah, 5x25x9", VG, A **$160.00**

Princeton Tiger Brew, label, 1933-37, U-type permit number, 12-oz, EX, A **$25.00**

Prize Cup Cigars, box label, inner lid sample, 1901, Lady Luck & Lady Liberty hold wreath over trophy before regatta, American Litho, M, A...............................**$79.00**

Prize Cup Tea, sign, 1920s, light-up, celluloid, girl talking on telephone, product name above, ornate frame, 13½x11½", EX, A **$275.00**

Pro Forma Cigars, box label, inner lid, woman on throne & cherubs, 6x9", EX, C3.......................................**$15.00**

Proctor & Gamble, recipe book, 1932, '144 Time Saving Recipes,' white cover, 55 pages, EX, D..................**$3.00**

Proctor & Gamble, sign, paper, Victorian lady in profile, ...Soaps on hat, collar & across front, Purity below, 22x17½", G-, A **$130.00**

Producers Peanut Butter, pail, screw lid/bail, 1-lb, A...**$130.00**

Producers Superman Orange Flavored Drink, carton, wax on cardboard, pictures Superman in various poses, 2-qt, EX, D $9.00

Prosit Golden Lager Beer, label, 1933-36, Superior Brewing Co, U-type permit number, 12-oz, EX, A **$31.00**

Prospect Brewing Co, calendar, 1898, inset of 3 children with floral border, minor creasing/soiling, framed, image: 20½x16", EX, A **$1,100.00**

Prospect Brewing Co, label, dated 1904, company name arched above Ulmer Beer, EX, A **$12.00**

Prospect Brewing Co, label, pre-1920, company name arched above Lager Beer, EX, A **$17.00**

Protectol Anti-Freeze, thermometer, tin, penguin logo on green above, Protection Against Freezing & Corrosion in black circle below, 36", VG, A **$25.00**

Providence River Oyster Co's Celebrated Oysters, trade card, Black man fighting with dog for an oyster with ships beyond, Everybody Wants... above, EX, A **$50.00**

Providence Washington Insurance Co, trade card, 2-sided, finely engraved Victorian dock scene, 1886 balance sheet on reverse, black & white, EX, A **$17.00**

Prudential Insurance Co, bank, 1950s, plastic glow-in-the-dark Rock of Gibralter, Has The Strength Of Gibralter, 2x4x5", EX, D **$18.00**

Prudential Insurance Co, calendar, 1893, round with girl holding insurance policy surrounded by months of the year, 9" dia, EX, A **$75.00**

Prudential Insurance Co, trade card, Father Time holding hourglass, Take Time By The Foreclock, EX, A...**$18.00**

Prudential Life Insurance Co, calendar, 1894, April, May & June sheet on the diagonal shows girl with hand in mouth & halo of flowers, 6x6", EX, A..................**$45.00**

Prudential Life Insurance Co, calendar, 1894, July, August & September sheet on the diagonal showing boy in billed cap, 6x6", EX, A **$40.00**

Prudential Life Insurance Co, tape measure, metal, D.**$4.00**

Prudential Life Insurance Co, tip tray, vertical oval featuring The Rock logo, plain rim, EX, A **$15.00**

Prune Nugget Tobacco, sign, 1890s, paper, product name above garden girl with flower basket, metal strips top & bottom, framed, 30x15", NM, D3..$1,950.00

Puck Rye, pocket mirror, cherub leaning against bar holding bottle of rye, lettered, 2⅛" dia, VG+, A **$20.00**

Pulver Chewing Gum, pin-back button, ca 1900, red, white & blue, fading, D **$8.00**

Pulver Chewing Gum, vendor, 1¢, porcelainized metal, green with white lettering, glass window reveals traffic cop, 20x 8½", EX+, A...**$625.00**

Pulver Chewing Gum, vendor, 1¢, 1950s, double column & composition clown in center, red & white, 20x8½x4½", EX+, A...**$450.00**

Pulver Kola-Pepsin Gum & Sweet Chocolate, vendor, 1¢, ca 1910, white lettering on red, no interior mechanism, 24x10x5½", G, A **$1,500.00**

Pulver's Cocoa, tip tray, dainty little girl with cup on cocoa container, ...Purity Itself on rim, 4½" dia, G, A...**$215.00**

Pure as Gold Transmission Grease, can, ca 1933, product name in square & band on top half, Pep boys pictured below, no lid, 5-lb, 6½", EX, A.............................**$75.00**

Pure Food Cigar, container, brown glass with embossed lettering, tin lid, hexagonal, 6½", VG, A **$30.00**

Pure Gold, sign, die-cut cardboard stand-up, diapered crawling baby in brown cap advertising California fruits, 16¾", VG, A $525.00

Pure Oil Co, bottle, ca 1906, salesman's sample, glass with cork top, original tag, soiling to tag, 7", A............**$20.00**

Pure Oil Co, globe, blue & white lenses in metal case, Pure in bold letters, Products Of The..., 19", G, A.................**$140.00**

Pure Oil Co, sign, 1930-40, neon, blue logo on white ground, Products Of The..., original crate, 50" dia, EX, A...**$850.00**

Pure Premium, pump sign, porcelain, 2-color background with Pure Premium above round logo, Be Sure With Pure below, 10x12", VG+, A................................**$45.00**

Pure Winner Yams, crate label, pictures 5 card royal flush of hearts, 9x9", M, C3...**$3.00**

Purina, doll, 1972, scarecrow, cloth body with vinyl head, NM, D..**$25.00**

Purina Health Products, sign, embossed tin, 2-piece, checkerboard on left, Purity Health Foods lettered on right, each: 36x36", EX, A **$30.00**

Puritan Crushed Plug Mixture, tin, black & white on gray paper label, product name above & below encircled Puritan man, slip lid, 1-lb, round, EX, D3..$95.00

Puritan Cut Plug, tin, yellow, slip lid features schooner sailing on high seas in brown tones, rectangular with round corners, EX, M2..**$20.00**

Puritan Motor Oil, sign, painted tin, early policeman with Stop on large hand at left of product & company name, 11x35", VG+, A...**$325.00**

Purity Beer, label, pre-1920, logo above Purity in script, United States Brewing Co, 12-oz, G, A................**$30.00**

Purity Brand Rolled Oats, container, Manufactured By Purity Oats Company, Keokuk & Davenport Iowa, 7¼x4" dia, G, D...**$60.00**

Purity Ice Cream, dish, logo flanked by product name in ornate letters on top rim, Maddock's, EX, A.........**$30.00**

Purity Ice Cream, sidewalk sign, porcelain, Agency above emblem with lilly & product name, serving French Vanilla..., 32x20½", EX, A **$275.00**

Purity Ice Cream, sign, embossed die-cut cardboard, boy seated at table with block of ice cream, animals watching, 11½", NM, A **$120.00**

Purity Ice Cream, sign, paper, animated boy with bird perched on back of chair enjoying ice cream, product name below, vertical, EX+, M1 ....**$200.00**

Purity Ice Cream, tray, 1913, girl in yellow dress enjoying ice cream, product name on rim, American Art Works litho, 13x13", EX, A $275.00

Purity Ice Cream, tray, 2 kids with piles of vanilla & chocolate ice cream on circular inset, product name on rim, 13x13", VG, A $325.00

Purity Kiss, sign, tin, 2 children kissing in large wicker chair, ...Everybody Likes It, National Biscuit Co, 8" dia, VG, A $700.00

Purity Oleomargarine, sign, tin, small girl on a running cow, In A Field Of Our Own, Capitol City Dairy Co, framed, image: 9x13", EX, A $2,700.00

Purol Gasoline, gas globe, 1920s, porcelain, arrow with product name above & below, Pure Oil Co at bottom, blue on white, 15" dia, EX, A....................$500.00

Purol Gasoline, sign, 1930s-40s, tin flange, 2-sided, white arrow & lettering on blue, Pure Oil Co below, 17½x19¾", EX, A $275.00

Purol-Pep Oil, sign, porcelain, zigzag border surrounds The Pure Oil Company USA lettered above & below Purol-Pep, 15" dia, NM, A $425.00

Putnam Dyes, cabinet, tin, trademark image of General Putnam escaping the Red Coats, minor soiling, 10x21x8½", VG, A $200.00

Putnam Dyes, display, 1920s, die-cut cardboard stand-up, shows 3 children & dog, EX, D2 ....$70.00

Putnam Dyes, fan, pre-1940s, cardboard with wooden handle, pictures a peacock, Charm Of Colors, Putnam Fadeless..., 7x10", NM, P4 ....$45.00

Putnam Dyes, jigsaw puzzle, General Putman on horse waving to cavalry on horses, inscribed Norman E Bohn..., 5½x6½", EX, F1 ....$85.00

Putnam Phalanx Cigars, sign, 1861, paper, 15 staff members & officers from the Massachusetts military, Gillett Jones & Co, rare, 27x36", G, A $1,600.00

Pyrex Ware, sign, die-cut cardboard stand-up, wedding couple being presented with Pyrex Ware, Give Modern..., 25x21", EX, A $24.00

Pyro Anti-Freeze, sign, ca 1940, tin, Super Pyro Anti-Freeze $1 Gal above thermometers, No Boil Away on bottom band, 31¾x17¾", NM, A $70.00

Pyro Anti-Freeze, thermometer, tin, white & black on white & red, Modern Anti-Freeze Protection logo below, minor scratches, 36", G, A $20.00

Pyro Plastics, catalog, 1970, 28 pages, EX, D $25.00

Pyroil 'A', sign, Add To Gas 25¢...Saves Motors, Saves Money, vertical rectangle, EX+, A $30.00

Q

Q Boid Granulated Plug Tobacco, pocket tin, product name above tobacco plant logo, 4x2", VG, A $35.00

Q&Q Perfectos, sign, 1930s-40s, embossed tin, red with cream lettering & border, Smoke Q&Q Perfectos, edge wear/yellowing, 9½x28", A $35.00

Quaddy Playthings, postcard, pictures Spotty the Turtle, Of Course I Am A Quaddy, & Spotty Is My Name..., EX+, P3 ....$50.00

Quail Brand Contra Costa Bartletts, crate label, 1930s, California quail walking through grass, Sacramento, 7¼x11", M, C1 ....$5.00

Quaker Alcohol, thermometer, tin, pictures product can at bottom, ...Safe, Economical, 38x8", M, D $275.00

Quaker Cereal, recipe book, 1927, 'Quaker Cereal Products & How to Use Them,' 56 pages, VG, D $10.00

Quaker Cigars, box label, inner lid, pictures a Quaker girl, 6x9", M, D $6.00

Quaker City Motor Oil, paperweight, clear acrylic with drop of oil encased, 2½x2½", EX, D $35.00

Quaker Maid Table Syrup, tin, encircled bust portrait of Quaker lady with product name above & below, press lid, round, EX+, A $112.00

Quaker Maid Whiskey, sign, ca 1905, reverse-painted glass with copper backing, S Hirsch Co..., ornate frame, oval, 15½x23½", VG, A $990.00

Quaker Muffets Cereal, dexterity puzzle, steel canister with plastic cover, place balls in holes on clowns, premium, EX, H1 ....$14.00

Quaker Oats, display, ca 1936, cardboard, 5 folding panels featuring the Dionne Quints, G, A $165.00

Quaker Oats, jigsaw puzzle, shows Quaker man feeding little girl, 5x6½", EX, F1 ....$45.00

Quaker Oats, tin, 1992, 7x5" dia, EX, D $15.00

Quaker Puffed Wheat, cereal box, Shirley Temple pictured below product name, This Is My Cereal!, red, black & yellow, 8½", EX, A $195.00

Quaker Puffed Wheat, sign, cardboard, full-length portrait of Shirley Temple holding cereal box, This Is My Cereal, 18x3½", VG, A $39.00

Quaker Puffed Wheat, sign, die-cut cardboard, Shirley Temple saluting, Shirley Temple Loves..., 20½x18", G-, A $50.00

Quaker Queen Cigars, box label, inner lid, young Quaker woman dressed in blue, 6x9", M, C3 ....$35.00

Quaker Ranges, pin-back button, Quaker man in profile with product name above & below, red, white & green, round, EX, A $28.00

Quaker Rolled White Oats, container, cardboard, Quaker man on square inset, blue, red, yellow & white, 7½", EX, D..$15.00

Quaker Rose Cigars, sign, cardboard, black & white image of woman wearing bonnet, 10x5", EX, D **$4.50**

Quaker State Cold Test Oil, sign, porcelain, 2-sided, Use...For Winter Driving in white lettering on green with white fancy border, 6x27", NM, A **$130.00**

Quaker State Motor Oil, sign, ca 1982, tin, Quaker State lettered vertically above Motor Oil, green background, 72x12", NM, A...**$80.00**

Quaker State Motor Oil, sign, porcelain, 2-sided, white on green, oil well pictured in letter Q above product name, rounded top, 30x26", M, D3.........$225.00

Quaker State Motor Oil, sign, porcelain, 2-sided, 100% Pure logo above Quaker State arched above QSM logo & Motor Oil, 29x27", VG, A.................................**$70.00**

Quaker State Motor Oil, sign, 1940s, product name in silver & yellow flanked by logos on green ground, framed, 12½x16½", EX, A **$100.00**

Quaker State Motor Oil, strip sheet, 1970s, painted tin, original uncut sheet for making cans, green, white & black, 35x26", VG, A..**$130.00**

Quaker State Motor Oil, toy clicker, green & white, EX, D...**$15.00**

Quaker State Winter Oil, banner, cloth, product name on band below winter scene with car driving through horseshoe, text at left, 34x57", EX, A.................**$150.00**

Quality Electric Ranges, booklet, black & white illustrations, 20 pages, minor soiling, 11x8½", D **$15.00**

Quandt Bock Beer, label, pre-Prohibition, 12-oz, VG, A..**$40.00**

Quandt Lager Beer, sign, tin, gold with white outlined letters on blue background around cherub with beer glass, 27½x19½", EX, A..**$45.00**

Queen Beauty Toilet Soap, label, girl in off the shoulder pink dress, elegant peacock & mansion with steps leading to river, 8¼x14", M, C1 ....**$3.00**

Queen Cola, sign, painted tin, cream & light purple on purple, Ask For above bottle, It's Different & Better below, 20x7", G, A...**$150.00**

Queen Ester, crate label, 1930s, California orange, Egyptian queen on blue, Placentia, 10x11¾", M, C3 ....**$6.00**

Queen Pine Tar Hair Dressing, tin, 1940s, red & white, 1½" dia, EX, D **$9.50**

Queen Quality Salted Peanuts, tin, Queen Quality lettered diagonally above Salted Peanuts, press/pry lid, small scratches/dent, 9¾x8" dia, VG, A.......................**$130.00**

Queen Quality Shoes, pocket mirror, bust portrait of lovely young woman with Queen Quality logo below, oval, 2¾", EX, A...**$50.00**

Queen Quality Shoes, pocket mirror, classical lady in pink scarf descending steps, logo below, oval, 2¾", EX, A...........**$85.00**

Queen Quality Shoes for Women, sign, reverse-painted glass, gold Queen & Quality flank oval portrait of lady on black gold-trimmed band, 15x42", VG, A.....$300.00

Questa-Rey Habana Cigars, tip tray, girl in profile, product name above & below, The Aroma Lingers Longer on green rim, crazing, oval, 6x4", EX, A.............**$160.00**

Quick Meal, sign, porcelain, Trade Mark arched above chick running out of egg shell after bug, Quick Meal below, oval, 33x45", VG, A **$185.00**

Quilted Side Corsets, trade card, portrait of a woman, advertising on reverse, black & white, EX, A.......**$10.00**

R

R&G Corsets, trade card, sepia, interior scene with girl looking in full length mirror, EX, A **$26.00**

R&G Licorice Lozenges, tin, 5 Lbs lettered above arched glass panel with R&G in ovals flanking top sides of arch, slip lid, some wear, A.................................**$55.00**

R&H Adams Gauze Netting, sign, paper, surreal image of little boy riding a bee, ...Protection Against Insects, 13½x10½", EX, A......**$1,100.00**

R&J Gilchrist, trade card, die-cut vase of flowers, 8", VG, D......**$4.50**

Raco Ham & Bacon, pocket mirror, sow feeding piglets, product name above, Reading Abattoir Co below, Sweet, Juicy..., 2⅛" dia, EX, A......**$450.00**

Radiana Cigars, box label, inner lid, women in wooded scene, 1 playing harp, 6x9", VG, D......**$7.50**

Radiant Roast Coffee, tin, mountain scene, key-wind lid, 2-lb, EX, D......**$35.00**

Radio Skim Milk Powder, sign, paper, features cow image & advertising, Radio Foods Corp, matted & framed, 23" dia, EX+, M2......**$45.00**

Radway's Sarsaparillian Resolvent, sign, paper, woman presenting product to large group of people, ...Ready Relief, Regulating Pills, 10x13", VG, A......**$925.00**

Rahr Green Bay Beer, label, 1933-36, U-type permit number, 12-oz, EX, A......**$35.00**

Raid, beach bag, 1980s, canvas, Bug Out To The Beach, 11x17", M, D......**$28.00**

Raid, coffee mug, 1986, 30th anniversary, NM, D......**$10.00**

Raid, telephone, 1980s, plastic, Raid bug on white base, SC Johnson & Son Inc, 9", M, D......$55.00

Railway Express Agency, sign, porcelain, diamond shape, red, white & black, 8", NM, D......**$125.00**

Railway Express Agency, sign, porcelain flange, lettering on diamond in center, Packages Received Here below, 18x15", G+, A......**$275.00**

Railway Express Agency, sign, tin, men loading train with express truck in foreground, Fast Dependable..., dent/surface speckling, 13x19", G, A......**$300.00**

Rainbow Plant Feed, sign, tin polychrome, pictures colorful back of plant food, red lettering, white ground, rust/dents, 19x17", A......**$10.00**

Rainier Beer, sign, neon, product name in white with large R in red, EX, D......**$150.00**

Rainier Beer, sign, tin, stock image of girl leaning on roaring bear, logo above, rolled corners, 14½x14½", EX, A..**$250.00**

Rainier Beer, statuette, 1956, plaster, Rainier waiter carrying tray with bottle, For Good Cheer on his apron, 6½", EX, D......**$125.00**

Rainier Beer, tray, pictures Evelyn Nesbitt in pink & white hooded coat, lettering on rim, overall fading/wear, 13½" dia, G-, A......**$40.00**

Rainier Lime Rickey, label, 1920-28, Ranier superimposed over lines, 12-oz, VG, A......**$10.00**

Rajah Cigars, mirror, reverse-painted with product name & prices, Imperial Tobacco Co of Great Britian & Ireland, framed, 10x26", G, A......**$20.00**

Raleigh Bicycles, sign, paper, African on bike being chased by lion, You're Missing Something If You Don't Buy A Raleigh, 13x29", EX, S5......$150.00

Raleigh Cigarettes, nail clippers & file in plastic cover, chrome-plated steel, stamped with Brown & Williamson logo, EX, H1......**$6.50**

Raleigh Cigarettes, sign, paper, bathing beauty posed on knees looking up with product name & pack above, 18x12", NM, A......**$20.00**

Raleigh Cigarettes, sign, paper, Save B&W Coupons above dancing couple, product pack & Raleigh oval over & left of couple, 18x12", NM, A......**$16.00**

Raleigh Cigarettes, sign, tin, Now At Popular Prices above product name & open pack of cigarettes, Save B&W Coupons below, 14x20", NM, B1......**$65.00**

Raleigh Cigarettes, sign, tin, Now At Popular Prices on band above advertising left of open pack, Save B&Q coupons below, rectangle, EX, A......**$55.00**

Raleigh Cigarettes, sign, 1940, paper, pinup lady & pack of cigarettes, Now At Popular Prices..., 18x12", EX, D...**$40.00**

Raleigh Cigarettes, statuette, 1960s, metal bust of Sir Walter Raleigh, product name embossed on base, 5", VG+, D......**$35.00**

Ralston Purina, ashtray, heavy pottery, shaped like a dog's feeding bowl with colorful graphic on white background, 5⅞" dia, P2......**$35.00**

Ralston Rice Chex, cereal box, 1960s, pictures spoon filled with cereal, wear on corners, EX, D......**$25.00**

Ralston's Improved Threshing & Cleaning Machine, broadside, ca 1843, paper, stains, 17½x11½", G, A .**$20.00**

Ralston Straight Shooters, pocket knife, mother-of-pearl, product name flanked by checked logo, EX, A ...**$49.00**

Ralston Whole Wheat Cereal, display, cardboard box, pictures a boy in circular inset on red & white checked ground, rare, 19x14x6", G-, A......**$145.00**

Ram's Horn Cigars, box label, early 1900s, lithographer's proof, encircled close-up of ram's head, Ram's Horn label below, EX, A **$62.00**

Ram's Horn Fragrant Mixture, pocket tin, pictures a ram's head with product name above & below, slip lid, VG+, A **$25.00**

Ramon's Aspirin Tablets, display box, cardboard with top folding back to make advertising marquee, several aspirin tins inside, EX, A **$22.50**

Ramon's Brownie/Pink Pills, thermometer, wood, pictures The Little Doctor with advertising above & below, arched top, squared bottom, EX, M1 .... **$390.00**

Ramon's Laxative, thermometer, tin, roll of Brownie Pills & Pink Pills above & below top-hatted figure in stride, rounded top, 21", VG, A **$130.00**

Ramon's Little Doctor, tin, blue or pink, EX, D3..... **$18.00**

Ramon's Medicines, jar, clear glass, gent in top hat & spectacles on tin lid, 3 full figures & lettering on jar, 7¾", EX, A **$45.00**

Ramon's Pills, container, clear glass with raised lettering, no top, 9¾", VG, A **$20.00**

Ramon's Pills, thermometer, stenciled wood, young boy in doctor's uniform, A Real Laxative For Adults below, 21", VG, A **$130.00**

Ramona Lager Beer, label, 1933-50, San Francisco Brewing Co, Internal Revenue Tax Paid statement, 11-oz, VG, A **$25.00**

Ramona Memories, crate label, 1920s, California lemon, romantic Spanish senorita with roses in her hair, San Fernando, 9x12½", M, C1 .... **$3.00**

Ramrod Apricots, can label, Art Deco style with apricots, VG, C3 .... **$5.00**

Ramsay's Biscuits & Chocolates, sign, cardboard, Ramsay's above factory scene & Dutch girl, The Sunshine Home Of..., matted & framed, 24x36", VG, M2.. **$240.00**

Ramsay's Paints, sign, metal flange, 2-sided, product name above painter pointing upward, The Right Paint... Sold Here, 16x12", VG, A **$110.00**

Rancheria Bartlett Pears, crate label, 1930s, Indian on white horse with village & lake beyond, Suisun Cal, 7¼x11", M, C1 .... **$2.00**

Rand McNally, sign, 1920s, die-cut porcelain, arrowhead shape, pictures Indian drawing, ...Official Hotel in white, 17x13½", EX, A **$1,000.00**

Ranger Bicycles, catalog, 1916, 64 pages, VG, D **$85.00**

Rapid Kool Milk Conditioner, sign, 1930s, tin, blue lettering on yellow, 9x28", EX, D **$35.00**

Raven Cigars, label, The Raven lettered on either side of bird sitting on Poe's book, The Raven, diagonal corners, 4x4", EX, D **$10.00**

Rawleigh's Fan-Jang Talc, tin, pictures Oriental lady with open fan surrounded by flowers, EX, A **$35.00**

Rawleigh's Good Health Talcum Powder, tin, logo surrounded by nursery rhyme characters, tall rectangular can with shaker top, EX, A **$65.00**

Ray Cotton Co, inkwell, cast-iron truck with driver, truck bed loaded with cotton bales, embossed lettering on panels, 4x8x3", VG, A **$80.00**

RC Brown & Co's New York Cigars, sign, ca 1886, paper, young lady pulling up stockings after a days shrimping, framed, image: 20½x14¼", EX, A **$800.00**

RCA, banner, cloth, RCA & Nipper logos on 2-tone aqua zigzag background, 40x48", EX, A **$65.00**

RCA, banner, cotton, multiple images of Nipper with Victrola & RCA symbols, 37½x40", VG, A **$55.00**

RCA, display, rubber figure of Nipper, white with black ears & collar, slight bend in paw/minor age cracks, 13", M2 .... **$350.00**

RCA, see also Victor

RCA Victor, display, papier-mache figure of Nipper, early repaint, 13½", EX, A **$55.00**

RCA Victor, salt & pepper shakers, 1930s, ceramic, Nipper figures, RCA Victor & His Masters Voice impressed on bases, Lenox, EX, H1 .... **$65.00**

RCA Victor, statuette, 1930s, chalk, Nipper seated on round base, 3", EX, D **$35.00**

RCA Victor Records, sign, hanging, 2-sided, black with white lettering & maroon label, weathered/faded, 20" dia, G, A **$350.00**

Reading Brewing Co, sign, die-cut cardboard, girl with bottles in her apron surrounded by embossed flowers, framed, image: 20x15", EX, A.......................... **$1,950.00**

Reading Brewing Co, sign, tin litho, turn-of-the-century brewery by Kauffman & Strauss, raised lettering on frame, 27x39", EX, A **$3,080.00**

Reading Brewing Co's US Standard Beer, sign, paper, elderly man lifting stein of beer, decorative background, framed, image: 22x17", EX, A **$450.00**

Reception Cigars, box labels, inner & outer sample set, 1870s, visitors being received in classical setting, Heppenheimer & Maurer, EX, A **$103.00**

Recruit Cigarettes, chair, folding, wood with spindle back, overall wear, 32x20x17", G-, A............................ **$25.00**

Recruit Little Cigars, pin-back button, ca 1900, portrait image & white lettering on red ground, EX, D **$8.00**

Recruit Little Cigars, sign, porcelain, soldier in formal attire & open box of cigars flank product lettering, 12x30", EX, A $300.00

Red & White Brand Pure Spices, tin, red, white & blue, Red & White above rest of product name & Nutmeg, vertical rectangle, EX+, M2 .... **$8.00**

Red Aro Gasoline, gas globe, 1920s-40s, glass body, Aro lettered on red arrow with Red Anti-Knock... above & below, 13½" dia, EX, A **$350.00**

Red Ball, display, red plastic globe, black Guaranteed Service lettered around white Red Ball in center, 22" dia, EX+, A **$50.00**

Red Ball, sign, tin light-up, small lights decorate Ford lettered in white, white border on blue oval, 36x70", G+, A.. **$1,450.00**

Red Band Beer, label, 1933-50, diamond logo above product name, Internal Revenue Tax Paid statement, 12-oz, EX, A **$17.00**

Red Bell Cranberries, label, early 1900s, pictures a large red bell, 7x10", M, C1 ....**$2.00**

Red Cap Candy Bar, sign, painted tin, Eat above Red Cap lettered on the diagonal, Everybody's Candy Bar Choice 5¢, 10x28", G, A...**$35.00**

Red Circle Coffee, bank, metal square shape with advertising, 4", NM, A **$12.00**

Red Cloud Cigars, box label, inner lid, 1920s, Indian with arrow & shield on horseback with ornate border, 6½x10", M, C3 ....$14.00

Red Cloud Sliced Plug Smoking Tobacco, match striker, tin, pictures Chief Red Cloud, The Best Thing You Ever Struck..., 6x2", NM, A..**$550.00**

Red Comb, sign, paper hanger, Your Neighbor Is Feeding... above Why Don't You & logo, rectangular, 16", NM, B1 ....**$5.00**

Red Cross Base Burner, trade card, pictures woman spanking child, Co-Operative Foundry Co, Rochester NY, EX, A...**$14.00**

Red Cross Brand Condensed Milk, sign, embossed tin, yellow with can at left of red product name, America's Best Milk in black, 3½x19½", EX, A **$30.00**

Red Cross Macaroni, pin-back button, Little Orphan Annie flanked by 2 Red Cross emblems, Little Orphan Annie Loves... above, round, EX, A **$44.00**

Red Cross Stoves & Ranges, pin tray, ca 1890, tin, red, black & silver, round with zigzag edge, advertising in center, EX+, A...**$80.00**

Red Crow Brand Coffee, tin, paper label, EX, A....**$675.00**

Red Crown Gasoline, blotter, 1930s, pictures mountain sheep & wolves, 6x4", EX, D **$4.00**

Red Crown Gasoline, sign, porcelain, 2-sided, white with Red Crown Gasoline lettered around encircled red & blue crown, 42" dia, EX+/VG+, A **$800.00**

Red Devil Polish, clock, 1930s, wood frame, Red Devil logo, electric, 16x16", EX, D3.............................**$450.00**

Red Devil's Lighter Fluid, thermometer, tin, black & red on white, can of product above, The Fluid With A Thousands Lights below, 11½", EX, A....................**$5.00**

Red Diamond, crate label, 1920s, California apple, pictures 3 apples & card with big red diamond, Watsonville, 9x11", G1 ....**$3.00**

Red Dot Cigar, sign, 1930s, cardboard, die-cut cigar with small portrait of a pretty girl, Truly Different, 6x34", EX, D..**$48.00**

Red Dot Junior Cigars, pocket tin, flat, encircled head portrait flanked by Red Dot, 10 For 50¢ above, Barnes-Smith Co Makers, VG, H1....................$18.50

Red Fox Beverages, door push plate, 1950s, embossed tin, Red Fox in script, red, white, black & silver, 13½x4", EX, D **$32.00**

Red Giant Grease, bucket, 1930-40, pictures a red giant with product name arched above on black & cream ground, lid missing, 10-lb, 7", A.........................**$180.00**

Red Goose Shoes, bank, 1960s, plastic, red goose on red base with embossed lettering, 5", M, D **$15.00**

Red Goose Shoes, clock, glass, metal frame, 1-5 & 7-11 surround large red goose lettered Red Goose Shoes, round, EX, D **$350.00**

Red Goose Shoes, display, papier-mache, figural goose with nodding head, glass eyes, extremely rare, 1 eye missing, 24x18x13", G, A................................**$1,000.00**

Red Goose Shoes, display figure, red goose on green base, plaster of Paris, 11", NM, D **$100.00**

Red Goose Shoes, door push plate, porcelain, Push in script above red goose image lettered Red Goose Shoes, vertical, EX, M1 ....**$950.00**

Red Goose Shoes, horn, cardboard with wooden mouthpiece, Red Goose Shoes-Half The Fun Of Having Feet, 6" long, EX, D **$8.50**

Red Goose Shoes, pencil box, children on the path to school with large goose in foreground, EX+, D **$175.00**

Red Goose Shoes, sign, neon, die-cut porcelain goose, 24x12", M, D...**$3,000.00**

Red Goose Shoes, sign, porcelain, red goose on yellow background, 17¼x12", EX, A.............................**$170.00**

Red Goose Shoes, sign, 1930s-40s, die-cut porcelain, red goose with Red Goose Shoes lettered in yellow, 35x17½", EX, A...**$1,400.00**

Red Goose Shoes, string holder, cast-iron goose with removable side plate, red with yellow lettering, green base, 14½" long, VG, A.......................................**$475.00**

Red Goose Shoes, string holder, die-cut goose suspended above spool of string, 28x16", EX, A **$2,600.00**

Red Goose Shoes, string holder, die-cut tin goose, red, black & white, 27x14", VG, A............................**$825.00**

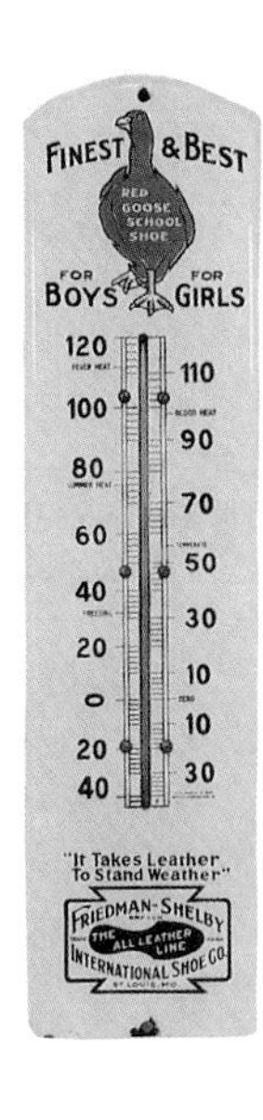

Red Goose Shoes, thermometer, porcelain, white with Finest & Black flanking goose, For Boys & Girls, rounded ends, 27x7", EX, A..........................$260.00

Red Goose Shoes, thermometer, 1930s, wood, Red Goose logo above bulb & advertising, beveled edge, arched top, square bottom, 21x8", EX, D **$200.00**

Red Head White Corn Meal, sack, 1940s, cloth, bird & corn design, Shreveport La, 25-lb, EX, P1 ....**$15.00**

Red Heart Rum, sign, tin on cardboard, 2 Jamaican boys & a heart, minor fading, 9½x6", VG, D...........................**$20.00**

Red Horse Chewing Tobacco, sign, paper, Chew That Good Chew, Red Horse at left of tilted product pack, 10x20", NM, A..**$10.00**

Red Horse Liquor, statuette, composition, cowboy on horse, bright red with black & white lettering, some paint wear, 8", D **$50.00**

Red Indian Cut Plug, lunch box, tin, Indian in full headdress on 2 sides, black & red, hinged lid & wire handle, rare, 5x8x4", EX, A **$650.00**

Red Indian Cut Plug, tin, Indian in full headdress & product name on paper label, slip lid, 4x6", VG, A **$175.00**

Red Jacket Mild Smoking Tobacco, sign, silkscreened cardboard, lettering above & below baseball scene, 22x28", EX, A..**$100.00**

Red Jacket Tobacco, pocket tin, upright, NM, H3 ....**$70.00**

Red Man Chewing Tobacco, belt buckle, H3...........**$15.00**

Red Man Chewing Tobacco, sign, cardboard, man in vest & tie displaying pack at right of Fresh Red Man Wax Wrapped, 8x17", NM, A **$20.00**

Red Man Chewing Tobacco, sign, cardboard, tilted open pack lower right of Chew Red Man on the diagonal, The Good Tasting... below, 10x20", NM, A **$15.00**

Red Man Chewing Tobacco, sign, paper, Buy Red Man America's Best Chew on the diagonal above product pack, Big New Pack..., 14x11½", NM, A **$13.00**

Red Man Chewing Tobacco, sign, paper, 1952, baseball player Johnny Mize promoting Free baseball cap, Enjoy Red Man..., 16x11", NM, A **$65.00**

Red Man Chewing Tobacco, sign, 1920s, paper, man with tobacco pack in each hand, 8x17", EX, D **$20.00**

Red Man Chewing Tobacco, tin, 1989, 6x6", EX, D ...**$10.00**

Red Moon Sweet Peas, can label, red crescent moon logo with peapods in background, Baltimore, EX, G1...**$3.00**

Red Mountain, crate label, 1930s, California orange, colorful vista with large orange in foreground, Corona, 10x11¾", M, C3..**$4.00**

Red Owl Harvest Queen Coffee, tin, lettering on large red owl, ...Finest Quality, key-wind, 2-lb, EX+, A **$60.00**

Red Poppy Marrow Squash, can label, 1929, pictures flowers & squash, M, C3 ....**$15.00**

Red Raven, tray, nude child reaching for bottle with red raven looking on, ...Ask The Man & logo on rim, 12" dia, VG, A **$300.00**

Red Raven, tray, nude child reaching for bottle with red raven looking on, ...Ask The Man & logo on rim, 12" dia, EX+, A...**$600.00**

Red Raven Aperient Water, tip tray, ca 1904, raven standing next to glass & product bottle, Red Raven lettered below, 6x4", EX+, D..**$240.00**

Red Raven Splitz, tray, deep-dish, classic image of raven & bottle, For High Liver... on rim, minor spotting/wear, 12" dia, VG, A **$80.00**

Red Robin Peanut Butter, pail, tin, white front panel with Red Robin logo, back panel is red & white vertical stripes, bail handle, 1-lb, NM, A **$3,100.00**

Red Rock Cola, door push plate, 1930s, embossed tin, Enjoy..., in red on white, 3½x19", EX, D **$36.00**

Red Rock Cola, sign, tin, flanged, die-cut oval reading Enjoy Red Rock Cola, 10x21", NM, A **$110.00**

Red Rooster Coffee, tin, pictures a red rooster at left of product name, key-wind lid, 1-lb, EX+, A............**$75.00**

Red Rose Brand, crate label, 1890s, California fruit, red roses on yellow background, Rosedale Raisin Vineyard Co, 13x8½", M, C3..................................$20.00

Red Rose Coffee, sign, tin, key-wind can image on green background, can reads Estabrook's Red Rose Coffee with rose image, 16x18", EX, M2..........................**$60.00**

Red Rose Coffee, sign, tin, red, black & cream on orange & cream striped background, Red Rose Coffee Is Good Coffee, 19x27", EX+, M2 ....**$60.00**

Red Rose Coffee, sign, tin, white, red & black on blue, Red Rose Coffee above emblem reading Really Refreshed, bordered, 19x27", EX, M2 ....**$80.00**

Red Rose Tea, door push bar, tin, red product name in red at left of white Is Good Tea on meduim blue, 3x30", VG, M2..**$28.00**

Red Rose Tea, sign, tin, Red Rose Tea Is Good Tea in white on red, white outline, 4x23½", NM, A........**$65.00**

Red Rose Tea, sign, tin, red white & black image of tea box on black background, Red Rose Tea Is A Good Tea, unused, 19x28", NM, M2 ....**$160.00**

Red Rose Tea, sign, tin, white Red Rose Tea outlined in black above white For Sale Here on red, white & black border, 18x22", EX, M2...**$80.00**

Red Rose Tea, sign, tin hanger, Red Rose Tea Is Good Tea on 2 sides of 3-D horizontal rectangle with open bottom, 30x6x6", EX+, M2 ....**$115.00**

Red Rose Tea & Coffee, sign, cardboard, multicolors on black, 2 tea boxes flank coffee can, For Goodness Sake...Try Red Rose!, 11x42", EX, M2 ....**$40.00**

Red Seal Beer, label, 1933-50, Stecher Brewing Co, Internal Revenue Tax Paid statement, 12-oz, EX, A..........**$30.00**

Red Seal Beverages, sign, tin, white with Red Seal logo between red Drink & Beverages, 12x24", NM, M3..**$45.00**

Red Seal Beverages, sign, 1930s, embossed tin, ribbon logo flanked by Drink Beverages, red, white & blue, 12x24", EX, D **$48.00**

Red Seal Brand Peanut Butter, pail, tin, metallic gold with black lettering on shield, slip lid & bail, 1-lb, EX, A..**$20.00**

Red Seal Dry Battery, sign, porcelain, flanged, battery shape, red, white & blue, 24½x13", EX, A..........**$300.00**

Red Seal Dry Battery, thermometer, 1915, porcelain, pictures a battery at top, The Guarantee Protects You below, 26½x7", G, A **$80.00**

Red Seal Dry Battery, thermometer, 1915, porcelain, pictures a battery at top, The Guarantee Protects You below, 26½x7", EX, D $135.00

Red Seal Lye, pin-back button, ca 1900, multicolored canister on white background, blue lettering, EX, D **$8.00**

Red Seal Lye, pocket mirror, can of product surrounded by lettering, Sold By Storekeepers, 1¾" dia, EX, A ...**$40.00**

Red Seal Peanut Butter, pail, comical image of gents playing violins, yellow background, slip lid & bail, 3x3½" dia, EX, A...**$160.00**

Red Seal Peanut Butter, pail, pictures various nursery rhymes & characters, Newton Tea & Spice Co, press lid & bail, 12-oz, EX, A...**$150.00**

Red Star Yeast, sign, embossed tin, white with advertising around blue shield logo with 2 boxes of product & 2 For 5¢, 6x8¾", VG, A **$400.00**

Red Steer Brand, watch fob, celluloid, G, D............**$75.00**

Red Stripe Lager Beer, label, 1933-36, Galena Brewing Co, U-type permit number, 12-oz, EX, A....................**$45.00**

Red Tag Lager, label, 1928-33, Adam Scheidt Brewing Co, L-type permit number, 12-oz, EX, A **$36.00**

Red Tip Calks, sign, 1900-10, Neverslip Red Tip above horse's head in horse shoe, Calks Safest & Best below, framed, 29x20", EX, A..**$220.00**

Red Turkey Coffee, tin, blue & white background with product lettered in red with gold outline above red turkey, slip lid, 1-lb, EX, A...........................$155.00

Red Wolf Coffee, tin, 1935-42, wolf in horizontal with product name above & below, yellow, red & blue, 1-lb, EX, A **$300.00**

Redbreast Flake, sign, porcelain, The Popular Smoke lettered on ribbon banner in lower right corner, framed, horizontal rectangle, A.......................................**$170.00**

Reddy Kilowatt, bank, 1960s, plastic figure of Reddy against background of blue & white clouds, rare, 5x6½x3½", VG, A **$1,605.00**

Reddy Kilowatt, certificate, Reddy Salute, framed, EX, P2 ....**$35.00**

Reddy Kilowatt, cookie cutter, 1950s, red plastic die-cut of Reddy, Your Favorite Cookie Cutter lettered on box, 3x3", EX, A...**$51.00**

Reddy Kilowatt, earrings, metal, M, P2 ....**$35.00**

Reddy Kilowatt, mechanical pencil, 1950s, plastic & metal, Let Reddy Do It inscribed in red & blue on white, 5¼", EX, D **$18.00**

Reddy Kilowatt, necklace, EX, D **$35.00**

Reddy Kilowatt, pin-back button, 1950s, red, white & blue, EX, D **$25.00**

Reddy Kilowatt, plate, china, M, P2 .... **$125.00**

Reddy Kilowatt, playing cards, complete, in original box, EX, P2 .... **$35.00**

Reddy Kilowatt, recipe book, 1950, Southern Colorado Power Co, EX, D **$22.00**

Reddy Kilowatt, statuette, 1961, plastic glow-in-the-dark, 6", M, D....................... $55.00

Reddy Kilowatt, tie clip, M, P2....................... **$35.00**

Redford's Celebrated Tobaccos, sign, paper, Black men growing & picking tobacco, tobacco leaf border, 20x25½", EX, A....................... **$70.00**

Redford's Celebrated Tobaccos, sign, paper, Black men growing & picking tobacco, tobacco leaf border, 20x25½", NM, A....................... **$175.00**

Redman, crate label, apple, fierce Indian & 2 apples, 10½x9", M, C1....................... **$4.00**

Reeves, Parvin & Co's Mountain Coffee, trade card, elegant girl in plumed hat with cup of coffee, mountain scene beyond, EX, A....................... **$21.00**

Regal, sign, die-cut brass boot with spur, VG, A .. **$1,500.00**

Regal Bock Beer, label, 1933-50, ram's head in center, American Brewing Co, Internal Revenue Tax Paid statement, 12-oz, EX, A **$27.00**

Regoes Rubbed Sage, tin, 1920s, pictures a turkey, round, EX, D....................... **$35.00**

Reichard & Weaver Brewery, pocket mirror, celluloid, 1806 Centennial 1906 lettered below factory scene, Wilkes-Barre, 2¼" dia, G, A....................... **$275.00**

Reindeer, crate label, 1920s, California orange, reindeer by lake & grove scene in sunburst, El Cajon Valley, 10x11", M, C1....................... **$8.00**

Reisch's Sangamo, label, pre-Prohibition, Indian overlooking stream, Reisch Brewing Co, 12-oz, EX, A....... **$70.00**

Reliance, ashtray, 1950s, painted hard plaster, boy standing on rim with body formed by lock washers, 6½x4½" dia, VG, A....................... **$1,300.00**

Remer's Tea Store, sign, cardboard stand-up, kitten licking from teacup tipped on its side, advertising on bottom of cup, 6¼x10", EX, A....................... **$25.00**

Remington Ammunition, sign, 1940s, die-cut paper, leaping 8-point buck, ...Is Loaded To The Limit For Power!, VG, A **$30.00**

Remington Arms Co, catalog, 1894, nonpictorial cover, introduced the Hammerless Double-Barrel Shotgun, 18 pages, EX, A **$180.00**

Remington Arms Co, postcard, 1916, aerial photo of the factory, VG, A **$12.00**

Remington Arms Co Works, postcard, 1915, busy street scene, used, VG, A **$8.00**

Remington Arms-Union Metallic Cartridge Co, sign, paper, 3 setters looking out window, ...Union Metallic Cartridge Co below, framed, 24½x17", VG, A....................... **$200.00**

Remington Autoloading, pin-back button, pictures a rifle with lettering above & below, oval, VG, A **$45.00**

Remington Express, box of 500 shotgun shells, .410-gauge, wood, unopened, A....................... **$230.00**

Remington Guns & Rifles, ad cover, 1906, lady hunter, birds & more advertising on reverse, VG, A....................... **$80.00**

Remington Guns & Rifles, ad cover, 1910, man holding rifle, sepia tones, illustrations & advertising on reverse, scarce, VG, A **$60.00**

Remington Kleanbore .22's, counter display, metal & glass, red & green, If It's Remington...It's Right in script at bottom, VG, A **$190.00**

Remington Knives, display case, oak frame with slanted glass front, rear door opens for storage, lettering top & bottom, 20x14x10", VG, A **$75.00**

Remington Peters, sample display case for setting up large displays, contains panel arrangement worksheets in 5 pages, VG, A **$300.00**

Remington Shur Shot Shells, box, Shur Shot Shells with extended S's to form Sure, Safe & Speedy below, 20-gauge, minor soiling, VG, A **$45.00**

Remington Tires, sign, tin, white, black & green, 16x31", EX, D....................... **$75.00**

Remington Typewriter Ribbon, tin, Art Nouveau design, EX, D **$8.50**

Remington-UMC, calendar, 1917, paper, hunt scene with birds in flight, American Litho Co, September pad, framed, 30x17", EX, A....................... **$550.00**

Remington-UMC, catalog, 1911-12, nonpictorial cover, well illustrated with well-designed page layouts, 192 pages, EX, A **$50.00**

Remington-UMC, pin-back button, white on red, round, VG, A **$15.00**

Remington-UMC, postcard, shows exhibit at the 1915 Panama Pacific Expo, scarce, VG, A **$50.00**

Remington-UMC, sign, die-cut stand-up, various game with each beside box of shells, 28x11", VG, A **$220.00**

Remington-UMC, sign, paper, elaborate image with various game, bullets & guns, soiling & spotting, 24x20", G, A....................... **$125.00**

Remington-UMC, sign, paper with metal strips top & bottom, hunter with dogs & puppies, shotgun leaning on fence, 25x17", VG+, A....................... **$450.00**

Remington-UMC .22 Caliber Repeating Rifle, sign, boy with rifle following tracks in the snow, framed, 10x14", VG, A **$350.00**

Remington-UMC .22 Caliber Rifles & Cartridges, display, die-cut, stands up by opening to form a shooting range, target shooting scene, 10x14", EX, A....... **$400.00**

Remington-UMC Big Game Rifles, envelope, colorful image of large elk & 2 rifles, scarce, VG, A **$170.00**

Remington-UMC Lesmock Cartridges, pin-back button, scene with bears surrounded by lettering, Shoot..., round, EX, A **$45.00**

Remington-UMC Metallic Cartridges, envelope, pictures angry cougar encircled in upper left, VG, A **$100.00**

Remington-UMC Nitro Club Loaded Paper Shells, box, with contents, round logo above mallard in flight, Nitro Club... below, 12-gauge, VG, A **$40.00**

Remington-UMC Repeating & Autoloading Shotguns, ad cover, 1919, colorful bird-shooting scene above 2 rifles & logo, scarce, VG, A **$150.00**

Remington-UMC Steel-Lined Speed Shells, ad cover, 1919, colorful image of dogs flushing birds, VG, A.........**$170.00**

Remington-UMC Steel-Lined Speed Shells, envelope, turkey encircled above 2 shotgun shells, VG, A ..**$100.00**

REO Motor Cars. sign, embossed tin, yellow & blue, OF Seikman, Bartlesville Okla, minor wear, 10x28", B1 ....**$60.00**

REO Speed-Wagon, pencil clip, red, white & blue, EX, D **$35.00**

Resisto Ties, sign, stenciled plastic insert with illuminated red border, green metal case, Always The Newest, 16½" long, G+, A **$20.00**

Resolute Fire Insurance Co, sign, paper, vignette of Indian & sailor with American flag flanked by 2 rows of Corinthian columns, 23x18", EX, A **$700.00**

Restokraft Noiseless Mattress, playing cards, woman asleep on bare mattress, complete, M, D $4.00

Retold Cigars, box label, inner lid, 1934, shows Edison's first lamp, M, C3 ....**$55.00**

Rettig Brewing Co, tray, stock image of girl hugging horse's head, ...Ale & Porter on rim, oval, fading/scratches, 16½x13½", G, A **$200.00**

Revelation Smoking Mixture, pocket tin, cream with red lid & red bottom band, Revelation lettered above Smoking Mixture in oval, short, EX+, M1 ....**$50.00**

Revelation Smoking Mixture, pocket tin, cream with red lid & red bottom band, Revelation lettered above Smoking Mixture in oval, tall, EX, M1 ....**$19.00**

Revlon, doll, 1950, Little Miss Revlon, 10", EX, D......**$30.00**

Rex Aguilla Cigars, box label, inner lid, large eagle with wings spread, 6x9", M, D **$8.50**

Rex Beer, label, 1933-50, Standard Brewing Co, Internal Revenue Tax Paid statement, 12-oz, EX, A...........**$37.00**

Rex Bitters, sign, paper, nude woman on divan, If You Can't Do Business Drink..., matted & framed, image: 9¼x12", VG, A **$700.00**

Rex Brand Extract of Beef, trade card, die-cut folder, labeled jar, Cudahy Packing Co, advertising inside, EX, A **$21.00**

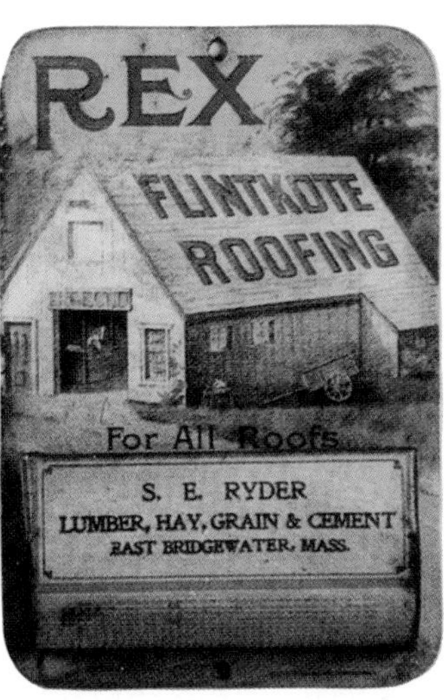

Rex Flintkote Roofing, match holder, rectangular back with round corners features barn with advertising, distributor ad on holder, 5x4", VG, A...........$180.00

Rex Tobacco, pocket tin, upright, oval head portrait with product name above & below, slip lid, EX+, A .**$166.00**

Rexall Violet Talcum Powder, tin, flat oval shape with violet floral motif surrounding product lettering, EX+, M2 ....**$60.00**

RG Sullivan's Quality 10¢ Cigar, sign, porcelain, red with RG Sullivan's banner over 20 in 7-20-4 above Quality 10¢ Cigar, 12x30", VG, A **$165.00**

Rheingold Beer, tray, girl with 2 shot glasses on a tray, Iron City Brewing Co, Lebanon Pa on rim, 13" dia, VG, A **$75.00**

Rheingold Extra Dry, sign, neon, no transformer, 23x15½", EX, A **$20.00**

Rice's Flower Seeds, sign, paper, little girl in bonnet holding rake surrounded by flowers, Good News..., framed, image: 29x13¾", NM, A **$1,450.00**

Rice's Seeds, display rack, tin, stair-step type with 7 tiers, bottom front shows 2 seed packets & Try Rice's Seeds, 32x24x22", EX+, D **$1,250.00**

Rice's Seeds, display rack, wood & metal, stair-step type with 5 tiers, product name & seed packets below, 28x22x18", EX, A **$475.00**

Rice's Seeds, sign, paper, farmhand & girl looking at growth of White Plume celery & Brazil squash, framed, image: 24x20", NM, A **$1,050.00**

Rice's Seeds, sign, paper, jovial man hugging large turnip, ...True Early Winningstadt..., matted & framed, image: 27x20", EX, A **$950.00**

Rice's Seeds, trade card, 1880s, woman throwing gourd at man below her window, VG, P1 .... **$10.00**

Rice Seed Co, display cabinet, ca 1909, metal & wood, unfolds to display packets, overall wear, A **$25.00**

Richardson's Root Beer, dispenser, oak barrel shape with aluminum logo plaques, onyx knob tap, footed, 26x18" dia, VG+, A **$270.00**

Richardson Skates, postcard, pictures elegant couple skating, If You Can Walk-You Can Skate..., EX, D **$40.00**

Richelieu Coffee, tin, key-wind lid, 1-lb, VG, D **$24.00**

Richfield Gasoline, sign, Here Soon above close-up profile of race car driver, emblem & car above Richfield below, 55x40", G, A **$175.00**

Richland, crate label, Florida citrus, white heron perched on branch by a river, 9x9", M, C1 .... **$2.00**

Richlube Motor Oil, sign, 1915-25, porcelain, space object & lettering on blue shield in center, yellow ground, Safety..., 24" dia, EX, A $2,000.00

Richmond Straight Cut Cigarettes, sign, paperboard, lady standing left of product name & large box of cigarettes, matted & framed, 15½x12½", EX, A **$150.00**

Richter's Select, label, pre-1920, product name in script, G, A **$20.00**

Rideau Hall Coffee, tin, lettering above & below scenic building, screw lid, round, 1-lb **$175.00**

Ridgeway Tea, tin, square, 8-oz, VG, D **$11.50**

Rieger & Gretz Brewing Co, calendar, 1914, bust-length portrait of a girl in wide-brimmed hat, logo upper left, full pad, framed, 22x16½", EX, A **$450.00**

Riey's Panetelas Cigars, box label, outer, eagle & woman seated on a cloud, 4½x4½", M, C3 .... **$6.00**

Riley's English Toffee, tin, shows children playing, with lid & handle, 4-lb, EX, D3 .... **$145.00**

Rin Tin Tin Dog Supply Center, display, metal, row of hooks holds dog collars at bottom of ad panel featuring Rin Tin Tin in white circle, 8x21", EX, A **$95.00**

Ringed Licorice, sign, paper, child trying to break licorice & content baby chewing on some, product name diagonally, 10x13", EX, A **$450.00**

Ringling Bros, Barnum & Bailey Circus, sign, paper, full-color image of trainers & seals, 2 sections of border missing, 42x28", G, A **$60.00**

Rio Grande Cigars, box labels, inner & outer sample set, 1870s, boating scene, Heppenheimer & Maurer litho, EX, A **$150.00**

Ripple Cigarette Blend, cigarette papers, pictures 5¢ box of tobacco, NM, A **$10.00**

Rippled Wheat, sign, cardboard stand-up, boxer Jack Dempsey posed before red dot advertising Rippled Wheat, 6", EX, A $250.00

Rishwain Special Beer, label, 1933-50, San Francisco Brewing Co, Internal Revenue Tax Paid statement, 11-oz, VG, A **$35.00**

Rising Sun Brewing Co, sign, paper, brew master holding foaming glass of beer, lettering above, framed, image: 23x15", EX, A **$600.00**

Rising Sun Stove Polish, sign, paper, elegant woman above factory scene, muted pastels, framed, image: 28x18", EX+, A **$1,600.00**

Rising Sun Stove Polish, sign, paper, elegant woman leaning on banister surrounded with roses, factory scene beyond, 29x13", VG, A **$850.00**

Rising Sun Stove Polish, sign, paper, elegant woman looking out window at factory, text below, Forbes litho, framed, 29½x18", NM, A **$1,850.00**

Rising Sun Stove Polish, trade card, folder, pictures factory 20 years ago on front, factory in 1881 & owner's mansion inside, EX, A **$35.00**

Ritter Manufacturing Co, tip tray, lady in profile before US flag, Art Metal Signs-Lithographed Boxes lettered on rim, 4½" dia, EX, A **$170.00**

Ritz Beer, label, 1933-50, Schoenhofen Edel Co, Internal Revenue Tax Paid statement, 12-oz, EX, A **$24.00**

Ritz Crackers, charm, 1970s or early 80s, brass-plated replica of Ritz box, 2", EX, A **$12.00**

Ritz Crackers, sign, 1934, paper, pictures box of crackers & a salad, Serve It With Ritz, 10x14", EX, D **$20.00**

Ritz Crackers, tin, 1986, 6¾x4¼", EX, D **$7.00**

Rival Dog Food, bank, tin, VG, D **$14.00**

Rival Peanut Butter, pail, white with Rival Brand in slanted letters above yellow & black circular logo, slip lid & bail, 1-lb, EX, A **$85.00**

River Maid, crate label, California pear, Dutch girl beside canal with windmill, boat sailing past, Lodi, 8x11", EX, G1 .... **$3.00**

Robert Bosch Pro-Action Spark Plugs, sign, embossed tin, large firing spark plug at right of product name, Guaranteed... on yellow, 12x20", VG+, A..........**$110.00**

Robert Burns Cigars, display, die-cut cardboard stand-up of Robert Burns holding box of cigars, 69", EX, A...$100.00

Robert Burns 10¢ Cigars, charger, tin, bust-portrait of Robert Burns & cigar box on Scottish plaid background, 24" dia, EX, A..........**$200.00**

Robert Burns 10¢ Cigars, sign, 1930s, cardboard hanger, oval portrait of Robert Burns with decorative border, 13x10", NM, B1..........**$60.00**

Robert H Graupner's Brewery, calendar, 1908, paper, girl in red dress & feathered hat holding red roses, full pad, framed, 24½x18½", G-, A..........**$800.00**

Robert Smith Ale Brewing Co, sign, tin, tiger bursting through paper, ...Tiger Head Brand, Ales & Stouts, oval, scratches/rust, 23 19½", VG, A..........**$500.00**

Robeson Shur Edge Razor, display case, wall mount, wood with glass front, 18 razors with prices below, Ask the Man Who..., 2½x32½", G, A..........**$1,400.00**

Robin Hood Cigars, box label, inner lid sample, 1800s, gentlemen gathered around table, fancy border, Geo Schlegel litho, EX, A..........**$58.00**

Robin Hood Picnic Beer, label, 1933-36, Robin Hood with bow & arrow, Fontenelle Brewing Co, U-type permit number, 1/2-gal, EX, A..........**$25.00**

Robin Hood Powder Co, can, company name in bold lettering surrounds text & directions for use, red, white & green, 9" dia, VG, A..........**$100.00**

Robinson Crusoe Cigars, box label, inner lid sample, 1870s, round portrait of lady flanked by Robinson Crusoe & Friday, GS Harris litho, EX, A..........**$60.00**

Rochester Brewery, sign, 1890, paper, alliance between German maiden & liberty symbol, men with steins below, framed, image: 32x22", VG, A..........**$450.00**

Rochester Dairy, clock, numbers reverse-painted on outer glass face, lettering reverse-painted on inner illuminated face, 15" dia, EX, A..........**$45.00**

Rock Brand Salmon, can label, view of coastal Washington, M, C3..........**$8.00**

Rock City, thermometer, painted & stenciled tin, When You Have Seen Rock City..., other lettering above & below, 39", G, A..........**$50.00**

Rock Island Plow Co, thermometer, wood with impressed lettering, lacquered finish, Better Farm Implements..., 21", VG+, A..........**$95.00**

Rock Island Railroad, sign, 1901, reverse-painted glass, features Rock Island against the Colorado Rockies, framed, 27x100", G, A..........**$9,000.00**

Rock Island Select Beer, label, 1933-36, product name on triangle in center, Rock Island Brewing Co, U-type permit number, 12-oz, VG, A..........**$10.00**

Rockford Watch, sign, embossed tin, girl holding pocket watch in oval inset surrounded by watches, True Time... below, 17x23", G-, A..........**$275.00**

Rockford Watches, pin tray, 1890, Rockford Watches on emblem above elegant lady seated before tree, fluted edge, round corners, EX+, D..........**$70.00**

Rockwood & Co's Breakfast Cocoa, tin, lion & lettering on paper label, slip lid, 4¼x3¼", EX+, A..........**$65.00**

Rocky Ford Cigar, sign, paper, Indian overlooking canyon flanked by 5¢, matted & framed, image: 21x26½", EX+, A..........**$200.00**

Rodeo, crate label, Washington apple, cowboy on bucking pinto horse kicking up dust, 9x11", EX, G1..........**$6.00**

Rodeo Lager Beer, label, 1933-50, Monterey Brewing Co, Internal Revenue Tax Paid, 11-oz, EX, A..........$31.00

Roe Feeds, sign, painted tin, red & white feed bag on green, vertical with rounded corners, EX, A..........**$110.00**

Roehrich & Raab Keystone Brewery, sign, paper, man & woman on bench with parasol sampling products, scuffing/soiling, framed, image: 20x15", EX, A..........**$850.00**

Roelof's Hats, pocket mirror, countryside billboard featuring Get Under A Roelofs & Smile, horizontal oval, 2¾", EX, A..........**$45.00**

Roerich & Raab Brewers, sign, paper, young couple with foaming stein of beer in oval inset surrounded by flowers, framed, image: 23x17", EX, A..........**$500.00**

Roesch's Old Master Beer, label, 1933-36, U-type permit number, 62-oz, EX, A..........**$15.00**

Roessle Brewery, sign, paper, factory insets surrounded by hops & leaves, Brewers & Bottlers Of Premium..., framed, image: 28x20", NM, A..........**$650.00**

Roha's Milk, thermometer, wood, brown lettering on white bottle shape, elongated diamond logo below, 7¼", VG, A **$35.00**

Rohrers Liquor Store, shot glass, etched letters, ...24 Center Street, Lancaster Pa, EX, D **$12.00**

Roi-Tan Cigars, sign, cardboard, couple reminiscing in front of fireplace, The Same Old Love below, framed, image: 30x39", EX, A **$225.00**

Rold Gold Butter Pretzels, jigsaw puzzle, 1931, boy, girl & dog eating from box of pretzels while playing on floor, 8x10", EX, F1 .... $85.00

Ronz Beer, label, Columbus Brewing, 1-qt, EX, A **$27.00**

Roosevelt 5¢ Cigar, sign, embossed self-framed tin, oval portrait of Teddy Roosevelt, DB Long & Son Makers, 19½x13½", EX, A $13,000.00

Rosa de Oro, crate label, California orange, fancy lettering above oranges & rose, view of ranch, Thermalito, 10x11", EX, G1 .... **$20.00**

Rosa Moro Cigars, box label, inner lid, lady in oval flanked by lions, Rosa Moro on banner below, Mild Tampa Cigar, 6x9", EX, D **$7.00**

Rosary Chocolates, pocket mirror, product name above box of candy with rose, Mueller-Keller Candy Company below, 2¼" dia, VG+, A **$15.00**

Rose & Co, sign, paperboard, smartly dressed couple featuring man above company name & address, damaged corners, 21½x9", VG, A **$80.00**

Rose Leaf Fine Cut Tobacco, plate, Majolica, Chew Rose Leaf Fine Cut lettered at left of 3-D wild-rose pattern, rare, 9" dia, EX, A **$225.00**

Rose of America Cigars, box label, inner lid sample, 1880s, profile of lady in bonnet flanked by roses & figures, Witsch & Schmidt litho, EX, A **$42.00**

Rose Pears, crate label, pink roses with green leaves on dark blue, white logo, Wenatchee Ca, 8x11", G1 .. **$3.00**

Roseco Evaporated Milk, can label, pictures brown cow beside milking stool & bucket & red rose, M, C1 .... **$2.00**

Rosenbaum Co Gas Iron, pocket mirror, lady ironing with lettering around rim, 2⅛" dia, EX, A **$600.00**

Roth's Pilsener Beer, label, 1933-36, Roth Brewing Co, U-type permit number, 12-oz, VG, A **$21.00**

Rothschild Bros Hat Co, sign, cardboard, 1920s man in hat & suit with busy street scene beyond, company name & Star Hats below, 16x12", NM, A **$75.00**

Rough Rider Baking Powder, tin, round with paper label featuring a roughrider soldier on horse waving his hat, slip lid, 3¾x2" dia, EX, A **$60.00**

Round Robin Pears, crate label, 1930s, pictures large robin on purple background, Medford Ore, 7½x11", M, C3 .... **$4.50**

Round Trip Smoking Tobacco, lunch pail, circular image of a cruise ship flanked by Cut Plug, rectangular shape, EX, A **$225.00**

Roxbury Rye, sign, 1905-1910, cardboard, product name above Uncle Sam pointing to bottle, America's Purest Whiskey, 41x31", NM, S5 .... **$1,350.00**

Royal '400' Gasoline, thermometer, wood, red & green on white, Red Hat circle logo above, Use Royal '400'... below, keyhole shape, 21", G+, A **$170.00**

Royal Baking Co, recipe book, 1913, packed with old-time recipes, 48 pages, EX, D **$6.00**

Royal Baking Powder, box, wood, black lettering on sides, paper labels on ends with can in oval, product name above & below, 9x15x8", VG, A **$20.00**

Royal Baking Powder, recipe book, 1902, 'Royal Baker & Pastry Cook,' oval image of woman taking rolls out of oven, EX, D $16.00

Royal Baking Powder, recipe book, 1932, 45 pages, EX, D **$7.00**

Royal Baking Powder, recipe book, 1937, blue & red cover, 64 pages, G, D **$8.00**

Royal Baking Powder, recipe book, 1941, 'A Guide to Royal Success in Baking,' 22 pages, G, D **$3.50**

Royal Baking Powder, tin, 1938, 12-oz, VG, D **$16.50**

Royal Banner Cigars, sign, tin litho, cigar box displayed over crossed flags, lettering above & below, chips/creases, 23¾x17½", VG+ A **$175.00**

Royal Beer, mug, stoneware, transfer print with motto on reverse, crazing, 3¾", G-, A **$25.00**

Royal Bengals Cigars, trolley sign, 1919-22, cardboard, woman holding cigar box beside large box, Quality, Economy..., 11x21", VG, A **$40.00**

Royal Blue Cigars, box label, outer, eagle above US civil war generals, 4½x4½", M, C3 .... **$18.00**

Royal Blue Selz Shoe, sign, acid-etched & reverse-painted glass, blue, white & silver, framed, image: 16x20", VG, A **$200.00**

Royal Bock Beer, label, 1933-50, Central Breweries Inc, Internal Revenue Tax Paid, 12-oz, VG, A **$10.00**

Royal Crown Cola, ashtray, reverse-painted glass, 3x3", G, D **$22.00**

Royal Crown Cola, bottle, 1971, clear with red & white label, 10-oz, EX, D **$4.50**

Royal Crown Cola, calendar, 1955, woman holding RC bottle & young couple in circular inset behind her, full pad, framed, 25x12½", VG, A **$30.00**

Royal Crown Cola, calendar top, features June Haver with bottle leaning against phonograph, rectangular logo lower right, EX, A **$35.00**

Royal Crown Cola, can, pictures Archie Manning, series #8, EX, D **$3.50**

Royal Crown Cola, can, pictures Bobby Grich, series #1, EX, D **$3.50**

Royal Crown Cola, clock, glass, metal frame, 12-3-6-9 with crowns surround RC diamond logo on dot, round, EX, D **$230.00**

Royal Crown Cola, cooler, 1950s, painted yellow metal with embossed logo, Art Deco design on sides, bottle opener on side, 17x13", VG, D **$65.00**

Royal Crown Cola, decal, product name above tilted bottle over sun rays, 12x7", NM, A **$22.00**

Royal Crown Cola, display, die-cut cardboard stand-up, June Mayer seated in green swimsuit says RC Tastes Best, 37x26", VG+, M3 .... **$155.00**

Royal Crown Cola, playing cards, G, D **$15.00**

Royal Crown Cola, scale, 1950s, bottle shape with platform at bottom, drop coins in cap, 45½", EX, A **$1,900.00**

Royal Crown Cola, sign, cardboard, girl in white tennis sweater with bottle left of 6-pack, You'll Flip At The Zzzip..., 22x34", VG+, M3 .... **$30.00**

Royal Crown Cola, sign, cardboard, Go Fresher...Go RC on white panel above girl in swing with 6-pack & can, 22x34", EX+, M3 .... **$30.00**

Royal Crown Cola, sign, cardboard, 1940s, batboy with bats & bottle of RC cheering on his team, 11x28", EX+, D... **$40.00**

Royal Crown Cola, sign, cardboard, 1940s, factory worker having lunch & bottle of RC, 11x28", EX, D **$36.00**

Royal Crown Cola, sign, cardboard, 1940s, girl drinking bottle of RC while talking on the phone, 11x28", EX+, D **$40.00**

Royal Crown Cola, sign, cardboard, 1940s, Santa Claus with bottle of RC in winter scene, 11x28", EX+, D **$40.00**

Royal Crown Cola, sign, cardboard, 1948, couple raiding fridge, RC-Best Home Treat!, 11x28", NM, D **$80.00**

Royal Crown Cola, sign, cardboard, 1948, pictures Barbara Stanwyck with bottle of RC, RC Tastes Best!..., 11x28", EX, D **$80.00**

Royal Crown Cola, sign, cardboard cutout, 1930, bottle shape, 30x8", NM, B1 .... **$20.00**

Royal Crown Cola, sign, flange, stenciled lettering, ...Best By Taste-Test, green, red, yellow & blue, 10½x17½", EX, A **$120.00**

Royal Crown Cola, sign, paper, little boy on swim board, Here's Your RC Swim Board above 6-pack & lettering, 22x17", NM, B1 .... **$12.00**

Royal Crown Cola, sign, tin, copyright 1936, die-cut bottle, 11½", EX, A $125.00

Royal Crown Cola, sign, tin, yellow & white on red, Drink..., Best By Taste Test left of bottle on white oval, 12x28", NM, M3 .... **$85.00**

Royal Crown Cola, syrup dispenser, yellow with red labels, Drink Royal Crown Cola... in yellow & cream, 1 label mostly missing, 14", VG, A **$25.00**

Royal Crown Cola, thermometer, 1952, tin, thermometer degrees on yellow arrow, lettering above & below, overall scratches, 26x10", A **$45.00**

Royal Crown Cola, thermometer, 1954, tin, embossed, ...Best By Taste-Test lettered above bulb & bottle, minor rust, A **$65.00**

Royal Crown Cola, thermometer/barometer, mirrored top with thermometer & barometer, Drink..., Best By Taste-Test below, 24x12", VG+, A **$250.00**

Royal Dragon Cigars, box label, inner lid, pictures a small red dragon, black & bronze, 6x9", M, C3 .... **$12.00**

Royal Dutch Coffee, tin, screw lid, round, 1-lb, EX, A..... **$80.00**

Royal Gelatine, bank, 1970s, molded vinyl, King Royal on round base, 10", M, D **$55.00**

Royal Gelatine, recipe book, 1940, 'Royal Desserts Recipes,' pictures Ginger Rogers on cover, 22 pages, EX, D.. **$10.00**

Royal Gelatine, recipe book, 1942, 'Royal Recipe Parade,' 48 pages, EX, D **$6.50**

Royal Insurance Co, sign, wood, gold company name on red crest with crown, Agency Of The Leading Fire Co... above, framed, 31x22", VG, A **$80.00**

Royal Palm, crate label, Florida citrus, palm trees & swamps, 9x9", M, C3 .... **$5.00**

Royal Patent Flour, sign, tin over cardboard, Nickel-Plate Milling Co above product name in filigreed emblem, framed, 11¼x11¼", VG+, A **$50.00**

Royal Pride Coffee, tin, ca 1910, paper label with ornate lettering, Levering Coffee Co, 1-lb, VG, H1 .... **$32.00**

Royal Purple Poultry Conditioner, tin, Royal Purple above oval inset, chicken images atop Poultry Conditioner, pry lid, round corners, 8x6x6", VG, M2 .... **$30.00**

Royal Purple Stock Conditioner, tin, Royal Purple above circular inset of factory atop Stock Conditioner emblem, pry lid, round corners, 8x6x6", NM, M2 .... **$55.00**

Royal Queen Brand Coffee, tin, product name above Queen holding tray with coffeepot on paper label, pry lid, 1-lb, EX, A **$45.00**

Royal Scarlet Canned Goods, pin-back button, ca 1896, multicolored, scuffs at bottom edge, D **$4.00**

Royal Shield Ceylon & India Tea, tin, embossed multicolored graphics on blue ground, 9x9x5", VG, M2 .... **$35.00**

Royal Shield Cloves, tin, red, white, blue & gold, vertical rectangle, EX+, M2 .... **$9.00**

Royal Stock Cigars, box label, inner lid, 1902, pictures crowned bull, 6x9", M, C3 .... **$50.00**

Royal Stock Cigars, box label, inner lid sample, 1880s, stately lion overlooking landscape, Witsch & Schmidt litho, EX, A **$286.00**

Royal Style Ale, calendar, 1935, Indian princess picking water lilies, Globe Brewing Co, full pad, framed, image: 28x14", NM, A **$425.00**

Royal Tailors, sign, reverse-painted glass, reclining tiger with green clouds in background, illumated metal case, 19½" long, EX, A **$375.00**

Royal 76 Gasoline, pump sign, porcelain, white with blue Royal above orange 76, blue Gasoline below, orange border, 11½" dia, EX, D **$65.00**

Royal 76 Gasoline, pump sign, porcelain, white with blue Royal above orange 76, blue Gasoline below, orange border, 11½" dia, EX+, A **$80.00**

Royaline Gasoline, sign, porcelain, 2-sided, blue & black on white, product name around R&C logo, Penn...Motor Oils..., 30" dia, EX, A **$1,400.00**

Royalty Club Whiskey, sign, gold glittery lettering on green, product name lettered diagonally, company name below, framed, 21x31", EX, A **$80.00**

Royalty Club Whiskey, sign, reverse-painted glass, barrel logo above Royalty Club in script, A Friedman Co, framed, 18x28", NM, D **$250.00**

Royster Fertilizers, calendar, 1949, baby girl with segmented wooden doll, signed Charlotte Becker, full pad, 8x4¾", NM, H1 .... **$16.00**

RPM Motor Oil, sign, porcelain, white with 100% Pure Paraffin Base Motor Oil lettered around RPM on red swirling circle, 28" dia, NM, A **$275.00**

RPM Motor Oil, sign, tin, pictures Donald Duck throwing a punch at a snowman, A Knockout For Winter above, 23½" dia, EX+, A $1,200.00

Rubon Polish, tin, 1920s woman cleaning, EX, D **$45.00**

Rubsam & Horrmann Atlantic Brewery, sign, paper, 3 men & maid sampling brew with factory scene beyond, matted & framed, image: 15x11", VG, A **$50.00**

Ruff Brewing Co, tray, stock image of tavern scene with monks playing cards, ...Quincy Ill on rim, oval, 16¾x13¾", VG, A **$200.00**

Ruff-Riedel Lager Beer, label, 1933-50, R logo above product name in script, Internal Revenue Tax Paid statement, 12-oz, VG, A **$14.00**

Ruff-Stuff Sandpaper, display, painted metal, slanted rectangle with 8 compartments, advertising on top & front panels, 23x12x14", EX, A **$100.00**

Ruger Firearms, calendar, 1979, 30th anniversary, scene of hunting moose in a canoe, full pad, EX, A **$65.00**

Ruhstaller Lager & Gilt Edge Steam Beer, tray, factory scene, floral design on rim, rare, oval, heavy wear, 13¾x16¾", G-, A **$100.00**

Ruhstaller's Beer, tray, deep-dish, girl holding dove, lettering on rim, overall scratches/minor dents, 12¼" dia, G-, A **$85.00**

Ruhstaller's Gilt Edge Beer, sign, 1912, self-framed tin, 'The Cockfight,' 2 elderly men watching cocks fighting, American Art Works, 24x20", EX, A **$880.00**

Ruhstaller's Gilt Edge Beer, tray, 1910-15, exterior scene of man pouring beer for 2 ladies in open touring car, round corners, 13¼x13¼", EX, A **$210.00**

Ruhstaller's Gilt Edge Lager Beer, sign, cardboard, pictures early gold miners panning for gold, Favorite Of The West..., framed, image: 19x14", NM, A **$500.00**

Ruhstaller's Gilt Edge Lager Beer, tip tray, lady in orange, lettering on decorative rim edged in blue, California Invites..., crazing, 4⅜" dia, EX, A **$260.00**

Ruhstaller's Lager, tip tray, barmaid carrying flagons with product name on apron, Best Beer Brewed... on rim, 4¼" dia, EX, A **$225.00**

Rumford Baking Powder, recipe book, 1907, 'Rumford, the Wholesome Baking Powder,' pictures girl holding wheat stalks, EX, D **$16.00**

Rumford Baking Powder, recipe book, 1919, 'Cakes & Cookies,' 16 pages, EX, D **$8.00**

Rumford Baking Powder, recipe book, 1929, 'Several New Things Under the Sun,' 12 pages, G-, D **$5.00**

Rumley Plowing & Threshing Co, hatpin, ca 1900, factory scene, 2½" long, VG, D **$8.50**

Rummy, display, die-cut cardboard stand-up, beach beauty next to large bottle, Rummy on panel below, 12x8", NM, M3 .... **$75.00**

Rummy, sign, cardboard stand-up, couple drinking from 2 straws in 1 bottle flanked by lemons, Get Chummy, NM, M3 .... **$35.00**

Rummy Grapefruit Mixer, sign, tin, Enriched With Vitamin B1 & A Delicious Drink above & below product name on yellow, 6x9", NM, M3 .... **$55.00**

Runkel Brothers Breakfast Cocoa, sign, paper, elegant couple outdoors being served by butler, child in foreground, matted & framed, image: 24x18", EX, A **$700.00**

Runkel Brothers Cocoa & Chocolate, trade card, girl looking through curtain with cup of cocoa, product name above & below, EX, A **$34.00**

Runkel Brothers Cocoa & Chocolate, trade card, maid pouring cocoa surrounded by floral border, product name above & below, EX, A **$32.00**

Runkel's Cocoa, recipe book, 1920s illustrations, 24 pages, EX, D **$4.00**

Runkel's Cocoa, sample tin, slip lid, square shape with rounded corners, EX, A **$65.00**

Runkel's Highest Grade Cocoa, pocket mirror, shows pretty lass in red with arm raised holding can of cocoa, oval, 2¾", EX, A **$1,000.00**

Ruppenthal Hardware, calendar, 1933, cardboard, evening scene with mother, child & dog, 17x10", EX, D **$24.00**

Ruppert Beer & Ale, coaster, cardboard, pictures 2 hands holding large mugs of beer, 4½" dia, NM, D **$7.00**

Ruppert Beer & Ale, foam scraper/holder, red plastic glass set into yellow catalin holder, 7x5½x4¾", EX, A **$40.00**

Rusco Brake Lining, jigsaw puzzle, 1933, couple hangs from limbs after being thrown from car stopped at edge of cliff, 9x11", EX, F1 .... $40.00

Rusco FF Engineered Clutch Facing, sign, tin, Rusco above round logo flanked by Fused Fabric & Clutch Facings with diagonal line, 17½x23¼", EX, A **$40.00**

Russells' Ales, sign, self-framed tin, Russells' Ales lettered above 2 men unloading barrels, simulated wood frame, 29x21", VG, A **$160.00**

Ryan Ginger Ale, bottle topper, die-cut cardboard, hand holding glass & product name in decorative border, NM, B1 .... **$4.00**

Ryan's Jet Hi-Test, gas globe, 1932-40, glass, product name in blue shield outline, red & blue lettering, 15" dia, EX, A $110.00

Ryan's Pure Beers, pocket mirror, head portrait of Syracuse Indian in profile, product name & address circles banded rim, 2⅛" dia, EX, A **$350.00**

S

S Bolton's Sons Beer, tray, interior scene with monks, ...Troy, NY on fancy rim, oval, dents/chips/scratches, 15¼x18¾", G, A **$70.00**

S Herbert Adams Taxidermist, business card, 1860-70, ...Fitchburg, Mass, VG, A **$20.00**

S Richard Hall's Quality Ice Cream, globe, lettered milk glass, 2-sided, 12½" dia, EX, A **$190.00**

S&H Green Stamps, clock, electric, wood frame, round white face on dark green above We Give..., 23x15", EX+, A **$75.00**

S&M Smoking Tobacco, pail, pictures man in top hat & lettering on paper label, slip lid & bail, EX+, A ... **$40.00**

Sabo Coffee, pin-back button, ca 1900, red logo on black & white, EX, D **$5.00**

Safe Hit, crate label, 1940s, Texas Vegetables, Gulf Distributing Co, Weslaco, 9x7", M, C3 .... **$3.00**

Safeway, emblem, embossed porcelain, stylized S, 18" dia, M, D **$85.00**

Sagamore Salmon, can label, pictures Indian chief & salmon, Chinook Wash, M, C1 .... **$2.00**

Sailor Boy Oysters, tin, Sailor Boy lettered diagonally above his image in dancing position over 5 wavy lines around can, 1-gal, EX, A **$45.00**

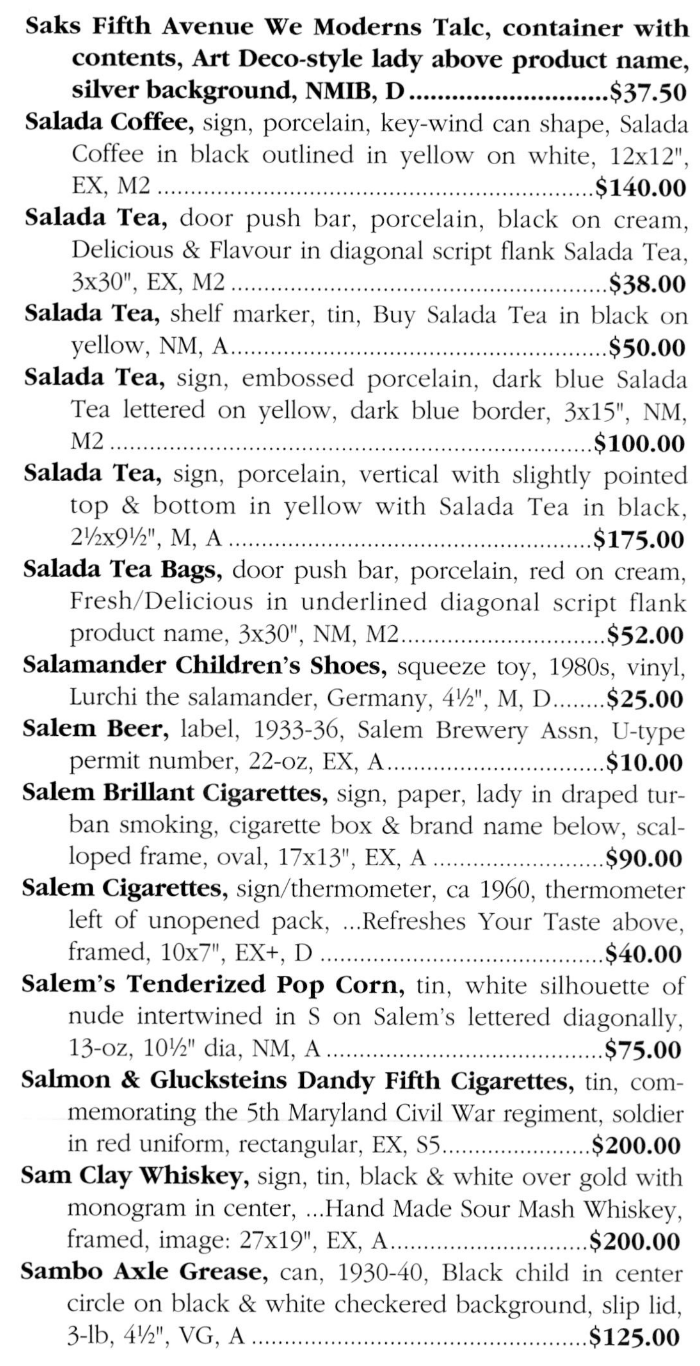

Saks Fifth Avenue We Moderns Talc, container with contents, Art Deco-style lady above product name, silver background, NMIB, D $37.50

Salada Coffee, sign, porcelain, key-wind can shape, Salada Coffee in black outlined in yellow on white, 12x12", EX, M2 ....**$140.00**

Salada Tea, door push bar, porcelain, black on cream, Delicious & Flavour in diagonal script flank Salada Tea, 3x30", EX, M2 ....**$38.00**

Salada Tea, shelf marker, tin, Buy Salada Tea in black on yellow, NM, A..**$50.00**

Salada Tea, sign, embossed porcelain, dark blue Salada Tea lettered on yellow, dark blue border, 3x15", NM, M2 ....**$100.00**

Salada Tea, sign, porcelain, vertical with slightly pointed top & bottom in yellow with Salada Tea in black, 2½x9½", M, A **$175.00**

Salada Tea Bags, door push bar, porcelain, red on cream, Fresh/Delicious in underlined diagonal script flank product name, 3x30", NM, M2..............................**$52.00**

Salamander Children's Shoes, squeeze toy, 1980s, vinyl, Lurchi the salamander, Germany, 4½", M, D........**$25.00**

Salem Beer, label, 1933-36, Salem Brewery Assn, U-type permit number, 22-oz, EX, A................................**$10.00**

Salem Brillant Cigarettes, sign, paper, lady in draped turban smoking, cigarette box & brand name below, scalloped frame, oval, 17x13", EX, A **$90.00**

Salem Cigarettes, sign/thermometer, ca 1960, thermometer left of unopened pack, ...Refreshes Your Taste above, framed, 10x7", EX+, D **$40.00**

Salem's Tenderized Pop Corn, tin, white silhouette of nude intertwined in S on Salem's lettered diagonally, 13-oz, 10½" dia, NM, A **$75.00**

Salmon & Glucksteins Dandy Fifth Cigarettes, tin, commemorating the 5th Maryland Civil War regiment, soldier in red uniform, rectangular, EX, S5......................**$200.00**

Sam Clay Whiskey, sign, tin, black & white over gold with monogram in center, ...Hand Made Sour Mash Whiskey, framed, image: 27x19", EX, A.............................**$200.00**

Sambo Axle Grease, can, 1930-40, Black child in center circle on black & white checkered background, slip lid, 3-lb, 4½", VG, A **$125.00**

Samoset Chocolates, banner, cloth, product name lettered on canoe with Indian chief, Chief Of Them All, company name below, 29x47", EX, D3..$450.00

Samoset Chocolates, display, plaster, figural piece with Indian in canoe on marked base, signed Ferrington Elwolf, 11x37", EX, A...**$550.00**

Samoset Chocolates, plaque, embossed cast iron, round with product lettering on rim around Indian in canoe, 18" dia, EX, A **$275.00**

Samoset Chocolates, pocket mirror, Indian in canoe encircled by product name, 2¼" dia, EX, A **$1,350.00**

Samoset Chocolates, sign, plaster, 3-D, Indian in canoe flanked by Trade Mark, minor flaking to surface, 20" dia, G, A..**$95.00**

Samoset Chocolates, sign, porcelain, Indian in canoe at left of Agency Samoset, blue background, overall touchup, 14x36", VG, A **$525.00**

Sampson Carriage Jack, trade card, 1875, text over product, brown, EX, A..**$80.00**

Samuel Rosenthal & Bros, watch fob, 1890s, embossed image of boy holding up trousers, G, D..............**$35.00**

San-Cura Ointment, sign, early 1900s, die-cut hand wrapped with lettered bandage, Cures Cuts, Burns, Bruises..., 7", NM, B1 ....**$20.00**

San-Cura Ointment, sign, die-cut cardboard stand-up, features large bandaged hand with advertising, ...Cures Cuts, Burns..., 8x7", NM, A **$18.00**

San-Cura Ointment, sign, paper, 5 hand images listing the virtues of San-Cura Ointment, wood frame, 38x5", EX, A...**$85.00**

San Diego Brewing Co, label, 1933-50, Internal Revenue Tax Paid statement, 11-oz, EX, A **$25.00**

San Felice Cigar, match safe, ca 1925, metal with celluloid oval insert, man sees lady in his cigar smoke, hinged lid, EX+, D **$390.00**

San Felice Cigar, sign, embossed tin, red & yellow, 11x23", EX, D...**$45.00**

San Luis Artichoke, crate label, artichoke field on blue background, M, C3 ....**$6.00**

San Marto Coffee, tin, pictures knight on horse, lettering above & below, screw lid, 1-lb, EX, A **$110.00**

Sanchez & Haya Havana Cigars, sign, reverse-painted glass, product name above & below various cigar seals, framed, image: 24x36", G, A..............................**$200.00**

Sander's Satin Candies, pail, 1930s-40s, pictures children in various play scenes, bail handle, lid missing, 2 1/2-lb, 5½", EX, A $40.00
Sandwich Manufacturing Co, trade card, pictures a hay rake, Clean Sweep Hay Loader lettered in upper left, VG, A $16.00
Sandy Hill Iron & Brass Works, print, bust portrait of dark-haired girl within wood-grained oval matt, gold product lettering lower right, 29x24", M, A $500.00
Sanford's Ginger, sign, paper, Black boy sitting beside watermelon holding large bottle, framed, image: 28½x21½", EX, A $3,250.00
Sanford's Inks, display cabinet, gold-leafed wood & glass, shelves missing, 36x22x9½", VG, A $500.00
Sanford's Inks, display cabinet, oak trapezoid frame with glass panels, decaled sides with gold lettering on front, 16x14x11", VG+, A $230.00
Sanford's Inks & Mucilage, sign, tin flange, pictures various bottles & jars, Faultless!..., overall chipping & wear, 13½x20", G-, A $500.00
Sanford's Inks & Pastes, jar, stoneware, blue bands & lettering, bail handle, no top, EX, A $45.00
Sanspariel Vinegar, trade card, young boy in sailor suit, 4x6", VG, D $4.00
Santa Claus Soap, shipping crate, wood, Santa Claus Gifts..., end label pictures Santa carrying tree, NK Fairbank Co, 10x21x14", G, A $225.00
Santa Claus Soap, sign, paper, little girl with doll sitting in front of Santa, tears/paper loss, original frame, 36x20", G-, A $1,400.00

Santa Maria, crate label, 1940s, California vegetables, Rosemary Packing Corporation, Santa Maria Cal, 11½x7¼", M, C3 ....$3.00
Santa Wood's Boston Coffee, trade card, Santa Claus in balloon with lots of toys, full moon in the sky, 5¼x3", EX, D $15.00
Santovin, sign, tin, Santovin above sun rising over field of sheep & list of many cures, Stephen Pettifer & Sons, framed, 27x20", G+, A $110.00
Santox Talc, tin, pictures a nurse, EX, D $100.00

Sapolin, sign, canvasboard, Washington flanked by Lincoln & Roosevelt in ovals, frame gilded with Sapolin gold, 14x21", EX, A $65.00
Sapolin No 124 Hot Pipe Aluminum, display, cast-iron stove on tin litho base advertising heat-resistant paint, 9x12x5", VG, A $743.00
Saratoga Natural Mineral Waters, thermometer, wood, pictures a bottle & green lettering, round top & square bottom, 23½", EX, A $95.00
Satin Luminall One Coat Interior Paint, thermometer, painted metal, round top & bottom with product name above, paint can below, 39x8", EX, A $35.00
Satin Skin Powder & Cream, sign, copyright 1903, paper, yellow field with black lettering above & below lady with fan & products, 43x28", EX, A $30.00
Saturday Evening Post, sign, cardboard, thinking man & cavalier flank Laugh! With Octavus Roy Cohen This Week...5¢, 10x13", VG, A $90.00

Sauer's Pure Vanilla, thermometer, wood, shaped as box of vanilla, allover advertising, vertical, EX, M1 ....$575.00
Savage Arms Co, postcard, 1919, colorful factory view, scarce, used, VG, A $30.00
Savage Arms Co, stickpin, Indian in full headdress, on original card, EX, A $120.00
Savage Rifles, catalog, 1905, Indian with rifle on front cover, well designed pages with various game in each corner, 48 pages, EX, A $120.00
Savage Rifles, pocket catalog, 1923, hunter standing over wounded bear, includes original mailing envelope, 32 pages, EX, A $45.00
Savage-Stevens-Fox, display, wood, 4 simulated rifles mounted as floor-type rack, holds 8 guns, EX, A $325.00
Savoy Asparagus, can label, 1923, bundle of asparagus & coat-of-arms, EX, C3 ....$7.00
Sawyer's Crystal Blue Dye, sign, paper, oval image of woman in admiral's uniform holding package of dye, trimmed top & bottom, 22x17½", G-, A $95.00

Sawyer's Slickers, sign, die-cut cardboard, girl in slicker & hat holding apple & school books with advertising lower left, 30x18", EX+, A.......$1,350.00

Sayman's Vegetable Wonder Soap, sign, cardboard, pictures man & large vegetable plant, ...Lathers At A Touch, white & green ground, 20x14", EX, D................................**$35.00**

Scarlet Crown Cigars, box label, inner lid, pictures a lion & large crown, 6x9", M, D....................................**$12.00**

Sceptre Pears, can label, white lettering on green background, Selma Canning Co, Cal, G1 ....**$6.00**

Schaefer Beer, bar sign, On Sunday, 11x14", G+, A .**$35.00**

Schaefer Beer, sign, light-up, Take Home Department on zigzag ribbon left of Schaefer Beer on red emblem, 12x26", NM, M3 ....**$65.00**

Schaefer Beer, table display, woman's gloved arm extended to hold bottle or glass, marked F&M Schaefer Brewing Co, NY #455, P4.....................................**$45.00**

Schaefer Beer, tray, red with white lettering, 12" dia, G, D...**$10.00**

Schaeffer Pianos, pocket mirror, product name lettered above piano flanked by more lettering, scratches, 2¼" dia, G, A...**$20.00**

Schaut's Bus & Taxi Lines, sign, glass, early bus image above company name, VG Schaut Prop, Ask The Clerk below, small, EX, M1 ....**$300.00**

Scheidt Brewing Co, sign with attached 1900 calendar, paper, multiple vignettes, Norristown Pa, USA below, framed, image: 29½x20", EX, A...........................**$800.00**

Schell's Quality Seed, catalog, 1925, 81 pages, EX, D..**$16.00**

Schenck's Mandrake Pills, sign, ca 1880, tin, oval portrait of Dr Schenck flanked by lettered bands, Indian beyond, framed, image: 28x22", G-, A................**$900.00**

Schenck's Pulmonic Syrup, sign, tin, small butterfly in center, ...A Positive Cure For Consumption, framed, image: 14x20", G, A **$550.00**

Schenley's Red Label Blended Whiskey, sign, 1933, aluminum over pressed wood, red, silver & black, Jos Finch & Co, VG, D **$75.00**

Schepps Old Fashioned Ale, label, 1933-36, U-type permit number, 12-oz, EX, A...**$36.00**

Schilling's Nicolet Coffee, tin, paper label with medieval graphics & lettering, pry lid, 1-lb, EX, A..............**$48.00**

Schimmel's Fruit Preserves, trade card, coated stock, lettering superimposed over various fruits, VG, A **$12.00**

Schinasi Bros Natural Cigarettes, sign, paperboard, close-up of Arab & white horse with lettering above & in lower left corner, framed, 23x16", VG+, A.....**$100.00**

Schlitz, can, 1960s, metal, Mfg Kramer Products lettered on top seal, VG, P4..**$4.00**

Schlitz, glass, 8-oz, D **$4.00**

Schlitz, sign, cardboard, diagonal factory scene with fairy above, draped nude atop globe lower right, gold trim, 33x45", NM, A **$2,200.00**

Schlitz, sign, embossed tin litho, tan lettering on brown & blue background, bottle left of Schlitz label, 11½x23½", G+, A..**$120.00**

Schlitz, sign, 1920s-30s, tin, oval image of girl holding beer bottle, red letters, gold label below, 24x21", VG, A $325.00

Schlitz, soda jerk's hat, 1974, paper, brown on white, adjustable, EX, D **$4.00**

Schlitz, stained glass window, belted banner through world globe with ornate curly-Q surround, wood frame, 31½x58", G-, A $1,000.00

Schlitz, stein, 1970s, Chicago Fire, MIB, D.................**$75.00**

Schlitz, stein, 1974, 125th Anniversary, pictures the brewery, 7¾", M, D **$125.00**

Schlitz, tray, yellow & white, Real Gusto, 13" dia, EX, D..**$25.00**

Schlitz, tray, 1900-10, man & woman drinking with blacksmith working behind them, large bottle in background, 24" dia, VG, A **$650.00**

Schlitz Light Beer, plaque, 1976, plastic with logo & lettering, 12" dia, EX, P4 .... **$5.00**
Schlitz Malt Syrup, sign, ca 1928, tin, pictures product, Schlitz in script above Famous Malt Syrup, nail holes at corners, 12x24", EX, A **$145.00**
Schmidt & Sons Puritan Beer, goblet, etched glass, Puritan Beer in script above logo, company name below, 6½", EX, S5 .... **$60.00**
Schmidt's Beer, sign, embossed tin under black-painted glass, ...Quality Since 1860, 21x21", G-, A **$50.00**
Schmidt's City Club Beer, sign, embossed tin, yellow, white & maroon, product name encircled by 3-lined border, NM, B1 .... **$60.00**
Schmidt's Dunklbrau Beer, label, 1933-36, Jacob Schmidt Brewing, U-type permit number, 24-oz, VG, A **$20.00**
Schneider's Beer, tray, portrait of Admiral Dewey, patriotic design around border, minor dents/chips, 12" dia, G, A **$150.00**
Schneider's Brewery, sign, paper, woman in profile with red rose in her hair, lettering above, framed, image: 20x15", EX, A **$400.00**
Schobers Export Beer, tip tray, product name lettered at right of seated lady holding dove, leaf border, 5" dia, VG+, A **$150.00**
Schoenling Beer, label, 1933-36, Cincinnati's Finest..., U-type permit number, 12-oz, EX, A **$42.00**
Scholl's Axle Grease, pail, 1935-45, tin, pictures horse & wagon, product name in red on black, slip lid, 6½x5¾" dia, EX, A **$35.00**
Schooner Brew, label, product name on diagonal center band, National Beverage Co below, EX, A **$13.00**
Schrader Tire Gauges, display, die-cut tin tire gauge, paper inserts inside & numerous valve covers, 15", VG+, A **$176.00**
Schrafft's Chocolate, sign, 1903, paper, Schrafft's Chocolate Girl with red bow in her hair, original frame, 29½x23¼", G+, A **$100.00**
Schrafft's Ice Cream, clock, light-up, blue & red on white, Schrafft's Ice Cream bordered with blue line left of clock, 12x26", NM, M3 .... **$55.00**
Schubert Piano, trade card, mechanical, woman's arms come down to play piano as card is opened, colorful, EX, A **$85.00**
Schwarzeneach Beer, tray, deep-dish, bust-length portrait of girl wearing yellow dress, lettering on rim, 13" dia, EX, A **$550.00**
Schweppes Dry Ginger Ale, door push bar, tin, Ask For...Dry Ginger Ale in white, Schweppes in yellow on green, edge chips, M2 .... **$40.00**
Score Card Cigars, tin, paper label, product name on diagonal band across score card graphic, A Big Hit below, 5x4" dia, EX, A **$325.00**
Scott's Emulsion, booklet, colorful alphabet, poetry & views of children, 16 pages, 4x6", EX, P1 .... **$15.00**
Scott's Emulsion, trade card, patriotic twins standing on product boxes, EX, A **$28.00**
Scott's Emulsion, trade card, pictures little boy in highchair reaching for product, He Wants It lettered above, EX, A **$19.00**

Scott's Emulsion, trolley sign, 1920, baseball player & product flank Keep Your Boy In The Game...Promotes... Growth, framed, 12x24", VG+, D3 .. $375.00
Scovill's Sarsaparilla, trade card, pictures maiden with scrofula, opens to show her beautiful & cured, EX, A ... **$13.00**
Scudder's Brownie Brand Confection Butter, pail, lettered graphics flanked by figures, blue, yellow & red, press lid & bail, heat damage/wear, 3½", G-, A ... **$20.00**

Scuffy Shoe Polish, box with contents, Mickey Mouse atop Scuffy lettered on white in red circle, ...Brushless Ox-Blood, 5x2", EX, D $30.00
Sculptor Cigars, box label, outer, marble bust of a bearded man, 4½x4½", M, C3 .... **$15.00**
Sea Bird, crate label, 1930s, California lemon, large white flying seagull, yellow lettering, Carpinteria, 9x12½", M, C1 .... **$4.00**
Sea Breeze, crate label, 1930s, California lemon, seaside lemon orchard & Red Ball logo, Carpinteria, 9x12", M, C3 .... **$6.00**
Sea Cured, crate label, 1937, California lemon, ocean liner leaving port, pink & gold clouds in blue sky, Oxnard, 9x12½", M, C1 .... **$5.00**
Sea Foam, sign, paper, comical man pointing to container of product, Purity, Excellence... on banner, 20½x13", VG, A **$450.00**
Sea Gull, crate label, 1930s, California lemon, white gulls with black-tipped wings flying over ocean, Upland, 9x12½", NM, C1 .... **$5.00**

Sea Host Inc, push puppet, 1969, plastic, Ossie Oyster, 4½", EX+, D **$20.00**
Sea Treat, crate label, California lemon, old yacht at sea viewed through porthole, Carpenteria, 9x12", G1..**$6.00**
Seagram's Crown Royal, pitcher, pottery, shaped like a Crown Royal bottle, brown, D **$15.00**
Seagram's Golden Cooler, display, light-up, EX, D.**$18.00**
Seagram's Whiskey, employee or visitor badge, ca late 1940s, red, white & blue, EX, D...........................**$14.00**
Seagram's 7, pitcher, white pottery with Seagram's embossed on red background, 7 embossed on each side, D **$8.00**
Seal of North Carolina Plug Cut Tobacco, sign, die-cut cardboard litho, colorful image of 3 men holding product, early, framed, vertical rectangle, EX, A **$200.00**
Seal of North Carolina Smoking Tobacco, sign, paper, man holding up package of tobacco, The Hon Bardwell Slote, Makes A Few Remarks, 20x8", EX, A........**$350.00**
Sealtest Ice Cream, clock, light-up, square, G, D.....**$75.00**
Sealtest Ice Cream, hand puppet, 1962, Mr Cool, walrus head, EX, D **$48.00**
Sears, Roebuck & Co, catalog, 1930, VG, D.............**$70.00**
Sears, Roebuck & Co, catalog, 1952, Christmas, VG+, H2..**$75.00**
Sears, Roebuck & Co, catalog, 1962, Summer, VG+, H2 .**$15.00**
Sears, Roebuck & Co, catalog, 1965 Christmas, VG, D **$18.00**
Sears, Roebuck & Co, catalog, 1966, Fall/Winter, VG+, H2 ....**$25.00**
Sears, Roebuck & Co, catalog, 1972, Christmas Wish Book, Winnie the Pooh on cover, EX, D........................**$32.00**
Sears, Roebuck & Co, catalog, 1980, VG, D.............**$16.00**
Sears, Roebuck & Co, letterhead, 1900, order form with return envelope on Vicuna bicycle, scarce, EX, D.................**$13.50**
Sears, Roebuck & Co, tape measure, black plastic case, The World's Largest Store, We Guarantee To Satisfy You..., G, D **$15.00**
Sears, Roebuck & Co, tape measure, company name & address lettered on belt encircling a David Bradley plow, 1¾" dia, G, A...**$75.00**
Sears, Roebuck & Co, tip tray, 1905-15, Lady Justice overlooks Chicago, lettering above & below, simulated wood rim, oval, 4x6", NM, A **$55.00**
Sears, Roebuck & Co, wall pocket with 1934 Sears catalog, tin in simulated wood, rust at bottom/catalog worn, 16", G, A **$10.00**
Sears, Roebuck & Co's Special Combination Coffee, tin, bordered lettering over striped background, slip lid & bail, 5-lb, VG, A..**$90.00**
Sedgwick Bros Co Steel Wire Net Work Fences & Gates, trade card, house & barn with fenced in yards, ...Farm Fencing A Specialty, Richmond Ind, EX, A **$26.00**
Seiberling Sealed-Aire Tires, ashtray, tire shape, clear insert, D **$12.00**
Seiberling Tires, sign, porcelain, 2-sided, bold product name above diamond S logo on inverted triangle with round corners, 16x30", VG, A **$200.00**
Seilheimer Beverages, sign, 1930s, embossed tin, So-dalicious in elongated diamond in center, red, white & black, 8½x23½", EX, D...**$36.00**
Seipp Brewing Co, tray, 2 couples in open touring car & large beer bottle, fancy border, 10½x13¾", VG, A **$425.00**
Seitz Beer, tray, deep-dish, trademark image of bird on crescent moon, lettering on rim, minor chips/wear, 13" dia, VG, A **$110.00**
Seitz Brewing Co, tray, stock image of bulldog, lettering on rim, minor soiling/scratches, 14x13", EX, A..**$195.00**
Selby Shells, calendar, 1910, 'Thoroughbreds,' hunt scene with pointers, Dec. pad, major tears, 27½x20", A.............**$350.00**
Selby Shot Gun Shells, box, with contents, Shot Gun lettered on shell with Selby Loads above & below, 25 on pointed bands in each corner, VG, A **$260.00**
Select Combination Cigars, box label, outer, 1911, 3 stars & blue scroll decoration, 4½x4½", M, C3...............**$3.00**
Sellers Kitchen Cabinet, sign, tin, product name above cabinet with open doors, The Best Servant..., courtesy panel below, vertical, EX, M1 ....**$1,750.00**
Seminola Cigars, box label, inner lid, Indian Princess in native dress, 6x9", M, D **$6.50**
Seminola Cigars, can label, Indian Princess in native dress, M, D...**$9.50**
Senate Brand Steel Cut Selected Coffee, tin, product name & other lettering in ornate shield on striped background, screw lid, 1-lb, EX+, A **$83.00**
Senator Motor Oil, can, 1935-45, oval portrait of Jerry Senator, text below, green, black & white, pry lid, 1-qt, 5½", EX, A..**$180.00**
Seneca Allspice, tin, Seneca lettered above early sailing ship, Allspice below, vertical rectangle, NM, M2 ...**$9.00**
Seneca Sage, tin, Seneca lettered above early sailing ship, Sage below, white on red, pry lid, round, EX+, M2..............**$9.00**
Sensible Tobacco, tin, gold on white, 5x4x2¾", NM, D...**$30.00**

Seroco Harness Oil, can, 1910-20, lady's face in crescent moon in center, Sears Roebuck & Co, pour spout, heavy wear, 1-gal, 11½", A $50.00

Service Merchandise, catalog, 1974, VG+, H2 ....**$20.00**
Sespe, crate label, 1930s, California lemon, mountain scene with river, trees & rocks, Fillmore, 9x12½", M, C1.**$2.00**
Seven Stars Tobacco, tin, product name above 7 stars & company on paper label, 3¼x4½", VG+, A **$44.00**
Seven Up, **see 7-Up on page 305**
SF Hess & Co Premium Chewing Tobacco, pocket tin, pictures little girl in circular inset, black, gray & white, Ginna litho, scarce, 2x3", NM, D.........................**$975.00**

Shadowland Hard Candies, tin, 1930s-40s, orange & black barrel shape, logo in center, press lid, overall wear, 1-lb, 5½x3" dia, A....................................**$10.00**

Shady Lawn Ice Cream, fan, 1920s, cardboard, 2-sided, stock image of mother & daughter having a dish of ice cream, 9x9", EX, D **$14.00**

Shakespeare's Fishing Tackle, catalog, 1939, 92 pages, G, D...**$15.00**

Shakey's Pizza Parlor, bank, 1970s, ceramic, Shakey Chef, Shakey's Pizza Parlor & Public House lettered on base, 6", EX+, D **$35.00**

Shambrock Kidney Beans, can label, 1924, pictures a castle, bowl of beans & clover, EX, C3 ....**$12.00**

Shamrock Cloud Master Premium, pump sign, porcelain, Shamrock on shamrock image above Cloud Master over stylized cloud, Premium below, 13x11", EX, A ..**$130.00**

Shamrock Oranges, fan, 1930s, die-cut cardboard, pictures large shamrock, 8x8", EX, D..........................**$6.00**

Shapleigh Keen Kutter, catalog, 1958, saleman's sample, VG, D **$200.00**

Sharples Tubular Cream Separators, calendar, 1912, milkmaid beside separator with cow resting head in window, full pad, framed, image: 14x7", EX, A....................**$100.00**

Sharples Tubular Cream Separators, match holder, die-cut tin, pictures cows above girl using separator, lettering below, 6¾", EX, A.......................................**$425.00**

Sharples Tubular Cream Separators, match safe, cattle scene above mother & child using separator, Pet Of The Dairy, Tubular... below, 7x2", G, A **$100.00**

Sharples Tubular Cream Separators, pin-back button, shows woman using separator, Different From The Others arched above, EX, A **$25.00**

Sharples Tubular Cream Separators, pocket mirror, pictures woman & child with separator, Different From The Others on border, oval, 2¾", VG+, A......................**$80.00**

Sharples Tubular Cream Separators, pocket mirror, shows milkmaid watching gent pour milk into separator, Different From The Others, oval, 2¾", VG+, A.................**$50.00**

Sharples Tubular Cream Separators, pot scraper, EX, D...**$150.00**

Sharples Tubular Cream Separators, sign, paper, milkmaid with cows in field, inset picturing separator upper left, matted & framed, image: 12x19", EX, A......**$200.00**

Sharps' Rifle Manuf'g Co, box with contents, nonpictorial, 10 Cartridges, 12 Caps For Sharp's Improved Rifle...Hartford Ct, VG, A **$50.00**

Sheaffer Ink Pens, display, ca 1970, plastic & brass figural fountain pen, 60" long x 6" dia, EX, A...............**$425.00**

Sheboygan 10¢ Cigar, label, Sheboygan in diagonal script over mountainous view of the Indian chief kneeling over cliff, 6x9", EX, D **$20.00**

Shedd's Peanut Butter, pail, pictures elves, press lid & bail, 5-lb, EX, D **$25.00**

Sheffield Farms Co, display, wood, horse-drawn milk wagon, 21" long, EX, A......................................**$325.00**

Sheffield Milk, pin-back button, 1930s, pictures flag of Venezuela, EX, D **$3.00**

Shell, book, 1952, 'The Oilmen,' EX, D **$10.00**

Shell, book of maps with US & Canada, red binder-type cover with gold Shell logo, 18½x13½", EX+, A **$45.00**

Shell, calendar, 1928, fishing scene within decorative border, bow at top, Shell logos flank full pad, 17x10", NM, A..**$33.00**

Shell, calendar, 1930, stone path leads to floral-covered cottage, logos flank full pad, 16¾x10¼", NM, A **$31.00**

Shell, clock, glass front with metal frame, 12-2-4-6-8-10 numbered around Shell logo, square, VG, D..................**$240.00**

Shell, gas globe, late 1920s, milk glass, shell form with red lettering, 18x18", EX, A **$300.00**

Shell, portable oil rack, 1930s, handle atop panel with 9 can holders, shell logos flank Shell lettered above, vertical, EX, A **$235.00**

Shell, sign, die-cut porcelain, 2-sided, shell form with Shell Gasoline lettered in red, 41x41", EX, D1 ....$475.00

Shell, sign, 1930s-40s, various birds from North America, Australia..., World Experience... & shell logo above, 33x58", EX, A...**$25.00**

Shell, sign, 1940s, die-cut porcelain, 2-sided, yellow shell form with Shell lettered in red, 48x48", G, A **$275.00**

Shell, sign, 1940s, embossed die-cut porcelain, shell form with Shell in red, neon border, 50x49", NM, A..............**$1,100.00**

Shell, toy tanker truck, pressed steel, orange with embossed logos flanking shell, by Tootsietoy, overall wear, 1¾x6", VG, A...**$55.00**

Shell Blend Coffee, tin, pictures steamship in oval with lettering above & below, pry lid, 1-lb, EX, A **$220.00**

Shenandoah Valley Railroad, sign, reverse-painted glass, multiple designs & company name, multicolored with gold, framed, image: 21x28", G-, A.................**$1,150.00**

Sheridan Pale Beer, label, 1933-50, product name & logo in decorative center, Internal Revenue Tax Paid statement, 12-oz, EX, A **$13.00**

Sherlock Holmes Cigars, box label, lithographer's proof, early 1900s, close-up of famous sleuth, American Litho, rare, EX, A **$150.00**

Shermack Razor, box with original round razor, 1930s, silver & black, 3x2x1", EX, D **$30.00**

Sherwin-Williams Opex Laquers/Enamels, sign, tin flange, 2-sided, globe logos in upper corners with Opex in center, Modern Automobile... below, 16x22", EX, A **$200.00**

Sherwin-Williams Paints, sign, die-cut porcelain hanger, 2-sided, red & blue on white, can pours paint on globe left of name, 10x24", EX, M2 .... **$120.00**

Sherwin-Williams Paints & Varnishes, sign holder, porcelain, Sherwin-Williams above Cover The Earth, Paints & Varnishes below, chipped, 8x4x1", M2 .... **$20.00**

Sherwin-Williams Products, display, painter dips brush in paint can, Use Sherwin-Williams Products & Hire A Good Painter, 22½x30", EX, A **$25.00**

Sherwood Brand Coffee, shelf marker, tin, blue with Buy Sherwood Brand Coffee For Quality in red & white, NM, A **$30.00**

Sherwood Heating Oil, sign, porcelain, S2 .... **$75.00**

Shilling's Blossom Tea, trade card, 1880s, pictures romantic couple, Ah! Augustus, How Too Is Blossom Tea, 4½x3¼", EX, P1 .... **$7.50**

Sho-Am-Sweet, crate label, vegetable, smiling Black chef holding platter of cooked yams, 7x4", M, C1 .... **$1.50**

Shoe Lace Service Station, display box, tin, man driving a shoe into service station, shelved interior, minor dents & soiling, 11x11", VG, A **$900.00**

Shredded Wheat, recipe book, 1933, 'Recipes for New & Delicious Energy Dishes,' pictures cute little girl with bowl of cereal, EX, D $10.00

Shredded Wheat, sign, 1930s, die-cut cardboard, 3 kids surround large product box with flag, Headquarters For..., 24x30", EX, M2 .... **$1,100.00**

Shults Bread, pocket mirror, Little Red Riding Hood on path showing basket of bread, mirror chipped, vertical rectangle, 2¾", EX, A **$1,650.00**

Shumate Razors & Strops, cabinet, wood with decal of man's face & razor on glass front, 23", VG, A **$800.00**

Sierra Bullets, display board, various game encircled by 53 bullets mounted with plastic descriptive overlay, VG, A **$130.00**

Sierra Chemical Co, trade card, ca 1890, flowers, boats & water motif, The Great Sierra Kidney & Liver Cure, 3½x5¼", EX, P1 .... **$16.00**

Sierra Vista, crate label, 1920s, California orange, grove scene with snowy mountains beyond, Porterville, 10x11", M, C1 .... **$8.00**

Silberman Bros Wool Commission Merchants, pocket mirror, pictures a sheep with lettering above & below, 2⅛" dia, VG+, A **$175.00**

Silver Bar Apricots, can label, stone litho of 2 apricots on a twig, silver ground, San Francisco Ca, EX, G1 .... **$8.00**

Silver King Marshmallows, tin, bold lettering, slip lid, EX, A ... **$60.00**

Silver Leaf Lard, trade card, comical image of pigs pulling pail on wheels, factory beyond, Tally Ho!, Swift & Company, EX, A **$42.00**

Silver Seal Coffee, tin, company seal in circle with lettering above & below, some dents, A **$30.00**

Silver Slipper Saloon, Las Vegas, postcard, 1950s, dance hall design, We Mail It, You Address It, red & black, M, P1 .... **$6.50**

Silver Spring Brand Quality Beverages, sign, porcelain, blue logo & product lettering on white with blue border, horizontal rectangle, EX, D3 .... **$110.00**

Silver Spring Brewery, barrel label, 1910, pictures a fireman, ...Victoria, BC, 16" dia, EX, D **$45.00**

Silver Thistle Coffee, can label, pictures a building with silver thistles, M, C3 .... **$12.00**

Simon Pure, sign, curved porcelain, Simon Pure encircling wings trademark, The Wm Simon Brewery lettered below, 25", VG, A **$175.00**

Simon Pure Cigars, box label, inner lid, fancy document with flowers on each side, 6x9", M, D **$4.50**

Sinclair, radio, shaped as gas pump, MIB, D2 .... **$35.00**

Sinclair, toy tanker truck, green with Sinclair lettered in green, emblem on truck cab, by Marx, with original box, EX+, A **$650.00**

Sinclair Aircraft, sign, porcelain, 2-sided, green with white airplane in center, Sinclair Aircraft around border, 48" dia, NM/EX, A **$2,700.00**

Sinclair Aircraft, sign, porcelain, 2-sided, green with white airplane in center, Sinclair Aircraft around border, 48" dia, VG/G, D **$1,750.00**

Sinclair Gasoline, bank, 1940s-50s, tin, logo on cream center band, green background, lift-off top, minor wear, 4", A **$45.00**

Sinclair Gasoline, sign, porcelain, Dino above Gasoline, 12x13½", NM, D1 .... **$75.00**

Sinclair H-C Gasoline, bank, 1948, tin litho in red, green & white, EX+, D **$50.00**

Sinclair H-C Gasoline, pump sign, porcelain, Sinclair Gasoline lettered around shadowed H-C in double-lined circle on square, 14x14", EX, A **$500.00**

Sinclair Household Oil, can, 1950s, metal, image of Dino on front, red, white & green, minor surface wear, 5x2", EX, D **$15.00**

Sinclair Litholine, can, 1935-45, logo atop white lettering, red background, pry lid, 1-lb, 3½", EX, A **$15.00**

Sinclair Motor Oil, can, 1930s, Dino & product name encircled above, Mellowed 80... below, green & red ground, 5-qt, 9½", EX, A **$50.00**

Sinclair Motor Oil, can, 1936-45, Dino holding Pennsylvania Motor Oil on red ground, 1-qt, 5½", EX, A **$175.00**

Sinclair Oil Co, toy, 1960s, inflatable vinyl, Dino, 12", M, D ... **$20.00**

Sinclair Oils, pump sign, porcelain, green on white, Sincalir Oils lettered around vertically striped center, 12" dia, EX+, A **$400.00**

Sinclair Opaline F Motor Oil, sign, 1920s, porcelain, Made Expressly For Ford Cars arched above product name & other lettering, rare, 20x46", D..............**$650.00**

Sinclair Opaline Motor Oil, sign, tin, pictures can at right of product name, lined border, 11½x19½", G, A **$100.00**

Sinclair Opaline Motor Oil, sign, tin, oil pictures can at right of product name, lined border, 11½x19½", EX, A...$235.00

Sinclair Pennsylvania Motor Oil, pump sign, porcelain, Dino below product name on red & white circular background, 11" dia, G, A **$250.00**

Singer's Patent Gravel Paper, sign, paper, woman frolicking on a path with bird cage at her feet, ...For The Bottom Of Bird Cages, 13x10", VG, A $500.00

Singer Sewing Machines, booklet, 1926, 'Short Cuts To Home Sewing,' 48 pages, G, D **$8.00**

Singer Sewing Machines, catalog, ca 1900, illustrations of sewing machines, red & green, 34 pages, EX, D ..**$10.00**

Singer Sewing Machines, drawing book, colorful covers of children at sewing machines, 12 pages, unused, 3¼x5½", P1 ....**$20.00**

Singer Sewing Machines, jigsaw puzzle, pictures Native Americans in front of teepee using treadle machine, 7x10", EX, F1 ....**$35.00**

Singer Sewing Machines, pin-back button, Bonded Representative, Singer Sewing Machine Co lettered around large S, Dec 1939, 1¾", EX, A..............................**$15.00**

Singer Sewing Machines, sign, porcelain, large red S with white lettering over woman at sewing machine, green background, 36x24", G, A **$375.00**

Singer Sewing Machines, trade card, copyrighted 1916, The Poppy Girl, signed by W Haskell Coffin, ad on back, 5x4", EX, H1 ....**$4.50**

Sioux Fire Insurance Co, sign, litho transfer on oak panel, pictures Sioux Indian in full headdress, Sioux City Iowa below, 24x18", G-, A..**$200.00**

Sioux Motor Oil, can, 1940s-50s, Sioux lettered on arrowhead on white band above company name on red, pry lid, 1-qt, 5½", EX, A..**$40.00**

Sir Loraine Cigars, box label, outer, knight in armor, 4½x4½", M, D **$4.00**

Sir Walter Raleigh Tobacco, tin, 1920s, encircled portrait of Sir Walter Raleigh in center, Sooner Or Later... below, 11½x12½" dia, VG, A..............................**$275.00**

Skelly Motor Oil, tape measure, diamond logo, Compliments Of Community Service Station Co, red, cream & blue, 4-ft, 1½" dia, EX, D **$45.00**

Skelly Supreme, gas globe, 1940s, porcelain, red, white & blue diamond logo with 4 blue stars below, blue border, 13½" dia, EX, A...**$130.00**

Ski-Top Beer, label, 1933-50, North Pole Brewing Co, Internal Revenue Tax Paid, 12-oz, VG, A.............................**$11.00**

Skookum, crate label, apple, smiling cartoon-faced Indian eyeing red & yellow apples, 10½x9", M, C1...........**$2.00**

Skooner Beer, label, 1933-50, Blumer Brewing Co, Internal Revenue Tax Paid statement, 12-oz, G, A **$10.00**

Sky Chief Gasoline, sign, 1940s, porcelain, Sky Chief on large band above Texaco star, green, red & black, 18x12", EX+, A..**$70.00**

Sky-High Motor Oil, can, ca 1923, Sky-High on band above airplane, Guaranteed 100%... below, pour spout & handle, dents, 2-gal, 11", VG, A **$30.00**

Slade's Epicurean Spices, box with 6 round spice containers, tin, Ginna & Co litho, box: 4x6x3¾"/spice tins: 3⅜x1⅞" dia, G-/VG **$475.00**

Sleepy Eye Flour, sign, embossed tin, Old Sleepy Eye portrait with white lettering on silver background, 19x13½", NM, A $1,650.00

Sleepy Eye Milling Co, plaque, polychromed plaster bust of Old Sleepy Eye in wood frame, lettered with company name, 33x25", VG, A **$385.00**

Slippery Elm Lozenges, tin, product name arched above glass front, allover flower designs, gold & silver, slip lid, rare, 9x6½", EX, A **$525.00**

Sloman's Diamond Wedding Pure Rye, sign, tin, elegant woman with shot glass surrounded by lettering, 12" dia, VG, A **$300.00**

Smile Soda, display bottle, horizontally ribbed bottle with Smile embossed on band, 1-gal, 18", EX, A **$125.00**

Smile Soda, fan pull, die-cut cardboard, pictures Smile boy, EX, M3 ....**$20.00**

Smile Soda, playing cards, 1946, shows Smile boy, with calendar card, original box, G, A **$61.00**

Smile Soda, sign, tin flange, 2-sided, Drink above Smile in script, flange at bottom, round, 12x10", NM, D1 ....**$210.00**

Smirnoff Vodka, ashtray, clear glass with red & black lettering on white bottom, 3¾x3¾", D **$3.00**

Smith & Travis Insurance & Loans, sign, ca 1905, waxed cardboard, white lettering on black ground, See Us Now..., EX, D..**$15.00**

Smith & Wesson, catalog, 1939, SW logo on front, well illustrated, 52 pages, EX, A..................................**$75.00**

Smith & Wesson Automatic Pistol, pocket catalog, non-pictorial cover, EX, A **$50.00**

Smith & Wesson Police Models, catalog, 1908, SW logo on front, well illustrated, 12 pages, EX, A **$95.00**

Smith & Wesson Revolvers, catalog, #D4, 1925, large SW logo on front cover, features the safety hammerless models, minor crease, A **$50.00**

Smith & Wesson Revolvers, foldout, 1923, illustrated 3-panel lettered in Spanish, EX, A.........................**$110.00**

Smith & Wesson Superior Revolvers, pamphlet, 1933, SW logo on front, 12 pages, EX, A **$45.00**

Smith American Piano & Organ Co, sign, paper, early interior scene of 2 women & maestro at piano, lettering at top, Giles litho, 27x19½", VG, A **$275.00**

Smith Brothers Cough Drops, blotter, product box flanked by portraits & Black Menthol, The Only Cough Drop Containing Vitamin A below, VG, A **$30.00**

Smith Brothers Cough Drops, box, 1930s, pictures the Smith brothers, full, 1x4", D **$8.00**

Smith's Ice Cream, sign, painted tin, Smith's in script & Model Dairy Inc on tail above Ice Cream, It's Pleasingly Different, 20x31", EX, A **$90.00**

Smith's True Fruit Extracts, display, metal frame with glass panels, 10½x12x6½", VG, A **$425.00**

Smith-O-Lene Gasoline, pump sign, 1946-50, porcelain, black airplane with Aviation Brand in red above & below, minor flaking, 10" dia, A **$1,000.00**

Smith-Wallace Shoe Co, match holder, tin, logo surrounded by lettering, Best Of Everything In Shoes..., 5", VG, A **$120.00**

Snake Charmer Cigarettes, box, pictures a snake charmer flanked by logo, lettering above & below, 4½x3x3", VG+, A **$25.00**

Snoboy, crate label, 1930s, Washington apples, pictures snowman holding apple, Yakima, 9x10¾", M, C3.................**$3.00**

Snow Boy Washing Powder, calendar, 1901, embossed image of girl with doll house, Compliments Lautz Brothers...above, full calendar, framed, EX, A ...**$125.00**

Snow Boy Washing Powder, sign, canvas, boy on sled holds large box of product on snowy background, ad text around, framed, 42x28", EX, A **$5,100.00**

Snow Crest Syrup, tin, product name above bear & mountain graphics, full, small, EX, A **$23.00**

Snow King Baking Powder, sign, ca 1900, die-cut cardboard, 2 reindeer pulling Santa in sleigh, Use..., One Trail Convinces, 20x36", EX, D3 ....$500.00

Snow Owl Brand Pears, crate label, 1920s, fierce snowy owl on blue ground, Yakima Wash, 7¼x11", M, C1 ....**$2.00**

Snow-Line Apples, crate label, 1930s, snowy mountain scene above apple orchard, large apple in foreground, Oakglen Ca, 10½x9", M, C1 ....**$2.00**

Snowball, crate label, Florida citrus, Black child holding a peeled orange, green ground, 3½x9", M, C1 ....**$2.00**

Snowman Anti-Freeze, can, 1935-45, snowman & cars in winter scene, cream lettering on blue, pour spout & handle, 2-gal, 10½", EX, A **$100.00**

Snyder's Pretzels, tin, 9½x6¾x4", EX, D **$10.00**

Soapine, trade card, ca 1880, pictures Louis Wain cats on chimneys, 5x3", EX, P1 ....**$22.50**

Soapine, trade card, dog kissing horse, EX, A.................**$13.00**

Soapine, trade card, man washing large whale, Kendall Mfg Co, Providence RI lettered below, EX, A.**$19.00**

Soapine, trade card, pictures wizard & lady, Soapine lettered in stars, Kendall Mfg Co, G, D **$3.00**

Social Rye, sign, tin, stock image of girl holding carnations, Pure & Wholesome..., below, curled corners, 18x16", G, A **$500.00**

Society Snuff, canister, cardboard, original tax stamp, 1¼" dia, NM, A..**$12.00**

Socony Air-Craft Oils, sign, ca 1930, porcelain, red & white on blue, Air-Craft on wing of plane with lettering above & below, 20x30", EX, D3......................**$1,275.00**

Socony Banner Gasoline, banner, cloth, red & white on red reading The New Socony... Banner Gasoline, The Best Popular Priced... 34x99", NM, A...................**$40.00**

Socony Gasoline & Motor Oil, calendar, service man holding hose to red Socony gas pump above product name, pad missing, 27x14", G, A **$90.00**

Socony Globes & Candles, box, wood, holds globes & paraffin candles, stamped lettering on ends, hinged lid, 12x15x12", EX, A **$50.00**

Socony Motor Gasoline, sign, die-cut porcelain flange, 2-sided, We Sell... emblem with Standard Oil Co Of NY lettered below, 24x22", G/G-, A.........................**$275.00**

Socony Motor Oils, sign, porcelain, white on blue with red trim, 36x18", EX, D **$175.00**

Socony-Vacuum Marine Products, sign, 1930s, die-cut tin shield, 2-sided, red Mobil horse above black & red product lettering, 11x11", EX, A **$325.00**

Softex Shampoo, display, wood, 2-tiered foldout box, inner lid paper label with girl running fingers through hair, 10", VG+, A **$20.00**

Solace Cut Plug Tobacco, box, square, G+, H3........ **$15.00**

Solace Cut Plug Tobacco, sign, tin, product name arched above flowers, John Anderson & Co below, Tuchfarber & Co litho, 17½x23½", G, A................................. **$75.00**

Solar Tip Shoes, sign, paper, children with lettered banners, oval inset lower left, general soiling & minor tears, 9x13", VG, A **$200.00**

Solar Tip Shoes, trade card, sitting couple with poem laminating bad shoes so they can't dance opens to happy couple dancing, VG, A... **$25.00**

Solarine Metal Polish, match holder, tin, pictures bottle of polish beside Wise Wives Work With, minor creases, 5", G, A **$80.00**

Solder Seal Radiator Leak Stopper, display, cardboard stand-up, 12 full canisters at top of star graphics, red, white, yellow & black, 14x21", VG, D **$80.00**

Solid Comfort Cigars, box label, inner lid, red, blue & bronze, 6x9", EX, C3 .... **$10.00**

Solomon-Grindell Clothing Co, sign, reverse-painted glass etched with copper clad acid, 7½x84½", G-, A........ **$25.00**

Somers Bros Original French Marshmallows, tin, rectangular with rounded corners, A **$55.00**

Somerset Chocolates, display, plaster figure of Indian paddling canoe, product name embossed on each side, 12x36x9", VG+, A **$225.00**

Something Fine Cigars, box label, inner lid sample, 1880s, man with 2 ladies at the theater, Witsch & Schmidt litho, M, A... **$70.00**

Something Good Cigars, box label, inner lid sample, 1880s, couple relaxing in landscape, Witsch & Schmidt litho, M, A **$75.00**

Songster Phonograph Needles, tin, pictures a songbird, M, D **$16.50**

Sonny Boy Cigars, box label, inner lid, pictures young boy on his fathers lap, 6x9", M, D.......................... **$4.00**

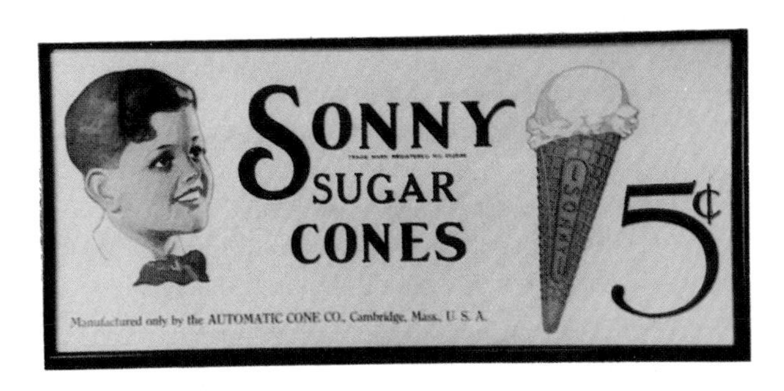

Sonny Sugar Cones, sign, paper, Sonny Sugar Cones in black flanked by Boy's head, ice cream cone & 5¢ on white, framed, 9x19", NM, A................... $140.00

Sopronol Powder, sample tin, 2", EX, D **$20.00**

Soul Kiss Talcum Powder, tin, heart logo, shaker top, oval, very rare, NM **$1,300.00**

Soulas' Rathskeller Betz Building, tray, interior view of pub with intricate ceiling, carved chairs & ceiling fans, minor chips/soiling, 12" dia, EX, A **$200.00**

South Bend Bait Company, catalog, 1942, features fishing equipment, 135 pages, EX, D **$28.00**

South Bend Fishing Tackle, catalog, 1931, 'Fishing What Tackle & When,' boy with stringer of bass on cover, 78 pages, EX, A **$35.00**

South Bend Fishing Tackle, sign, die-cut porcelain, man with fish, EX, D **$650.00**

South Bend Watch Co, jigsaw puzzle, 1911, shows large graphic of the inner workings of a pocket watch, 9½x7½", EX, F1 .... **$100.00**

South Bethlehem Brewing Co, tray, stock image of 3 dogs chewing playing cards, pictorial vignettes & lettering on rim, 13½x16¼", G-, A **$75.00**

South Shore Peaches, can label, 1934, golfers at country club, EX, C3 .... **$30.00**

Southern Bread, sign, tin, pictures child & loaf of bread, G, D **$65.00**

Southern Brewing Co Bock Beer, label, 1933-36, ram's head flanked by S&B, U-type permit number, 12-oz, EX, A **$16.00**

Southern Dairies Ice Cream, sign, glass, blue & gold, 11x6", G, D **$175.00**

Southern Fertilizing Co, sign, paper, stock image of woman fixing garter while Black beggar leers at her, framed, image: 17x14", EX, A............................ **$750.00**

Southern Freight & Passenger Line, sign, 1870s, paper, ship sailing to Savannah Georgia & other southern locales, fancy graphics, 21½x13", EX, A....$2,100.00

Southland Beauties, crate label, California lemon, red, pink & yellow roses on blue background, 9x12", EX, G1 .... **$5.00**

Southwest Utility Ice Co, sign, porcelain, blue & white, ...Save With Ice, edge chips, 14½x44", VG, A.... **$120.00**

Souvenir Popcorn/National Candy Co, pocket mirror, shows clown sitting on top of drum, lettered rim with Oh My! lettered below drum, 1¾" dia, VG, A....**$140.00**

Sovereign Cocoa, tin, encircled elephant with product name above & below on paper label, embossed slip lid, 4¼x3¼", EX+, A **$64.00**

Sozodont Tooth Powder, sign, paper, elegant woman in pink holding up product & pointing at tooth, The National Dentifrice..., 13x8½", EX, A **$100.00**

SP Lapcevic Steamship Agent, calendar, 1908, die-cut with embossed cowgirl & vignettes of horses, full pad, framed, 21x11", EX, A.......................................**$550.00**

Spalding, sign, porcelain flange, 2-sided, Spalding Trade Mark on baseball surrounded by Athletic Goods For Sale..., 19x20", G, A **$1,200.00**

Sparrow's Empress Chocolates, pocket mirror, empress on her throne, lettering above & below, rectangular, rounded corners, 2¾", EX, A **$40.00**

Sparrow's Empress Chocolates, sign, tin, crowned empress being presented box of chocolates, HD Beach litho, self-framed, 19x13", EX, A **$500.00**

Spartans Varnish & Paint Co, thimble, ca 1910, aluminum with blue band, Spartans Varnish & Paint Co, Marietta, VG+, D **$5.00**

Sparton Radios, mirror, 1930s, clear with blue mirrors at bottom, pale gold lettering, Buy Sparton Radios, rare, 28½x28½", VG, A **$700.00**

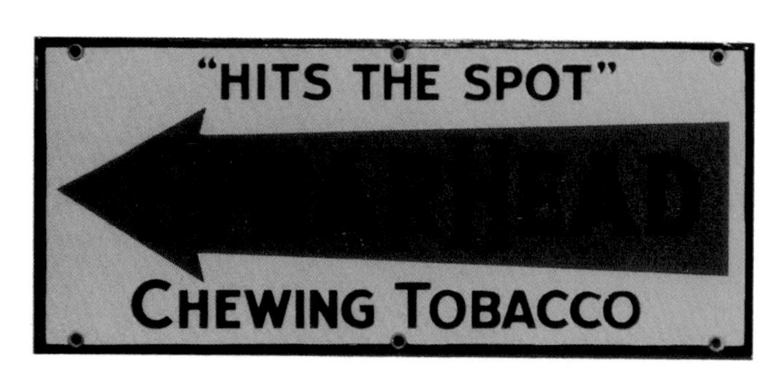

Spear Head Chewing Tobacco, sign, porcelain, black & red on yellow, Hits The Spot above Spear Head on arrow, 6x14", NM, D3......................................$300.00

Spear Head Plug Tobacco, sign, embossed tin hanger, 2-sided, Try Spear Head..., 6x6", NM, A **$55.00**

Speed King Cigars, box label, inner lid sample, 1900s, 2 men in early race car flanked by palm trees & ocean, Schmidt & Co litho, EX, A **$292.00**

Sperry Drifted Snow Flour, door push plate, 1920s, porcelain, Don't Forget in diagonal script above product name, 8x3", NM, M2 ....**$110.00**

Spice House, tin, house shape with pink roof lettered The Spice House Est 1834, Ginger, Dalton Bros Toronto, 3" long, EX, A...**$20.00**

Spicers & Peckham's Ranges & Stoves, trade card, little boy waving goodbye to ship, For Sale By Daley Brothers, Uxbridge lettered below, EX, A.....................**$28.00**

Spiegel, catalog, 1932, Spring/Summer, VG+, H2......**$60.00**

Spiegel, catalog, 1942, VG, D **$50.00**

Spiegel, catalog, 1950, Christmas, VG+, H2................**$75.00**

Spiegel, catalog, 1961, VG, D **$30.00**

Spiegel, catalog, 1968, Fall/Winter, VG+, H2 ....**$25.00**

Spiegel, catalog, 1972, Christmas, VG, D...................**$40.00**

Spies, Kissam & Co, letterhead, 1875, pictures 5 guns, VG, A **$15.00**

Spiffy Cola, sign, tin flange, red & black with boy's face left of white hand, Stop Here's Spiffy, Swell Cola Drink, 10x13", NM, M3 ....**$400.00**

Spirit of Camphor, bottle, clear glass with cork, Larkin Co Inc, round, 5", EX, P4 ....**$12.00**

Splendid, crate label, 1930s, California lemon, country scene with house, orchard & mountains, Ivanhoe, 9x12½", M, C1 ....**$2.00**

Sportsman, crate label, 1930s, Washington apples, hunter in silhouette with mountains beyond, Chelan, 9x10½", M, C3 ....**$25.00**

Spratt's, sign, steel, Spratt's in shape of a terrier, Builds Up A Dog, red, black & cream, 9x18", EX, D **$30.00**

Spratt's Silvercloud Ground Bait, sign, porcelain, pictures a fish & Anglers in script at top, We Sell & Recommend..., 12x12", EX+, S2...................................**$385.00**

Sprenger Brewing Co, tray, factory scene & large bottle, logo & hops below, High Grade Beer & Porter... on rim, oval, 14x16½", G, A....................................**$475.00**

Sprenger Brewing Co, tray, 3 monks feasting on bread & vegetables with flagons of beer, minor soiling/chips, 12" dia, VG, A..**$500.00**

Sprenger Brewing Co Beer, sign, embossed tin under curved glass, logo surrounded by hops & wheat at top, ...Lancaster Pa, rare, 23x17", NM, A.................**$1,700.00**

Springfield Breweries Co, calendar, 1911 printer's proof, company name arched above lady in plumed hat, by W Haskell Coffin, 31x23", NM, D...$1,850.00

Springfield Breweries Co, calendar top, 1914 printer's proof, illustration of lady in plumed hat, by C Warde Traver, 43x23", VG, A **$375.00**

Sprinkle Whiskey, pocket mirror, man towering over factory with arrow pointing to large bottle at right, horizontal oval, 2¾", G, A **$70.00**

Sprite, decal, 1963, hand holding bottle, 14", EX, D....**$7.50**

Sprite, talking doll, 1990, Lucky Lymon, molded vinyl, 7½", M, D **$10.00**

Spry Pure Vegetable Shortening, recipe book, 1949, 'Enjoy Good Eating Every Day,' 48 pages, EX, D...**$6.00**

Spunkey's Ethyl, gas globe, 1930s-40s, porcelain, Spunkey's in large red letters in center, logo above & below, EX, A **$225.00**

Spurrs Coffee, tin, paper label, slip lid, heavily worn, scarce, A....................**$20.00**

Sputa Fuoco Fresh Italian Grapes. sign, paper, unusual devil figure squeezing juice from grapes flanked by lettering, 16x16½", VG, A **$350.00**

Squadron Leader Tobacco, tin, 1930s, pictures a biplane, multicolored, 3x4", EX, D **$55.00**

Square Deal Bread, badge, 1930s, silvered brass, Safety Club, EX, D....................**$9.00**

Squeeze, sign, 1940s, die-cut cardboard stand-up, girl posed with bottle, Had Your Squeeze Today?, 20x12", NM, D **$120.00**

Squeeze, see also Lime Squeeze

Squeeze, see also Orange Squeeze

Squire's, see also John P Squire & Co,

Squire's Arlington Hams-Bacon-Sausage, calendar, 1926, Squire's pig in oval atop emblem with advertising & Dec. page, matted & framed, 36x23", VG, A **$100.00**

Squire's Arlington Hams-Bacon-Sausage, sign, self-framed tin, frontal view of a pig surrounded by corn husks, 24½x20¼", G, A **$1,100.00**

Squirrel Brand Peanut Candy Crunch, tin, 1930s-40s, squirrel logo on red & yellow ground, red, cream & black lettering, slip lid, 1-lb, 6x4" dia, EX, A........**$40.00**

Squirrel Brand Salted Jumbo Peanuts, display, tin, squirrel on red 5¢ oval logo atop black 6-sided stand featuring Squirrel Brand Products, 22½", NM, A $2,200.00

Squirrel Brand Salted Peanuts, container, glass, pictures a squirrel & product name on tin lid, 9½", VG, A...**$65.00**

Squirrel Brand Taffy, display, yellow tin with die-cut squirrel atop 3-tiered stand featuring 3 Squirrel Brand products, 24x8", EX, A **$475.00**

Squirrel Peanut Butter, pail, yellow with squirrel logo, red lettering above & below, slip lid & bail, 1-lb, G, A......**$120.00**

Squirrel Peanut Butter, pail, yellow with squirrel logo, red lettering above & below, slip lid & bail, 1-lb, EX+, A **$222.00**

Squirt, bottle topper, die-cut plastic Squirt boy with large bottle, Just Call Me Squirt on base below, 8½x4¼", NM, A **$100.00**

Squirt, calendar, 1940s, girl in red holding bottle before log wall & round yellow emblem above 3 month pads, 23x16", NM, M3 ....**$125.00**

Squirt, calendar, 1948, Squirt Quenches Quicker, complete, EX, D **$35.00**

Squirt, decal, 1963, pictures boy with bottle of Squirt, Squirt Out Of This World, 4x2", EX, D **$5.00**

Squirt, menu board, tin, Squirt on red logo with green on white ground left of ribbed bottle above chalkboard, 28x20", NM, M3 ....**$45.00**

Squirt, menu board, tin, Squirt on yellow ground left of straight-sided bottle & Squirt boy above chalkboard, 27x19", NM, M3 ....**$75.00**

Squirt, push plate, 1941, embossed tin, Drink Squirt on yellow splash above tilted bottle, 8½x3½", EX, D **$80.00**

Squirt, push plate, 1941, embossed tin, Drink Squirt on yellow splash above tilted bottle, 8½x3½", NM, A **$140.00**

Squirt, salt & pepper shakers, green glass bottle form with metal lids, logo on 1 side, Squirt boy on the other, 6", EX, D....................$27.00

Squirt, salt & pepper shakers, 1974, green glass bottle form with plastic lids, logo & Squirt boy, 4½", MIB, D **$10.00**

Squirt, sign, cardboard, 1943, full-color image of rooster & hens, 10x8½", EX, D....................**$12.50**

Squirt, sign, cardboard hanger, die-cut, 1949, 2-sided, Drink Squirt above Squirt boy with large bottle, 8x3½", NM, D....................**$40.00**

Squirt, sign, cardboard hanger, snowman in top hat, NM, B1 ....**$5.00**

Squirt, sign, cardboard hanger, 1943, cartoon image of fish having a discussion, 10x8½", NM, B1 ....**$8.00**

Squirt, sign, cardboard stand-up, 1944, Squirt Gives You Go! above girl girl in swing & bottle, framed, 28x37", M, D **$95.00**

Squirt, sign, tin, embossed, Drink Squirt left of tilted bottle, green border, 18x54", EX, M3..............................**$95.00**

Squirt, sign, tin, flag with Drink above Squirt lettered in script on splash logo, It's Tart Sweet below, horizontal, VG, A **$45.00**

Squirt, sign, tin, red with Enjoy Squirt on yellow logo left of swirled bottle on white, Never An After-Thirst, 12x28", M, M3..**$125.00**

Squirt, sign, tin, Squirt boy flanked by Enjoy Squirt on yellow emblem & swirled bottle, Never An After-Thirst, 9x27", NM, S3 ....**$55.00**

Squirt, sign, tin, yellow circle with red border featuring Drink Squirt, The Quality Soft Drink, 12" dia, EX, M3 ....**$45.00**

Squirt, store display, 1947, composition, Squirt boy beside bottle, Just Call Me Squirt in red on yellow base, 13", M, D...$400.00

Squirt, thermometer, 1960, embossed tin, Squirt on diagonal band above numbered bulb & bottle, round corners, 14x6", NM, D **$45.00**

SR Van Duzen & Co's Fruit Flavoring Extracts, sign, die-cut stand-up, puppies in basket holding tag with company & product name, EX, A **$36.00**

St Augustine Cigars, box labels, inner & outer sample set, 1870s, vignettes of early St Augustine, Heppenheimer & Maurer litho, EX/M, A..**$166.00**

St Bruno Tobacco, shadow box display, Black field hands picking tobacco surrounded by tobacco leaves, wood frame, EX, A **$600.00**

St Jacobs Oil, sign, paper, monk holding up a glowing bottle of the product, The Great German Remedy, 18x9½", VG, A **$50.00**

St Jacobs Oil, trade card, sick man opens up to healthy man, How The Neuralgic Man Was Cured, VG, A...........**$44.00**

St James Coffee, tin, pictures the factory with product name & lettering above & below, red & gold, oval slip lid & handle, 9x8", EX, A..................................**$220.00**

St James Coffee, tin, red square shape with square logo, St James above, Coffee below, Gimbel Brothers, round slip lid, 5-lb, VG, A **$95.00**

St Joseph Aspirin, clock, metal case, glass front, electric, blue numbers on white surround white product name on blue dot, 15" dia, EX, A................................**$120.00**

St Louis Beef Canning Co, trade card, western cattle scene, We Supply The World With..., list of products on reverse, EX, A **$20.00**

St Louis Beef Canning Co's Cooked Canned Meats, trade card, comical image of man in small tent, It Is So Nice To Camp Out But Do Not Forget..., black & white, EX, A **$17.00**

St Louis Beef Canning Co's Cooked Corn Beef, sign, paper, Black waiter serving large man in decorative border, soiling/creasing, 13½x10½", VG, A $600.00

Sta-Green Lawn Seeds, box with contents, 1920s, landscape with large mansion, 6x4", EX, D **$6.50**

Stacy's Chocolates, pocket mirror, sun rises over water with lighthouse at left, On Land Or Sea, North, South, East..., 2¼" dia, EX, A...**$25.00**

Stafford's Universal Ink, trade card, hold-to-light, pictures little girl sleeping, eyes open & close, EX, A **$15.00**

Stag, crate label, Colorado apple, 3 large apples, stag's head & fancy blue logo on yellow background, 9x11", EX, G1...**$25.00**

Stag Trousers, sign, tin, pictures an elk flanked by Union Made & Never Rip, None Better, curled corners, 15x15", EX, A...**$175.00**

Staley's Salad & Cooking Oil, recipe book, 'Staley's Approved Recipes,' Wm Landers & Sons General Mdse, Utica Ill, 30 pages, EX, D **$4.00**

Standard, gas globe, glass on metal base, red & white flame on blue & white porcelain holder, minor paint chips, 28x22", VG+, A...**$450.00**

Standard Brau, label, pre-1920, Standard Brewery, G, A.**$45.00**

Standard Brewing Co, tray, shows the execution of 38 Sioux Indians at Mankato Minnesota, Dec 3 1862, red-lettered rim, 12" dia, EX+, M2 ....**$550.00**

Standard Cough Drops, tin, glass front flanked by logos, product name arched above, black on red, Canadian, slip lid, 8x7", VG, A **$175.00**

Standard End Cutting Nipper, sign, celluloid & tin over cardboard, product name lettered above hand holding Nipper, 11x6", NM, D **$225.00**

Standard Gasoline, sign, porcelain, red & white, several small chips, 36x18", D **$125.00**

Standard Gasoline, sign, 1940s, tin, pictures Mickey Mouse holding sign, For Extra Service..., minor dent/edge wear, 23½" dia, A......................$1,200.00

Standard Licorice & Lozenges, tin, Standard lettered above arched glass window on front, pretty girl on slip lid, 5-lb, 7½x5x5", VG, A **$180.00**

Standard Motor Oil, checker game, EX, D **$30.00**

Standard Motor Oil, sign, porcelain, We Sell Standard Motor Oil above Makes Motors Run Smoother & Costs Run Lower, 18x36", EX+, A **$750.00**

Standard Plumbing Fixtures, catalog, 1933, 48 pages, G, D..**$5.00**

Standard Varnish Works, sign, self-framed tin, painter behind line-up of product, The Man Who Knows..., 23x33", G, A **$175.00**

Stanford's Unshrinkable Underwear, sign, cardboard, 2 boxers casting shadows on wall above product name, 16x11", VG+, M2 ....**$24.00**

Stanley Electric Tools, catalog, July 1951, 95 pages, VG, D......**$8.00**

Stanley Garage Door Holders, sign, early 1920s, tin, shows product in use with auto in garage, HD Beach litho, wood frame, 27½x35", EX, D3 .$850.00

Stanley Plumbing & Heating Supplies, catalog, 1926, fully illustrated with prices, 88 pages, G, D **$15.00**

Stanley's India Pale Ale, label, pre-1920, Suffolk Brewing Co arched above product name, G, A **$5.00**

Stanley Tools, catalog, 1926, 192 pages, VG, D........**$25.00**

Stanley 1800 Sliding Door Hardware, display, 1960s, wood, white logo & lettering, 10x14" , EX, A.....................**$30.00**

Staples Prepared Wax, tin, pictures a beehive, 3" dia, EX, D...**$9.50**

Star Brand Shoes, clock, stained wood case with reverse-painted glass door, All The Time...Are Better, working, 32", G-, A **$150.00**

Star Brand Shoes, pencil clip, ca 1900, celluloid, red & white, EX, D **$18.00**

Star Brand Shoes, pin-back button, ca 1900, multicolored, EX, D...**$12.00**

Star Brand Typewriter Ribbon, tin, EX, D **$6.00**

Star Cars, sign, porcelain, encircled star flanked by product name in center, Low Cost Transportation... above & below, NM, D..**$550.00**

Star Dust, crate label, 1930s, California orange, Star Dust lettered in starry sky, Exeter Orchards Ass'n Inc, 10x11", M, C1 ....**$4.00**

Star French Fried Popcorn, box, light cardboard, product name over sunburst graphics, 6½x4½", NM, A.....**$18.00**

Star Maid Salted Peanuts, tin, cream with blue, silver & white, image of maid before starburst, product name above & below, 10-lb, EX, A..............................**$210.00**

Star Naptha Washing Powder, door push plate, porcelain, Push above product, vertical, EX, M1.........**$375.00**

Star Naptha Washing Powder, sign, porcelain, Sold & Here lettered in between 3 boxes of product with stars on background, horizontal, EX, M1.................**$1,350.00**

Star of America Cigars, box label, inner lid sample, Lady Liberty posing in landscape, Schmidt & Co litho, 1895, EX, A..**$213.00**

Star Palace Laundry & Dry Cleaners, pocket mirror, lady in hat tied with scarf encircled by Star Palace Laundry, Dry Cleaners, foxing, 2⅛" dia, G, A **$21.00**

Star Soap, sign, die-cut cardboard hanger, 2 babies in swing, 1 holds star marked Schultz & Co, Star Soap sign above, 9x6", NM, A............................$1,850.00

Star Soap, sign, porcelain, star image on each side of Star Soap, horizontal, EX, M1 ....**$325.00**
Star Steel Belt Lacing, sign, painted tin, S intertwined with star on Star Steel Belt Lacing above diagonal image, text around, 14x20", G+, A **$70.00**
Star Tobacco, sign, porcelain, Star Tobacco Sold Here & row of tobacco plugs with white star logos on yellow, 12x40", EX, D3 ....**$285.00**
Star Tobacco, sign, porcelain flange, white lettering on blue, We Sell Star Tobacco, 8x18", VG, A **$220.00**
Star Twist, spool cabinet, tin with glass front, 4 drawers, Guaranteed Fast Colors-Will Boil, American Thread Co, 9x16x4", EX+, A....................................**$30.00**

Star Weekly, door push, tin, white on red, white border, Star Weekly lettered diagonally above On Sale Here, rounded ends, VG, D3 ....$150.00
Starkist Tuna, bank, 1988, ceramic, Charlie Tuna surrounded by stacks of coins on tuna-can base, 9½", M, D....................................**$20.00**
Starkist Tuna, bathroom scale, 1972, vinyl cover shows Charlie in red hat & pink glasses, Sorry Charlie at top, oval, 13" long, EX, A....................................**$87.00**
Starkist Tuna, lamp, 1970, painted plaster with metal fixture, figural Charlie Tuna, shade not included, 12½x3", EX, D....................................**$70.00**
Starkist Tuna, squeeze toy, 1973, Charlie Tuna, vinyl, 7½", M, D **$35.00**
Starkist Tuna, tie clip & cuff links, 1970s, gold, die-cut figures of Charlie, name engraved on hat, EX, D **$45.00**
Starlight Marshmallows, tin, Starlight Marshmallows lettered above Cracker Jack Co, slip lid, round, EX, A **$45.00**
Staroleum Motor Oil, sign, porcelain, lettering in star, blue & white, chips/fading, 30" dia, D **$125.00**
Starr Arms Co, letterhead, 1864, factory image flanked by guns at top, VG, A **$180.00**
Starrett Precision Tools, catalog, 1938, 282 pages, VG+, H2....................................**$40.00**
Starrett Tools, pin-back button, ca 1900, red & white, EX, D....................................**$4.00**
State House Coffee, container, cardboard, political figure in center circle with product name above & below, 1-lb, EX, A....................................**$70.00**
State House Coffee, pin-back button, ca 1900, blue & white with red border, EX, D **$8.00**
State Mutual Life Assurance Co, letter folder, frontal view of the building, Kellogg & Bulkeley Co, rare, 12½x3", EX, A **$350.00**
State Seal, crate label, apple, Idaho state seal with blue ribbon on red background, 10½x9", M, C1 ....**$2.00**
Steak 'n Shake, platter, oval, Buffalo China, M, D2 ..**$10.00**
Stegmaier Brewing Co, tip tray, hand holding 4 bottles, ...Wilkes-Barre Pa on rim, hairlines/chips, 4¼" dia, VG, A....................................**$80.00**
Stegmaier Brewing Co, tray, beer bottles on fishing bank with gear in background, lettering & logo on rim, Shonk litho, 10½x14", VG, A **$125.00**
Stegmaier Gold Medal Beer, sign, tin over cardboard, product name & In Quarts lettered diagonally on bands at left of bottle, 8½x13", VG, A.............................**$25.00**
Stegmaier's Beer, foam scraper, celluloid, Drink..., Wilkes-Barre Pa, 8½x1", EX, H1 ....**$16.00**
Stegmaier's Beer, globe, tin & glass light-up, reverse-painted letters in script, 17x16" dia, G, A **$375.00**
Stegmaier's Beer, tray, red, black & gold, Steigmaier's Quality Beers..., 13¼" dia, EX, H1........................**$12.00**
Stein Club Havana Cigars, sign, 1909, tin, butler serves 5 card players cigars, lettering above & below, Kaufmann & Strauss litho, 20x28", EX, A **$1,300.00**

Steinhaus Lager, bottle, 1920s-30s, glass with label at top & base, Victor Brewing, Jeanette Pa embossed in center, 9½", EX, A $180.00
Stephenson Union Suits, pocket mirror, product name lettered on the diagonal over 2 acrobats performing, some flaking/wear, oval, 2¾", VG, A...................**$70.00**
Sterling Ale, label, pre-1920s, circular logo at left of product name, Rueter & Co, G, A **$5.00**
Sterling Beer, sign, porcelain, product name over armour clad soldier, Drink..., minor edge chips/soiling, 19" dia, VG, A....................................**$1,000.00**
Sterling Gasoline, measuring cup, 1940s-50s, glass, green logo & lettering, Use New..., measuring chart on back, 4¾", EX, A....................................**$15.00**

Sterling Gasoline, pump sign, porcelain, black & red on yellow & white, Sterling Gasoline around Sterling symbol in center, 9x11", EX, A **$270.00**

Sterling Gasoline, pump sign, porcelain, Sterling Super Blend Gasoline, S2 ....**$125.00**

Sterling Marshmallows, tin, blue lettering on cream, For Baking, Toasting & Eating...Redel Candy Corp, slip lid, 5-lb, 10" dia, VG+, D $57.50

Sterling Tobacco, store bin, tin, plaid, EX, D **$115.00**

Steuben Brew, sign, embossed die-cut cardboard, Indian in profile surrounded by acorn & leaf border, framed, image: 18x12", VG, A..**$450.00**

Stevens .410 Gauge Shotguns, phamplet, pictures a squirrel on front, red, black & white, EX, A..............**$130.00**

Stevens Rifles & Shotguns, sign, cardboard stand-up, pictures a beaver beside 2 shotguns, lettering on blue panels top & bottom, 25x14", VG, A........................**$100.00**

Stevens Shot Guns (sic), catalog, 1912, nonpictorial cover, well illustrated with logo & fancy green border on each page, 48 pages, EX, A..**$115.00**

Stevens Shotguns, pin-back button, lettered banner wrapped around 2 rifles, product name above, blue & white, round, EX, A **$220.00**

Stevens-Savage-Fox Shotguns & Rifles, sign, 1940s, self-framed cardboard stand-up, angry bear standing on hind legs, 16x12", VG, A....................................**$65.00**

Steward Iron Fence, postcard, 1914, mechanical, bottom flap folds down & replaces wood fence with new iron fence, ad text inside, EX, D **$35.00**

Stickney & Poor's Mustards, trade card, 2 little girls with baskets, 1 carrying a cat, EX, D..............................**$3.50**

Stillboma Oriental Polish, tin, pictures a deer, 6x2x2", EX, D...**$12.50**

Stix Dental Powder, tin, features lettering above & below denture graphics, VG, A **$40.00**

Stokely Van Camp, statuette, 1950s, ceramic, Easy on green base, 7½", NM, D....................................**$175.00**

Stoll Bros Automobiles, sign, die-cut cardboard, pictures 2 children in touring car, chips/tears/color loss, framed, image: 11½x14", G, A **$400.00**

Stollwerck Gold Brand Chocolate & Cocoa, tip tray, Stollwerck on stylized bow tie shape over globe, lettering above & below, fancy border, 5" dia, EX, A **$15.00**

Stone Hill Wine Co, sign, embossed tin, 'Bacchus Festival,' nymphs feasting & drinking, Compliments Of..., 23" dia, G-, A **$200.00**

Stonewall Whiskey, trade card, ca 1880, portrait of the Emperor of Germany, advertising in form of a poem on back, 6x3½", EX, P1 ....**$45.00**

Strathmore Hotel, sign, paper, pictures resort with people swimming in the foreground, minor marring/chips, framed, image: 24x30", VG, A............................**$250.00**

Strawberry Cigars, box label, outer, 1874, mice pulling large strawberry, 4½x4½", M, C3 ....**$7.50**

Strawbridge & Clothier, pocket mirror, pictures Santa in chimney, lettering around rim, 2⅛" dia, EX, A...**$775.00**

Strength, crate label, 1930s, California orange, elephant with tusks on yellow ground, Santa Paula Orange Ass'n, 10x11", M, C1 ....**$25.00**

Stroh's, stein, 1984, German-American Tricentennial, MIB, D ..**$60.00**

Stroh's, stein, 1984 Heritage Series, Our Family's 200-Year Brewing Heritage Assures You..., 7½", M, D........**$20.00**

Stroh's, stein, 1986, features Statue of Liberty, 1886-1986, 9", MIB, D **$60.00**

Stroh's Bohemian Beer, tray, hooded girl carrying case of beer in circular inset, chips/minor rust spots, 13¼x13¼", VG, A **$250.00**

Stroh's Bottled Beer, tray, hooded girl carrying case of beer, lettering on rim, minor scratches/rim wear, oval, 13x10½", VG, A **$200.00**

Stromeyer's Grape Punch, syrup bottle, label under glass, metal cap, 11½", EX, A **$100.00**

Stud Tobacco, cigarette papers, pictures white stallion rearing on hind legs, Stud lettered above, NM, A **$8.00**

Studebaker, pin-back button, Studebaker encircled in center, America's Finest above, Six & Eight below, red & blue, round, EX, A **$25.00**

Studebaker, salesroom brochure, 1950, foldout, dealer stamp in upper left front, 8 pages, 8x6", NM, D **$8.50**

Studebaker, thermometer, stenciled wood, lettering on red & white checked ground, Have You Seen The New..., 11¾", G+, A **$200.00**

Studebaker Batteries, clock, metal frame with glass front, numbered 12-3-6-9, Studebaker in blue above Batteries in red, 15x15", VG, A..**$115.00**

Studebaker Izzer, pin-back button, figural, EX, A..**$114.00**

Studebaker Jr Wagons, postcard, goat pulling kids in wagon in front of a tree with sign that reads: ...Just What The Boy Wants, minor wear, P3 ....**$35.00**

Studebaker Vehicle Works, pocket mirror, aerial view of factory, lettering below, oval, 2¾" long, EX, A **$50.00**

Studebaker Wagons, ad, ca 1900, paper, westerners transporting goods across a mountain range, original frame, 24x20", VG, A **$605.00**

Student Prince Beer, label, 1933-50, crown logo, Heidelberg Brewing Co, Internal Revenue Tax Paid statement, 1-qt, EX, A **$16.00**

Student Prince Draft Beer, label, 1933-50, crown logo, Heidelberg Brewing Co, Internal Revenue Tax Paid statement, 1/2-gal, EX, A **$10.00**

Style Cigars, box label, inner lid sample, 1890s, couple being driven in horseless carriage on city street, Geo S Harris litho, EX, A **$281.00**

Suburban, crate label, 1920s, California orange, mountain cottage & orchards, JJ McIndoo-Lindsay, 10x11¾", M, C3 .... **$85.00**

Sucaryl Brand Sweetener, tape measure, red & cream, push button, lettering faded, 1¾" dia, D **$2.50**

Success Manure Spreader, tip tray, pictures farmer using spreader, lettered rim, Kemp & Burpee Mfg Co, rectangular, 4¾" long, VG+, A **$210.00**

Sugar Candies, pail, 1930s-40s, silhouettes of children on light blue, United Candy Co, press lid & bail, 10-oz, 4x3" dia, VG, A **$20.00**

Sultana Peanut Butter, pail, product name flanked by seated children, yellow, red & black, press lid & bail, scratches, 1-lb, 4½", G, A $35.00

Sultana Peanut Butter, pail, product name flanked by seated children, yellow, red & black, press lid & bail, 1-lb, 4½", NM, A **$109.00**

Summer Belle Cigars, box label, inner lid, Niagara Falls & mountain scene, 6x9", M, C3 .... **$27.00**

Summer-Time Tobacco, tin, beach scene with seated man in top hat & girl with her back to him, slip lid, round, EX, A **$50.00**

Sun Crest, sign, cardboard hanger, You Can't Lose With Sun Crest above young baseball player & bottle, vertical, EX, A **$150.00**

Sun Crest, sign, die-cut cardboard hanger, Glamour Girls Like Glamour Drinks above girl & bottle, So Refreshing, 14x10", EX, A **$60.00**

Sun Crest, sign from drink rack, tin, black & white on red, Drink Sun Crest It's Best over white sun graphic, 9x17", EX, M2 .... **$42.00**

Sun Crest, thermometer, 1940s, embossed die-cut tin bottle, orange, green, blue & cream, 16", EX, A **$120.00**

Sun Cured Tobacco, pocket tin, upright, product name & smiling sun above lettered barrel, Ready For Pipe below, EX, A **$800.00**

Sun Drop Cola, sign, embossed tin, Sun & Drop flank Golden Cola emblem over cup & saucer, Refreshing As A Cup Of Coffee, 12x28", VG+, A **$82.00**

Sun Drop Lemonade, sign, tin, Have You Had Your Lemonade Today? on banner with lemon graphic above Sun Drop 5¢, World's Most..., EX, A **$160.00**

Sun Flower Chewing Tobacco, container, wood with paper label, Black men dancing surrounded by sunflowers, 12x11½" dia, VG, A **$400.00**

Sun Insurance Agency, sign, porcelain, smiling sun logo with blue lettering on white, English, minor rust at left edge, 14x20", VG, A **$100.00**

Sun Insurance Office, blotter, logo in black on pink, old soft-type, unused, minor stains, 6x3", D **$4.00**

Sun Maid Cigars, box label, inner lid, pictures woman holding box of cigars, 6x9", M, D **$4.00**

Sun Oil Co, sign, porcelain, blue on yellow with red & blue logo in center, 24x12", EX, D **$75.00**

Sun Smile Brand Mountain Bartlett Pears, crate label, 1930s, large smiling sun & rays on blue background, Colfax Cal, 7¼x11", M, C1 .... **$2.00**

Sun Spot Soda, matchbook cover, full-length ad with Bottled Sunshine lettered above 5¢ tilted bottle, 20 strike, NM, R1 .... **$8.00**

Sun Spot Soda, sign, embossed tin, Drink above orange circle reading Sun Spot, Bottled Sunshine below, vertical rectangle, EX, A **$85.00**

Sun-Drop Cola, sign, cardboard, pinup type featuring large bottle cap and bottle pouring into glass, 8¼x7½", G, A **$9.00**

Sun-Maid (Seedless) Raisins, trolley card, shows little girl paying 5¢ for box of raisins left of advertising & open 5¢ box, 11x21", EX, D3 .... $150.00

Sun-Maid Raisins, bank, 1987, hard vinyl, raisin figure standing by product box with paper label on yellow base, CALRAB, EX, A **$50.00**

Sun-Maid Raisins, recipe book, 1915, 'Recipes with Raisins,' 32 pages, G, D **$10.00**

Sun-Rise Beverages, sign, tin, Discover Refreshing & smiling sun above Pure Sun-Rise Beverages with juicy orange, 28x20", NM, M3 .... **$135.00**

Sunbeam, crate label, Spanish citrus, smiling girl holding oranges, M, C3 .... **$5.00**

Sunbeam Bread, bread end label, shows color photos of Hopalong Cassidy seated before curtain holding a gun, white border, EX, S1 .... **$15.00**

Sunbeam Bread, bread end label, shows hefty boy tugging on dog's leash, Walking The Dog Burns Up 150 Energy Units Per Hour!, EX, S1 .... **$3.00**

Sunbeam Bread, bread end label, shows Miss Sunbeam feeding bread to actor Peter Lawford, blue background, EX, S1 .... **$15.00**

Sunbeam Bread, doll, Little Miss Sunbeam, plastic, M, P2 .... **$125.00**

Sunbeam Bread

Sunbeam Bread, door push bar, metal, Reach For in red script at left of Sunbeam Bread in white script on dark blue, shows wear, D3 ....$55.00

Sunbeam Bread, pin-back button, 1930s, red & white, EX, D **$8.00**

Sunbeam Mixmaster, jigsaw puzzle, 1931, pictures 8 women using appliance in different ways, 8½x11½", EX, F1 ....**$35.00**

Sunbru Beer, label, 1933-36, Arizona Brewing Co, U-type permit number, 12-oz, EX, A **$12.00**

Sunflower Baking Powder, trade card, die-cut sunflower with girl's face in center, scarce, EX, A................**$38.00**

Sunkist, banner, die-cut cardboard, 2-sided, Sunkist lettered on 7 oranges with blossoms atop, lemons on reverse, 68", EX+, M2..**$110.00**

Sunkist, booklet, 'Tradition & a Dime Will Get You a Cup of Coffee,' full-color pictures of 70 different labels, M, C1 ....**$3.00**

Sunkist, clock, plastic, pictures boy & girl, Good Vibrations, G, D **$65.00**

Sunkist, crate label, 1930s, big wrapped orange on black ground, California Fruit Growers Exchange, Los Angeles, 10x11", M, C1 ....**$2.00**

Sunkist, recipe book, 1935, 'Sunkist Recipes for Everyday,' 48 pages, VG, D **$8.00**

Sunkist, recipe book, 1939, 'Sunkist Lemons Bring Out the Flavor,' 32 pages, VG, D **$7.50**

Sunland Motor Oil, sign, can shape, Sunland arched above Frictionezed in green on white, Motor Oil in white on orange below, EX+, D1 ....$250.00

Sunlight Axle Grease, pail, smiling sun & product name in oval center, slip lid & bail, 5x5" dia, EX, A **$88.00**

Sunlight Soap, sign, porcelain, white on blue, corners chipped, 9x6", D **$50.00**

Sunny Boy Peanut Butter, pail, boy eating sandwich with product name above & below, red & cream, slip lid & bail, 16-oz, 3½x4" dia, G, A................................**$100.00**

Sunny Cove, crate label, 1930s, California orange, Spanish-style home overlooking orange groves, Redlands, 10x11", M, C1 ....**$3.00**

Sunoco, sign, 1950s-60s, porcelain flange, 2-sided, Sunoco Charge Accounts Honored, black & white, 18x14", VG, A **$80.00**

Sunoco, sign, 1955, tin, Just Ahead... above arrow at left, diamond logo at right, red, yellow & blue, minor dents, 22x70", A...**$110.00**

Sunoco, see also Blue Sunoco

Sunoco A To Z Lubrication, sign, 1950s, porcelain, white A To Z outlined in red at right of Sunoco Lubrication, navy ground, 11x30", VG, A..............................**$130.00**

Sunoco Dynafuel, gas globe, ca 1915, milk glass with blue border, diamond logo in center, minor scratches to lens, 14½" dia, A **$285.00**

Sunoco Dynafuel, gas pump, 1950s, Wayne Pump Co on porcelain display front, diamond logo below, original pump sign, restored, 63", A............................**$1,000.00**

Sunoco Motor Oil, display rack, 1920-30, porcelain light-up, yellow with red highlights, Sunoco lettered in blue, 36x29", EX, A...**$400.00**

Sunoco Motor Oil, sign, 1930s-40s, porcelain, black lettering on yellow, Distilled lettered in red diamond above, 12x10", EX, A $360.00

Sunoco Self-Emulsifying Spray, sign, embossed tin, For Your Trees above product name, Sun Oils diamond logo & For Sale Here below, 17x24", VG, A **$80.00**

Sunray Natural Power Oils, sign, painted metal, sun shining behind product name, yellow & black on green, octagon, 7x7", VG+, A **$170.00**

Sunray Natural Power Oils, sign, 1950s, porcelain, Sunray in black letters superimposed over sun rays, Natural Power Oils below, 17x7", VG, A **$350.00**

Sunrise Ale, label, 1933-50, Sunrise Brewing Co, Internal Revenue Tax Paid statement, 12-oz, EX, A...........**$15.00**

Sunset Club Cigars, box label, outer, men in tuxedos seated around table, 4½x4½", M, D **$8.00**

Sunshine Beer, clock, electric, glass front, Drink Sunshine Premium Beer, plug frayed, 15" dia, G, A **$105.00**

Sunshine Biscuits, calendar, 1922, girl in yellow & pink gown with brown stole ready for an evening out, June sheet, worn, 15x9", VG, A....................................**$5.00**

Sunshine Biscuits, display rack, metal, 3 red-lettered shelves, Loose-Wiles Biscuit Co, advertising on side panels, 45x39¾", G, A..**$375.00**

Sunshine Biscuits, pocket knife, Imperial, 2-blade, G, D..**$35.00**

Sunshine Biscuits, tin, pictures Liberty Bell, octagonal, EX, D...**$40.00**

Sunshine Cigarettes, sign, 1932, embossed tin, full-color image of open pack of cigarettes, Twenty lettered above, 18x14", EX, D..**$170.00**

Sunshine Enameled Ranges, pocket mirror, Sunshine lettered over rising sun, company name below, 2¼" dia, EX, A...**$22.00**

Sunshine Kisses, tin, 1920s-30s, Chandler & Rudd Co's... on sunrise scene flanked by graphics, slip lid, 7x10" dia, G, A..**$50.00**

Sup R Popt Ready To Eat Popcorn, tin, fan-shaped graphic lettered with product name over popcorn background, pry lid, 14-oz, 10x8" dia, VG, A..............**$30.00**

Super Par Regular '100,' sign, porcelain, Super Par with oversized S&P on red above circle with plane above Regular '100' on black, 12x11", VG, A...............**$350.00**

Super Power, gas globe, 1940s, porcelain with red metal body, product name in white on black & red flag, 15" dia, EX, A..$325.00

Super X Ammunition, plate, ironstone, red & blue on white, logo on rim, band around center of plate, 6" dia, EX, D...**$125.00**

Superior Ale, label, 1933-36, Superior above Ale in script, logo at top, U-type permit number, 12-oz, G, A...**$10.00**

Superior Grain Drills, pocket mirror, pictures farm girl on drill encircled by lettering, The Name Tells The Story, 2⅛" dia, EX, A..**$1,100.00**

Superior Salted Peanuts, tin, cream with steamship on tropical waters, pry lid, 10-lb, EX, D3................**$250.00**

Superla Cream Separator Oil, can, 1930s-40s, black & white image of 2 children using separator, screw lid & handle, 1-gal, 10½", EX, A...................................**$25.00**

Superman Fruit Punch, carton, EX, D2...................**$20.00**

Supp-Hose Stockings, display, painted 3-D hard rubber figure in cloth dress seated on metal chair, lettering on wood base, 18", EX, A...**$425.00**

Supreme Dental Powder, tin, 1936, pictures smokers, green, black & silver, 5x1½" dia, EX, D...............**$10.00**

Supreme Light Beer, label, 1933-50, South Bethelem Brewing Co, Internal Revenue Tax Paid statement, 12-oz, VG, A...**$6.00**

Surbrug's Grain Cut Pipe or Cigarette Tobacco, pocket mirror, shows nude emerging from brown tobacco leaves, oval, 2¾", EX, A......................................**$800.00**

Sure Shot Chewing Tobacco, store bin, tin, Indian shooting bow & arrow, ...It Touches The Spot, red, yellow & blue, 10x15x7½", VG, A.....................................**$550.00**

Sure Shot Chewing Tobacco, store container, tin, Indian kneels on rock with bow & arrow, red lettering, slip lid with knob, 5x10x15", EX, A................................**$435.00**

Surefine Coffee, tin, product name on split bands above small cup of coffee in circular inset, key-wind lid, 1-lb, EX+, A...**$30.00**

Surety Aspirin, display with 12 full 10¢ tins, 1940s, 4x4", EX, D...**$44.00**

Sutter Maid Asparagus, label, large gold lettering, blue goose logo & asparagus on black ground, EX, G1..................**$2.00**

SW Venable & Co Tobacco, sign, clay-coated stock, St George slaying dragon surmounted by trumpeters, factory above, framed, image: 29x23", VG, A.........**$950.00**

Swan, crate label, apple, large white swan on black background, 10½x9", M, C1...**$5.00**

Swan Brand Flavoring Extract, pocket mirror, pictures various fruits before a swan, product name above & below, 2¼" dia, EX, A...**$225.00**

Swastika Pure Grain Alcohol, can, 1950s-60s, logo in center with product name above & below in blue, white ground, pour spout, 1-gal, 10", EX, A..................**$65.00**

Sweatman's Quality Ice Cream, thermometer, wood, boy with soda above Insist On... above bulb, girl with sundae below, round top, square bottom, EX, M1..**$250.00**

Sweet, Orr & Co's Overalls, pin-back button, ca 1900, black, white & blue, EX, D....................................**$4.00**

Sweet, Orr & Co's Pantaloon Overalls, sign, cardboard, men in tug-of-war with pair of trousers, ...Easy Fitting Pants..., framed, image: 24x20", EX, A.............**$1,600.00**

Sweet Burley Tobacco, store bin, tin, Sweet Burley surrounded by tobacco leaves, red background, tall cylinder shape, VG+, A..**$125.00**

Sweet Caporal Cigarettes, sign, paperboard, lettering above & below woman in clown suit on blue ground, Standard For Years, framed, 28x18", G+, A........**$190.00**

Sweet Caporal High-Class Cigarettes, sign, paperboard, Sweet Caporal above cla$sical lady standing before garden, Kinney Bros, gilt frame, 28x19", G+, A...**$200.00**

Sweet Caporal Cigarettes, banner, canvas, white, green, black & red on white, product name on horizontal oval in rectangle, 36x60", EX, M2...............................**$12.00**

Sweet Cuba Fine Cut Tobacco, sign, early 1900s, woman holding product in front of tobacco field, New Sealed..., matted & framed, 22x18", EX, A...........................**$75.00**

Sweet Cuba Fine Cut Tobacco, store bin, tin, oval portrait of woman in profile against green background, slant top with wood knob, VG, A **$150.00**

Sweet Cuba Fine Cut Tobacco, store bin, tin, yellow with red lettering, slanted hinged lid, 12x18x14", EX+, A $350.00

Sweet Cuba Light Fine Cut Tobacco, tin, pie shape, red & black on yellow, 1-lb, 2x8" dia, EX, H3 .... **$50.00**

Sweet Georgia Brown Hair Dressing Pomade, tin, 2 oval portraits with product name above & below, round, M, D **$8.00**

Sweet Girl Peanut Butter, pail, Sweet Girl above & Peanut Butter below girl's portrait on white emblem on blue, bail handle, 1-lb, NM, A $3,000.00

Sweet Heart Flour, thermometer, porcelain, red & white on blue, heart logo above thermometer, lettering below, arched top, 27", VG, A **$260.00**

Sweet Home Bread, box, wood, lettering between horizontal bands, Kuss Bakery, Mishawaka Ind, 23x24x33", VG, A **$330.00**

Sweet Home Soap, trade card, The Mother above mother holding 2 infants, product name below, EX, A **$10.00**

Sweet Hona Cigars, box label, inner lid, 1886, pictures bouquet of flowers, 6x9", M, C3 .... **$7.00**

Sweet Jasmine Talcum Powder, tin, lettering surrounded by floral motif, tall round can with shaker top, scarce, EX, A **$25.00**

Sweet Mist Chewing Tobacco, store bin, oval image of children at fountain, product name above & below, Scotten-Dillon Co, square slip lid, VG, A **$165.00**

Sweet Reflection Cigars, box label, inner lid sample, 1880s, lady looking at reflection in mirror, John's & Co litho, M, A **$40.80**

Sweet Tip Top Tobacco, sign, cardboard, horse-drawn fire engine, ...Beats All Smoke & Chew, rare, original frame, 23½x36", VG, A **$1,450.00**

Sweetheart Products, sign, porcelain, heart shape, white on red, ...Hard Wheat Flour, White Corn Flour, White Corn Meal, 5x5", EX, A **$170.00**

Sweetheart Soap, pack of 4 bars bound in red band advertising, Sweetheart 1 Cent Soap Sale..., package in shades of green, 6x2", EX, H1 .... **$16.00**

Sweetie, door push, 1930s, tin, orange, white & black on white, Drink Sweetie above tilted bottle, orange border, 17", EX, D3 .... $150.00

Sweney Motor Oil, scraper, product name on wooden handle, scratches on blade, 3½x2¼", D **$18.00**

Swift & Co, pin-back button, red, green & white, EX, D .. **$18.00**

Swift & Co, recipe book, 1950, '77 Recipes Using Swift-ning,' 35 pages, G, D **$5.00**

Swift's Beef Extract, trade card, portrait of a woman with serving tray, advertising on reverse, EX, A **$28.00**

Swift's Premium Frankfurts, pocket mirror, mustached fella overlooking Swift's Premium Frankfurts banner, Tender & How!, 2½" , NM, A **$67.00**

Swift's Premium Oleomargarine, sign, paperboard, little girl in chef's hat seated at table, For Table Or Cooking Purposes, framed, 19x14", VG, A **$475.00**

Swift's Sausage, pin-back button, 1930s, blue & white, EX, D **$5.00**

Sylvan Sandalwood Talc, tin, pictures Taj-Mahal above lettering, shaker top, appears EX, A **$40.00**

Synol Liquid Soap, blotter, ca 1905, pictures girl washing her hair, 3½x6", EX, D **$10.00**

Syrup of Figs, sign, embossed celluloid, woman picking figs, Nature's Pleasant Laxative..., minor soiling, 11x8", EX, A **$300.00**

Syrup of Figs, sign, 1896, self-framed wood, woman holding figs in countryside scene, Tuchfarber Co, 20x14", EX, A **$495.00**

T

T Kingsford & Son Starch, trade card, 2-sided, starch exhibit on front, factory scene on back, EX, A **$18.00**

T&B Cigars, punchboard, Play Football & Smoke, 5 Cents Per Sale, pictures 2 1930s football players, unused, 10x7¼", EX, H1 .... **$20.00**

Ta-Cu Cigars, box label, outer, 1913, map of Cuba & Florida, 4½x4½", M, C3 .... **$12.00**

Taber Pump Co, catalog, ca 1920, 16 pages, VG, D ... **$6.50**

Taco Bell, bank, bus shape, M, D2 .... **$20.00**

Tacoma Beer, sign, reverse-painted glass, milk glass with red letters & green & blue slag glass, The Model..., framed, 36x73", VG, A $4,000.00

Tacoma Beer, tray, comical image of 2 Persian cats, Anti Katzenjammer stamped in center, Best East Or West above, 13½" dia, VG, A $550.00

Tafel Beer, label, pre-1920, logo flanked by product name, Terre Haute Brewing Co in script above, G, A **$10.00**

Tagolene, can, 1922-29, yellow tag in center, Skelly Oil Co below, blue, yellow & red, screw lid & handle, 1/2-gal, 6", EX, A **$210.00**

Taka-Kola, sign, self-framed tin, ...Every Hour above lady with bottle standing before clock, Take No Other, 13x9", EX, M1 .... **$800.00**

Taka-Kola, tip tray, pictures Taka-Kola girl lifting bottle above head surrounded by Roman numerals, lettered rim, 4" dia, EX, A **$300.00**

Talisman, crate label, 1930s, California orange, 3 talisman roses on blue & black background, Redlands, 10x11", M, C1 .... **$2.00**

Tallman Stogies, tin, scarce, EX, D **$350.00**

Tally Ho Condom, tin, very scarce, EX, D **$275.00**

Tampa Life Cigars, box label, inner lid, golf, tennis & bathing scenes, 6x9", M, C3 .... **$18.00**

Tang, telephone, Tang Lips on round base, very scarce, EX+, M2 .... $200.00

Tang, toy figure, 1980s, Tang Lips, PCV, 3", M, D **$2.00**

Tangee Face Powder, tin, Art Deco design on orange background, EX, D **$7.50**

Tannhauser Beer, label, 1920-28, product name on diagonal band, Royal Brewing Co, 12-oz, EX, A **$15.00**

Tannhauser Beer, light, hanging, back-lit tin & glass, eagle logo above product name & Beth Uhl Brewing Co, 17x16" dia, EX, A **$1,600.00**

Tannhauser Beer, thermometer, ca 1896, brass case with paper dial, eagle logo surrounded by lettering, 9" dia, G, A **$95.00**

Tanqueray Gin, banner, canvas, white lettering on green background, 45x28", EX, D **$6.50**

Tap Beer, label, 1933-50, logo above product name, Birk Bros Brewing Co, Internal Revenue Tax Paid statement, 12-oz, VG, A **$9.00**

Tappan Appliance Co, statuette, 1950s, painted plaster, Tappan Chef kneeling with open arms, 8", VG, D **$55.00**

Tappen Shoe Mfg Co, bookmark, die-cut celluloid, shaped as bottom of 2 feet with advertising, White & Hoag litho, 2⅞x2¼", NM, A **$48.00**

Target Long Cut Tobacco, cigarette papers, pictures bull's eye with Target lettered above & Long Cut Tobacco, Chew-Smoke below, NM, A **$6.00**

Target Super Hybrid Popcorn, can, bull's-eye logo & product name lettered diagonally over unpopped & popping corn, unopened, 10-oz, EX, A **$200.00**

Tarrant's Seltzer Aperient, trade card, sick family opens up to healthy family, minor crease, EX, A **$15.00**

Tarrant's Seltzer Aperient, trade card, sickly maiden opens up to rosy-cheeked maiden, EX, A **$9.00**

Tarrant's Seltzer Aperient, trade card, sickly man opens up to healthy man, scarce, minor crease, EX, A .. **$28.00**

Tarzan Cups, sign, paper, pictures Tarzan riding a lion, Delicious Ice Cream In..., Free!, Save Tarzan Cup Lids..., 5x18", EX, A **$70.00**

Tastee Bread, sign, porcelain, white on red, 17", EX, D... **$90.00**

Tastee Freeze, toy figure, 1988, Oreo Cookie Man, bendable rubber, 4½", NM, D **$6.00**

Tatham & Brothers American Standard Drop Shot, trade card, 1860s, nonpictorial, specks for shot on reverse, black & white, VG, A **$110.00**

Taystee Bread, bread end label, shows 2 TV actors who portray Range Rider & Dick West with guns at fence, Favorite Bread Of..., EX, S1 .... **$10.00**

Teacher's Pet, crate label, 1950s, Washington apples, little boy handing apple to teacher, Manson, 9x10½", M, C3..... **$25.00**

Teacher's Scotch, mirror, smoked glass, plastic frame, 19x11", EX, D **$25.00**

Teacher's Scotch Whiskey, bust figure, 3-D painted papier-mache, teacher in graduation cap, lettering on base, minor chips, 12", VG, A **$25.00**

Teddy Bear Peanut Butter, pail, black & silver on yellow, product name above & below bear, flared bottom, bail handle & pry lid, scarce, EX, A **$968.00**

Teem, sign, tin, green Enjoy... on white left of white Lemon-Lime... above lemon on green, yellow & red border, 12x31", NM, M3 .... **$120.00**

Telling's Ice Cream, pin-back button, boy & girl reaching into large bucket of ice cream, round, EX, A **$92.00**

Tennessee Furniture Corp, catalog, 1929-30, features Cavalier refrigerators, 64 pages, VG, D **$50.00**

Tennyson 5¢ Cigars, dispenser, tin, Tennyson pictured on tall square container on pyramid base with advertising, Always Fresh, 10x5x5", G, A **$264.00**

Terre Haute Brewing Co, pocket mirror, pictures sexy lady hugging large beer bottle, company name & address around rim, 2⅛" dia, EX, A $675.00

Terre Haute Brewing Co, tip tray, colonial men & women lifting their glasses to cherubs, Ever Welcome Beer lettered below, 4½" dia, EX, A **$80.00**

Terre Haute Brewing Co, tray, deep-dish, colonial men & women lifting their glasses to cherubs, Ever Welcome..., oval, 15¼x12½", G, A **$155.00**

Tesoro Rancho, crate label, 1930s, California orange, red tile-roofed home flanked by palms & orchards, Placentia, 10x11", M, C1 .... **$3.00**

Tested Carbonated Beverages, sign, embossed tin, diagonal 2-color field, bottle at left, ...All Flavors, ...Coca-Cola Bottling Wk's, 20x28", EX+, A **$130.00**

Texaco, calendar, 1922, The Texas Company Petroleum & Its Products surround star logo atop calendar, full pad, 25x13", EX, A $185.00

Texaco, calendar, 1941, pictures woman above Texaco signs & symbols, January/February pads, corner bent/edge wear, 19x9½", A **$20.00**

Texaco, gas globe panel, leaded glass, Texaco lettered over top of star logo on round bordered panel, 22" dia, EX, A **$935.00**

Texaco, letters from side of oil tanker truck spelling Texaco, white porcelain outlined in black, 14x12" each, EX+, A **$215.00**

Texaco, name badge, 1930s, metal frame with celluloid window & paper insert, round Texaco star logo atop, 1½x2", EX, A **$94.00**

Texaco, oil cart, metal, logo on front end, 3-wheeled, 2 pumps on top, restored, 37x19x53", EX, A.... **$358.00**

Texaco, pump sign, ca 1940, porcelain, fire hat & star logo with product name above, red, gold & black, 12x8", NM, A **$150.00**

Texaco, pump sign, porcelain, keyhole shape, Reg TM star logo atop panel reading Agent above The Texas Company, 13x11", EX, A **$425.00**

Texaco, sign, ca 1939, die-cut porcelain, red & blue star logo above IA Kutzer Consignee in blue, white ground, 13x11", EX, A **$200.00**

Texaco, sign, ca 1940, porcelain, No Smoking flanked by star logos, white with black letters, 4x23", M, A **$185.00**

Texaco, sign, ca 1950s, die-cut porcelain, red & black star logo above Oil Co Distributor, white background, EX, A **$160.00**

Texaco, sign, 1930s, porcelain, round with star logo, 16" dia, M, D3 .... **$475.00**

Texaco, sign, 1955, porcelain, keyhole shape with star logo above Cyr Oil Company, Distributor below, 12½x11", NM, A **$240.00**

Texaco, sign from lube machine, porcelain, Texaco star logo on white, 15" dia, VG, A **$100.00**

Texaco, sign from truck, dated 1954, porcelain keyhole shape, round star logo above distributor name, 12½x10½", EX, D3 .... $365.00

Texaco, stained glass window, ca 1923, milkglass, green T on red star in center, Texaco in black, white ground, 22" dia, EX, A **$850.00**

Texaco, toy tanker boat, motorized plastic, red & black with logo on stack, box reads Exclusive...Dealer Offer..., 5x27", NM, A **$180.00**

Texaco Certified Lubrication, sign, 1932, porcelain, star logos flank Texaco Certified Lubrication, In Accordance With Approved Practice, 9x39", EX, A **$255.00**

Texaco Crankcase Service, sign, porcelain, star logo above Crankcase service in bold, other text below, bordered with dash marks, 22x28", EX, A **$850.00**

Texaco Ethyl, sign, porcelain, 2-sided, round star logo overlapping round Ethyl logo on red background, 30" dia, VG, A **$375.00**

Texaco Fire Chief, fireman's helmet, celluloid, red with gold label, gold & black lettering, 19th Street Texaco SS, VG, A **$25.00**

Texaco Fire Chief, fireman's helmet, 1960s, hard plastic, NM, D **$70.00**

Texaco Fire Chief, sign, ca 1955, porcelain, pictures fireman's hat & star logo, red, white & black, minor edge wear, rectangular, A **$40.00**

Texaco Fire Chief Gasoline, sign, painted tin, Fire Chief Gasoline above fireman's hat on 2-tone field, Localized For You... below, 16x16", VG, A **$25.00**

Texaco Gasoline & Motor Oil, sign, porcelain, 2-sided, Gasoline-Motor Oil lettered around star logo, Made By The Texas Company below, 42" dia, VG+, A **$450.00**

Texaco Golden Motor Oil, pump sign, porcelain, Drain & Refill With above image of pouring oil left of Clean, Clear..., curved, 15" dia, G, A **$250.00**

Texaco Havoline Motor Oil, bank, cardboard oil can, EX, D **$5.00**

Texaco Mail Port, sign, 1937, porcelain, white with red & yellow marine flags at left of red Texaco above black Mail Port, 17x23", EX, A **$565.00**

Texaco Marine Lubricants, sign, porcelain, seagulls above product name flanked by star logo, ships below, 15x30", EX, A $1,725.00

Texaco Marine Lubricants, sign, 1961, tin, product name at right of star logo overlapping diagonal tricolored panel showing 3 boats, 15x30", EX, A **$60.00**

Texaco Marine White Gasoline, sign, ca 1951, porcelain, star logo on ships wheel above Marine White in script, minor flaking, 18x12", VG+, A **$475.00**

Texaco Motor Oil, blotter, pictures early automobile, driver & garage man, unused, water spotted on back, 6x3½", D **$10.00**

Texaco Motor Oil, can, 1930s, star logo with product name atop, easy pour spout, tall cylinder, 1/2-gal, EX, A **$200.00**

Texaco Motor Oil, can, 1935-45, Texaco symbol top center on red background, product name on white below, 1-qt, 5½", EX+ **$50.00**

Texaco Motor Oil, clock, 1935-45, star logo in center on white background, metal rim, minor scratches, 14½" dia, A **$425.00**

Texaco Motor Oil, sign, porcelain flange, 2-sided, company name around star logo, product name below, 37x48", VG, A **$900.00**

Texaco Motor Oils, sign, porcelain, Gasoline Filling Station lettered around star logo reading Texaco Motor Oils, 42" dia, G, A **$700.00**

Texaco Outboard Motor Oil, can, 1935-45, boat motor with product name in green & red on white ground, logo above, screw lid, 1-qt, 7½", EX, A **$15.00**

Texaco PT Anti-Freeze, sign, die-cut cardboard, Get It Now! on clouds with wind-blown leaves, can at left, PT Anti-Freeze below, 17x14", VG, A **$80.00**

Texaco Sea Chief, pump sign, embossed metal, elongated hexagon shape with Sea Chief lettered above small star logo, 10x15", EX, A **$200.00**

Texaco Sky Chief Supreme Gasoline, sign, 1950s, porcelain, Sky Chief on band above Texaco star, ...Petrox below, red, green & white, 18x12", NM, A **$55.00**

Texaco Touring Service, map holder, metal, single pocket in green with red shield, white lettering, includes maps, 9x4x2½", EX, A **$80.00**

Texaco 574 Oil, can, 1930s, star logo with product name above & text below, green ground, screw lid, minor wear, 1-qt, 6", A **$25.00**

Texas Pride Lager Beer, tray, Texas Pride in script above factory image, Keg & Bottle, Texas' Own lettered on rim, 10¾x13½", G-, A **$25.00**

Texas Punch, sign, tin, yellow with Texas Punch on red cloud flanked by rodeo rider & tilted bottle, 9x27", NM, M3 .... **$145.00**

Texberry, dispenser, barrel shape with white & silver bands, red & green lettering, pump missing, 11¾", G, A **$80.00**

TH Chubb Rod Co, ad cover, 1880s, bust portrait of Mr Chubb, VG, A **$50.00**

Thendora Cigar, sign, 1920s, embossed cardboard, pictures girl on square inset, The Bouquet Of Quality, 7x15", EX, D **$16.50**

Thermo Anti-Freeze, bank, can shape with snowman graphics above lettered band, EX, A **$14.00**

Thermo Anti-Freeze, thermometer, stenciled tin, dark blue & red on yellow, Time For Non-Rusting Anti-Freeze, wood frame, 72", VG+, A **$90.00**

Thermo Anti-Freeze, thermometer, tin, red & white on black, arrow indicates Time For Thermo, lettered above, rounded top & bottom, 39", G, A **$35.00**

Theroux's Ice Cream, sign, painted metal, Theroux's arched above dish & block of ice cream, Ice Cream & Taunton Mass below, 28x19", VG, A **$180.00**

Thirty Below, see 30 Below on page 305

Thistle Cocoa Hardwater Soap, container, glass ball shape with metal lid, 10", EX, A **$120.00**

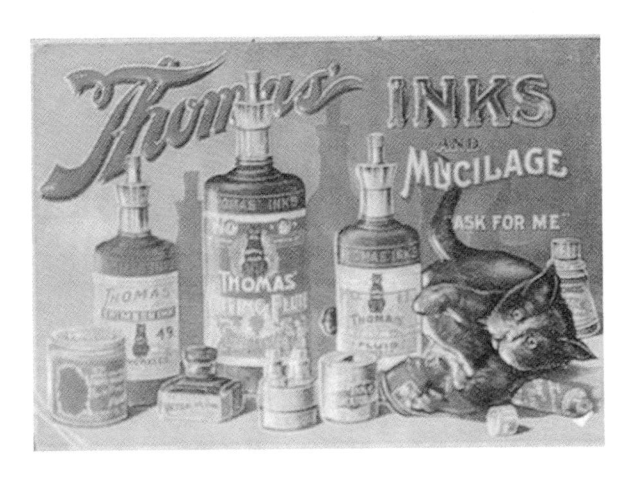

Thomas' Inks & Mucilage, sign, embossed tin, display of products with black cat spilling jar of ink, ...Ask For Me, 13½x19½", EX, A $15,500.00

Thomas Bread, door push plate, porcelain, Push above Don't Forget lettered diagonally above loaf of bread, vertical, EX, M1 .... **$100.00**

Thomas Glass, sign, die-cut porcelain, 2-sided, Authorized Sales & Service seal superimposed over early car, 22x30", VG, A **$1,300.00**

Thomas Moore Distilling Co, sign, tin, men playing cards in front of log cabin with barrel & bottles in foreground, framed, image: 23x31", G, A **$375.00**

Thomas Ryan Fire Arms Manufacturers, letterhead, 1877, pictures a large red revolver, A **$8.00**

Thompson's Malted Milk, container, aluminum, product name in script on front, EX, A **$70.00**

Thompson's Malted Milk, container, porcelain with heavy metal lid, Thompson's in script above Double Malted, Malted Milk, EX, A **$225.00**

Thompson Slotted Clinch Rivet, tin, pictures a clinch rivet flanked by product name, Edwin B Simpson & Son above, slip lid, 4x6", EX+, A **$35.00**

Thompsons Wild Cherry Bitters, clock, mantel, cast iron, bottle flanked by cherubs with cherries abound, It's Time To Drink, 17½x15x4", EX, A **$550.00**

Three Arches, crate label, 1930s, California orange, rock formation extending to ocean, Villa Park Orchards Assn, 10x11¾", M, C3 .... **$20.00**

Three Feathers Plug Cut, pocket tin, orange, white, yellow & black, Three Feathers arched above logo showing 3 white plumes, VG+, A **$165.00**

Three States Mixture, pocket tin, flat, Kentucky, Virginia & Louisiana lettered on wavy bands, slip lid, scarce, oval, EX+, A **$405.00**

Three Twins Cigars, box label, inner lid, pictures 3 children in a basket, 6x9", M, D **$7.00**

Tide Water Associated Credit Cards, sign, tin, 2-sided, red & blue on green, Friendliness Lives Here & winged A logo at top, ...Welcome, 14x20", NM, B1 .... **$85.00**

Tiger Chewing Tobacco, lunch box, tiger on red & black basket-weave, slip lid on shoulder opening, 2 handles, 4x7x5", VG, A **$45.00**

Tiger Chewing Tobacco, lunch box, tin, tiger on red & black basket-weave, slip lid on flush opening, 7¾x10x5½", EX, A **$65.00**

Tiger Chewing Tobacco, store bin, blue with tiger logo, holds 48 5¢ packages, slip lid on shoulder opening, scarce, 11¾x8½", EX+, A **$1,100.00**

Tiger Chewing Tobacco, store bin, orange with tiger logo, holds 48 5-cent packages, slip lid on shoulder opening, 11¾x8½" dia, G, A **$50.00**

Tiger Cigarettes, sign, paper litho, girl hugs tiger, each holds cigarette packs, Utterly Different 20 For 10¢, metal frame, 17x10", VG, A **$100.00**

Time Premium Gasoline, sign, porcelain, round clock in center with product name above & below, 14x9", NM, S2 .... **$395.00**

Time Super Gasoline, pump sign, porcelain, U-shaped with Time in bold letters above clock image, Super Gasoline below, 14⅛x9¼", NM, A, ... **$325.00**

Times Square Smoking Mixture, pocket tin, upright, pictures night scene at Times Square, NM, A **$198.00**

Times Square Smoking Mixture, pocket tin, upright, pictures night scene at Times Square, EX, A **$102.00**

Timken Oil Burner, jigsaw puzzle, comic book format showing people complaining about existing furnace then getting a Timken, 9x9", EX, F1 .... **$35.00**

Timur Coffee, tin, very rare, 1-lb, EX, A **$1,400.00**

Tiolene Motor Oil, sign, porcelain, Drain & Refill With above circle with arrow underlining Tiolene, Motor Oil below, 43x34", EX, A **$160.00**

Tiolene Motor Oil, sign, porcelain, white on blue, Product of USA & oval logo at right of Tiolene 100% Super-Pennsylvania..., 18x70", VG, A **$135.00**

Tiolene Motor Oil, sign, 1925-35, porcelain, 2-sided, white arrow going through bull's-eye & lettering on blue ground, 25½" dia, G, A **$190.00**

Tip Top Bread, bread end label, black & white image of baseball star Roy Campanella, Brooklyn Dodgers, red border, 2¾x2¾", EX, S1 ....**$150.00**

Tip Top Bread, bread end label, black & white image of Cisco Kid on horse, Cicso Kids Choice, red border, 2¾x2¾", EX, S1 ....**$8.00**

Tip Top Bread, flipper pin, 1940s, plastic, red, white & blue with How Ya Feelin'? on back, EX, D **$14.00**

Tip Top Tailors, clock, 1950s, light-up, M, D **$150.00**

Tippecanoe, sign, paper, pictures a birch canoe, ...The Best For Malaria, Tired Feeling, minor paper loss, 9x21", G, A..**$50.00**

Tirador Havana Cigars, sign, self-framed tin, Tirador lettered above bust portrait of musketeer, Havana Cigars below, 28x22", EX, A **$300.00**

Tirador Havana Cigars, sign, self-framed tin, Tirador lettered above bust portrait of musketeer, Havana Cigars below, 28x22", NM+, D......................................**$650.00**

Tivola Brewing Co, tray, deep-dish, man holding tray flanked by logo & factory inset, lettering on rim, 12" dia, VG, A **$125.00**

Tivoli Lager, tip tray, lady lifting glass on green ground, gold-lettered product name on red rim trimmed in gold, 4¼" dia, EX, A..................$325.00

Toiletine, trolley sign, 1920s, cardboard, text flanked by man with shaving brush & product bottles, 11x21", EX, D...**$25.00**

Tokay Punch, sign, 1920s, cardboard hanger, pictures glass in front of vase of flowers, 14x10", EX, D **$16.00**

Tokio Cigarettes, sign, paperboard, genie standing on 5¢ rug is served by child, sun setting on Arab city beyond, framed, 33x25", VG, A **$105.00**

Toledo & Ann Arbor Railroad, sign, paper, train crossing trestle bridge surrounded by vignettes, Go West Via Hoosac Tunnel Line, 22x32", VG, A **$2,000.00**

Toledo Wheel Co, catalog, 1908, features wicker carriages, 74 pages, VG, D **$85.00**

Tom Collins Jr, sign, tin, Drink Tom Collins Jr 5¢ in script, elongated horizontal rectangle, EX, A.................**$20.00**

Tom McAn, game, 1933, Fortune Teller, shoe broadcast souvenir, EX, D2 ....**$25.00**

Tomahawk Plug, sign, ca 1900, paperboard, figural painter's pallet picturing Indians, P Lorillard & Co, 25x17", G, A **$1,430.00**

Tootsie Roll, bank, metal top & bottom with cardboard sides, Tootsie Roll shape, EX, D **$15.00**

Tootsie Roll, display case, tin & glass with decaled label, Pure Delicious Chocolate Candy, 9x7¼x5¼", VG, A..........**$750.00**

Tootsie Roll, matchbook cover, full-length ad, Delicious in script above large Tootsie Roll, 1¢ & 5¢, 20 strike, front strike, NM, R1 ....**$7.00**

Top Card, crate label, California pear, stack of cards with ace of spades showing, blue background, Suisun, 8x11", G1 ....**$2.00**

Top Peak, crate label, California apple, silhouette of San Gorgonia Peak on black ground, orange letters, Redlands, 9x11", G1..**$2.00**

Topic Cigars, tin, pictures romantic couple with Topic arched above, slip lid, EX+, A............................**$115.00**

Topsy Hosiery, match holder, tin, Quality Shows In Topsy Hose arched above logo, Leading Dealers lettered on striker, 5", G, A **$95.00**

Topsy's Famous Chicken, matchbook cover, Eat With Your Fingers, shows Mammy, 10 stike, gray front striker, G-, R1 ....**$12.00**

Torch Light Tobacco, sign, 1942, cardboard, pictures factory worker with tobacco pack, It's Great Chewing, 10¢, 14x16", EX, D **$30.00**

Tortoise Shell Cut Roll Tobacco, tin, beach scene with men killing tortoises, slip lid, 2x3¼x1", EX, A...............**$125.00**

Tortoise Shell Tobacco, pocket tin, flat, VG, D **$250.00**

Tosetti Export, label, pre-1920s, logo above product name, G, A..**$43.00**

Tourist, sign, mid-1930s, porcelain, 2-sided, white Tourist lettered over black auto on yellow ground, 20x36", EX, D3..$3,500.00

Towle's Bucket Syrup, tin, bucket shape, no lid or handles, A **$75.00**

Towle's Log Cabin Syrup, display, die-cut cardboard, wooded scene at syrup camp with theatrical window to forest of trees, 28x22x7½", EX, A...................**$1,600.00**

Towle's Log Cabin Syrup, pin-back button, ca 1896-98, pictures log cabin, roof lettered with product name, Absolutely Pure,⅞" dia, EX, A **$21.00**

Towle's Log Cabin Syrup, spoon, silvered brass with cabin on end of handle, Souvenir...Golden Gate, May 5, 1908 in bowl, 4½" long, EX, A **$35.00**

Towle's Log Cabin Syrup, syrup glass, 1940s, clear with product name on red panel, double-spout, 2x1¾" dia, EX, A **$56.00**

Towle's Log Cabin Syrup, tin, cabin form picturing lady & girl, EX, A **$90.00**

Towle's Log Cabin Syrup, tin, Frontier Inn scene, 4½x5x3", NM, A **$60.00**

Towle's Log Cabin Syrup, tin, Mom flips pancakes at window while boy stands in open door, Yum! Those Griddle Cakes Sure Taste Great! 12-oz, NM, A **$95.00**

Towle's Log Cabin Syrup, tin, Mom flips pancakes at window with dog at open door, Wonder If They'll Give Me Some, Huh?, 12-oz, EX, A **$65.00**

Towle's Log Cabin Syrup, tin, pancakes, EX, D.....**$12.50**

Townsend West Milk, Cream, Butter, Eggs & Cottage Cheese, bill hook, pictures girl drinking glass of milk, oval, 2¾", VG, A **$50.00**

Toyland Peanut Butter, pail, tin, white lettering above rows of toy soldiers on blue background, bail handle, press lid, 1-lb, EX, A..............................$120.00

Toys R Us, doll, 1986, Geoffry (giraffe), yellow floppy legs & large feet with shoes, store logo, 20", M, N1....**$20.00**

Track Side Economy Motor, gas globe, 1919, metal body, Economy lettered on yellow diamond with Track-Side... in blue above & below, 16" dia, VG, A **$325.00**

Traffic Motor Oil, can, 1939-52, traffic light above product name, company name below, blue & white, pour spout & handle, 2-gal, 11", EX, A **$45.00**

Traveler's Insurance Co, pocket mirror, pictures a train with lettering above, oval, 2⅜", VG+, A **$120.00**

Traveler's Insurance Co, pocket mirror, pictures a train with lettering above, oval, 2⅜", G, D...................**$60.00**

Travelodge Motel, squeeze toy, 1970s, Sleepy Bear, molded vinyl, 5½", M, D **$20.00**

Treasure, crate label, yam, golden yams & other treasures coming out of pirate's chest, G1 ....**$2.00**

Treasure Line Stoves & Ranges, tip tray, stove & factory scene, 7x4", VG, D **$85.00**

Trek High Test Anti-Freeze, can, product name above snow scene, 1-qt, VG+, A **$10.00**

Trenton Bock Beer, label, 1933-36, charging ram, Peoples Brewing Co, U-type permit number, 12-oz, EX, A...**$20.00**

Triangle Club Peanut Butter, pail, tin, red inverted triangle logo on blue & white striped background, pry lid & bail, 5-lb, G, A $43.00

Tricksy Lee Cigars, box label, outer, portrait of a woman in large white hat, 4½x4½", EX, D **$5.50**

Tricksy Lee Cigars, sign, glass, product lettering & company name at left of woman's portrait, horizontal, diagonal corners, EX, M1..............................**$340.00**

Triner's Bitter Wine, poster, mother, father & daughter on heart-shaped inset above list of products, matted & framed, image: 18x13", VG, A **$50.00**

Trio Club Cigars, box label, inner lid sample, 1901, playing card showing king with arms around queen & jack, American Litho, M, A **$131.00**

Triple AAA Root Beer, bottle, 1946, clear with red & white label, 6-oz, EX, D **$12.50**

Triple AAA Root Beer, sign, tin, Just Say & bottle flank lettered red octagon on yellow & white background, 19x18", NM, M3 ....**$95.00**

Triple AAA Root Beer, sign, 1930s, cardboard hanger, tilted bottle with Just Say & 5¢ encircled above & below, 13x7", NM, B1 ....**$6.00**

Triple AAA Root Beer, sign, 1950s, die-cut tin, labeled bottle, St Louis Mo on bottom, Stout Sign Co, G, A..**$40.00**

Triple Diamond International Service, sign, porcelain, red Triple Diamond Service lettered around black International over 3 diamonds, 42" dia, EX, A...........**$120.00**

Triple XXX Root Beer, bottle, 1945, clear with yellow & red label, 8-oz, EX, D **$9.50**

Triple XXX Root Beer, bottle, 1973, clear with yellow & red label, 10-oz, EX, D **$5.50**

Triple XXX Root Beer, push bar, porcelain, yellow on red, ...XXXtra Creamy...XXXtra Delicious...XXXtra Good, 29½" long, VG, A **$120.00**

Triple 16 Ounce Cola, sign, tin, tilted bottle on red & white ground, Triple 16 Ounce Cola on white dot above, It's Bigger..., 32x12", NM, M3 .... **$75.00**

Triumph Cycles, poster, paper, screen print of Victorian lady with bicycle, Coventry lettered vertically at right, framed, 46x30", VG, A **$700.00**

Triumph Force Feed Grain Drill & Seeder, trade card, colorful farm scene, Manufactured By JW Stoddard & Co, Dayton, O lettered below, EX, A **$32.00**

Trixie Root Beer, alarm clock, automated, Black girl with braided bows winks as clock ticks, Home Brewed, working, 6x4½" dia, EX, A.................................. **$500.00**

Trojan Motor Oil, can, early 1930s, Trojan logo on circular inset, cream on red, pry lid, 1-qt, 5½", EX, A **$15.00**

Trojan Motor Oil, can, metal, white Cities Service on red above white Trojan's head logo & product name on blue circle, 1-qt, unopened, D3 .... **$45.00**

Trommer's Beer, ad, 1952, peel & stick, pictures glass & horseshoes, 9x5", EX, D **$4.00**

Trommer's Evergreen Brewery, tray, factory & summer garden scene with busy street scene in foreground, lettering on rim, oval, 13¾x16½", G-, A **$100.00**

Trop-Artic All-Weather Motor Oil, bank, can shape, shield logo, EX, A.. **$12.00**

Trop-Artic Auto Oil, cup, ca 1915, tin, split image with touring car in arctic scene & in tropical scene, handled, 2¼", M, A **$300.00**

Trop-Artic Motor Oil, can, 1915-25, split image with touring car in arctic scene & in tropical scene, 1/2-gal, NM, A...$1,355.00

Tropicana, lunch box & thermos, plastic, NM, D...... **$15.00**

Trout, crate label, apple, large leaping trout, small portrait of an Indian in profile on an arrowhead, 10½x9", M, C1 .... **$2.00**

Trout-Line Tobacco, pocket tin, upright, pictures man trout fishing on lettered circle, product name above & below, EX+, A **$660.00**

Tru Ade Soda, bottle, 1964, clear with red & white label, 7-oz, EX, D.. **$7.50**

Tru Ade Soda, sign, stenciled metal, tilted bottle & ...Drink A Better Beverage, original shipping paper on back, 14x20", EX, A.. **$100.00**

Tru Ade Soda, sign, tin flange, yellow, white Tru Ade on red dot & tilted bottle, Drink A Better... on black below, 14x20", NM, M3...................................... **$175.00**

Tru Age Beer, tray, man in center, 13x13", VG, D... **$26.00**

Tru Value Hardware, catalog, 1974, features toys, VG, D **$45.00**

Tru-Blu Beer, tray, deep-dish, stock image of horse & dog, ...Northampton Brewing Co on rim, chips/scratches, 13" dia, G, A **$200.00**

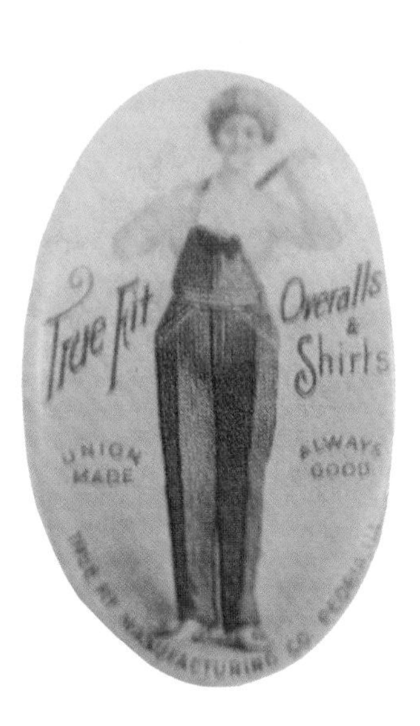

True Fit Overalls & Shirts, pocket mirror, pictures bare-breasted lady fastening overalls flanked by lettering, oval, 2¾", VG+, A...........................$150.00

Trujoy Cigars, box label, inner lid, 2 roses & gold medal, 6x9", M, C3... **$8.00**

Truth Spice, bread box, pictures George Washington on front & sides, G, D **$195.00**

Trutox Biological Supplies, catalog, 1928, 230 pages, VG+, H2 .... **$50.00**

Tube Rose Scotch Snuff, sign, tin, can of product & coupons right of name, It's Mild...& Suits Your Taste!, round corners, 18x28", EX, A **$85.00**

Tube Rose Snuff, sign, tin, product name above can with red arrow pointing to coupons, Always Mild & Satisfying! below, 24x17", NM, M3 .... **$125.00**

Tubular Cream Separators, match holder, die-cut tin, cows above mother & daughter using separator, Pet Of The Dairy, pitting, 6¾", G-, A............................. **$160.00**

Tuckett's Abbey Pipe Tobacco, pocket tin, upright, factory image with product name above & below, slip lid, 4", NM, A **$275.00**

Tuckett's Marguerite Cigars, sign, self-framed tin, bust portrait of lady in gold gown & red flower in her hair, emblem lower right, 28x22", EX, M2.............. **$2,100.00**

Tulane Motor Oil, can, 1925-45, Tulane in graduated letters above highway scene, red background, screw lid & handle, 2-gal, 10½", EX, A **$75.00**

Tulip Soap, sign, paper, woman surrounded by tulips & insets of horse-drawn wagons, CL Jones & Co, framed, 27½x21½", G-, A... **$50.00**

Tulsa, sign, porcelain, black Tulsa on white diamond shape with red & black accents, 40x60", EX, D3............. **$475.00**

Tulsa Hi-Test, gas globe lens, 1920s-30s, product name in red with gold graphic below, gold border, 13½" dia, EX, A **$60.00**

Tums, matchbook covers, set of 12, 6 from series A, 6 from series C, 20 strike, front strike, colorful, NM, R1..**$11.50**

Tums, ruler, wood, 12", EX, D....................................**$5.00**

Tums, thermometer, aluminum, white, yellow, & blue on blue, Tums (in bold) For The Tummy above, lettering below, 9x4", VG, A..**$20.00**

Tums, thermometer, aluminum, dark blue with cream & yellow lettering, Tums For The Tummy above, lettering below, 9x4", EX,..**$50.00**

Tums, thermometer, tin face, thermometer arched above Tums in bold print, 10¢ & roll of product below, rust, 9" dia, G-, A..**$5.00**

Turck's Compound Emulsion, blotter, celluloid over cardboard, elegant woman & floral pattern, logo in black, white & red, 3x7¾", EX, D **$10.00**

Turkey Brand Roasted Coffee, tin, lettering above & below turkey surrounded with filigree border, scarce, EX, A...**$1,050.00**

Turkey Red Cigarettes, sign, early 1900s, paper, girl in fez holds pack to mouth, fez on either side, product name on frame, 34x23½", EX, A $360.00

Turkish Delight Cigarettes, sign, celluloid, bulldog smoking a cigarette, His Master's Tip lettered above, matted & framed, image: 18x13", G-, A **$130.00**

Turkish Trophies Cigarettes, sign, paper, product name lettered diagonally above Turkish girl with arm bent behind head, framed, 29½x19½", G, A...............**$240.00**

Turkish Trophies Cigarettes, sign, porcelain, white with red product lettering, single red pin stripe around border, 12x35½", EX, A..**$100.00**

Tuxedo Handerchief, display, metal, tall square shape on slightly larger base, EX, A....................................**$50.00**

Tuxedo Pure White Pepper, tin, yellow ground, Tuxedo arched above circular graphic flanked by leaves, Pure White Pepper below, EX, M2 ....**$9.00**

Tuxedo Tobacco, pocket tin, blue with gold, Patterson's Tuxedo Tobacco in gold above man encircled in gold, lettering below, EX, M1 ....**$50.00**

Tuxedo Tobacco, pocket tin, flat, with contents, encircled portrait, Fresh...Specially Prepared For Pipe Or Cigarette, NM, A **$30.00**

Tuxedo Tobacco, sign, cardboard, elegant couple at a restaurant, Bring Me The Latest..., matted & framed, image: 15½x11½", EX, A...................................**$180.00**

TWA Airlines, clipboard, logo & printing on clip, paint scratches on clip, VG+, P4..................................**$12.00**

TWA Airlines, coffeepot, silverplated with gooseneck spout, International Silver Co, minor dent on back, 7", EX, D..**$110.00**

Twin Kiss Rootbeer, mug, fluted glass, G, D **$25.00**

Two Homers Cigars, label, Two Homers arched above 2 homing pigeons on oval field with fancy end borders, They Always Come Back, 4x4", EX, D...................**$5.00**

Two In One Shoe Polish, dispenser, cylinder form with black & red on cream, 2 in 1 Shoe Polish 10¢ All Colors, 13", EX, A **$45.00**

Two Queens Cigars, box label, outer, 1894, Indian maiden & white woman, 4½x4½", EX, C3 ....**$22.00**

Two Star Radiator Solder, clock, 1920s-30s, oak regulator, logos on numbered space & bottom glass panel, 38x16", A, EX,..**$600.00**

Two-Star Radiator Solder, clock, 1920s-30s, oak regulator, logos on numbered space & bottom glass panel, 38x16", A, G, ...**$110.00**

Two Wheelers Cigars, box label, inner lid, young girl with 2 mules, 6x9", EX, D **$16.00**

Tydol, banner, cloth, New Tydol in bold above woman driving at left of First In Mileage, Power, Anti-Knock, 36x59", EX, A..**$225.00**

Tydol, gas globe, 1935-45, black Tydol With Ethyl lettered on white, orange & black border, black metal casing, 14" dia, VG, A..**$275.00**

Tydol, pump sign, 1920s, porcelain, black Tydol on white, orange & black circle on black, 13x12", EX, D3 ....$285.00

Tydol Flying A, pump sign, Tydol Flying above winged-A graphic, bordered, 9¾" dia, EX+, A **$170.00**

Tydol Gasoline, sign, painted die-cut metal, 2-sided, Tydol man above The Lubricating Gasoline That Drives-Oils-Cleans, 14x10", VG, A.......................................**$175.00**

Tydol Gasoline, sign, porcelain, 2-sided, product lettered in black on white with black & orange border, metal frame, round, EX, A **$190.00**

Tydol Gasoline, signs, cardboard, set of 4 Tales Of The Road with various comical car scenes, ad text below, 22x14", G-VG, A **$350.00**

U

U&I Soda, bottle topper, die-cut cardboard, smiling boy & girl above panel reading Lets Drink & Play, U&I Everywhere, 10x7", NM, A **$15.00**

U&I Soda, display, die-cut cardboard stand-up, bottle & 2 full glasses on tray, Lets Drink & Play..., 24x18", NM, M3 .... **$35.00**

Uco Pumpkin, can label, pumpkin & red logo on white background, Newark NJ, EX, G1 .... **$3.00**

Ulmer Beer, window, large letters on rippled & slag glass, original frame, 3x8 ft, G, A **$500.00**

Ultrex Platinum Condoms, tin, crown logo, M, D **$32.00**

UMC, pin-back button, large UMC in center, Annie Oakley Shoots UMC Ammunition on border, red & white, round, EX, A **$375.00**

UMC, pin-back button, large UMC in center, Shoot Arrow Or Nitro Club Shells on border, round, VG, A **$22.00**

UMC Cartridge Co, sign, moose at lake flanked by various types of ammunition, Union Metallic Cartridge Co below, framed, 43x58", EX, A **$775.00**

UMC Cartridge Co, sign, paper, red UMC over bullet chart, ships at sea below, framed, 39x53", EX+, A $2,500.00

UMC Cartridges, sign, 1905, paper, 'In A Tight Place,' pictures a hunter aiming at angry bear, bands missing, 25x16", VG, A **$350.00**

UMC Cartridges, sign, 1906, paper, 'For Strenuous Sport,' pictures hunter aiming at lion in tree, metal band top & bottom, 25x16", VG, A **$900.00**

Uncle Green Cigars, tin, 1950s, oval portrait of the founder over tobacco field, product name above & below, slip lid, round, EX+, A **$110.00**

Uncle Jake's Seegar, box label, inner lid, 1925, comical bearded man & cat, M, C1 .... **$3.00**

Uncle John's Syrup, display, die-cut cardboard stand-up, Uncle John behind counter with lettering, 12½x16¾", G, A **$15.00**

Uncle John's Syrup, trolley sign, large syrup can at right of product name, man guiding yoke of oxen through the snow, framed, A **$75.00**

Uncle Sam Range, sign, paper, patriotic interior with Black man pulling turkey from oven for Uncle Sam to present, framed, 13x21", EX, A **$9,000.00**

Uncle Sam Shoe Polish, tin, white with figure of Uncle Sam on both sides, 2" dia, EX+, D3 .... **$38.00**

Uncle Sam Tobacco, pocket tin, upright, Canadian, rare, D **$2,750.00**

Uncle Wabash Cupcakes, sign, cardboard, pictures lettering at right of seated Black man playing banjo w/plate of cupcakes above, 13x11", EX, A **$40.00**

Uncle Wiggily Peanut Butter, pail, tin, Uncle Wiggily At Seashore, slip lid & bail, 1-lb, NM, A $650.00

Underwood Portable Typewriter, blotter, 1935, full view of typewriter, unused, 6x3½", P1 .... **$7.00**

Underwood Typewriter, pin-back button, ca 1900, pictures a typewriter in black & white with red border, white lettering, EX, D **$6.00**

Uneeda Biscuit, sign, cardboard, boy in yellow slicker holds product box by blackboard, Don't Forget Uneeda Biscuit, 16x21", EX **$120.00**

Uneeda Biscuits, see also Nabisco & National Biscuit Co

Unicy Marshmallows, tin, Unicy in diagonal script, slip lid, round, VG, A **$25.00**

Uniform Cut Plug, tin, oval image of a sailor & lettering on paper label, original tax stamp on slip lid, 7x4¼", EX+, A **$150.00**

Union Brewing & Malting Co's Cascade Beer, sign, ca 1900, embossed tin on cardboard, Uncle Sam & other gentlemen toasting, We Never Disagree..., 17x21", VG, A **$880.00**

Union Central Life Insurance, sign, self-framed tin, large image of the home office, light soiling/rubs, 37½x25½", EX, A **$550.00**

Union Commander Tobacco, lunch box, tin, VG, D **$375.00**

Union Furniture, pocket mirror, bust of nude woman within heart, EX, D...**$95.00**

Union Gasoline, sign, die-cut porcelain, 2-sided, shield logo above Speed & Power, red & blue on white, 26x32", VG, D..**$175.00**

Union Leader Cut Plug, lunch pail, tin, eagle atop product, gold lettering & logo on red, wire handle, scratches/chips/dents, 4x8x5", EX, D...........$60.00

Union Leader Cut Plug, sign, ca 1900, paperboard, pictures Uncle Sam with naval fleet in background, ...Leads Them All, framed, 25x17", EX, A........**$2,090.00**

Union Leader Cut Plug Smoke & Chew, sign, embossed tin, Union Leader Cut Plug lettered in yellow above & below red cigarette pack on dark blue, VG, A.................**$230.00**

Union Leader Redi Cut Tobacco, pocket tin, upright, oval portrait of Uncle Sam, product name above & below, EX+, A...**$275.00**

Union Leader Smoking Tobacco, pocket tin, pictures Uncle Sam, EX, D..**$55.00**

Union Leader Smoking Tobacco, tin, red & gold with eagle logo, 6¼x5" dia, EX, D...............................**$30.00**

Union Metallic Cartridge Co, billhead, 1878, aerial factory view, VG, A..**$35.00**

Union Metallic Cartridge Co, display board, ca 1890, display of cartridges surround elk & deer scene in diamond-shaped inset, 41x55", NM, A **$8,250.00**

Union Metallic Cartridge Co, sign, felt, colorful bird atop shell, Steel Line Shot Shells above, UMC encircled in each corner, framed, 11x12", EX, A **$400.00**

Union Metallic Cartridge Co, sign, felt, 22 Smokeless lettered on diagonal center band, New Ungreased, Clean, Sure... above & below, 11x12", VG, A...............**$230.00**

Union Oyster Co, trade card, girl holding piece of paper lettered Baltimore Oysters, company name above, scroll background, EX, A..**$90.00**

Union Pacific Tea, tray, little girl with pink hair bow surrounded by multiple images of little girl & boy, bear & snowman, 8" dia, VG, A **$70.00**

Union Sport Tobacco, box label, outer, man in formal attire with yacht & horserace scene in background, 4½x4½", M, D **$5.00**

Union Stamped Shoes, pocket mirror, pictures shield & shoe, M, D **$75.00**

Union Standard Chewing Tobacco, sign, paper, smiling man holding product saying I'm A Union Man, Chew Union Standard below, 13x13", NM, A **$20.00**

Union 76, auto compass, orange, blue & white, suction cup mount, EX, D **$12.00**

Union 76, print, 1940s service station, signed Stan Cline, 5x7", EX, D **$10.00**

Union 76, sign, porcelain, Certified Car Condition Service lettered on zigzag border around 76 above Union, 22" dia, VG+, A..**$100.00**

Union 76, sign, porcelain, Certified Car Condition Service lettered on zigzag border around 76 above Union, 22" dia, NM, A...**$190.00**

Union 76 Gasoline, pump sign, porcelain, orange with white Union above & Gasoline below 76 in blue, 11" dia, NM, D...$110.00

Union 76 Plus Gasoline, sign, porcelain, blue, white & orange, 11½" dia, EX, D **$125.00**

Union 76 Super-Royal Triton Motor Oil, bank, tin, purple, orange, blue & silver, 3x2" dia, EX, D...........**$25.00**

Union 7600 Gasoline, pump sign, porcelain, orange with white Union above & Gasoline below 7600 in blue, 11" dia, VG+, D3...**$85.00**

United, gas globe, 1920-30, milk glass, bull's-eye design with United lettered across center, base is soiled, 15½" dia, EX **$300.00**

United Brand Shirts, display, die-cut cardboard, mechanical, man's head pops out of folded white shirt, 8x3", EX, A...**$100.00**

United Coffee, tin, blue & white with gold seal over patriotic bow tie, product name above & below, 1-lb, EX, A **$115.00**

United Motors, sign, porcelain & neon, Service lettered on flashing touring car, United Motors above & below, oval, 21x36", EX, A..**$600.00**

United Motors, sign, 1910-20s, die-cut porcelain, 2-sided, early touring car & lettering on oval top, Hyatt...below, 17x18", NM, A **$1,500.00**

United States Cartridge Co, booklet, 'The Black Shells,' pictures hunter with rifle, 12 pages, EX, A..........**$40.00**

United States Cream Separator, calendar, 1910, girl in profile with cows beyond, Vermont Farm Machine Co below, March/April pad, framed, 30x20", EX, A $200.00

United States Fidelity & Guaranty Co, calendar, 1900, cardboard, shield shape, children in uniform & portrait inserts, April pad, framed, image: 20x16", EX, A**$300.00**

United States Horse Shoe Co, watch fob, silver, horseshoe shape with letter S around it, company name on back, EX, D **$28.00**

United States Hotel, Boston trade card, vignette of hotel & street scene, Under New Management..., EX, A......**$55.00**

United States Tires Sales & Service Depot, sign, painted metal in wood frame with slanted-roof front, 2-sided, lettering above & below ribbon, 42", VG, A **$200.00**

Universal Batteries, ashtray, 1950s, ceramic, pictures 12V battery, EX, D **$10.00**

Universal Batteries, playing cards, double deck, 1 blue, 1 maroon with heart logo, velvet box, D **$10.00**

Universal Blend Coffee, tin, paper label with Universal arched over male figure in wide stance flanked by Brand & Coffee, knob lid, 1-lb, A **$15.00**

Universal Clothes Wringer, trade card, Black woman being reprimanded for torn clothing, opens up to Black woman being praised, EX, A **$22.00**

Universal Electric Cleaner, sign, tin, gold stenciled letters above Universal woman decal on brown, green border, curved top & bottom, 28x16", G-, A **$5.00**

Universal Natural Milker, sign, 1920s, tin, blue & black lettering on orange, We Sell...., Stevens Hardware Co, Oneonta NY, 11½x35½", G, A..............................**$50.00**

Universal Stoves & Ranges, match holder, tin, product name on world globe above lettering, Made By Cribben & Sexton Co..., 4¾", EX, A.................................**$200.00**

Up To Date Pure Candy, tin, 1920s-40s, orange lettering on tropical background, Candy Mfg Co, New York, screw lid, 5-lb, 8¾", EX, A **$15.00**

Upland Pride, crate label, 1930s, California orange, red rose & bud on navy ground, Euclid Ave Orange Assoc, Upland, 10x11", M, C1 ....**$5.00**

Upper 10, bottle, 1955, green with yellow & red label, 10-oz, EX, D...**$9.50**

Upper 10, bottle, 1957, green with white & yellow label, 10-oz, EX, D..**$8.00**

Upper 10, sign, embossed tin, Up! Up! UP! left of Upper 10, tilted bottle at right, ...For A Bigger Better Lift!, 12x29", M, D1 ....**$95.00**

Upper 10 Lime-Lemon Soda, sign, tin, yellow with Drink Upper 10 Lime-Lemon Soda, Pick You Up left of bottle, 12x30", EX+, M3 ....**$85.00**

Uptown, door push bar, tin, Drink & Buvez lettered diagonally on either side of yellow, black & red Uptown logo, 3x30", EX, M2...**$52.00**

US Ammunition, ad cover, 1910, with letterhead of Norton Hardware, campfire scene, scarce, VG, A **$85.00**

US Ammunition, envelope, campfire scene, VG, A..**$30.00**

US Cartridge Co, gambling book, 1895, cover shows cards & chips, It's All In The Draw, cartridge ad at end, string bound, 6x10", EX, D **$175.00**

US Cartridge Co, sign, paper, hunter seated on a rock holding up a shotgun shell, The Black Shells... below, 12½x8½", VG, A **$250.00**

US Cartridge Co, sign, tin, pictures large shell, embossed lettering, The Black Shells, Romax, Climax & Ajax, 9x13", VG, A...**$450.00**

US Climax Black Shells, ad cover, 1923, pictures hunter & dog behind display of shells, scarce, VG, A....................**$170.00**

US Marine Cut Plug, lunch pail, product name on green basketweave background, rectangular, NM, H3...**$50.00**

US Marine Cut Plug Tobacco, roly poly, 1920s, man in vest & tie with apron smoking a pipe, head lifts, minor paint chips, 7", A..**$700.00**

US Shot-Shells & Cartridges, calendar, 1931, 'Opportunity,' man beside dog with dead game, full pad, framed, 31½x16", VG, A **$650.00**

US Tires, sign, frosted glass, yellow US split horizontally by white Tires on blue circle on white rectangle, 12x15", EX, A **$35.00**

Usher's OVG Whisky (sic), pitcher, clear glass with reverse-painted lettering in bottom, 5¼", EX, A...**$45.00**

Usher's OVG Whisky (sic), shot glass, pictures man with shotgun & product name on porcelain holder, minor wear, 3½x3¼" dia, VG, A...................................**$175.00**

Utica Beer, tray, pictures brewery with street scene in the foreground, West End Brewing Co, blue, orange & yellow, EX, D **$70.00**

Utz & Dunn's Footwear, display stand, reverse-painted glass with wood frame, beveled mirror on back, Ladies & Misses..., 42x42x17½", VG, A..........................**$400.00**

V

V Lower's Gambrinus Brewery Co, sign, die-cut tin, barrel shape with round inset showing company name around king lifting goblet, 26x20", EX, D3 ....**$2,200.00**

Valdura Asphalt Paint, sign, porcelain flange, 99.5% Pure...Waterproofs Anything, red, white & blue, oval, 13½x18", VG, A **$145.00**

Valentine's Automobile Varnishes, thermometer, celluloid, black with red & cream lettering, red border, Why Drive A Shabby Car? above, 20x5½", EX, A **$110.00**

Valley Flame, lug box label, grapes, scenic view of vineyards, cold storage plant & grapes, EX, G1 ....**$2.00**

Valley Forge Special Beer, pocket mirror, Valley Forge Special lettered above bottle, Adam Scheidt Brewing Co below, oval, EX+, D **$130.00**

Valley Shoe Service, sign, wood with incised lettering, 2-sided, 3-D shoe atop, 60" long, G+, A................**$300.00**

Valley View Cherries, can label, vignettes of Yosemite Valley, poppies & cherries, Selma, EX, G1 ....**$10.00**

Valspar Paints, oil painting for ad, dated 1937, 3 kids in bath scene, signed FN Donaldson, framed, 28x43", EX, A..$4,950.00

Valspar Varnish, tin, pictures 1940s man & woman, 1/2-pint, EX, D **$22.00**

Valvoline, sign, porcelain, 2-sided, Pennsylvannia 100% Pure Motor Oils above & below Valvoline over dots in center, 30" dia, NM, A.....................................**$1,600.00**

Valvoline Motor Oil, can, 1960s, World's First... in script above printed Valvoline, gold & cream background, pry lid, 1-qt, 5½", EX, A **$40.00**

Valvoline Motor Oil, key chain/pen knife with nail file, simulated mother-of-pearl handle, 1 blade, in original box, EX, D **$30.00**

Valvoline Motor Oil, pump, 1925-40, green with black hose, painted round tin sign above, Pennsylvania 100% Pure..., chips on sign, 34", EX, A **$160.00**

Valvoline Motor Oil, sign, tin, yellow on green, Valvoline lettered vertically above Motor Oil, yellow-lined border, NM, M3 ....**$175.00**

Valvoline Motor Oil, sign, 1930s, tin, 2-sided, large logo in center, cream, green & red lettering, Pennsylvania 100% Pure..., 7" dia, VG, A..**$75.00**

Vam Hair Tonic, sign, 1940s, tin stand-up, 2-sided, pictures a barber pole, Try New...For Healthy Handsome Hair, 9x28", EX, D **$50.00**

Van Bibber Pipe Tobacco, pocket tin, flat, oval portrait left of product name, slip lid, scarce, EX, A **$67.00**

Van Camp Hardware, display, die-cut tin salesman with movable arm behind bench, minor bending/chips, 62x41¾x13", VG+, A.......................................**$1,500.00**

Van Camp's Concentrated Soups, sign, 1910-1920, embossed die-cut tin, Van Camp kids holding soup tureen & can of tomato soup, 32x23", G+, A......**$1,500.00**

Van Camp's Pork & Beans, pocket mirror, shows the Van Camp kids ready to serve beans flanked by lettering, cracked mirror, 2" dia, VG+, A.............................**$45.00**

Van Camp's Soups, clock, shows soup can, A **$300.00**

Van Dole's Hot Chocolate, display, ceramic, Dutch girl sitting atop barrel embossed with product lettering, 12", VG+, A **$150.00**

Van Duzer's Fruit Extracts, trade card, girl stacking fruit on tiered tray, ...Are The Best For Flavoring... lettered on tablecloth, EX, A **$28.00**

Van Dyck Cigar, sign, cardboard hanger, 1920s, encircled portrait of Van Dyck & lettering within oval, Very Choice...15¢, 12x8", NM, B1 ....**$35.00**

Van Dyck Havana Cigars, sign, 1910-15, shaped as painter's palette with portrait of said artist, colors of paint & brushes, 8x12", EX+, M1 ....$800.00

Van Houten's Cocoa, sign, cardboard, lady standing at table pouring tea, Best & Goes Farthest lettered on tablecloth, framed, 36x22", VG, A......................**$350.00**

Van Houten's Cocoa, sign, paper, little girl raising baby to table for cup of cocoa, fading & tears, gesso frame, image: 27x21", G-, A **$800.00**

Van Houten's Cocoa, sign, paperboard, Dutch man & woman conversing at fence, Best & Goes Farthest, original wood frame, 27x16", G+, A.........................**$225.00**

Van Houten's Cocoa, trade card, pictures dogs greeting little girl in bed, Early Visitors on border, EX, A.................**$32.00**

Van Houten's Cocoa, trade card, unhappy man with cup labeled Imitation opens to man drinking Van Houten's Cocoa, EX, A..**$36.00**

Van Houten's Cocoa, trade card, unhappy woman with cup labeled Imitation opens to happy woman drinking Van Houten's Cocoa, EX, A **$46.00**

Van Houten's Cocoa, trade card, Victorian children fishing on dock with dog, product name upper left, colorful, EX, A **$28.00**

Van Ness Dust Absorber, tin, 1915-25, early touring car above lettering, text on sides, yellow background, slip lid, 5x3½", NM, A **$30.00**

Vandalia, crate label, 1930s, California orange, elegant male peacock in front of full moon, Porterville, 10x11", M, C1 .... **$2.00**

Vanderbilt Sure Tred Premium Tires, clock, ca 1958, glass lens, leopard straddling large V flanked by Sure Tred in 'speeding' letters, 15" dia, EX, A **$120.00**

Vanity Fair Cigarettes, sign, paper, monochromatic image of standing frog with cattail, ...Will Not Bite The Tongue, 10½x8½", EX, A **$130.00**

Varsity Blend, tin, flag above product name lettered diagonally in script, slip lid, 5x3½", EX, A **$12.00**

Vaseline, display box, tin with celluloid front, stands vertical with products shown on front, 13x7x6", EX+, M2 .... **$120.00**

Vaudeville Cigars, box label, outer, boys dressed in tuxedos, 4½x4½", M, C3 .... **$10.00**

Veedol Heavy Duty Plus Motor Oil, bank, can shape with winged 'V' logo, EX, A **$10.00**

Veedol Motor Oil, banner, cloth, bird above striped shorts on clothesline, It's Time To Change To Warm-Weather Veedol, 36x38", G, A **$120.00**

Veedol Motor Oil, can, 1935-45, winged V with High Detergency... lettered above & below on red ground, pry lid, 1-qt, 5½", EX, A **$25.00**

Veedol Motor Oil, sign, cardboard, can of product before image of king-of-hearts, lettering below, framed, 64x32", VG, A $550.00

Veedol Motor Oil, sign, die-cut tin flange, 2-sided, oil-can with Veedol above winged A, World's Most Famous... below, 19x24", EX, A **$100.00**

Veedol Motor Oil, sign, die-cut tin flange, 2-sided, Veedol above winged A logo, World's Most Famous Motor Oil below, 19x12", NM, B1 .... **$75.00**

Veedol Motor Oil, sign, 1920s-30s, tin, Veedol above logo, black, orange & cream, scratches/rust, framed, 72x15", A **$130.00**

Veedol Motor Oil, sign, 1930s, porcelain, 2-sided, Ask For... & 100% Pure Pennsylvania Supreme Quality on black, arched top, 29x22", NM, A **$360.00**

Veedol Motor Oils-Greases, sign, porcelain, orange lettering on black, bold Veedol above Motor Oils, Greases below, lined border, 14x10", EX+, A **$250.00**

Veedol Tractor Oil, thermomerter, wood, red, white & black with Veedol logo, 16x5" , EX, D3 .... **$295.00**

Velie Motor Vehicle Co, pin-back button, Velie 40 lettered in center, company name above, Runs Like Sixty below, blue & gold, round, EX, A **$41.00**

Velvet, crate label, California orange, Old English in diagonal script over Velvet, orange & blue, Irvine, 10x11", G1 .... **$4.00**

Velvet Cake Flour, recipe book, 1954, 'Good Things To Eat Made with Velvet Cake Flour,' 22 pages, EX, D **$4.50**

Velvet Night Talcum, tin, pictures palm trees & sailboat, EX, D **$24.00**

Velvet Tobacco, sample tin, burning pipe with product name above & below, slip lid, EX+, A **$165.00**

Velvet Tobacco, sign, porcelain, pictures pipes & upright tin, Velvet in script at left of Smoothest Smoking Tobacco, 12x39", G, A **$85.00**

Velvet Tobacco, tin, embossed, pictures burning pipes, Velvet in script, octagon, round slip lid, EX+, A **$50.00**

Velvet Tobacco, watch fob, porcelain, smoke streaming from pipe spelling Velvet, Tobacco lettered below, advertising on reverse, EX, A **$7.00**

Venus, tin, 1935-45, lady statue on yellow, green & blue background, Whiz symbol at bottom, screw-on lid, 6x3¾", EX, A **$25.00**

Venus Pencil, lead dispenser, painted tin pencil mounted on rod base, shades of green with gold lettering, 32½", G+, A **$200.00**

Veribest Root Beer, dispenser, ca 1900, barrel shape, wood with metal strips, claw feet, Drink Veribest Root Beer on front, 25½", VG, A **$600.00**

Vermont Mutual Fire Insurance Co, calendar, 1902, eagle on concrete ground, December pad, tears/creases, matted & framed, 16x11½", G, A **$30.00**

Vermont Railway, sign, metal, inverted 'V' designs & lettering in white on blue-green, fading/soiling/chips, 15x50", G-, A **$65.00**

Vernor's Ginger Ale, sign, porcelain, Vernor's in diagonal script above Ginger Ale, elongated horizontal rectangle, EX, A **$80.00**

Vernor's Ginger Ale, thermometer, dial, metal case with glass lens, face divided vertically in 2 colors, EX, M1 .... **$135.00**

Vernor's Ginger Ale, tray, Deliciously Different above Vernor's in diagonal script, From Extract Mellowed 4 Years In Wood, plain rim, VG+, A **$35.00**

Vernors, menu board, 1960, embossed tin, green on yellow, Drink Vernors, Deliciously Different, chalkboard below, 25x19", NM, M3 .... **$60.00**

Verona Needles, tin, shows nude woman, EX, D **$35.00**

Vesper Coffee, tin, key-wind lid, 1-lb, EX, D **$12.00**

Vess Cola, sign, 1940s-50s, counter-top neon, 5-sided metal frame with glass front, Drink Vess Soda, First For Thirst! NM, A **$450.00**

Veteran Brand Coffee, can, bust portrait of Civil War Veteran in uniform on oval, vertical stripes top & bottom, press lid, 1-lb, EX, D **$135.00**

Veteran Brand Peanut Butter, pail, tin, dark blue with officer in profile on light blue & white horizontal oval, slip lid & bail, 1-lb, EX, A **$135.00**

Vic's Special Beer, sign, tin over cardboard, tilted bottle on oval at left of product name, red background, 5x11", NM, B1 .... **$25.00**

Viceroy Cigarettes, sign, tin, Filtered Smoke With The Finest Flavor at left of shadowed cigarette pack on white ground, 17x29", NM, M2 .... **$22.00**

Viceroy Cigarettes, sign, tin, lady blowing smoke from cigarette left of Viceroy in underlined script above open pack, rectangle, EX, A **$45.00**

Vick's Choice Seeds, trade card, colorful image of vegetables & flowers, minor creases, EX, A **$65.00**

Vicks, sign, tin, Vicks VapoRub Relieves Misieries Of Cold on white oval on dark ground, 17x23", VG, D1 .... **$35.00**

Vicks, thermometer, tin, Now Over 159 above 117 53 17 (crossed out) Million...Used Yearly, products shown below, 13½", VG, A **$70.00**

Vicks Va-Tro-Nol & Vaporub, push plate, porcelain, pictures product, Come In For Better Control Of Colds, blue, green & red, 7½x4", EX, A **$130.00**

Vicoilized Gasoline, jigsaw puzzle, 1931, man & woman driving in roadster through countryside, 10x13½", EX, F1 .... $50.00

Victor, mirror, silkscreened, Nipper the dog listening to Victrola, couples dancing below, framed, image: 22x16", VG, A **$170.00**

Victor, pocket mirror, Nipper the dog facing Victrola with Victor lettered above, oval, 2¾" long, EX, A **$200.00**

Victor, postcard, black & white photo image of Evan Williams, ...Makes Records Only For The Victor..., VG+, P3 .... **$30.00**

Victor & Co Home Furnishers, trade card, pictures cute little girl with apple, score card for Progressive Pedro card game on reverse, EX, A **$12.00**

Victor Real Cigars, box label, outer, building & street scene, 4½x4½", M, C3 .... **$25.00**

Victor Record Gift Selections, catalog, 1940s, pictures a dog, 64 pages, 7½x5", NM, D **$10.00**

Victor Records, booklet, 1921, September, shows prices, black & white cover, 15 pages, G, D **$12.00**

Victor Records, sign, porcelain, 2-sided, record shape, Aida-Celeste-Aida by Enrico Caruso promoted on both sides, 28" dia, G, A **$400.00**

Victor Talking Machine Co, display, plaster, Nipper the dog with ear cocked, 12½x7½x5", VG, A **$200.00**

Victor Talking Machines, sign, tin, product name arched above Nipper listening to Victrola, framed, image: 13½x19", G, A **$500.00**

Victorious Yams, crate label, cowgirl on white horse, 9x9", M, C3 .... **$3.00**

Victory Brand Tobacco, box label, Victory above soldier standing over slain enemy, TC Williams Co lettered below, framed, image: 13x7", M, A **$45.00**

Victory Cakes, sign, 1940s, cardboard, pictures basket of cakes on purple background, Why Bake At Home..., 15x15", EX, D **$30.00**

Victory Cigars, box label, inner lid, embossed & gilted image of gladiator over fallen opponent in Roman forum..., NM, H1 .... **$12.00**

Victory Club Premium Beer, label, 1933-50, Salem Brewery Assn, Internal Revenue Tax Paid statement, 1-qt, EX, A **$10.00**

Victory Gum & Lozenges, store bin, tin chest with 3 drawers, 10x9x5", VG+, A **$70.00**

Victory Sanitary Wax Dressing, sign, ca 1919, paper, little girl with large bow on oval inset flanked by lettering, Victory Chemical Co, 13x11", EX, D **$25.00**

Victory Tobacco, bucket label, Goddess of war standing on a conquered warrior, 13x7", EX, D **$35.00**

Victrola, jigsaw puzzle, 1922, man & woman listening to Victrola & miniature musicians & singers sitting around, 8x9", EX, F1 .... $75.00

Victrola, pocket mirror, pictures a Victrola with ad text, Atherton Furniture below, rectangular, rounded corners, 2¾", EX, A **$300.00**

Victrola Records, jigsaw puzzle, 1908, record shape with pictures & names of recording stars, 8¼" dia, EX, F1 .... **$90.00**

Vienna Beauties Cigars, box label, inner lid, bust of Miss Liberty in mirror, 6x9", EX, C3 .... **$28.00**

Vienna Style Draught Beer, label, 1933-36, Vienna Brewing Co, U-type permit number, 1/2-gal, VG, A **$12.00**

Vigoral, dispenser, ceramic, Vigoral in gold diagonal script on white urn with floral motif & gold trim, no lid or insert, EX, M2 .... **$350.00**

Vigorator Hair Tonic & Head Rub, sign, 1910s, tin, pictures man lathering his head, 5x9", EX, D...........**$50.00**

Villa Vista Cigars, box label, inner lid, street scene with Spanish men & a mule, 6x9", M, D......................**$10.00**

Vin Fiz, display, die-cut cardboard, 4 women & caricatured boy at soda fountain, 5¢, Sparkling Grape Drink, 25x37½", EX, A...**$6,500.00**

Vin Fiz, display, die-cut cardboard, 4 women & caricatured boy at soda fountain, The Sparkling Grape Drink, 25x38x7½", G, A **$2,000.00**

Vina Vista, crate label, California pear, gateway to Vaca Valley at sunset & 3 pears, Vacaville, 8x11", G1..**$20.00**

Vincent's Straight 5¢ Cigar, lighter, metal with round fuel container attaches to flat square base with Vincent's 76 logo, flint attached to side, A **$285.00**

Violet, crate label, Washington apple, pictures violets, 9x11", EX, G1...**$8.00**

Violet Brand Pears, crate label, 1930s, large bunch of violets on blue ground, Yakima Wash, 7¼x11", M, C1 ....**$4.00**

Violet Talcum Powder, tin, ovoid with flat ends & flat top, floral motif surrounding lettered oval, Babies & Adults, EX, M2...**$90.00**

Virginia Cigarettes, sign, embossed tin litho, bathing beauty holds large cigarette pack, Virginia lettered above, wear, 21x13½", G+, A..............................**$80.00**

Virginia City Bank, calendar, 1926, pick & shovel crossed over image of state of Nevada with 2 insets of cow & sheep, full pad, rare, NM, A **$55.00**

Virginia Creeper Smoking Tobacco, pocket tin, lettered vignettes on green background, squared corners, slip lid, 3½x4½", EX, A **$195.00**

Virginia Dare, container, glass with raised lettering, Have You Tried Virginia Dare?, 8½", EX, A..................**$60.00**

Virginia Dare Carbonated Beverages, bottle topper, round portrait of Virgina Dare with round logo above Carbonated Beverages, 7x4¾", NM, A....................**$5.00**

Virginia Dare Ginger Ale, sign, cardboard, girl's portrait at left of product name on yellow, Quality In Flavor Since..., 5x8", EX, M3 ....**$20.00**

Virginia Dare Grape Punch, bottle topper, cardboard, head portrait of girl with braided hair, ...Hits The Spot, NM, B1 ....**$5.00**

Virginia Dare Orange Soda, bottle topper, Virginia Dare lettered at left of portrait, Orange Soda below, 7½x5", NM, A **$5.00**

Virginia's Delight, crate label, apple, Black boy holding large apples, 9x10½", M, C3 ....**$10.00**

Vita Oleomargarine, box, May 13, 1925, waxed cardboard, company & product name above & below clenched fist, 2½x5x3", EX, H1..............................**$6.00**

Vitabrew Beer, label, 1933-50, Internal Revenue Tax Paid statement, Burton Brewing Co, 32-oz, EX, A **$17.00**

Vitamin Beer, label, 1933-36, logo at left of product name, Kankakee Beverage Co, U-type permit number, 12-oz, VG, A **$10.00**

Voegele's Dainty Specialties, tin, screw lid, round, appears worn, A...**$25.00**

Vogel's Star Brand Sugar Cured Meats, bill hook, paperboard, star logo with lettering above & below, 5½", VG, A..**$10.00**

Vogt's Franks, pin-back button, 1940s, blue, white & yellow, EX, D **$5.00**

Vogue Hat Shop, pocket mirror, company name lettered across center, Smart Ready-To-Wear... Portland Oregan, 2¼" dia, EX, A...**$12.00**

Vogue Royale Talc, tin, pictures a cherub, EX, D...**$100.00**

Vogue Tires, cigarette lighter, red & cream, EX, D....**$22.00**

Voight Brewery Co, sign, paper, mermaids & nymphs in water below rock with large bottle of Rhinegold, framed, image: 26x20", G, A **$2,050.00**

Volk All American Beer, label, 1933-36, product name above logo, Volk Brewery, U-type permit number, 12-oz, G, A...**$12.00**

Volkswagen Service, sign, porcelain, white on dark blue, Volkswagen's encircled W logo above Service, white line border, 30x25", G+, A.................................**$215.00**

Von Beer, label, 1933-36, logo above product name, U-type permit number, 12-oz, G, A **$7.00**

Von Lengerke & Antoine, catalog, No 38, 1911, lettering surrounded by fancy border on front, well illustrated, 112 pages, EX, A **$50.00**

Von Lengerke & Antoine, catalog, 1936, Fall & Winter, photo image of man in canoe on cover, well illustrated, 96 pages, EX, A **$30.00**

Vose & Son Piano, trade card, pictures cherubs playing musical instruments, EX, D **$6.00**

VP Savard, Georgeon & Co Cognac, sign, self-framed tin, elaborately dressed woman seated on stone wall having a glass of cognac, 19x13", EX, A..................**$375.00**

W

W Baker & Co American & Vanilla Chocolates, sign, 1868, paper, eagle atop shield flanked by growers & pickers, factory vignettes below, framed, image: 20x24", G, A..**$200.00**

WA Kreps Buggies & Harness, sign, ca 1905, cardboard, waxed, black on yellow, 9½x14", EX, A..............**$24.00**

Wabash Saloon, sign, ca 1900, die-cut paper, Victorian girl amidst flower-covered anchor & embossed roses, framed, 18x12", NM, A.......................................**$275.00**

Wadhams Gasoline, sign, porcelain, 2-sided, Wadhams Gasoline around Ethyl logo, 42" dia, VG/G, A.................**$230.00**

Wadhams Tempered Motor Oil, sign, painted tin, cream, yellow & red on black, product graphics flank Wadhams Tempered Motor Oil, 18x84", G, A **$110.00**

Wake Up Beverages, menu board, tin, yellow with black menu area lettered Special Today & Take Some Home, green bottle above, 24x16", NM, M3..................**$135.00**

Waldorf, crate label, Washington apple, green-suited bellhop bringing huge red apple on tray, 9x11", EX, G1........**$2.00**

Walgreen's, coffee cup, china, early, EX, D2 ....**$20.00**

Walk-Over Shoes, print, copyright 1911, young cowgirl emerging from behind tree, R Ford Harper litho, wood frame, 29½x10½", EX, A **$550.00**

Walk-Over Shoes, sign, ca 1910, cardboard, man in tuxedo on circular inset, Abram & Gerber, 60 & 62 Main..., 6x20", EX, D **$16.00**

Walk-Over Shoes, sign, paperboard, woman with hat & gun in holster carving Walk-Over into a tree, framed, 27x11", EX, A..**$120.00**

Walla Walla Pepsin Gum, store jar, glass, embossed image of Indian in full headdress, round glass lid, 12¾", EX, A..**$250.00**

Wallace Invader Pencils, can, pictures knight on horse with A Fine Pencil lettered above, tall tube shape, scarce, EX, A..**$10.00**

Walling's Cash Drug Store, sign, tin, yellow & blue, Don't Fail To Visit Walling's Cash Drug Store, Park Rapids Minn, 7x20", NM, B1..**$30.00**

Walter A Wood, calendar, 1892, company name on decorative banner above 3 little girls, full pad, framed, 7x6", NM, A..**$60.00**

Walter A Wood Harvesting Machinery, banner, cloth roll-down, multiple vignettes of machinery, ...Mowing & Reaping Machine Co below, 23x31", G-, A....**$150.00**

Walter Baker & Co, bookends, cast-iron figures of the chocolate girl, 5x3", EX, A..**$149.00**

Walter Baker & Co, cocoa pot, the chocolate girl in oval on blue with gold decoration, scarce, 8", EX, A $715.00

Walter Baker & Co, cup & saucer, chocolate girl on red with gold decoration, rare, 4x5¼", EX, A....................**$578.00**

Walter Baker & Co, display, cast-brass figure of the chocolate girl, 40", EX, A..**$1,210.00**

Walter Baker & Co, figurine, Meissen porcelain figure of the chocolate girl, 8", EX, A **$1,100.00**

Walter Baker & Co, plaque, painted oval porcelain of the chocolate girl in oval wood frame, some damage to frame molding, 8½", EX, A **$248.00**

Walter Baker & Co, plaque, porcelain, waist-length portrait of chocolate girl in profile with tray, gilt stand-up frame, 4x3", EX, D..**$300.00**

Walter Baker & Co, plate, painted image of the chocolate girl, gold & red border, marked Chocolate Maiden on reverse, 9½" dia, EX, A **$770.00**

Walter Baker & Co, print, hand-tinted litho on paper, 'La Belle Chocolatiere,' pictures chocolate girl with tray, 36x25½", EX, D3..**$800.00**

Walter Baker & Co, sign, tin, chocolate girl in profile with tray on plain background, La Belle Chocolatiere... on frame, 44x32", NM, A..**$400.00**

Walter Baker & Co, tray serviette (napkin), linen with fringed edges, features chocolate girl, framed, 21x21", VG+, D3 ....$500.00

Walter Baker & Co, see also Baker's

Walter Baker & Co Breakfast Cocoa, box, wood with paper labels, includes recipe book, 6x12x12", G+, A **$121.00**

Walter Baker & Co Breakfast Cocoa, sign, tin, company name above & other text at left of chocolate girl in profile with tray, framed, image, 20x14", EX, A.......**$700.00**

Walter Baker & Co Breakfast Cocoa, tin, footed bombe shape with lid featuring sporting scenes, 5x5½" square, VG, A..**$110.00**

Walter Baker & Co Chocolate & Cocoa Preparations, sign, 1870s, paper, Victorian factory surrounded by medallions, original frame, 27x35", G, A **$700.00**

Walter Neilly & Co, trolley sign, cardboard, Banquet Ice Cream on border above lady promoting Brunette Beauty Sundae, 13x25", NM, A...........................**$130.00**

Walter Neilly & Co, trolley sign, cardboard, elegant couple in doorway at right of dish of Pineapple Snow, Smilin' Through, 22x21", NM, A **$85.00**

Walter Neilly & Co, trolley sign, cardboard, lady with candle at window right of Pineapple Marshmallow Sundae, Wireless..., 14x25", NM, A.................................**$104.00**

Walter Neilly & Co, trolley sign, cardboard, lady with nose in book at right of Fig Walnut Sundae, ...Booklover's Dream, 11x21", EX, A..**$60.00**

Walter Neilly & Co, trolley sign, cardboard, stylized ladies in cityscape at left of Fig-Walnut Sundae, My Lady Friend..., 12x25", NM, A **$85.00**

Walter Neilly & Co, trolley sign, cardboard, sundae at right of Sunny Sundae with empty price space, company name below, 11x21", NM, A **$85.00**

Walter's Bock Beer, label, 1933-50, Bock Beer lettered over ram's head, Walter Brewing Co, Internal Revenue Tax Paid statement, 12-oz, EX, A **$16.00**

Walter's Fine Bottle Beer, sign, oilette, people on veranda watching biplanes & touring cars spotlight billboard, framed, image: 24x33½", VG, A **$400.00**

Walter's Wurzburger Dark Beer, label, 1933-50, Walter Brewing Co, Internal Revenue Tax Paid statement, 12-oz, EX, A....**$13.00**

Waltman Watch Co, pin-back button, blue on white, company name & Employees Outing Sept 8th 1934... lettered around face of watch, EX, A......................**$20.00**

Walton Shoe, blotter, pictures boy & girl with basketball, multicolored, unused, 6x3½", D.............................**$6.00**

Wan-Eta Cocoa, tin, encircled Indian chief with product name above & below on paper label, slip lid, 1/2-lb, 4½x3¼", EX, A..**$132.00**

Wanamakers, pin-back button, full-color image of Indian in full headdress, The First American arched above, round, EX, A...**$151.00**

War Eagle Cigars, tin, eagle logo flanked by 2 For 5¢ lettered vertically, product name above & below, slip lid, 4¼x5" dia, G, A **$15.00**

War Eagle Cigars, tin, eagle logo flanked by 2 For 5¢ lettered vertically, product name above & below, slip lid, 4¼x5" dia, NM, A **$77.00**

War Horse Cigars, box label, inner lid, lancer mounted on white horse, 6x9", M, C3.......................................**$10.00**

Ward's Bread, fan, 1930s, cardboard, pictures loaf of bread & stars, 9x12", EX, D..**$12.00**

Ward's Cake, display box, tin & glass, children at table & play eating cake, overall wear/chips/scratches, 20½x17x13", G, A..**$1,400.00**

Ward's Lemon-Crush, syrup dispenser, lemon-shaped porcelain, floral decor around base, pump missing, minor fading, 11x9x7", VG, A **$400.00**

Ward's Lime-Crush, syrup dispenser, lime-shaped porcelain, floral decor around base, replaced pump, 10x9x7" excluding pump, EX, A.......................................**$800.00**

Ward's Orange-Crush, syrup dispenser, orange-shaped porcelain, floral decor around base, pump missing, overall soiling/wear, 10x9x8", G, A **$300.00**

Ward's Orange-Crush, syrup dispenser, orange-shaped porcelain, floral decor around base, with pump, bright colors, NM, M2...**$895.00**

Ward's Paper Collars, sign, paper, pictures a circus ring with vignettes of people watching, framed, image: 16x20x1/2", EX, A **$800.00**

Ward's Vitovim Bread, thermometer, 1930s-40s, porcelain, little boy eating bread & product name above, Keeps Him Smiling...below, 21x9", EX, A.....................**$900.00**

Warner Licorice, tin, blue with arched glass front, slip lid, some flaking, rectangular, A.................................**$40.00**

Warner's Log Cabin Remedies, sign, reverse-painted glass, cabin scene in circular inset with product name & advertising, framed, rectangular, EX, A...........**$3,505.00**

Warners Safe Remedies, dominoes, wood, advertising on each domino & box, complete, EX+, D...............**$90.00**

Warren Savings Bank, pocket mirror, stately building with tower, lettering above & below, Old, Strong, Reliable, 2¾", VG+, A...**$30.00**

Warrenton Rum Cakes, tin, waiter carrying large turkey to table, white with red lettering, signed Mary Clemmitt, 7" dia, EX, D **$18.00**

Washington Baking Powder, tin, paper label features George Washington encircled with stars, lettering above & below, slip lid, 5½x3" dia, G-, A............**$20.00**

Watchman Cigars, label, Watchman lettered above encircled portrait of terrier, filigree decoration on side of circle, 4x4", EX, D...**$5.00**

Waterbury Watch Co, trade card, pictures the pavillion, ...Improved Quick Winding Watches, EX, A........**$34.00**

Waterfill & Frazier Whiskey, tray, deep-dish, pictures bull charging matador, Mexican, 13¼" dia, D.............**$20.00**

Waterman's Ideal Fountain Pen, sign, self-framed cardboard, product name around pen over globe marked Ideal, Makes Its Mark..., 12x14", NM, D **$225.00**

Waterman's Ideal Fountain Pen, sign, tin with cardboard back, close-up of boy helping brother write on paper, dark background, unused, 9x13", NM, A $1,235.00

Waterman's Ideal Fountain Pen, thermometer, die-cut tin fountain pen, thermometer insert, scratches/soiling, 19½x4", EX, A..**$700.00**

Waterman's Ideal Fountain Pen, trade card, die-cut pen tip in gold, EX, A...**$65.00**

Waterproof Linen Cuffs & Collars, trade card, caricature of Chinese man asking for $3 to clean shirt opens to man with new collar & cuffs, EX, A.....................**$46.00**

Watkins Menthol Camphor Ointment, tin, 3½" dia, EX+, P4 ....**$8.00**

Watkins Talc, tin, outline of child's face on white 'V' on light blue, Watkins below, white Talc on black band, round, EX+, M2 ....**$50.00**

Watson's Imperial Cough Drops, tin, lettered vignettes & floral design, green, blue & gold, Canadian, made by Ilsley of NY, slip lid, 7x7", VG, A.......................**$225.00**

Watta Pop Lolly-Pops, display, bust of Chief Watta Pop, headdress holds lollipops, 9½", EX, A **$170.00**

Waverly Cigars, box label, inner lid sample, 1880s, lady, landscape & silhouette in collage design, Witsch & Schmidt litho, M, A **$181.00**

Wayne Beets, can label, 1906, large portrait of General Wayne, curved white logo, Newark NY, G1 ....**$5.00**

Wayne Brewing Co, jar, ceramic, with lid, blue & white logo transfer, minor soiling, 7½x6½" dia, EX, A...**$40.00**

Wayne Brewing Co, pocket mirror, celluloid, family seated at table waiting for a case of beer, overall soiling, 2" dia, VG, A **$175.00**

WB Guy Jeweler, trade card, pictures children having snowball fight, EX, A **$26.00**

WE Garrett Snuff, sample tin, 1¾", EX, D **$20.00**

Wearwel, pocket mirror, portrait of a girl in profile, Wearwel above, Mfg'd By Prince Hartigan & Sherman, oval, EX, A **$185.00**

Weaver Organ & Piano Co, trade card, 1890s, little girl in polka-dot skirt & sash holding basket of flowers, 3⅛x4¼", EX, H1 ....**$4.00**

Weber Fishing Tackle, catalog, No 20, 1939, 96 pages with 30 color pages, wear to cover, VG+, A **$24.00**

Weber's Bread, lapel pin, die-cut tin litho, loaf of bread atop panel reading Cisco Kid on TV-Radio, Pancho image below, 2" dia, NM, A **$6.00**

Weber Tackle Co, catalog, 1959, features fishing tackle, 73 pages, VG, D **$20.00**

Webster Tobacco, tin, Webster arched above encircled portrait of the founder, ornate border, hinged lid, worn, 3½x5", D **$45.00**

Wedding Bouquet Segars, sign, paper, pictures wedding ceremony, ...L Kahner & Co Makers, New York, minor soiling, original frame, 25x19", VG, A **$200.00**

Weed Chains, calendar, 1916, 4 colorful vignettes of women in hats above full calendar, minor wear/small edge tear, 34x13½", A $550.00

Weed Chains, price display, painted tin, dial on side turns gas prices for the day, close-up view of tire with chains, 23x17", VG, A **$950.00**

Weeks, crate label, Oregon pear, red script logo slanting up & pear on branch, blue ground, Trail, EX, G1 ....**$5.00**

Weisbrod & Hess Brewery, calendar, 1903, vignettes of parks, seashore scenes, display of products, etc, full pad, framed, image, 28x20", EX+, A **$1,050.00**

Welch Juniors, sign, tin, Drink A Bunch Of Grapes on band above bottle before grape cluster, Welch Juniors 10¢ at right, EX, A **$250.00**

Welch's Grape Juice, pocket mirror, bottle of grape juice over large grape cluster, lettering above & below, minor wear, oval, 2¾", VG, A **$45.00**

Welchs, tray, doiley pattern around Welchs lettered on geometric star shape with grapes & leaves around rim, oval, rare, EX, A **$85.00**

Welcome Baking Powder, trade card, man & woman on park bench, 2½x4", G, D **$3.00**

Welcome Cigarettes, display, die-cut paper, girl standing at attention with broom, skirt draped with stars, Sweet & Mild, framed, 11", EX, A **$60.00**

Welcome Soap, premium catalog, 1920, VG, D **$20.00**

Welcome Soap, sign, paper, collage image of 2 women in a landscape, ...Curtis Davis & Co on frame, 31½x16½", EX, A **$1,200.00**

Wells Fargo, shipping receipt, Oct 21, 1905, advertising on back, VG, D **$14.00**

Wells Richardson & Co Kidney Wort Remedy, tin, 1879, red & black, front lists curable ailments, minor chipping, 4", EX, A **$70.00**

Wells Shoes, sign, self-framed tin, factory scene with trains in foreground, store inset at bottom, We Sell..., 25½x38", VG, A **$125.00**

Welsbach Light Co, letter opener, die-cut tin, advertising on yellow handle with eagle & shield logo graduating to point, 10½", EX, A **$60.00**

Wenatchee Chief, crate label, 1940s, Washington pear, Indian chief & arrowhead on blue background, Wenatchee, 7¼x11", M, C1 ....**$3.00**

Wendy's Restaurant, statuette, 1980s, red plastic, Wendy seated with arms around her knees, 2", M, D $5.00

Wendys Restaurant, ashtray, glass w/logo on bottom, NM, P4 ....**$5.00**

Wenona Cigar Co, pocket mirror, company name arched above nude posed on rock at water's edge, Port Huron Mich, 2⅛" dia, VG+, A **$185.00**

Wesson Oil, recipe book, 1928, 'Everyday Recipes,' 46 pages, G, D **$8.00**

Wesson Snowdrift Oil, recipe book, ca 1920, brown cover, 43 pages, G, D **$3.00**

West Bend Old Timer's Beer, bottle, long neck, paper label, G, D **$8.00**

West Coast Coffee, tin, pictures a bell above product name & other lettering, key-wind lid, 2-lb, EX+, A **$55.00**

West End Brewing Co, calendar, 1907, paper, girl at table sampling brew with factory out window, full pad, framed, image: 23½x16", EX, A **$600.00**

West End Brewing Co, calendar top, 2 little girls on a bench with flowers, framed, image: 19½x14½", G-, A......**$200.00**

West End Brewing Co, pocket mirror & pin cushion, pictures Lady Liberty encircled by company name on dark band, 2" dia, NM, A..**$125.00**

West End Brewing Co, sign, paper, boy with teddy bear straddling keg of beer, lettering above & below, matted & framed, image: 25x20", G-, A **$225.00**

West End Brewing Co, tray, patriotic image of Liberty with flag & eagle with shield, lettering on rim, fading/wear, 13" dia, G-, A **$60.00**

West End Cigars, box label, inner lid sample, 1880s, 2 cherubs with crown above West End in script, Witsch & Schmidt litho, EX, A **$23.00**

West End Fire Co No 1, pocket mirror, pictures firetruck with lettering above & below, ...Stowe Pa, black & white, round, EX, A..**$66.00**

West Hair Nets, display case, 3 tiers of boxes on hinges, top box has lid with inner label of touring car at the beach, 10x14", VG+, A $225.00

West India Bananas, display, papier-mache, figural bunch of bananas on base marked West India Bananas, very rare, 14x10x8", EX, A **$330.00**

Westchester County Brewing Co, sign, litho transfer on wood, frontal factory view with New York brewery inset in upper right, 24x34", G, A **$375.00**

Western & Southern Life Insurance, calendar, 1922, shows girl in bonnet with flowers, 2 rows of 6 months each below, 9x9", NM, A **$21.00**

Western Ammunition, catalog, 1920-25, last 6 pages are full page illustrations, 88 pages, EX, A **$115.00**

Western Ammunition, display board, 1961, display of shells & cartridges, World Champion Ammunition on top band, Western below, 25x36", VG, A.............**$60.00**

Western Ammunition, sign, 1921, 'The Warning,' moose standing in stream with game birds overhead, metal strips top & bottom, 30x17", VG, A **$850.00**

Western Assurance Co, ledger marker, Royal Seal logo, Incorporated 1851, Toronto Canada, Kellogg & Bulkeley, minor wear, 12½x3", G, A **$250.00**

Western Brew, label, 1933-50, Indian in full headdress surrounded by Sioux City..., 12-oz, VG, A **$23.00**

Western Cartridge Co, calendar, 1929, pointer sitting in chair, original mailing promo piece still attached, full pad, 27x14", VG, A..**$600.00**

Western Club Beer, label, 1933-50, Wm Roesch Brewing Co, Internal Revenue Tax Paid, 31-oz, EX, A **$20.00**

Western Farms Milk, sign, self-framed tin, sleeping baby & milk bottle at left of gold lettering on green, gold beveled frame, 5x14", NM, A $900.00

Western Field Shells, pin-back button, Western in script on elongated diamond above shell, Shoot... arched at top & bottom, round, EX, A **$290.00**

Western Metallic Cartridges, sign, paper, father & son aiming shotgun while mother & daughter watch from car, framed, 24x15", VG, A **$900.00**

Western New Chief Loaded Paper Shells, box, Western in elongated diamond above New Chief..., pictures various game on back, 12-gauge, VG, A **$75.00**

Western Packing Lard, pail, crowned lions flank company seal with lettered banner below, slip lid, bail handle missing, G-, M2 ....**$15.00**

Western Queen, crate label, 1920s, California orange, Indian lady in green sunburst, Rialto Orange Co, 10x11", M, C1..**$10.00**

Western Record Loaded Paper Shells, box, with contents, Western in elongated diamond above Record Loaded Paper Shells, 10-gauge, VG, A **$80.00**

Western Shell, booklet, folds up to form shotgun shell, Look Inside A Western Shell & See The Difference, 12 pages, VG, A..**$60.00**

Western Shot Gun Shells & Metallic Cartridges, pin-back button, Western in script on elongated diamond surrounded by lettering, red, white & blue, round, VG, A **$30.00**

Western Super-X Long Range Shells, sign, die-cut stand-up, display of product, Short Shot String, Gets The Game! below, framed, 20½x12", VG, A **$125.00**

Western Super-X Shotgun Shells, box, with contents, Western in script above Super-X Shotgun Shells & other lettering, .410-gauge, VG, A..................................**$55.00**

Western Union Telegrams, sign, porcelain, ...Accepted Here, white on blue, 14½x9", EX, D..................**$165.00**

Western Union Telegraph & Cable Office, sign, porcelain, 2-sided, finger pointing toward office, white on blue, oval, fading/scuffing, 22x31", G-, A...........**$350.00**

Western Union Telegraph Office, sign, porcelain flange, white lettering on navy background, fading/chips, 12x24", A....................**$145.00**

Westfella Cream Separators, ashtray, plastic & tin miniature cream separator, 5", EX+, M2....................**$36.00**

Westinghouse, doll, Cozy Glow Kid, nude boy holding towel, 12½", EX, A....................**$35.00**

Westinghouse, statuette, 1940, molded composition of the Westinghouse man, arms folded, 4½", EX, D........$40.00

Westinghouse Co Threshing Machines, sign, paper, agricultural scene with steam-powered equipment running machines, framed, 21x26½", G-, A....................**$300.00**

Westinghouse Electric Range, booklet, 1948, 80 pages, EX, D....................**$6.50**

Westinghouse Mazda Lamps, display, 8 light bulbs on round simulated compass, banner reads Remember Westinghouse Mazda Lamps..., 33", EX, A....................**$35.00**

Westinghouse Refrigerator, booklet, 1936, 49 pages, EX, D....................**$10.00**

Westinghouse Refrigerator, sign, neon, metal with glass front, neon tube surrounds large W atop Westinghouse Refrigerator, 13" dia, VG+, A....................**$175.00**

Westminster Rye Whiskey, sign, 1900-15, self-framed tin, 'Settled Out of Court,' farm scene with early touring car, C Shonk litho, 38x25", EX, A....................**$4,500.00**

Westmoreland Brewing Co, pitcher, hand-colored transfer of eagle & flags with FOE lettered on front, gold leaf trim, 9x5" dia, G, A....................**$350.00**

Westwood Tomatoes, can label, embossed image of early golfer in full swing, gilt decoration, minor damage, 4x11", C1....................**$5.00**

Wexford Pale Beer, label, 1933-36, logo above Wexford in script, Fortune Bros Brewing Co, U-type permit number, 12-oz, G, A....................**$13.00**

WH Baker Chocolate & Cocoa, sign, paper, woman with flowers & illustrations of products in background, matted & framed, image: 24x14", VG, A....................**$275.00**

WH Baker's Best Cocoa, display, 1897, cardboard, 3-D, Victorian lady standing behind product box with serving set atop, 6½", EX, D....................**$150.00**

Wheat Sheaf Coffee, canister, tin, gold & cream, Wheat Sheaf Coffee above harvest scene, knobbed slip lid, 9x7" dia, EX+, M2....................$315.00

Wheaties, cereal box, 1940s, with Pinocchio mask, full, EX, D....................**$125.00**

Wheaties, necktie, 1970s, repeated logo on blue, EX, D..**$15.00**

Wheeler & Wilson, trade card, pictures Oriental lady seated on a branch with a fan, EX, D....................**$3.00**

Whip Tobacco, pocket tin, upright, encircled horse & rider flanked by whips, product name above & below, EX+, A....................**$600.00**

Whippet, sign, porcelain, white on red, Dollar For Dollar Value above Whippet, Product Of Willy's-Overland Company, 24x36", G+, A....................**$300.00**

Whippet Motor Oil, can, 1925-45, product name above & below greyhound dog, red, white & blue, pour spout & handle, 2-gal, 10½", EX, A....................**$210.00**

Whistle, clock, metal, glass lens, 12-3-6-9 & logos surround large Whistle logo in center, round, EX, D........**$255.00**

Whistle, display, cast-iron hand with original embossed glass bottle, 15" long, VG, A....................**$825.00**

Whistle, pennant, 1920s, paper, Just Whistle above bottle with straw, metal band at top, 26x11", EX+, D........**$60.00**

Whistle, push bar, steel, Thirsty?, Just...Whistle & musical notes at left of top part of slanted soda bottle, 30" long, G, A....................**$15.00**

Whistle, sign, cardboard, die-cut, boy & orange surround large bottle, Golden Orange Refreshment, framed, 21x16", NM, M3....................**$125.00**

Whistle, sign, cardboard, die-cut, 1920s, bottle on round dot reading Thirsty? Just- above panel reading Whistle, 18x17", EX+, D....................**$65.00**

Whistle, sign, cardboard, die-cut, 1940s, 2 elves clinging to bottle, 30x10½", EX+, D....................**$135.00**

Whistle, sign, cardboard, 3-D stand-up, elves enjoying Whistle at Golden Orange Refreshment stand, 14x19", EX, M2....................**$85.00**

Whistle, sign, tin, embossed, 1940s, hand holding bottle flanked by Thirsty? Just...On Ice, The Only Handy Bottle, 7x10", VG, A....................**$235.00**

Whistle, sign, tin, Thirsty? Just Whistle above elf pushing large bottle on cart in circular inset, blue ground, 30x26", EX, M2....................**$310.00**

Whistle, sign, tin, 1930s, Thirsty? Just- above hand with bottle above Good Housekeeping seal, The Choice Of...5¢, 10x29", NM, D3....................**$375.00**

Whistle, sign, tin, 1930s, 2 lines divide sign into 3 panels with painted diagonal corners, Thirsty? Just Whistle..., M, D **$175.00**

White Cap Beer, label, 1933-50, officer saluting, Vienna Brewing Co, Internal Revenue Tax Paid statement, 1-qt, EX, A **$78.00**

White Dove Marshmallows, tin, White Dove in bold lettering above Marshmallows, slip lid, some wear, round, A .. **$35.00**

White Goose Coffee, pail, product name in white above and below encircled goose, red background, press lid, 1-lb, EX+, A $600.00

White House Cigars, box label, inner lid sample, 1880s, view of White House with cherubs in lower corners, Witsch & Schmidt litho, EX, A **$132.00**

White House Coffee, thermometer, wood, black on white, Drink White House Coffee, None Better At Any Price above, wood split, 21", G-, A **$20.00**

White House Coffee, tin, key-wind, 1-lb, VG, D **$40.00**

White House Selected Vegetables, label, oval vignette of the White House above basket of veggies, Los Angeles, 7x9", EX, G1 .... **$4.00**

White House Shoes/Brown Shoe Co, pocket mirror, formal colonial scene encircled with lettered rim, Peter Kurrzin & Son, 2¼" dia, VG+, A **$55.00**

White Label Soup, sign, tin, can of soup on crest with knights helmet, shield, weaponry, etc, oak frame, image: 13½x19¼", G, A **$150.00**

White Label 5¢ Cigars, sign, embossed tin hanger, pictures open box of cigars, Smoke...Favorite Everywhere, Sentenne & Green, 10x14", EX, A **$245.00**

White Owl Cigars, ashtray, 1930s, owl atop burning cigar, blue, white & brown, 3½x3½", EX, D **$8.00**

White Poppy Flour, pocket mirror, bag of flour with poppy graphics flanked by advertising, In A Class By Itself..., oval, 2¾", EX, A **$95.00**

White Rock Beverages, display, die-cut cardboard standup, White Rock above nymph on rock looking into water, For Purity, 40x28", NM, A **$415.00**

White Rock Beverages, door push plate, tin, yellow with White Rock above green bottle, Push below, 15x4", NM, M3 .... **$95.00**

White Rock Beverages, sign, tin, white & black with fairy kneeling on rock looking into water, For Sparkling..., 8x22½", NM, A $110.00

White Rock Ginger Ale, display, tin, 2-tiered, green carton holds 12 bottles with yellow labels, 16½x11x8½", NM, A **$750.00**

White Rock Sparkling Water, sign, pictures bottle & character, S2 .... **$265.00**

White Rose Coffee, tin, 1-lb, 4", EX, D **$42.00**

White Rose Flour, sign, paper mounted on board with arched top, young baker holding up tray of bread, Ask For..., scratches, 15½", G, A **$30.00**

White Rose Flour, sign, wood, white on blue, White Rose Flour above Bakes Better (larger letters) Bread, framed, 26x74", VG+, A **$375.00**

White Rose Service Station, hat, military style with leather band & bill, White Rose in braided raised letters, 9½" dia, EX, D **$165.00**

White's Golden Tonic for Horses, broadside, features horse with advertising above & below, Kimball Bros & Co, Enosburg Falls Vermont, 23½x18", EX, A **$30.00**

White Sewing Machine & Bicycle, trade card, little girl sitting on hinged ladder holding a sign, EX, A **$26.00**

White Sewing Machines, trade card, frustrated family using old hand crank machine, opens up to family using new foot pedal model, VG+, A **$42.00**

White Sewing Machines, trade card, women using old sewing machine, opens to scene with new machine & baby in crib, EX+, A **$65.00**

White Star Gasoline, sign, porcelain, 2-sided, White Star Gasoline surrounds encircled white star lettered Staroleum, 30" dia, EX+/EX, A **$450.00**

White Star Pure Rye, sign, tin, barroom scene with bartender & 2 men toasting, Here's Oh, star logo on barrel below, framed, 37x27", EX, A..$23,500.00

White-Cat Cigars, box label, inner lid, 1930s, white cat perched on cigar on blue oval background, product name above & below, 7x9", M, C3 .... **$3.00**

Whiting-Adams Brushes, pocket mirror, owl perched on branch with brush before crescent moon, narrow banded rim, 2¼" dia, EX, A **$185.00**

Whitman's Chocolates, display, polychromed wood figure of delivery boy with candy box, figure detailed to simulate sampler, 24", EX, A ...$1,155.00

Whitman's Chocolates, display, 1920s-40s, painted die-cut wood depicting the chocolate girl, movable hands, lettered blue base, 16", EX, A **$110.00**

Whitman's Chocolates & Confections, sign, porcelain, white on green, Agency upper left of Whitman's in diagonal script, Since 1842 below, 14x40", EX, A **$120.00**

Whitman White Cap Mints, tin, round, 8-oz, VG, D ... **$10.00**

Whittall Rugs & Carpet, sign, 1930s-40s, light-up, tin & reverse-painted glass, red & blue lettering outlined in gold, M, A **$80.00**

Whittemores Polishes, blotter, girl polishing lady's shoe, multicolored, 1 corner bent, 6x3½", D **$6.00**

Whiz Auto Top Dressing, sign, paper, 2 gnomes painting car top, ...Makes Old Tops Look New, framed, image: 37x12", G, A **$450.00**

Whiz Patch Outfit, display, painted metal with advertising panel, 3-tier, lettering at right of man with product in front of car, EX, A **$300.00**

Wide Awake Cigar, label, ca 1900, embossed image of Uncle Sam with eagle & fleet, 6x10", EX, D **$18.00**

Wide Hollow, crate label, apple, country home with apple orchard, 9x10½", M, C3 .... **$15.00**

Wiedemann's Beer, photographic print, black & white image of couple seated at table with bottles & steins, framed, 22x18", G-, A **$25.00**

Wiedemann's Beer, sign, self-framed tin, 2 showgirls at dressing table with tray of beer reading a note, 23x33", G, A **$450.00**

Wiedemann's Fine Beers, sign, paper, man smoking pipe with stein of beer, minor overall soiling, matted & framed, image: 19x16", EX, A **$75.00**

Wiedemann's Royal Amber Beer, sign, bronze & wood, pictures flying pheasant, 20x15", M, D **$100.00**

Wieland's Beer, tray, lady in gloves with flowers in lap seated in profile reading a letter, wood-grain rim, 13x11", G, A **$75.00**

Wieland's Beer, tray, lady in gloves with flowers in lap seated in profile reading a letter, wood-grain rim, 13x11", EX+, A **$175.00**

Wieland's Extra Pale, tray, girl sampling glass of beer, ...California's Best Beer lettered on decorative rim, oval, 16¾x13½", VG, A **$175.00**

Wigwam Coffee, tin, pictures silhouette of Indian's head in profile with lettering above & below, pry lid, 1-lb, EX, A **$60.00**

Wilbur & Sons Cocoa, pocket mirror, features box of cocoa on plain background, uneven surface, 1¾" dia, EX, A **$180.00**

Wilbur's Cocoa, broom holder, metal, top is box of cocoa with cherub stirring cup of cocoa, holder is wire loop, 4x2½", NM, A $700.00

Wilcox Gasoline, sign, porcelain, 2-sided, white with red Wilcox Gasoline lettered around Ethyl logo, blue border, 30" dia, VG+, A **$220.00**

Wild Cherry Bitters, sign, glass, Try- in gold above Wild Cherry in graduating letters above Bitters, horizontal, EX, M1 .... **$160.00**

Wild Turkey Bourbon, bottle, inflatible, 24", EX, D.. **$7.50**

Wild Turkey Bourbon, pitcher, white with black lettering & turkey, gold trim on edge & handle, D........... **$65.00**

Wildroot, sign, embossed tin, pictures a barber pole at right of Ask For Wildroot, 9¾x27¾", EX+, A **$30.00**

Will's Cigarettes, sign, pictures 3 vertical rows of 15 planes & 9 cars, product & company name above & below, framed, 24x13", EX, A **$150.00**

Willard Batteries, clock, reverse-painted glass front on metal base, white & black on red, 22", EX, A **$425.00**

Willard's Carnival of Fine Candy, pail, 1940s-50s, circus scene, slip lid & bail, minor paint nicks, 5-lb, 7¼x5¼" dia, A **$40.00**

William G Lord Insurance, calendar, 1940, colorful image of mother & son looking into port, full pad, edge loss, matted & framed, 16½x10", A **$25.00**

William Mills & Son Fishing Tackle, catalog, No 141, 1941, well illustrated, 80 pages, with original mailing envelope, A **$50.00**

William Penn Cigars, display, papier-mache figure of William Penn holding cigar box in 1 hand & cigar ad in other, square base, 65", EX, A..........$2,500.00

Williams' Baby Talc, tin, image of baby on both sides, blue & yellow with blue accents, shaker top, minor scratches on 1 side, 5", G, A **$80.00**

Williams' Carnation Talc Powder, tin, product name above carnation graphic, Carnation, The JB Williams Co, Glastonbury... below, oval, 2x1¼", EX, D **$35.00**

Williams' Shaving Soap, thermometer, wood, blue on white, lettering & graphics above & below, rounded top, square bottom, narrow, 24", G, A **$80.00**

Williams Co Shelby Tubing, Brass & Copper, thermometer, wood, black on white, company & product lettering above, Boiler Tubes... below, rounded top, 15", G, A **$30.00**

Williams Russian Cough Drops, store bin, slip lid, rectangular, VG+, D **$90.00**

Willimantic Six Cord Spool Cotton, cabinet, wood, gold lettering outlined in black, 5 drawers, 16x28½x18", EX, A **$350.00**

Willimantic Six Cord Spool Cotton, sign, paper, children trapping roaring elephant with thread, decorative border, matted & framed, 13½x19½", VG, A **$2,100.00**

Willimantic Six Cord Spool Cotton, store card, copyright 1891, paper, well-dressed woman with packages crossing street, framed, 17x13½", EX, D3 .... **$1,550.00**

Willimantic Six Cord Spool Cotton, trade card, scene at Brooklyn Bridge with hot air balloon, EX+, A **$26.00**

Willimantic Thread, trade card, child watching cat & parrot playing tug-of-war with thread, G, D **$4.00**

Willimantic Thread, trade card, 1887, colorful image of girl in Victorian clothing, rare, G, D **$3.00**

Willimantic Thread, trade card, 2 children in horse-drawn cart with spools of thread as wheels, G, D **$5.00**

Willoughby Taylor, pocket tin, upright, with contents, Personal Blend arched above arrowhead on 3 bands, product name above, slip lid, EX+ **$65.00**

Willys Overland Co, sign, paper, aerial factory view, wood frame, 10½x39½", EX, A **$220.00**

Wilson & McCallay's Happy Thought Tobacco, trade card, unhappy man using low grade tobacco opens to happy man using Happy Thought, rare, EX, A .. **$90.00**

Wilson Garage, calendar, 1925, paper with tin rim, night scene with girls in early car, full pad, EX, D........ **$30.00**

Wilson's Certified Brand Peanut Butter, pail, tin, features nursery-rhyme vignettes, pry lid, bail handle, 12-oz, EX, A..$300.00

Wilson's Old Dublin Whiskeys, sign, paper, product name above 3 bottles, John Wilson & Co Ltd, Dublin Ireland, matted & framed, 15x19", EX, M2 .... **$84.00**

Wilson Sewing Machine Co, sign, paper on canvas, portrait of the founder surrounded by factory & sewing machine vignettes, 24x19", EX, A....................... **$350.00**

Winchester, ad cover, 1910, colorful hunt scene, Model 1912 Light-Weight Hammerless Repeating Shotgun..., VG, A **$80.00**

Winchester, calendar, 1913, paper, bearded man with rifle, Dec pad, matted & framed, 29½x15½", VG, A ... **$950.00**

Winchester, calendar, 1922, mountain scene with cowboy on horseback aiming at bear, November pad, framed, 26x15", EX+, A **$950.00**

Winchester, calendar, 1923, paper, hunter watching game from cliff, framed, 26x14", VG, A **$425.00**

Winchester, calendar, 1934, 'I Wish I Had My Winchester,' little boy sitting on fence, minor tear, G+, A...... **$170.00**

Winchester, catalog, 'The Game, The Gun, The Ammunition,' pictures dead game on a chair in red, white & blue, EX, A **$26.00**

Winchester, catalog, 1941, illustrated, 44 pages, EX, A.... **$26.00**

Winchester, catalog, 1968, features guns, VG, D **$10.00**

Winchester, Christmas card, early 1900s, wintry hunting scene, VG, A **$50.00**

Winchester, display, cardboard, 4 panels with continuous hunt scenes, each panel: 38x13", EX, A **$525.00**

Winchester, display, die-cut stand-up, pictures JAR Elliott with rifle standing atop large shotgun shell, rare, 16½x15", VG, A **$1,500.00**

Winchester, pin, for 20 years of service, screw-back, round, VG, A **$20.00**

Winchester, pin-back button, bull's-eye with W on inner circle, Always Shoot Winchester Cartridges on outer circle, 1" dia, NM, A **$32.00**

Winchester, pin-back button, large W in center of target, Always Shoot..., red, white & black, round, VG, A....**$28.00**

Winchester, pin-back button, portrait of WR Crosby surrounded by lettering, ...Winchester Leader, round, EX, A....**$70.00**

Winchester, pin-back button, Winchester over 2 crossed rifles featuring Junior Rifle Corps, ⅞" dia, NM, A....**$35.00**

Winchester, score sheet, for junior trapshooting, red, black & white, VG, A....**$20.00**

Winchester, sign, metal, 2-sided, rider on galloping horse above Winchester Western, banded rim, small scratches, 20" dia, EX, A....**$60.00**

Winchester, sign, 1936, reverse-painted glass, Authorized Dealer...Cutlery & Firearms surrounded by fancy scrolls, framed, VG, A....**$220.00**

Winchester, sign, 1987, for Ducks Unlimited Clay Target Shooting Tournament, mallards in flight, VG, A....**$35.00**

Winchester, tie clip, Commemorative, VG, A....**$15.00**

Winchester .22 Caliber Rifles & Cartridges, display, die-cut stand-up, boy with rifle behind stone wall, .22 Caliber lettered on large W at top, EX, A....**$700.00**

Winchester Air Rifle, target, lines for name, distance, date & score at bottom, illustrates & describes air rifle shot shell on back, VG, A....**$12.00**

Winchester Cartridges, calendar, 1896, 2 hunters stalking moose above with other hunting vignettes around December pad, framed, EX, A....$600.00

Winchester Cartridges, stickpin, The 97.20% Shells lettered on shotgun shell, yellow, EX, A....**$50.00**

Winchester Fishing Tackle, pocket catalog, 1920s-30s, non-pictorial cover, illustrated, 32 pages, EX, A....**$55.00**

Winchester Guns & Ammunition, pocket catalog, 1922, non-pictorial cover, illustrated, 30 pages, VG, A....**$20.00**

Winchester Guns & Cartridges, display, die-cut cardboard stand-up, elk's head in front of large 'W,' product name below, 12x9", EX, A....**$325.00**

Winchester Guns & Cartridges, pin-back button, black & white portrait image, The Wonderful Topperweins, Who Always Shoot..., round, VG, A....**$125.00**

Winchester Junior Rifle Corp, badge, Marksman, silver, Winchester over 2 crossed rifles, EX, A....**$40.00**

Winchester Leader & Repeater, score card, pictures 2 shells at top, information of 5 different loads on reverse, VG, A....**$12.00**

Winchester Model 12 Repeating Shotgun, brochure, pictures hunter aiming shotgun, EX, A....**$10.00**

Winchester Model 1894 Soft Point, box of 20 labels, black & orange, ...Smokeless Soft Point lettered on shell, other lettering above, G, A....**$30.00**

Winchester New Rival, box, pictures 2 shotgun shells with lettering above & below, 20-gauge, VG, A....**$60.00**

Winchester No 8 Chilled Shot, box, nonpictorial, 25 Shells, Shotgun 12 Gauge, Paper...Winchester Repeating Arms Co, VG, A....**$25.00**

Winchester Nublack, box, with contents, product name above & below birds in flight, 10-gauge, VG, A **$150.00**

Winchester Ranger Skeet Load, box, skeet shooters aiming at simulated bird in flight, 12-gauge, VG, A..**$90.00**

Winchester Repeater Paper Shot Shells, box, nonpictorial, 12-gauge, VG, A....**$30.00**

Winchester Repeating Arms Co, ad cover, 1902, pictures a rifle, Winchester seal on reverse, VG, A....**$70.00**

Winchester Repeating Arms Co, catalog, No 72, 1905, lettering surrounded by fancy scrolls on cover, 170 pages, EX, A....**$80.00**

Winchester Repeating Arms Co, display board, ca 1897, display of 182 cartridges surrounding hunt scene with dead bear, framed, 40x57", EX+, A....**$6,600.00**

Winchester Repeating Arms Co, display board, ca 1902, illustrates over 235 cartridges, shotshells & bullets, framed, 32x49", G, A....**$770.00**

Winchester Repeating Arms Co, letterhead, 1878, aerial factory view, VG, A....**$60.00**

Winchester Repeating Arms Co, paperweight, 1910, ...New Haven Conn, scarce, VG, A....**$55.00**

Winchester Repeating Arms Co, postcard, 1907-15, colorful factory view with busy street scene, VG, A....**$11.00**

Winchester Repeating Arms Co, sign, paper, 2 men at hollow log, 1 chases skunk out as other man jumps in unpleasant surprise, mounted, 26x35", VG, A....**$325.00**

Winchester Repeating Arms Co, stock certificate, 1929, 100 shares, matted & framed, VG, A....**$90.00**

Winchester Repeating Rifles & Shotguns, ad cover, 1908, bust portrait of bearded man in front of rifle, edge wear at right, A....**$65.00**

Winchester Repeating Shot Gun (sic), ad, 1898, from Southern Railway, pictures a rifle, magenta letters, 6x8", VG, A....**$40.00**

Winchester Repeating Shotguns, ad cover, 1910, pictures a bird with rifle in center of large W, VG, A....**$110.00**

Winchester Rifles & Cartridges, envelope, colorful western image with 2 cowboys, 1 with rifle & 1 pointing, VG, A....**$65.00**

Winchester Rifles & Cartridges, sign, paper, 2 cowboys laying behind rocks aiming at steers, The W Brand Safe-Sure-Accurate, 30⅜x15", EX, A....**$450.00**

Winchester Rifles & Shotguns, banner, silk, cowboy holding rifle on running steer, blue, gold & red, creasing/dirt smudges, 19x31", EX, A....**$450.00**

Winchester Self-Loading Shotguns, envelope, hunter with rifle & dead game bird, scarce, VG, A....**$50.00**

Winchester Shells, postcard, salesman's advance notice from Clark-Rutka-Weaver Co, pictures shotgun shells, black & white, VG+, P3 ....**$40.00**

Winchester Shells & Cartridges, catalog, 1938, retail price list included, 44 pages, EX, A................................**$15.00**

Winchester Shotgun Shells & Shotguns, pin-back button, full-color with product name surrounding large W, round, EX, A..**$34.00**

Winchester Tools, pocket catalog, nonpictorial cover, well illustrated, 30 pages, light water stain at top of pages, VG, A **$16.00**

Winchester Western Bullets, display board, horse & rider above display of 60 bullets, framed, EX, A **$160.00**

Winchester World Standard Guns & Ammunition, catalog, No 82, 1918-20, green hard-bound cover, red logo at top of each page, 208 pages, EX, A..................**$85.00**

Winchester World Standard Guns & Ammunition, catalog, No 82, 1918-20, green soft cover, red logo at top of each page, 208 pages, spine cover partially missing, A ...**$35.00**

Winchester World Standard Guns & Ammunition, catalog, 1933, nonpictorial cover, includes price list, 144 pages, EX, A **$75.00**

Winchester 20-Gauge Shotguns, sign, 2 setters in tall grass, ...Hammerless, Light & Strong below, metal strips top & bottom, framed, 30x16½", VG, A..............**$400.00**

Windisch-Muhlhauser Brewing Co, sign, paper, elegant girl holding pink roses, some wrinkling/soiling/edge tears, framed, image: 22x16", EX, A....................**$750.00**

Windisch-Muhlhauser Brewing Co, sign, paper, stock image of man & woman watching another man play guitar, framed, image: 20x15", VG, A.................................**$550.00**

Windsor Supreme, pitcher, ceramic, shaped as the head of a royal guard, red base with white lettering, 8½x4", EX, A **$20.00**

Wine French Cocoa, sign, metal, large 5¢ flanked by Relieves Headache & Assists Digestion, If You're Tired... below, 37x20", G-, A...........................**$1,500.00**

Wingold Flour, notebook, 1928-29, EX, D **$3.00**

Wings Cigarettes, sign, paper, Wings lettered on dark band above sexy lady posed with cigarette, product pack lower left, 18x12", NM, A.............................**$22.00**

Wings King Size Cigarettes, sign, paper, plane above row of 4 other planes advertising Free Piper Cub Airplane..., Wings King..., 16x11", NM, A **$32.00**

Wings King Size Cigarettes, sign, paper, Wings King Size lettered above tilted pack of cigarettes, Cost Less Last Longer below, 15x10", NM, A...............................**$34.00**

Wings King Size Cigarettes, sign, 1941, cardboard, Free! Piper Cub...Given Away... above open pack & NBC's Wings Of Destiny ad on red, 15x10", M, D3......**$145.00**

Winne, Burdick & Co, trade card, 1880s, pictures racehorse (Wedgewood) & jockey, EX, A............................**$125.00**

Winne, Burdick & Co, trade card, 1881, pictures racehorse (Sorrel Dan) & jockey, lettering above, EX, A....**$135.00**

Winne's Ice Cream, sign, painted metal, 2-sided, Winne's Ice Cream, Eagle Mills NY above dish of ice cream on blue ground, 28x20", EX, A **$240.00**

Winner Cigars, box labels, inner & outer sample set, 1870s, jockey in oval at left of racing scene, Heppenheimer & Maurer, EX/M, A **$96.00**

Winner Cut Plug Smoke & Chew, lunch box, tin, racing scene with lettering in brown & blue, hinged lid, wire handle, 4x8x5", EX, A **$325.00**

Winner Cut Plug Smoke & Chew, lunch box, tin, racing scene with lettering in brown & blue, hinged lid, wire handle, overall rust, 4x8x5", A **$60.00**

Winner Plug Tobacco, barrel, wood with paper label featuring horses jumping through stirrup, 17", VG, A $200.00

Winner Plug Tobacco, label, horses jumping through large stirrup, 11x11", EX, D **$45.00**

Winner Roasted Coffee, tin, lettering on the diagonal with vertically lined bands at top & bottom, beveled lid, with handle, 1-lb, EX, A..**$85.00**

Winston Cigarettes, lighter, red & cream, Filter Tipped..., 1¾x2", EX, D $7.00

Winston Cigarettes, thermometer, The Taste Is Tops flanked by open packs of cigarettes, Winston arched above, 9" dia, NM, B1 ....**$35.00**

Wise Potato Chips, sign, 1940, cardboard, pictures boy & girl, G, D..**$150.00**

Wishing Well Orange, door push bar, porcelain, We Sell in script left of product name on yellow background, 3x30", EX, M2....................................**$100.00**

Wishing Well Orange, matchbook, yellow cover with bottle image at left of Drink above Wishing Well arched over Orange, unused, M2 .... **$2.00**

Wiz Brilliant Polish, display rack, metal, features litho on marque of woman polishing piano & car, 2 shelves, dents/rust, 23x17x4½", G-, A **$75.00**

WL Douglas Shoes, sign, self-framed tin, oval portrait of WL Douglas with lettering on chest, black, white & brown, 31x23", EX, A **$100.00**

Wm M Herrmann Jeweler, sign, metal hanger, 2-sided, figural pocket watch, black face with silver lettering & bezel, 40", G+, A **$350.00**

Wm Peter Brewing Co, sign, paper, man holding mug of beer, lettering & star logo above, Temptation below, framed, image: 23x16", VG, A **$1,000.00**

Wm Peter Brewing Co Lager Beer, sign, reverse-painted glass, brewer with mug of beer, Union Hill, NJ, framed, image: 20x14", VG, A **$750.00**

WM Rothfuss Buggies, Wagons & Harnesses, thermometer, stenciled & lacquered wood, lettering & wagon graphics above, lettering below, rounded top, 21", G-, A **$25.00**

Wm Taylor's Monumental Brand Baltimore Oysters, sign, paperboard, monument & ships at sea flanked by lettering, Each Can..., framed, 22½x19", G, A **$450.00**

Wm W Souder Cyclone Washing Machine, trade card, black lettering superimposed over red washing machine, EX, A **$25.00**

Wolf's Head Motor Oil, bank, cardboard tube with metal ends, wolf's head logo, 100% Pennsylvania Refinery Sealed, 4x2" dia, EX, D **$15.00**

Wolf's Head Motor Oil, sidewalk sign, 1953, embossed metal oval in cast-iron stand, We Sell... lettered diagonally on colored bands, NM, A **$290.00**

Wolf's Head Motor Oil, sign, tin flange, red, white & green ground with Ask For above Wolf's Head Motor Oil, 100% Pure... below, 17x22", NM, D **$145.00**

Wolsey Socks, statuette, 3-D plaster composition, bust of Wolsey man, Wolsey lettered on base, 6½", D...$225.00

Wolverine Shoes, clock, bowed glass front with metal frame, pictures hands bending shoe encircled by lettering then numbers, round, M, A **$375.00**

Woman's Suffrage Stove Polish, trade card, 1880s, well-dressed girl with long hair, 12 reasons why every woman wants it on reverse, 5x3", EX, P1 .... **$27.50**

Wonder Bread, bank, shaped like loaf of bread, miniature, G, D **$35.00**

Wonder Bread, bread end label, shows Howdy Doody in top hat promoting Free Wonder Circus Album for 16 labels, red border, EX, S1 .... **$12.00**

Wonder Bread, bread end label, Wonder arched over image of Annie Oakley leaning against fence reading, Annie Oakley's Favorite, EX, S1 .... **$10.00**

Wonder Bread, sign, die-cut cardboard hanger, Howdy Doody with loaf of bread, movable joints, 13", NM, D **$33.50**

Wonder Bread, sign, embossed tin, Builds Strong Bodies 8 Ways! below loaf of bread, 12x20", EX, D1 .... **$95.00**

Wonder Bread, trade card, Pat 1928, chain-faced man, You Will Be More Suprised At..., 4x6¼", EX, D **$15.00**

Wood, Smith & Co Fort Plain Spring & Axle Works, trade card, dated 1880, factory flanked by Carriage & Wagon, Springs & Axles, black & white, VG, A **$60.00**

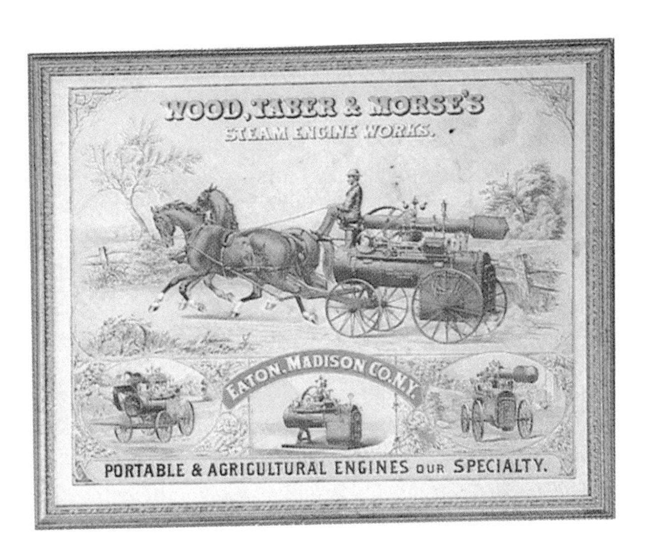

Wood, Taber & Morse's Steam Engine, sign, paper, horse-drawn steam engine above vignettes with various equipment, leaf border, framed, 22x28", NM, A $6,000.00

Wood's Primrose Tea, crate, wood, front panel stamped with product name, inside label depicts Chinese tea pickers, 13x25x16½", VG, A **$70.00**

Wood-Lac Stain, sign, enameloid, pictures woman staining piece of furniture & color chart, minor foxing, 17x20", EX, A **$350.00**

Woodbury Talc, tin, white Woodbury Talc above girl in white on blue mottled background, shaker top, tall oval, EX+, M2 .... **$105.00**

Wooden Shoe Lager Beer, can, cone-top, pictures 2 Dutch men toasting, red, white & blue, EX, D **$40.00**

Wooden Shoe Lager Beer, label, 1933-36, Star Beverage Co, U-type permit number, 12-oz, VG, A **$43.00**

Woodford Club Rye, pocket mirror, shows large whiskey bottle, The Unequalled Whiskey arched above, lettering below, oval, 2¾", VG+, A **$55.00**

Woodlake Nymph, crate label, California lemon, nude blond woman dancing beneath eucalyptus tree, Woodlake, 9x12½", M, C1...**$12.00**

Woodland Mills Shoe Laces, display case, tin, pictures a man driving a shoe into Shoe Lace Station, graphics on all sides, 14x11½x11", NM, A..........................**$3,600.00**

Wool Soap, thermometer, paper face, thermometer arched above bar of soap, Toilet Bath lettered below, repainted frame, 6" dia, G, A................................**$20.00**

Woolsey's Marine Paint Specialties, pocket mirror, pictures can of product with lettering above & below, oval, 2¾", EX, A **$170.00**

Woolson Spice Co, trade card, pictures fisherman in canoe with campsite in background, advertising on reverse, VG, A **$25.00**

Woolson Spice Co's Midsummer Greetings, trade card, embossed image of hunters shooting at game birds, EX, A **$23.00**

Woolworth's, catalog, 1954 Christmas, 16 pages, VG, D .**$15.00**

Woonsocket Rubber Boots, sign, paper, little boy on ocean pier wearing rubber boots, matted & framed, image: 22x15", EX, A..**$475.00**

Woonsocket Shoes, trade card, woman in front of store window, ...Specialties Superior To All Others lettered above, EX, A...**$26.00**

Worchester Brand Salt, sign, cardboard, bag of salt with tag: For Mrs Campbell, Housewife, 34 Economy..., framed, image: 21¼x14½", G, A.........................**$120.00**

Worchester Buckeye Mower, trade card, night scene with men looking through telescopes at farmer in the moon, gray, green & white, VG, A **$22.00**

Worchester Salt, blotter, red on pink, unused, slightly rough edges/water spotted on back, 6x3½", D......**$2.50**

Worchester Salt, coin, embossed brass picturing sack of salt, good luck symbols & slogan on back, EX, D............**$3.00**

WP Deppen Brewer, calendar, 1899, paper with metal strips, couple by bridge with cow in the foreground, December sheet, 15½x20", G, A.........................**$700.00**

WR Benedict's Best Bicycles on Earth, sign, screen-printed tin, pictures bicycle atop Earth graphic, lettering below, 36¼x12½", VG, A.....................................**$90.00**

Wright McGill Tackle Co, catalog, 1957, features fishing tackle, 60 pages, VG, D **$20.00**

Wright's Shampoo Powder, postcard, pictures girl looking in mirror admiring her hair, Shampoo At Home With..., EX+, P3 ....**$50.00**

Wrigley's Chewing Gum, display, tin, Wrigley man with arms at length holding racks for gum, minor chips/scratches/rust, 13¼x14x7", G, A................**$300.00**

Wrigley's Doublemint Gum, matchbook cover, full-length ad, Enjoy above lettered green arrow pointing to smiling face, full book, 20 strike, EX, R1......................**$4.00**

Wrigley's Juicy Fruit Gum, gum wrapper, early, held 5 sticks, EX, D2...**$5.00**

Wrigley's Juicy Fruit Gum, trolley sign, shows Juicy Fruit flying at target, framed, EX, G2..........................**$345.00**

Wrigley's Juicy Fruit Gum, see also Juicy Fruit

Wrigley's Soap, tip tray, black cat sits on bars of soap with red & black ad text on yellow, white & black rim, 3½" dia, NM, A..**$250.00**

Wrigley's Spearmint Gum, display box, folds open to display gum, features Wrigley man promoting product, missing flap on lid, 1x6x4", VG+, M2 ....**$45.00**

Wrigley's Spearmint Gum, sign, 1950s, cardboard, illustrated man displays large pack of Spearmint, Pure, Wholesome, Inexpensive, 11x21", VG+, M2 ....**$42.00**

Wrigley's Spearmint Gum, trolley sign, cardboard, Deco train with Out In Front With... lettered above multiple gum packages, 11x21", G, A.................................**$30.00**

Wrigley's Spearmint Gum, trolley sign, 1920s, cardboard, full-color image of Wrigley boy & large pack of gum, A Famous Flavor, 11x21", EX, D..............................**$48.00**

Wrigley's Spearmint Pepsin Gum, candy scale, 4-lb, painted tin body with brass face, raised lettering, 8", G, A..**$600.00**

Wrigley's Spearmint/Doublemint Gum, sign, die-cut porcelain, 2-sided, Ice Cream lettered on panel above tab reading Wrigley's..., 9x30", VG, A **$1,450.00**

Wrigley's Spearmint/Doublemint Gum, trolley card, Wrigley boys hold sign flanked by packs of gum, Doublemint Is... Popular Brother!, framed, EX+, A **$150.00**

Wrigley's Spearmint/Juicy Fruit/Doublemint Gum, sign, tin over cardboard, Wrigley's above 3 packs of gum, originaly held United profit sharing coupons, 17x9", G-, A **$25.00**

Wrong End Cigars, box label, inner lid sample, 1880s, caricature couple at table, George S Harris, EX, A............**$62.00**

Wrought Iron Range Co, sign, paper, factory scene flanked by insets of other factory scenes & ranges, company name above, framed, 17x23", EX, A...**$300.00**

WS Kimball Cigarettes, sign, 1882, scenes of mens club, ladies salon, concert hall & ocean front sports club, 27x21", NM, D **$375.00**

WS Mancke & Co Military-Navy Society Goods, sign, 1910s, embossed tin, black lettering on yellow ground, 6½x14", EX, D...**$36.00**

Wunderland Beer, label, 1933-36, Arizona Brewing Co, U-type permit number, 11-oz, EX, A **$14.00**

Wyandotte Sanitary Cleaner & Cleanser, postcard, black & white image of woman behind display of products, I Use..., NM, P3 ....**$30.00**

Wyldewood Talc, tin, white with blue product lettering above floral motif, shaker top, tall square shape, VG+, M2 ....**$135.00**

Wynola, door push plate, white with You'll Enjoy above slightly tilted bottle, Good Any Time below, 14x4", EX+, M2 ....**$70.00**

Wynola, sign, die-cut cardboard, Sir Cola-Nut in cap & gown with large bottle, ...Graduate to Wynola, A Real Cola Drink, EX, M2 ....**$35.00**

Wynola, sign, die-cut cardboard stand-up, 3 tiers of bottles, ...Any Time 5¢, top bottle attached, EX, M2.........**$48.00**

X

X-It Auto Dry Cleaner, tin, 1920-30, hand polishing early touring car, X-It on red band at top, slip lid, 4x3", NM, A **$45.00**

XXXX Baker Rye, pocket mirror, product name arched above beer bottle flanked by hops & lettering, Garrett-Williams Co, oval, VG+, A **$130.00**

Y

Y-B Cigars, sign, painted tin, tilted cigar image, B-Y's And Buy Y-B's, 12x27¾", VG, A **$30.00**

Y-B Havana Cigars, sign, embossed tin, open box of cigars with portrait lid, ...Give Universal Satisfaction, 19½x13½", G, A **$200.00**

Yacht Club Coffee, tin, key-wind lid, 1-lb, M, D **$35.00**

Yacht Club Drip Grind Coffee, tin, encircled yacht flanked by lettering, product name above & below, key-wind lid, 1-lb, EX+, A **$35.00**

Yale Brewing Co Lager Beer, sign, reverse-painted glass, etched factory scene flanked by Ales & Porter, framed, image: 24x32", EX, A **$3,000.00**

Yale Lock Man'f'g Co, encased window, blue glass over frosted ground, Designed & Built By...For Post Office At Glen's Falls NY, 39x29", EX, A **$350.00**

Yankee Boy Tobacco, pocket tin, boy in baseball uniform in shield on red & white checked background, slip lid, 4x3½x1", EX, A **$550.00**

Yankee Cigars, sign, paper & reverse glass with foil lettering, Uncle Sam flanked by Sweet Smoke, framed, 11x9½", EX, A **$300.00**

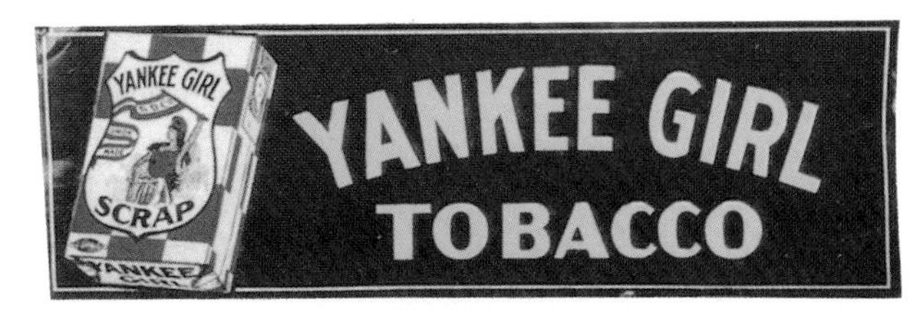

Yankee Girl Tobacco, sign, embossed tin, dark blue with product package at left of yellow product name, with line border, 6½x20", EX, A $50.00

Yankee Peanut Butter, pail, tin, red with white & black letters on white & black outlined emblem, random stars, pry lid & bail, 12-oz, VG, A **$140.00**

Yankee Star Cigars, sign, ca 1900, paper, Victorian temptress holding rose & fan, Pure Havana Filler..., framed, 22x18", VG, A **$385.00**

Yankees Sweet Smoke Cigars, sign, glass, product name lettered around inset of Uncle Sam, framed, vertical, EX, M1 .... **$385.00**

Yankiboy Play Clothes, pin-back button, Tom Mix photo encircled by Yankiboy Clothes & signature, 2" dia, EX, A **$42.00**

Yara Tobacco, display, ca 1915, die-cut cardboard standup, trifold, pictures woman in center, signed Haskell Coffin, 32x44", VG, A **$140.00**

Yardley's Lavender Talc Powder, tin, tall oval shape in cream with gold accents, period mother, child & dog on oval inset, shaker top, VG+, M2 .... **$20.00**

Yardley's Lavender Talc Powder, tin, tall oval shape in cream with gold accents, period mother, child & dog on oval inset, shaker top, VG+, M2 .... **$45.00**

Yates & Co Clothing, trade card, metamorphic die-cut in shape of a clock with dog & cat at bottom, door opens to show little girl, EX, A **$60.00**

Yeast Foam, sign, paper, girl at table with plate of pancakes, Makes Delicious Buckwheat Cakes, 15x10", VG, A **$30.00**

Yeast Foam, sign, paper, girl at table with plate of pancakes, Makes Delicious Buckwheat Cakes, framed, image: 15x10", EX, A $55.00

Yellow Cab Cigars, box, inner lid label features policeman with whistle, early cab beyond, 5¢ marked out above Now 2 For 5¢, VG, A **$110.00**

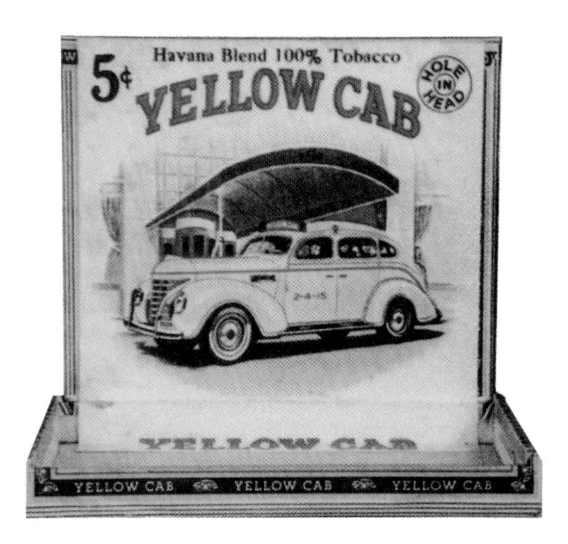

Yellow Cab Havana Blend 100% Tobacco, cigar box, cardboard, inner lid label pictures yellow 1940s cab parked at arced entrance, ¾x5½x7", EX, A $300.00

Yellow Cab 5¢ Cigar, sign, tin, Yellow Cab 5¢ Cigar, image of traffic cop & early auto above Takes The Right Of Way, horizontal, EX, M1 .... **$460.00**

Yellow Cap Cigars, box label, outer, half nude woman holding tobacco, 4½x4½", G, C3 ....**$12.00**

Yellow Kid Chewing Gum, pin-back button, kid in gown marked YK in center with There Is Only One...Big Bubble Chewing Gum around rim,¾", NM, A............**$62.00**

Yoe & Coe's Lakeside Maple Syrup, sign, paper, winter workers tapping maple trees with ice skaters beyond, Forbes litho, framed, image: 13x20", NM, A.......**$850.00**

Yokohl, crate label, 1920s, California orange, Indian brave fishing by stream, oranges in foreground, Exeter, 10x11", M, C1 ....**$3.00**

Yoo-Hoo Chocolate, store sign, 1970s, features cartoon image of Yogi Berra & a modern-day rock band, 17x11", M, D **$35.00**

Yorktown American Cigarettes, sign, 1936, tin, pictures a ship with pack of cigarettes in the foreground, red, white & blue, 16x12", EX, D **$50.00**

Yosemite Lager, sign, reverse-painted glass, red rippled letters on milk glass surrounded by green & yellow slag glass, 20x67", G, A **$6,100.00**

Yotoc Beer, label, 1933-50, logo above product name, Ohio Brewery Inc, Internal Revenue Tax Paid statement, 12-oz, EX, A **$5.00**

Young Tar Cigars, box label, inner lid sample, 1880s, young sailor in oval inset left of ships, Witsch & Schmidt litho, M, A **$308.00**

Yours Forever Cigars, box label, inner lid sample, 1880s, young endearing couple flanked by other couples, Witsch & Schmidt litho, VG, A **$75.00**

Yuengling's, see also DG Yuengling

Yuengling's Ale, sign, die-cut cardboard, lady with glass in framed oval beside bottle, Most Calls Are For...Since 1829, 36x24", VG, A **$35.00**

Yuengling's Beer, Porter & Ale, sign, reverse-painted glass, eagle logo flanked by Purity & Cleanliness, gold leaf highlights, framed, 32x22", VG, A..$1,750.00

Yuengling's Beer, Porter & Ale, sign, self-framed tin, eagle logo flanked by Purity & Cleanliness, Shonk litho, 23" dia, VG, A **$775.00**

Yuengling's Beer, Porter & Ale, tip tray, bust-length portrait of a girl in wide-brimmed hat, lettering on rim, minor soiling, 4¼" dia, EX, A **$135.00**

Yukon's Queen of the West Self-Rising Flour, sign, tin, flour bag with woman holding pie within oval, product lettering above & below, 22½x13½", VG, A **$180.00**

Yusay Pilsener, label, 1933-50, pictures an eagle, Pilsener Brewing Co, Internal Revenue Tax Paid statement, 1-qt, EX, A **$15.00**

Z

Zaco, sign, light-up, lady with product pointed at car fender, Just Twist..., Squelch The Squeaks, framed, 17x14", EX, A **$65.00**

Zenith, pin-back button, 1930s, blue, white & yellow, small nick, D **$4.00**

Zenith Color TV, display, 1966, cardboard foldout, fold's out to 25x25", NM, D **$3.00**

Zeno Chewing Gum, vendor, tin & iron on oak base with allover advertising, coin operated with clockwork mechanism, 16", EX, A **$1,155.00**

Zeno Chewing Gum, display case, wood frame, straight glass sides with slanted front, Zeno carved on marquee, 3 shelves, 17x10x9", VG, A......$325.00

Zeno Chewing Gum, tin, inside lid graphics shows man leaning over to grab pack of gum from water, Dutch graphics on sides, 3x10x5", EX, A **$150.00**

Zeno Chewing Gum, vendor, 1¢, metal, black lettering on yellow, patented May 5 1908, no back or interior parts, G, A **$65.00**

Zeno Chewing Gum, vendor, 1¢, oak with embossed tin front, Drop One Cent In Slot..., original condition, 16½x10½x9", VG, A **$600.00**

Zeno Fruit Flavored Gum, complete 10¢ pack, G2 ....**$22.00**

Zephyr Gasoline, gas globe, 1930-40, glass, blue & white letters on red outlined in blue, 13½" dia, EX, A **$130.00**

Zeppelin Motor Oil, can, 1925-45, Zeppelin flying over the ocean, red, white & blue, pour spout & handle, 2-gal, 10½", EX, A....................$375.00

Zerolene Oil, can, 1915-25, polar bear & Zero Cold... on blue, ships, touring car & text on back, screw lid & handle, 1-gal, 11", G, A....................$80.00

Zerolene Oil, can, 1915-25, polar bear & Zero... on blue, ships, touring car & text on back, screw lid & handle, 5-gal, 15", EX, A....................$225.00

Zerolube Motor Oil, can, 1935-45, product name above 2 polar bears on ice, Perfect Winter... below, cream & blue ground, 1-qt, 5½", EX, A....................$50.00

Zeroniz Anti-Freeze, can, 1935-45, pictures Eskimo, igloo & dogs, product name & lettering encircled above, 9½", NM, A....................$100.00

Ziegler Peerless Marshmallows, tin, Ziegler in diagonal script above Peerless Marshmallows, slip lid, A....................$20.00

Ziegler 520, bottle, long neck, paper label, VG, D ...$10.00

Zig-Zag Cigarette Papers, dispenser, metal, hands roll cigarette above Easy To Roll Your Own, Zig-Zag 5¢, Gummed Edges, Ready Creased, 6", EX, A $65.00

Zimmerman Mfg Co, pocket mirror, pictures buggy with True Blue Vehicles arched above, company name below, minor flaking, 2⅛" dia, G+, A....................$50.00

Zingo Sweets Candy, tin, orange & blue with product name above race car image, Meekin Can Co, Cincinatti Ohio, 12x10" dia, VG, A....................$231.00

Zipp's Cherri-o, dispenser, white ceramic barrel shape with bird logo & red lettering, Zipp's Cherri-o 5¢, 16", VG+, A....................$2,300.00

Zira Cigarettes, sign, paperboard, sexy girl in hat with hand on hip & flower in mouth, Wonderfully Great, 5¢, framed, 22x16", G+, A....................$300.00

Zobelein's Eastside Beer, label, pre-1920, Los Angeles Brewing Co, EX, A....................$10.00

Zombies, tin, 1940s-50s, colorful tropic scene, Delicious Coconut Confection... below, slip lid, 1-lb, 4x7" dia, G, A....................$10.00

Zuyder Zee Tomatoes, can label, red tomatoes on red & blue background, EX, G1....................$2.00

Zwiazkowieg Cigars, box label, lithographer's proof, 1890s, close-up of shield flanked by flags & banner, John's & Co Litho, EX, A....................$24.00

1000 Mile Motor Oil, can, 1925-45, car tires & lettering on circular inset, yellow & black, pour spout & handle, 2-gal, 10½", EX, A....................$35.00

3 Centa, sign, paperboard, pictures bottle at right, Drink...3¢ In Bottles in red & green on yellow, wood frame, 10x28", EX, A....................$260.00

30 Below, sign, tin, green & black with penguin by 30 Below lettered on green circle, lettering below, 11x9", NM, M3....................$175.00

49'er Beer, label, 1933-36, Modesto Brewery Inc, U-type permit number, 22-oz, EX, A....................$34.00

7 Eleven Root Beer, can, steel, EX, D....................$3.50

7-Up, bottle, commemorating Notre Dames Fighting Irish, pictures a football player, 1977 game scores on back, 16-oz, NM, D....................$7.00

7-Up, bottle, 1968, green with orange & white label, 10-oz, EX, D....................$6.50

7-Up, bottle, 1971, green with red & white label, 7-oz, EX, D....................$4.00

7-Up, bottle topper, cardboard, Fresh Up With 7-Up above smiling boy lifting bottle to mouth, 8x5", NM, A....$6.00

7-Up, bottle topper, cardboard, Here's How Friends Fresh Up & 7-Up logo above 2 smiling fellas with bottles, NM, A....................$6.00

7-Up, bottle topper, die-cut cardboard, Easter basket, NM, B1....................$3.00

7-Up, bottle topper, die-cut cardboard, pictures turkey wearing a tuxedo, Dress Up The Dinner, NM, B1....................$4.00

7-Up, bottle topper, die-cut cardboard, 1948, logo above turkey chef, 10x7", NM, A....................$6.00

7-Up, bottle topper, die-cut cardboard, 1950, For Halloween banner over ghost pumkin holding logo, 6x10", NM, A....................$6.00

7-Up, bottle topper, die-cut cardboard, 1953, arrow shape, Enjoy A 7-Up Float!..., NM, B1 ....**$3.00**

7-Up, bottle topper, die-cut cardboard, 1953, You Like It, It Likes You lettered on heart left of logo, 6x9", NM, A .**$6.00**

7-Up, bottle topper, die-cut cardboard, 1954, logo upper left of bunny in a dress, Easter Fresh Up below, 10x5½", NM, B1 ....**$4.00**

7-Up, bottle topper, die-cut cardboard, 1954, silhouetted pipe-smoking leprechaun above tilted logo, 9x6", NM, A **$6.00**

7-Up, clock, light-up, glass with metal frame, 7-Up on colorful sun & rainbow logo above 12-3-6-9 on yellow, 18x12", EX, M3 ....**$45.00**

7-Up, clock, light-up, logo in center, Nothing Does It Like Seven-Up below, oak frame, 16x16", NM, A......**$110.00**

7-Up, clock, vertical rectangle bordered by wire decor, 12-3-6-9 around 7-Up logo, 22x18", EX, A **$140.00**

7-Up, display, counter-top, heavy glass ice cube shape with raised lettering, bottle rests in form fitting niche, 9", EX, A....................................**$475.00**

7-Up, display, die-cut paperboard hanger, flowers brimming from wicker basket with logo, 20", G, A...**$110.00**

7-Up, door pull plate, embossed tin, Come In above 7-Up & bubbles on oval inset, 3 lines pointing down to Likes You, VG, A **$85.00**

7-Up, door push bar, tin, yellow, blue, green & red designs flank green 7-Up with red dot on white, 3x30", EX, M2....................................$38.00

7-Up, door push bar, tin, 3 '7UPS' in green outlined in black with red dots between 7 & U, white ground, 3x30", VG+, M2 ....**$30.00**

7-Up, door push bar, tin, 7-Up logos flank Fresh Up With Seven-up! on white background, minor edge chips, 3x30", M2 ....**$47.00**

7-Up, folding chair, 1940s-50s, tin, green & white striped seat, back of seat is white with logo, 32½" folded out, EX, A **$150.00**

7-Up, menu board, die-cut masonite, Seven-Up Makes Good Food Taste Better above 7-Up logo in center of menu slots, EX, A....................................**$170.00**

7-Up, menu board, die-cut masonite, Suggestions on panel atop 2 rows for menu items, round logo below, 12x21", EX+, M2 ....**$70.00**

7-Up, menu board, masonite, Get Real Action, 7-Up Your Thirst Away! & logo on white above black menu area, 23x14", EX, M3 ....**$45.00**

7-Up, menu board, plastic, red & white 7-Up logo on green center panel with green menu space above & below, NM, M3 ....**$60.00**

7-Up, menu board, tin, hand with bottle & 7-Up logo above chalkboard, vertical rectangle with rounded corners, EX, M2....................................**$36.00**

7-Up, pocket lighter, enameled 7-Up logo over design on metal, EX+, A....................................**$17.00**

7-Up, screen door brace, 1960s, embossed tin, logo above Take Some Home Today, 7x11", EX, D **$30.00**

7-Up, shot glass, You Like It, It Likes You, EX, D........**$4.00**

7-Up, sign, cardboard, black, red & white on white, Handy Portable Cooler & Case Of 7-Up (logo pictured)..., 18x14", NM, M3 ....**$125.00**

7-Up, sign, cardboard, features New! Like (on red oval) Diet Drink, Lemon Lime Flavor above 7-Up logo, 13x22", NM, M3 ....**$33.00**

7-Up, sign, cardboard, Fresh Up With... above 2 bottles on tray with decanter & 2 glasses, vertical, EX+, A **$18.00**

7-Up, sign, cardboard, Mix With Chilled & 7-Up logo above bottles & glasses, sailboats beyond, vertical, EX, A ...**$18.00**

7-Up, sign, cardboard, 1944, girl with braids & apron holding bottle of 7-Up, Fresh Up, That's It! above, 12x8", EX, D....................................**$30.00**

7-Up, sign, cardboard, 1949, little boy wearing propeller beanie with bottle of 7-Up, logo above, 8x5", EX, D **$10.00**

7-Up, sign, cardboard, 1950s, die-cut, Fresh Up... on diagonal band separating elderly couple with bottles, vertical, EX, A **$15.00**

7-Up, sign, cardboard, 1950s, footed glass with bottle on tray, Fresh-Up With A Float, vertical, EX, A **$15.00**

7-Up, sign, cardboard, 1952, kids on a hayride & girl with ukelele, Fresh Up With 7-Up, 11x21", EX, D........**$28.00**

7-Up, sign, cardboard, 1953, self-framed, young baseball players sharing bottle of 7-Up, You Like It..., 13x23", EX, D....................................**$45.00**

7-Up, sign, cardboard, 1955, girl with tennis racket over her shoulder & bottle of 7-Up, Nothing Does It..., 11x21", EX, D....................................**$28.00**

7-Up, sign, cardboard, 1956, gift-wrapped case of 7-Up & Christmas ornament, All Through The Holidays, 14x14", EX, D....................................**$25.00**

7-Up, sign, cardboard, 1957, pretty girl decorating for a party, Real Thirst Quencher..., 11x21", EX, D **$35.00**

7-Up, sign, cardboard, 1958, ice-skating couple pausing for a 7-Up, Quick Refreshing Lift!, 11x21", EX, D......**$32.00**

7-Up, sign, cardboard, 1958, pictures young couple playing with basset hound, 14x14", EX, D........................**$24.00**

7-Up, sign, cardboard, 1958, preppies in a Model A car at a drive-in restaurant, 14x14", EX, D **$30.00**

7-Up, sign, cardboard, 1960, Beef Sandwich & Seven-Up lettered at right of plate of food & bottle, 10x17", EX+, M2 ....**$10.00**

7-Up, sign, cardboard hanger, Christmas bulb with Seasons Greetings & cartons of 7-Up, 12x10", NM, A.........**$3.00**

7-Up, sign, cardboard hanger, logo upper right of Santa's head in wreath, banner reads Give 'Un' To Others, 10x6", NM, A....................................**$6.00**

7-Up, sign, cardboard hanger, pictures hand holding bottle, Fresh Up With lettered above, NM, B1 ....**$5.00**

7-Up, sign, cardboard hanger, 1948, beach scene with 2 kids covering dad with sand, We're A Fresh Up Family!, 12x22", NM, B1....................................**$10.00**

7-Up, sign, cardboard hanger, 1949, self-framed, pictures dad pulling kids on sled, We're A Fresh Up Family, 13x23", EX, D **$25.00**

7-Up, sign, cardboard hanger, 1949, 2-sided, pictures country fiddler with logo above, 8x5", EX, D..............**$16.00**

7-Up, sign, cardboard hanger, 1950, self-framed, pictures fisherman & his family, 13x23", EX, D.................**$28.00**

7-Up, sign, cardboard hanger, 2-sided, logo right of stylized Santa in wreath, Seasons Greetings banner below, 10x11", NM, A..**$25.00**

7-Up, sign, cardboard hanger, 2-sided, stylized waving Santa with bottle, The More 7-Up The Merrier above, 12x8", NM, A..**$25.00**

7-Up, sign, cardboard stand-up, die-cut, grocery man offering case of 7-Up, Here's Your Family Fresh Up, 12x10", NM, M2 ....**$28.00**

7-Up, sign, cardboard stand-up, die-cut, 1946, We're A Fresh Up Family! above grandmother & granddaughter, 12x9", NM, D **$12.00**

7-Up, sign, cardboard stand-up, die-cut, 1948, man holding case of 7-Up, Here's Your Family Fresh Up, 12x8", NM, B1 ....**$10.00**

7-Up, sign, cardboard stand-up, elderly woman with bottle, Exactly What It Is, A Fresh Up lettered above, 12", NM, B1 ....**$12.00**

7-Up, sign, cardboard stand-up, Fresh Up Thats 7-Up on diagonal band between elderly man & woman, 12", NM, B1 ....**$9.00**

7-Up, sign, cardboard stand-up, Fresh Up With lettered above bottle display, brown background, 11½", NM, B1...**$10.00**

7-Up, sign, cardboard stand-up, man with bottle of 7-Up, Your Stand-By...Likes You above, 18x12", NM, B1..**$15.00**

7-Up, sign, cardboard stand-up, pictures chef grilling meat while father & son watch, You Like It... above, 12x8", NM, B1 ....**$12.00**

7-Up, sign, cardboard stand-up, 1948, mother & daughter with bottle of 7-Up, die-cut logo above, 12x8", EX, D **$28.00**

7-Up, sign, cardboard stand-up, 1950, display of bottles & glasses, Fresh Up With lettered above logo, 12", NM, B1 ....**$8.00**

7-Up, sign, cardboard stand-up, 1950, family fishing in rowboat, The Fresh Up Family Drink & logo above, 12x8", EX, D...**$20.00**

7-Up, sign, cardboard stand-up, 1950, family watching television, Fresh Up With...All-Family Drink above, 16x12", NM, B1 ....**$15.00**

7-Up, sign, cardboard stand-up, 1950, shows family at the beach, The Fresh Up Family Drink! above, 12", NM, B1 ....**$10.00**

7-Up, sign, cardboard stand-up, 1964, happy Santa with bottle & sandwich, When Guests Drop In... above, 24", NM, B1 ....**$15.00**

7-Up, sign, cardboard stand-up, 7-Up above 2 smiling kids enjoying 7-Up, They Like It...It Likes Them, 18x12", EX, A..**$12.00**

7-Up, sign, paper, Fresh Up With A 7-Up Float lettered diagonally over a tray with bottle & glass, 5½x16", NM, B1 ....**$2.50**

7-Up, sign, porcelain, 1948, traditional logo, 36x30", NM, D3 ....**$550.00**

7-Up, sign, tin, die-cut, 7-Up lettered in white on red logo & The Uncola in green over sunrise, 12x23", EX+, M3 ....**$75.00**

7-Up, sign, tin, embossed, 1946, 7-Up on round emblem with 'winged' design, You Like It, It Likes You, 19x27", EX+, A...**$240.00**

7-Up, sign, tin, embossed, 7-Up on green triangle, 13", NM, A...**$140.00**

7-Up, sign, tin, embossed, 7-Up Sold Here on round bubble logo attached to gold wings, 15", EX, A.............**$192.00**

7-Up, sign, tin, Fresh Up With above tilted logo, large bottle neck image below, 41x13", NM, A.................**$175.00**

7-Up, sign, tin, Fresh Up With above 6-pack of bottles, The All-Family Drink! below, 60x35", M, S2 ....**$950.00**

7-Up, sign, tin, Fresh Up! lettered diagonally above tilted bubble logo, It Likes You lower left, triangular, EX, M1 ....**$165.00**

7-Up, sign, tin, 1930s, 7-Up logo centered between You Like It...&...It Likes You, 11x28", VG+, M2 ....**$25.00**

7-Up, sign, tin, 1947, Your Fresh Up lettered diagonally upper left of hand holding bottle, 30x28", VG+, A..........**$183.00**

7-Up, sign from drink rack, white 7-Up on red square with rounded corners on white panel with rounded corners, 12x19", EX, M2 ....**$28.00**

7-Up, sign from vendor, plastic, metal frame, 2 cans flank 7-Up logo, Served In Cans Below, star background, 12x24", EX, M2 ....**$25.00**

7-Up, squeeze toy, 1959, Fresh-Up Freddie with bottle of 7-Up, molded vinyl, 9", NM, D $125.00

7-Up, telephone, 1990, 7-Up Spot standing on black base with checkered top, plastic, 12", M, D.................**$55.00**

7-Up, thermometer, dial, 1950s, metal frame, glass lens, degrees surround 7-Up logo, The All-Family Drink!, 12" dia, NM, D **$120.00**

7-Up, thermometer, porcelain, Fresh-Up above bottle right of bulb, You Like It...It Likes You, round ends, 15x6", EX, M2...**$50.00**

7-Up, thermometer, porcelain, white with red The Fresh Up Family Drink above bulb left of bottle, rounded ends, G, M2 ....**$70.00**

AD RATE CARD FOR HUXFORD'S COLLECTIBLE ADVERTISING

PLEASE CONTACT HUXFORD ENTERPRISES *IMMEDIATELY* TO RESERVE YOUR SPACE FOR THE NEXT EDITION

RATES
(Ad Size)

FULL PAGE	**7½" wide x 9¾" tall – $750.00**
HALF PAGE	**7½" wide x 4½" tall – $400.00**
QUARTER PAGE	**3½" wide x 4½" tall – $250.00**
EIGHTH PAGE (or business card)	**3½" wide x 2¼" tall – $150.00**

NOTE: The above rates are for **camera ready copy only** *– Add $50.00 if we are to compose your ad. These prices are net – no agency discounts allowed. Payment in full must accompany your ad copy.*

All advertising accepted under the following conditions:

1. *The Publisher will furnish advertising space in sizes and at rates as set forth in this rate sheet upon full payment in advance of its annual advertising deadline as set forth herein.*

2. Submission of Copy. *The publisher shall have the right to omit any advertisement when the space allotted to Advertiser in a particular issue has been filled. In addition, the Publisher reserves the right to limit the amount of space the Advertiser may use in any one edition.*

3. Content and Design. *Publisher reserves the right to censor, reject, alter or refuse any advertising copy in its sole discretion or disapprove any advertising copy in accordance with any rule the Publisher may now have, or may adopt in the future, concerning the acceptance of advertising matter, but no intentional change in advertising copy will be made without the prior consent of the Advertiser.*

4. Publisher's Liability for Deletions. *Publisher's liability for failure of the Publisher to insert any advertisement in their books shall be limited to a refund of the consideration paid for the insertion of the advertisement or, at Advertiser's option, to such deleted advertisement being inserted in the next edition.*

5. Copyright and Trademark Permission. *Any Advertiser using copyrighted material or trademarks or trade names of others in its advertising copy shall obtain the prior written permission of the owners thereof which must be submitted to the Publisher with the advertising copy. Where this has not been done, advertising will not be accepted.*

Half Page

Quarter Page

Eighth Page

Make checks payable to:

HUXFORD ENTERPRISES
1202 7th St.
Covington, IN 47932

One of the new features we've added to our book this year is the advertising section. All the ads you will see there (for this edition only) are complimentary. Some are from the auction galleries who provided us with their catalogs and in many instances sent photographs, others from individual collectors and dealers to whose 'for sale' lists we assigned 2-letter codes that identified each item as to its source. (See Identification of Coded Dealers and Collectors for further explanation.) The ads were complimentary this year for a two-fold purpose. One, to convey our appreciation to those that were involved in the preparation of this year's guide, and two, to demonstrate the impact these displays can carry. Ads will be sold on a 'first come, first serve' basis for the third edition.

Vintage Picture Postcards

Topical & Artist Want Lists Filled
Mail Approval Service
Mail Order Catalogs
Mail/Phone Auctions
Investment-Grade Rarities

Write or call and tell us your interests,
or request a sample catalog.

Postcards International
P.O. Box 2930, Dept. W
New Haven, CT 06515-0030
Tel: (203) 865-0814 • Fax: (203) 495-8005

WANTED!

ADVERTISING FIGURAL
SALT & PEPPERS

*Bobs Big Boy
*Blue Nun
*Indian Maid Feed
*Hamms Bear
*Lenny Lennox
*Evinrude Motors
*ANY OTHERS

ALSO ANY ITEMS RELATING TO...

*Elsie the Cow
*Smokey Bear
*Reddy Kilowatt
*Aunt Jemima

* **FIGURAL ADVERTISING BOBBIN' HEADS**
* **FOOD PRODUCT ADVERTISING FIGURES**

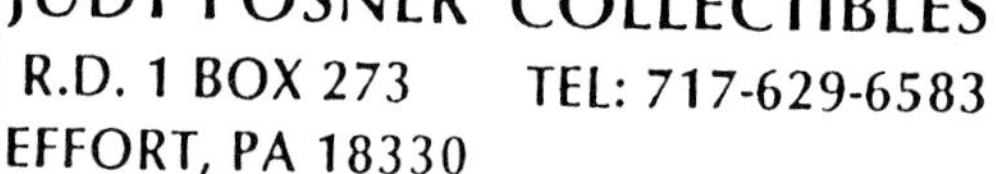

JUDY POSNER COLLECTIBLES
R.D. 1 BOX 273 TEL: 717-629-6583
EFFORT, PA 18330
BUY · SELL · MAIL ORDER · VISA/MC

Larry & Nancy Werner
P.O. Box 188, Winfield, Illinois 60190
708/690-2960

Beer Labels

A phone-mail auction catalog issued every June and December! US, Canadian and foreign beer labels are offered for auction. Each catalog includes prices realized and the ***Collectors Corner*** with news and tips about label collecting. Catalogs: US mail $7.00, to Canada $8.00, Overseas $10.00. Also buying label collections!

Bob Kay
PO Box 1805
Batavia, IL 60510-1805
Phone 708-879-6214

AND COLLECTABLES
BOUGHT & SOLD

By Appointment Only **(310) 376-3858**

SINCE 1967
AMERICA'S PREMIER
MAIL & PHONE BID
AUCTION

Our bi-monthly catalogues offer a fascinating array of original collectibles. Each "Mail & Phone Bid Auction" catalogue pictures, describes, and gives an estimated value for some 3000 items. Bidders participate by sending in a bid sheet and on the closing day of the auction, the status of bids may be checked by phone.

Specializing in over 100 collectible categories including:
DISNEYANA • COMIC CHARACTER ITEMS TOYS • RADIO PREMIUMS • WESTERN & SPACE HERO ITEMS • EARLY RADIO & TV ITEMS ADVERTISING COLLECTIBLES • PRESIDENTIAL CAMPAIGN ITEMS • PINBACK BUTTONS OF ALL TYPES • SPORTS • MOVIE ITEMS AVIATION • BICYCLES • AUTOMOTIVE • WORLD WAR I AND II • PATRIOTIC ITEMS, WORLD'S FAIRS • EPHEMERA • SHIRLEY TEMPLE & RELATED DOLL ITEMS • GUM CARDS • ELVIS THE BEATLES & MOST FORMS OF AMERICAN POPULAR CULTURE

We would like to show you what is available—

$7.50 Sample Auction—1 Catalogue
$20.00—3 Catalogues Subscription
$30.00—5 Catalogues (1 Year)
(overseas: $30.00 for 3 issues)

HAKE'S AMERICANA
PO BOX 1444 (DEPT. 181)
YORK PA 17405
717-848-1333

Cerebro
P. O. Box 327
East Prospect, PA
17317-0327

David C. Freiberg
Dealer In Antique Label Art
Specializing in Cigar Label Art

1-800-69-LABEL
FAX 717-252-3685
717-252-2400

Henry F. Hain III
Antiques, Collectibles & Books

2623 North Second Street
Harrisburg, Pennsylvania 17110
717-238-0534

$1 For List of Advertising Items for Sale
or
Send SASE with Specific Interests

Interests Computer-Filed for Future Offers

SASE for List of Lists Available of a General Line of Antiques, Collectibles and Books

A Full-Time Mail Order Dealer Since 1980

SIGNS OF AGE

115-117 Pine St.
Catasauqua, PA 18032

Robert & Louise Marshall
(215) 264- 8986

ADVERTISING COLLECTIBLES

- Advertising signs
- Thermometers
- Soda paper items
- Matchbooks
- ACL soda bottles
- Bottle toppers
- Bottle carriers
- Country store items
- Local advertising
- Local paper items
- Local bottles
- Reclosable bags
- Shipping bubbles
- Shipping supplies

Soda related items always wanted

Mike's General Store
In Business Since 1979
Specializing in:
TOYS - ADVERTISING - TINS
Our shop, which is located 8 hours north of Minneapolis, is crammed full of interesting and unique pieces of nostalgia and collectibles. We buy and sell worldwide. We purchase one item or complete collections. We can travel anywhere to do so. If you have anything for sale, drop us a line.
MAIL ORDER CATALOGS
We provide a full color catalog featuring over 500 items. All original and old. Advertising, tins and toys. Along with the catalog, we include a mini auction of over 100 items. Catalogs are printed every spring and fall, at a cost of $6.00 each or next 4 issues for $20.00.
MIKE'S GENERAL STORE
52 ST. ANNES ROAD
WINNIPEG, MANITOBA
CANADA R2M 2Y3
PH: 1-204-255-3463 • FAX: 1-204-253-4124
Coca-Cola
Hot Wheels
AURORA
BATMAN
GOLD DUST
TOBACCO
GI JOE

WANTED TO BUY!

ADVERTISING PUZZLES

Donald Friedman
660 W. Grand Ave.
Chicago, IL 60610

708-656-3700 *(day)*
312-226-4741 *(evenings & weekends)*

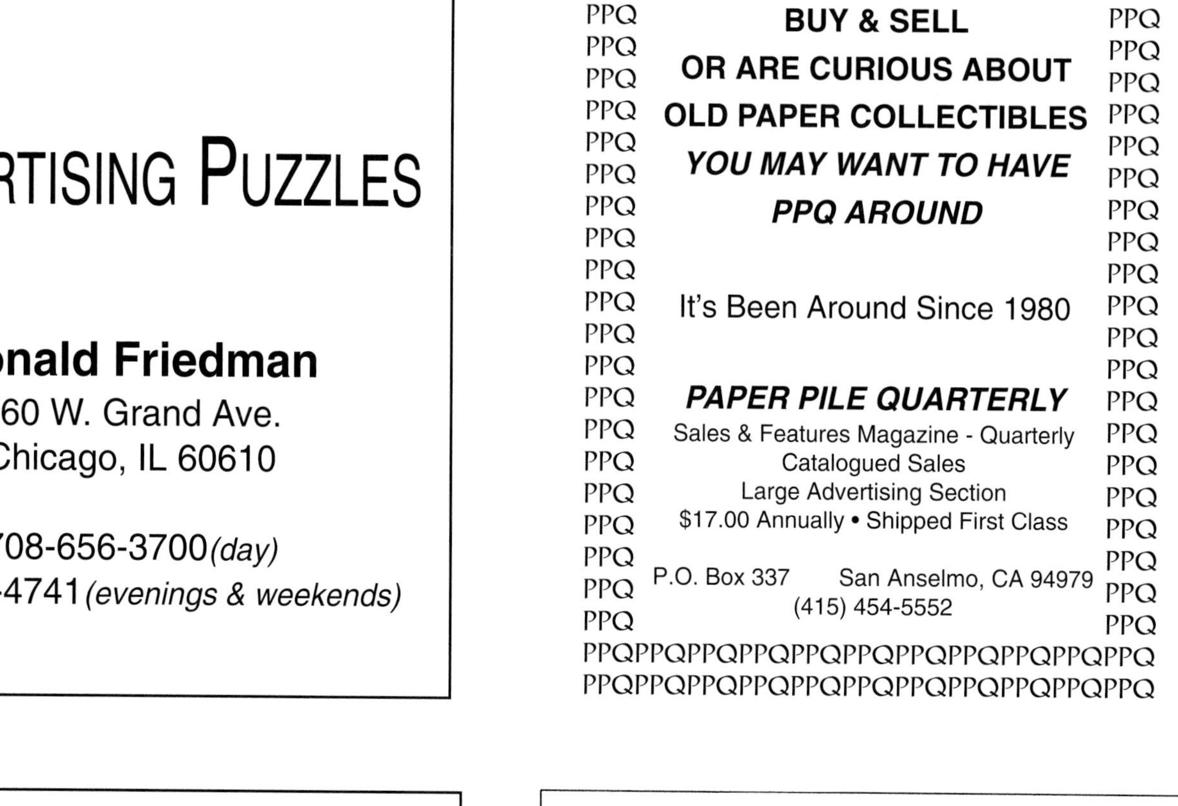

PPQPPQPPQPPQPPQPPQPPQPPQPPQPPQPPQ
PPQPPQPPQPPQPPQPPQPPQPPQPPQPPQPPQ
PPQPPQPPQPPQ

IF YOU COLLECT
BUY & SELL
OR ARE CURIOUS ABOUT
OLD PAPER COLLECTIBLES
YOU MAY WANT TO HAVE
PPQ AROUND

It's Been Around Since 1980

PAPER PILE QUARTERLY
Sales & Features Magazine - Quarterly
Catalogued Sales
Large Advertising Section
$17.00 Annually • Shipped First Class

P.O. Box 337 San Anselmo, CA 94979
(415) 454-5552

PPQPPQPPQPPQPPQPPQPPQPPQPPQPPQPPQ
PPQPPQPPQPPQPPQPPQPPQPPQPPQPPQPPQ

Old Labels

Citrus - Apple - Pear - Grape
Veggie - Beer - Spirits
Soda - Meds - Cosmetic - Cans
Miscellaneous - Seed Packets

CAIRNS ANTIQUES
P. O. BOX 44026
LEMONCOVE, CA 93244

MAIL ORDER
ONLY
(209) 597-2242

THE AMERICAN MATCHCOVER COLLECTING CLUB

. . . invites you to join and enjoy matchcover collecting. Four bulletins yearly, four matchcover auctions, a membership roster, specials, matchcovers, annual swapfest, custom matchcovers and more.

For more information:
AMCC
PO Box 18481
Asheville, NC 28814
or call
704/254-4487
FAX: 704/254-1066

VICTORIAN IMAGES

Builders, Buyers & Auctioneers of Great Ephemera Collections

RUSSELL S. MASCIERI

6 Florence Ave.
Marlton, NJ 08053

Bus. (609) 985-7711
Fax (609) 985-8513

Tobacco Tins & Bins

David & Betty Horvath

27 Cockpit St.
Baltimore MD 21220

Price List $2.00 ***410-686-1279***

"I'm Crazy! I'll buy anything!"

MINERAL CITY UNLIMITED

Antiques • Junk • Finders Service • Estates • Rental Units

DUANE NYCZ
Owner

(509) 246-0672
P.O. Box 923 / 323 Main East
Soap Lake, WA 98851

SIGNS WANTED!

I buy advertising signs of all kinds. I'm interested in quantities of decorator signs as well as individual self-framed signs.

Let me know what you have.

DAVE BECK

BOX 435
MEDIAPOLIS, IOWA 52637
319-394-3943

WANTED:

Bread End Labels

Howdy
Doody,
Cowboys
Spacemen
Movie Stars
Sports
Disney
Etc.

Royal Desserts and Dixie Lids
Movie Stars
Let me know what you have!

DON SHELLEY
P.O. Box 11
Fitchville, CT 06334
PH: 203-887-6163 after 5pm EST

9104

Index

CLOTHING & HATS

CLOTHING DYES

DAIRY

FARM

FAST FOOD

FINANCIAL INSTITUTIONS

FIREARMS, GUN POWDER & AMMUNITION

FOOD

FREIGHT, MOVING & STORAGE

FRUITS AND VEGETABLES

FURNITURE & CARPETING

GARDEN SEEDS AND TOOLS

GAS, OIL & AUTO

SOAPS, CLEANERS & POLISHES

SOFT DRINKS & SODA FOUNTAIN

SPORTS & SPORTING EQUIPMENT

TEA & COFFEE

TELEPHONE & TELEGRAPH

TOBACCO

TOILETRIES, PERFUME & COSMETICS

TOOLS

TRAVEL & TRANSPORTATION

VETERINARY

Books on Antiques and Collectibles

This is only a partial listing of the books on antiques that are available from Collector Books. All books are well illustrated and contain current values. Most of the following books are available from your local book seller, antique dealer, or public library. If you are unable to locate certain titles in your area, you may order by mail from COLLECTOR BOOKS, P.O. Box 3009, Paducah, KY 42002-3009. Customers with Visa or MasterCard may phone in orders from 8:00 – 4:00 CST, M – F – Toll Free 1-800-626-5420. Add $2.00 for postage for the first book ordered and $0.30 for each additional book. Include item number, title, and price when ordering. Allow 14 to 21 days for delivery.

BOOKS ON GLASS AND POTTERY

1810 American Art Glass, Shuman $29.95
2016 Bedroom & Bathroom Glassware of the Depression Years....$19.95
1312 Blue & White Stoneware, McNerney $9.95
1959 Blue Willow, 2nd Ed., Gaston $14.95
3719 Coll. Glassware from the 40's, 50's, 60's, 2nd Ed., Florence $19.95
3311 Collecting Yellow Ware – Id. & Value Gd., McAllister $16.95
2352 Collector's Ency. of Akro Agate Glassware, Florence $14.95
1373 Collector's Ency. of American Dinnerware, Cunningham $24.95
2272 Collector's Ency. of California Pottery, Chipman $24.95
3312 Collector's Ency. of Children's Dishes, Whitmyer $19.95
2133 Collector's Ency. of Cookie Jars, Roerig $24.95
3724 Collector's Ency. of Depression Glass, 11th Ed., Florence $19.95
2209 Collector's Ency. of Fiesta, 7th Ed., Huxford $19.95
1439 Collector's Ency. of Flow Blue China, Gaston $19.95
1915 Collector's Ency. of Hall China, 2nd Ed., Whitmyer $24.95
2334 Collector's Ency. of Majolica Pottery, Katz-Marks $19.95
1358 Collector's Ency. of McCoy Pottery, Huxford $19.95
3313 Collector's Ency. of Niloak, Gifford $19.95
1039 Collector's Ency. of Nippon Porcelain I, Van Patten $24.95
2089 Collector's Ency. of Nippon Porcelain II, Van Patten $24.95
1665 Collector's Ency. of Nippon Porcelain III, Van Patten $24.95
1447 Collector's Ency. of Noritake, 1st Series, Van Patten $19.95
1034 Collector's Ency. of Roseville Pottery, Huxford $19.95
1035 Collector's Ency. of Roseville Pottery, 2nd Ed., Huxford..... $19.95
3314 Collector's Ency. of Van Briggle Art Pottery, Sasicki $24.95
3433 Collector's Guide To Harker Pottery - U.S.A., Colbert $17.95
2339 Collector's Guide to Shawnee Pottery, Vanderbilt $19.95
1425 Cookie Jars, Westfall $9.95
3440 Cookie Jars, Book II, Westfall $19.95
2275 Czechoslovakian Glass & Collectibles, Barta $16.95
3315 Elegant Glassware of the Depression Era, 5th Ed., Florence ..$19.95
3318 Glass Animals of the Depression Era, Garmon & Spencer.....$19.95
2024 Kitchen Glassware of the Depression Years, 4th Ed., Florence ..$19.95
3322 Pocket Guide to Depression Glass, 8th Ed., Florence $9.95
1670 Red Wing Collectibles, DePasquale $9.95
1440 Red Wing Stoneware, DePasquale $9.95
1958 So. Potteries Blue Ridge Dinnerware, 3rd Ed., Newbound.....$14.95
3739 Standard Carnival Glass, 4th Ed., Edwards $24.95
1848 Very Rare Glassware of the Depression Years, Florence $24.95
2140 Very Rare Glassware of the Depression Years, Second Series.. $24.95
3326 Very Rare Glassware of the Depression Years, Third Series ...$24.95
3327 Watt Pottery – Identification & Value Guide, Morris $19.95
2224 World of Salt Shakers, 2nd Ed., Lechner $24.95

BOOKS ON DOLLS & TOYS

2079 Barbie Fashion, Vol. 1, 1959-1967, Eames $24.95
3310 Black Dolls – 1820 - 1991 – Id. & Value Guide, Perkins $17.95
1514 Character Toys & Collectibles, 1st Series, Longest $19.95
1750 Character Toys & Collectibles, 2nd Series, Longest $19.95
1529 Collector's Ency. of Barbie Dolls, DeWein $19.95
2338 Collector's Ency. of Disneyana, Longest & Stern $24.95
3441 Madame Alexander Price Guide #18, Smith $9.95
1540 Modern Toys, 1930 - 1980, Baker $19.95
3442 Patricia Smith's Doll Values – Antique to Modern, 9th ed.....$12.95
1886 Stern's Guide to Disney $14.95
2139 Stern's Guide to Disney, 2nd Series $14.95
1513 Teddy Bears & Steiff Animals, Mandel $9.95
1817 Teddy Bears & Steiff Animals, 2nd Series, Mandel $19.95
2084 Teddy Bears, Annalees & Steiff Animals, 3rd Series, Mandel...$19.95
2028 Toys, Antique & Collectible, Longest $14.95
1808 Wonder of Barbie, Manos $9.95
1430 World of Barbie Dolls, Manos $9.95

OTHER COLLECTIBLES

1457 American Oak Furniture, McNerney $9.95
2269 Antique Brass & Copper, Gaston $16.95
2333 Antique & Collectible Marbles, 3rd Ed., Grist $9.95
1712 Antique & Collectible Thimbles, Mathis $19.95
1748 Antique Purses, Holiner $19.95
1868 Antique Tools, Our American Heritage, McNerney $9.95
1426 Arrowheads & Projectile Points, Hothem $7.95
1278 Art Nouveau & Art Deco Jewelry, Baker $9.95
1714 Black Collectibles, Gibbs $19.95
1128 Bottle Pricing Guide, 3rd Ed., Cleveland $7.95
1752 Christmas Ornaments, Johnston $19.95
2132 Collector's Ency. of American Furniture, Vol. I, Swedberg....$24.95
2271 Collector's Ency. of American Furniture, Vol. II, Swedberg...$24.95
2018 Collector's Ency. of Granite Ware, Greguire $24.95
3430 Coll. Ency. of Granite Ware, Book 2, Greguire $24.95
2083 Collector's Ency. of Russel Wright Designs, Kerr $19.95
2337 Collector's Guide to Decoys, Book II, Huxford $16.95
2340 Collector's Guide to Easter Collectibles, Burnett $16.95
1441 Collector's Guide to Post Cards, Wood $9.95
2276 Decoys, Kangas $24.95
1629 Doorstops – Id. & Values, Bertoia $9.95
1716 Fifty Years of Fashion Jewelry, Baker $19.95
3316 Flea Market Trader, 8th Ed., Huxford $9.95
3317 Florence's Standard Baseball Card Price Gd., 5th Ed. $9.95
1755 Furniture of the Depression Era, Swedberg $19.95
3436 Grist's Big Book of Marbles, Everett Grist $19.95
2278 Grist's Machine Made & Contemporary Marbles $9.95
1424 Hatpins & Hatpin Holders, Baker $9.95
3319 Huxford's Collectible Advertising – Id. & Value Gd. $17.95
3439 Huxford's Old Book Value Guide, 5th Ed. $19.95
1181 100 Years of Collectible Jewelry, Baker $9.95
2023 Keen Kutter Collectibles, 2nd Ed., Heuring $14.95
2216 Kitchen Antiques – 1790 - 1940, McNerney $14.95
3320 Modern Guns – Id. & Val. Gd., 9th Ed., Quertermous $12.95
1965 Pine Furniture, Our American Heritage, McNerney $14.95
3321 Ornamental & Figural Nutcrackers, Rittenhouse $16.95
2026 Railroad Collectibles, 4th Ed., Baker $14.95
1632 Salt & Pepper Shakers, Guarnaccia $9.95
1888 Salt & Pepper Shakers II, Guarnaccia $14.95
2220 Salt & Pepper Shakers III, Guarnaccia $14.95
3443 Salt & Pepper Shakers IV, Guarnaccia $18.95
3737 Schroeder's Antiques Price Guide, 12th Ed. $12.95
2096 Silverplated Flatware, 4th Ed., Hagan $14.95
3325 Standard Knife Collector's Guide, 2nd Ed., Stewart $12.95
2348 20th Century Fashionable Plastic Jewelry, Baker $19.95
3444 Wanted To Buy, 4th Ed. $9.95